UNITED STATES ARMY IN WORLD WAR II

The Technical Services

THE ORDNANCE DEPARTMENT: PLANNING MUNITIONS FOR WAR

by

Constance McLaughlin Green

Harry C. Thomson

and

Peter C. Roots

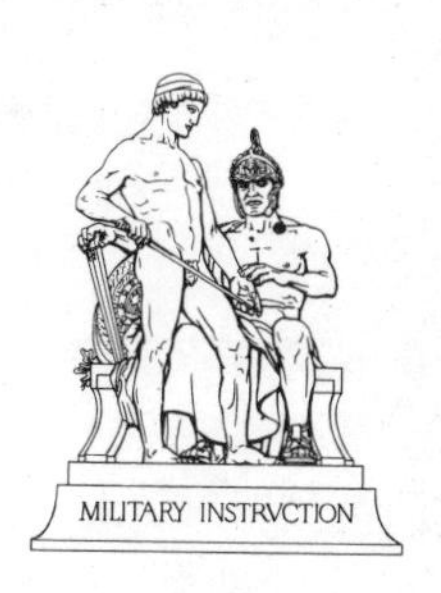

OFFICE OF THE CHIEF OF MILITARY HISTORY

DEPARTMENT OF THE ARMY

WASHINGTON, D. C., 1955

This volume, one of the series UNITED STATES ARMY IN WORLD WAR II, is the first to be published in the subseries THE ORDNANCE DEPARTMENT. All the volumes will be closely related, and the series will present a comprehensive account of the activities of the Military Establishment during World War II. A tentative list of subseries is appended at the end of this volume.

Library of Congress Catalog Card Number: 55–60000

For sale by the Superintendent of Documents, U. S. Government Printing Office,
Washington 25, D. C. - Price $4.25 (Cloth)

UNITED STATES ARMY IN WORLD WAR II

Kent Roberts Greenfield, General Editor*

*General Editor for Technical Service volumes, Lt. Col. Leo J. Meyer, Deputy Chief Historian.
**Maj. Gen. Orlando Ward was succeeded by General Smith on 1 February 1953.

The History of

THE ORDNANCE DEPARTMENT

Planning Munitions for War

Procurement and Supply of Munitions

Ordnance Overseas

. . . to Those Who Served

Foreword

The U.S. Army fought World War II with matériel much of which was developed in the decade prior to our entry, particularly in the period following the German blitz in Poland.

Our efforts to develop munitions to the point where our armies could cope on equal terms with those of potential enemies are covered here in this, the first of three projected volumes on the history of the Ordnance Department in World War II. How well the Ordnance Department succeeded in matching the Germans in quality continues to be a matter of debate both within the Ordnance Department itself, and between the using arms and the Department. That the battle of quantity was won—with the help of a superb industrial machine—can hardly be denied.

This volume, the result of diligent research by Dr. Constance McL. Green and her associates, should interest not only military men but also scientists, industrialists, and laymen in general. Among other things, it shows the urgent necessity of a directed, continuous, and intensive research program and the danger in failing to recognize and profit by developments abroad. Also shown is the inherent time interval between the drawing board and the production of the end item in quantity.

Washington, D.C.
15 January 1953

ORLANDO WARD
Maj. Gen., U.S.A.
Chief of Military History

Note on the Authors

Constance McLaughlin Green, the principal author of this volume, holds a Ph.D. degree in history from Yale University. Before entering government service, first as Historian, Springfield Armory, and later as Chief Historian, Ordnance Historical Branch, she taught at the University of Chicago, Smith College, and Mount Holyoke College. Her extensive writings and lectures in American local, social, and economic history have won her widespread recognition as an authority in these fields both in this country and abroad. She is at present the historian of the Research and Development Board, Department of Defense.

Harry C. Thomson received his doctorate in government from Harvard University. During World War II he was a historian with the Army Air Forces, serving both as an enlisted man and a commissioned officer. Since 1948 he has been a member of the Ordnance Historical Branch, which he now heads.

Peter C. Roots has a B. S. degree in Foreign Service and a law degree from Georgetown University. Before joining the Army, in which he served with Ordnance units between 1942 and 1945, he was the production manager of a machine tool plant in Cincinnati, Ohio. In 1948 he accepted employment in the Translation Section, Office of the Chief of Military History, and later transferred to the Ordnance Historical Branch. He is now practicing law.

Preface

This volume treats of the problems of a great Army agency and its prewar and wartime research and development programs. It is directed primarily to the men and women whose responsibility it is to make the U.S. Army the most effective possible tool of national defense. Technical history rarely makes light reading and this book is not intended to supply diversion for the casual reader. Yet inasmuch as many more Americans than ever before are today concerned with military affairs, others than Army staff planners may find this analysis of the Ordnance Corps' past of interest and use.

The scheme of treatment of the three projected volumes of Ordnance history is basically chronological. This first volume undertakes to discuss the steps that precede manufacture of munitions. The second volume will cover the problems of computing quantities to be ordered, the processes of production and procurement by purchase, and the tasks of distribution and maintenance of equipment in the zone of the interior. A third volume will be dedicated to the operations of Ordnance overseas.

To provide essential background this book includes a rather lengthy analysis of pre-1940 difficulties and a rapid sketch of the confused interim when the United States hovered between peace and war. Discussion of the vital preliminaries to efficient wartime functioning follows in chapters describing the evolution of a workable organization and the recruiting and training of soldiers and civilians to carry out the Ordnance mission. The last section of the book deals with research and development of weapons, the process that in a scientific age necessarily also precedes production of matériel.

Special recognition must be accorded Lida Mayo who, though a latecomer to the staff and hence not listed as an author on the title page, assembled the data and wrote the sections on self-propelled artillery, mines and mine exploders, terminal ballistics, and bombs. Dr. Albert E. Van Dusen, now Assistant Professor of American History at the University of Connecticut, made a valuable contribution in collecting and sifting the materials upon which much of Chapters II and VII are based. Several chapters are the work of more than one individual. Peter C. Roots wrote the story of German rearming contained in Chapter IX, the first half of Chapters X and XI, and the section on armor plate in Chapter XIII. Dr. Harry C. Thomson, the sole author of the chapters on over-all organization, military training, civilian personnel, and conservation of materials, also wrote most of the second part of Chapters X and XI. Mrs. Mayo, as noted, prepared the section on self-propelled artillery in Chapter X, the second half of Chapter XII, the bulk of Chapter XIII, and the entire chapter on bombs. The rest of the volume is the work of the Chief Ordnance Historian, upon whom rests also responsibility for the plan of the whole.

Throughout this book the authors have been obliged to omit discussion of numerous interesting, frequently significant, elements of the whole story of planning weapons. Selection has been chiefly dictated by consideration of controversial data, where the Ordnance Corps believes misapprehensions prevail. Thus the tank has received first attention, at the cost of nearly total exclusion of motor transport and of merely sketchy description of the evolution of self-propelled artillery. Even much of the tank story is untold, partly because space forbade, and partly because treatment of some features would have had to be so highly technical as to make it meaningless to anyone save the automotive engineering expert. The development of cross-drive tank transmissions, for example, has been dismissed with a word, not because this innovation was unimportant, but because explanation of its distinctive features would require many pages of complex engineering data.

Some readers, observing the nature of the documentation, may be disturbed by the degree of reliance the authors have placed upon Ordnance records. Could this volume be regarded as an attempt to produce a definitive history, the failure to exhaust the sources revealing the reverse of the coin would constitute a serious charge against the Ordnance historians. At no point have we aspired to so big an undertaking. Justifications for deliberately narrowing the task are several. First is the obvious impossibility of exhaustive research when staff was small and time relatively short. Ordnance records of World War II located in the Federal Records Center in Alexandria and in the Pentagon run to some 22,000 linear feet. Extracting the most pertinent data from that mass generally precluded more than sampling the voluminous records of other branches of the Army. Only where historians of other services and arms have screened these collateral materials have the Ordnance historians been able to examine thoroughly the counterarguments on controversial issues. Furthermore, the Ordnance Corps has expected its historians to present its side of the story as fully as possible. And, finally, the events under review are too recent to permit of any final appraisal, any fully rounded, wholly objective narrative. We can but hope that this first historical draft will have distilled a concentrate of some value from which the historian in time to come, by refining and by adding distillates from other studies, can prepare the authoritative history of a complicated but stirring era.

The authors are heavily indebted to Mrs. Irene House, research assistant in the Ordnance Historical Branch, whose ingenuity in locating elusive sources and whose patience in assembling a multiplicity of irksome detail have insured the volume an accuracy it would otherwise have lacked. The index is wholly the work of Mrs. House. Miss Feril M. Cowden of the Historical Branch has in turn contributed greatly to the format of the manuscript. Acknowledgments for assistance are also due to a host of men and women in the Office of the Chief of Ordnance, to the custodians of the records in Alexandria, to the staff of the National Archives where the materials of pre-1941 years are housed, and to the authors of preliminary studies of particular Ordnance items or particular tasks. And the work of historians of other segments of the Army has been a constant boon, correcting, at least in part, an otherwise one-sided view of Ordnance problems. Finally, thanks go to the editor, Miss Mary Ann Bacon of the Office of Military History, whose sound sense of literary style improved much of the text, and to Mrs. Loretto Stevens, who did the copy editing.

In writing this narrative the authors have sedulously endeavored to interpret the evidence by criteria of sound scholarship. Testimony to some measure of success may well lie in the mutually contradictory opinions of reviewers of the manuscript. Ordnance officers found many passages overcritical of Ordnance performance; officers of other branches thought that presentation frequently smacks of the Ordnance "party line." In the Ordnance view, the inadequacies of matériel on the battlefields of World War II were the result of the "dead hand" of the using arms, which blocked development of weapons badly needed before the war was over. Combat officers, on the other hand, point to the failure of the Ordnance Department to produce many items for some of which requirements date back to 1919. If the proponents of neither extreme be satisfied, we dare believe we have struck a judicious golden mean.

15 November 1951
Washington, D.C.

CONSTANCE McL. GREEN
Chief Ordnance Historian

Contents

Tables

Charts

Illustrations

291064 O—55——2

All illustrations are from Department of Defense Files.

THE ORDNANCE DEPARTMENT: PLANNING MUNITIONS FOR WAR

INTRODUCTION

The Ordnance Task In World War II

Ordnance is fighting equipment. It is the weapons, the ammunition, the armored and transport vehicles that give an armed force its striking power in battle. The Ordnance Department, in 1950 renamed Ordnance Corps, is that segment of the U.S. Army responsible for design, procurement, distribution, and maintenance of ordnance for the Army Ground Forces. During World War II it also supplied the Air Forces and, in some categories, the Navy as well.

Unlike England, France, and Germany, the United States has never sponsored private manufacturing establishments that specialized in the design and production of heavy munitions. Instead of relying upon a Vickers-Armstrong, a Schneider-Creusot, or a Krupp, this country from its beginning followed the policy of assigning responsibility for Army munitions supply to a special government agency, the Ordnance Department of the Army. A few commercial concerns, to be sure, acquired over the years technical skills in making small arms and ammunition, explosives and propellants, skills that in wartime simplified the problems of conversion from civilian to war production. But the Ordnance Department itself undertook development and manufacture of ordnance or directly supervised the work placed with private contractors.

Design to meet the weapon specifications of the infantry, the artillery, the armored forces, and the air forces; manufacture or purchase of items produced exactly to those design specifications; storage, inspection, and issue of all this matériel; maintenance by replacement of parts and by complete overhaul and reconditioning; and, finally, salvage—these constituted the mission of the Ordnance Department in World War II.[1]

Small arms included rifles, pistols, carbines, submachine guns, machine guns up to and including .50-caliber, recoilless rifles, grenade launchers, and bazookas. Artillery ranged from 20-mm. aircraft cannon and 76-mm. tank guns through the experimental 914-mm. mortar. Supplying ammunition for these weapons was complicated by the development of special purpose ammunition, such as incendiary, illuminating, armor-piercing, and smoke. Besides aircraft bombs, there were new guided missiles, special fuzes, demolition charges, land mines, submarine coastal defense mines, and flares and other pyrotechnics. Assigned responsibility for com-

[1] WD SOS Organization Manual, 1942, Sec. 304.03.

bat vehicles from World War I onward and, after mid-1942, for transport vehicles also, the Ordnance Department had to supply tanks, gun motor carriages, armored cars, ¼-ton "jeeps," trucks, heavy tractors for tank salvage, amphibious troop and cargo carriers, and all the many variations of these. Nor did the list end there. In the course of World War II the Department issued some 1,860 different models of major pieces of fighting equipment; of these about 1,200 were models of new or improved design. And into these went over 350,000 parts.[2]

The chain of command under which the Department performed these various duties was altered somewhat when the reorganization of the War Department took effect in March 1942. During the preceding twenty-odd years the Under Secretary of War, by authority delegated from the President of the United States through the Secretary of War, was charged with supervising procurement of Army supplies. He served as the civilian chief for Ordnance, as for all other supply services.[3] After the reorganization of the War Department in March 1942, which divided the Army in the continental United States into the Army Ground Forces, the Army Air Forces, and the Services of Supply, the Under Secretary of War acted as civilian supervisor to the Commanding General, Services of Supply, or, as it was relabeled in 1943, the Army Service Forces. That general now represented all of the supply services in their relations with the Under Secretary. The latter maintained contact with the heads of the civilian economy and chiefs of other war agencies, thereby guiding production for the Army in order to keep a balance among the groups competing for supplies.

Before March 1942 the traditional line of military command of the Ordnance Department had been from the Chief of Staff through the General Staff Supply Division, usually known as G–4. Creation of the Army Service Forces interjected another administrative unit between all the operating or technical services and the Assistant Chief of Staff, G–4. Thus, after March 1942 and throughout the war, the Ordnance Department performed its mission under the immediate direction of the Commanding General, Army Service Forces, and no longer enjoyed direct access to the Chief of Staff or to the Under Secretary of War. The "higher authority" to which the Chief of Ordnance was subordinate consisted of his immediate superior, Lt. Gen. Brehon B. Somervell, commanding the Army Service Forces, and his assistant chiefs of staff; the Supply Division, G–4, of the General Staff; the Chief of Staff himself; the Under Secretary of War; the Secretary of War; and the President in his capacity of Commander in Chief of the Army.[4]

Military equipment for many years past has differed markedly from articles for ordinary nonmilitary use. Even where items are of the same general category, differences exist between what is necessary for the Army and what suffices for the civilian. The military requirements of ruggedness and power far exceed what the civilian usually demands. Army rifles and Army trucks must first and foremost be capable of operating under the most adverse circumstances, regardless of the dollar cost of achieving that dependability. The .22 rifles, produced in the United States by

[2] Min, Joint Army-Navy (A&N) mtg on Army Ord R&D, 1 Oct 45, p. 1, A&N Mtgs, Barnes file, OHF.

[3] PL 891, 76th Cong, 3d Sess. See also Chart 1, p. 84.

[4] (1) WD SOS Organization Manual, 1942, Secs. 102.04 and 200.01. (2) Chart 2, p. 86.

thousands for farm boys who hunt rabbits and woodchucks, and the trucks manufactured for commercial use can be of relatively cheap construction, both because durability is rarely a matter of life and death to the purchasers and because initial price tends to be a big consideration in determining the purchase. Furthermore, many items of military equipment have no civilian counterpart at all. Large-caliber guns, artillery ammunition and fuzes, machine guns and their ammunition, tanks and other armored vehicles are produced solely for use by the armed forces. For these the toughest steels, the most powerful explosives, the most highly powered engines are needed. Hence, the first task in ordnance design is to test all materials meeting these requirements in order to specify the best. Establishment of exacting specifications for steels, oils, chemical agents, and other materials must be followed by detailed instructions for processing and gaging. As research and experience indicated feasible improvements, the Ordnance Department revised its designs and specifications.

Design of ordnance was not arrived at by theory alone. The basic idea for a new weapon might stem from any one of various sources, from a private citizen, from a commercial company, from combat troops, or, of course, from the Ordnance Department itself. The value of any proposal had to be thoroughly explored. Information assembled in the course of wars past was the first obvious check; forecast of future needs was a second. The using arms, the Infantry, the Coast and Field Artillery, the Air Forces, and the Cavalry, later called the Armored Force, collaborated closely with Ordnance Department designers in determining the characteristics needed in any given weapon or accessory to fulfill a definite military purpose. After March 1942 the Army Ground Forces and the Army Air Forces spoke for the combat arms. But the user had the final say about what would be acceptable to him. Sometimes one desired feature ruled out another; maneuverability and high road speed in a tank might preclude use of heavy armor plate or powerful guns. What was essential for the Infantry might be unimportant for the Cavalry and vice versa. Hence decisions as to what was of primary importance, what of secondary, were often hard to reach.[5] These questions were resolved by the Ordnance Committee, composed of members of the Ordnance Department and the using services. When the principal "military characteristics" were agreed upon in the Ordnance Committee, the Ordnance Department worked out a design, built a pilot model, and subjected it to tests. The using arms studied its performance, suggested, if need be, modifications, and later scrutinized the resulting modified weapon. If that appeared to be acceptable, the Ordnance Department made a limited number for test under service conditions. The using arm conducted the final service test. Only when both using arm and Ordnance designers concurred that the item was satisfactory in all essentials did the General Staff authorize the Ordnance Department to officially accept, or "standardize" it, and issue orders for quantity fabrication. In peacetime

[5] Particular testimony to the difficulties of determining military characteristics is contained in A Handbook of Ordnance Automotive Engineering, Aberdeen Proving Ground, 1945, II, 2: "A most notable example . . . was the development of combat lights. Due to lack of previous experience, neither the technical service nor the using arms were in a position to more than suggest approximately what was desired in light intensity, angle of cutoff, colors, and other definite requirements without extensive field tests involving actual samples."

this procedure of design, test, refinement, service test, acceptance, and, then, order for production might stretch over years. In wartime the process was necessarily hastened. But perfection of design cannot be greatly speeded. The U.S. Army fought most of World War II, like earlier wars, largely with the types of equipment standardized or ready for standardization when the conflict began. During World War II the Ordnance Department completed few significant innovations in weapons that reached the front lines in sufficient quantity and in time materially to affect the outcome on the battlefield.

Large-scale procurement of matériel declared satisfactory in design was the next function of the Ordnance Department. Procurement might be by manufacture in government arsenals or other government plants, or by purchase from commercial sources. Quantities and dates of delivery had to be worked out with utmost care. The General Staff of the Army determined the size of the Army, within statutory and budgetary limitations, and provided the implementing directives so that the technical services might then calculate the quantities of initial items of equipment needed and the volume of replacements. Under the aegis of the Army Service Forces in World War II, the Ordnance Department evolved its procurement schedules to meet the requirements calculated as the result of General Staff directives. Computation of requirements in order to have available the proper quantities at the exact time and place they were needed was an enormously difficult job. Controversy with the War Production Board and other agencies directing the civilian economy was occasionally inevitable. "Too much and too late" was the criticism tendered by men usually not themselves faced with responsibility for making the critical decisions of how much, when.

Desired requirements schedules mapped out, the Industrial Service of the Ordnance Department took over the job of meeting them. Since the six permanent government arsenals could produce only a small fraction of the volume needed, contracts with private industry had to be the mainstay. Government-owned government-operated plants were far outnumbered by government-owned contractor-operated plants and privately owned establishments. The Ordnance districts, the geographically decentralized offices first created in World War I, were in charge of making formal contracts, placing orders, and supervising production in plants other than the government arsenals. The staff of each of the thirteen district offices controlled the allocations of machine tools and raw materials and was accountable for government property within its district. The staffs trained inspectors, directed the inspection preliminary to acceptance of the contractors' output, supervised packaging and shipment of the finished product, made payments for satisfactorily completed orders, renegotiated and terminated contracts. These operations varied in particulars but in general were everywhere the same. The district offices furnished the administrative machinery for ordnance procurement.[6]

The six permanent Ordnance arsenals in peacetime sufficed to supply the Army. Each one specialized in particular types of ordnance: Springfield Armory in small arms; Watervliet Arsenal in cannon; Watertown in gun carriages and forgings; Rock Island in artillery recoil mechanisms,

[6] The Ordnance District System, Its Growth and Development, 1918–1945, prepared under the direction of Brig. Gen. A. B. Quinton, Jr., OHF.

gun carriages, and combat vehicles; Frankford in small arms ammunition, artillery projectiles, cartridge cases, optical and fire control instruments, gages, and pyrotechnics; and Picatinny in artillery ammunition, explosives, and propellants. In these establishments year after year research and development work went forward along with manufacturing and maintenance of equipment. While their peak productive capacity was never enough to meet the needs of a wartime army, the arsenals provided the technical assistance that enabled privately owned companies to manufacture specialized ordnance when expansion was necessary. Here the art of munitions manufacture was preserved. Not only blueprints of components of weapons, ammunition, and vehicles, but carefully planned shop layouts and details of processing were available for distribution to new contractors. The long-term civilian employees of the arsenals, men whose experience often could be counted in decades rather than years, constituted the schoolmasters of firms unfamiliar with the peculiar problems of ordnance manufacture. Consultations over particular difficulties helped the commercial contractor produce exactly to specification; occasionally during the war, arsenal employees were lent to contractors to assist in solving some processing problem. Interchangeability tests to guarantee that parts of one producer's output were interchangeable with those of another were also conducted at the arsenals. "Technical responsibility" for all Army Ordnance items was divided among the six arsenals, so that nothing from a cleaning rod to a "blockbuster" was fabricated without having experts from one or another of the government establishments qualified to accept or reject every piece. In fact, training men in inspection procedures was one of the arsenals' important functions during the war.

While the arsenals made a very small part of the matériel required and privately owned establishments produced most of some types of ordnance, neither possessed capacity to manufacture all items in sufficient quantity. Existing plants could be readily converted to turn out small arms, artillery shell and other metal components, fuzes, and transport vehicles. In these fields either prewar procurement planning had been thorough, or the military item was closely enough allied to a civilian article to eliminate novel production problems. In other fields the reverse was true. No existing facility, for example, was adapted to mass production of tanks; the original plan of fabricating all combat vehicles in shops making heavy railway equipment proved impractical. For procuring a great deal of ordnance, consequently, the best answer was found to be newly built government-owned contractor-operated plants—GOCO facilities.[7] Thus the vast, rapid expansion was achieved, and government establishments, private facilities, and combinations of the two met demand. By the end of 1942 the Ordnance Department was conducting the financially largest manufacturing program in the world.[8] Expenditures between 1940 and V-J Day totaled about $46,000,000,000.

Another duty of the Ordnance Department was to manage the distribution and upkeep of matériel. Field Service of the

[7] See: (1) Project Supporting Paper 8, Development of Production Capacity, OHF (hereafter Project Supporting Papers are cited as PSP); (2) Ord War Administration History, Series II, No. 11, Facilities, OHF.

[8] Col. C. Wingate Reed, "The Ordnance Department, What It Is, What It Does," *NADA Bulletin* (published by National Automobile Dealers Association), XV, 4 (1943), 11.

Ordnance Department was responsible for storing and issuing both initial equipment and spare parts and replacement parts. Some twenty-six storage depots in 1940 housed ordnance supplies, while the depot units had the task of keeping accurate records of stocks, receipt, and issue. As output of manufacturing plants mounted, the number of depots and warehouses had also to be multiplied. Storage space by 1942 was ten times that of 1940. In addition to ammunition depots, largely built inland out of range of carrier-based enemy planes, and storage space for weapons and accessories both for the U.S. Army and for lend-lease, the Ordnance Department after September 1942 acquired depots from the Quartermaster Corps for storage of transport vehicles and parts.

When U. S. troops began to move overseas, problems of distribution and record-keeping became more complex. Confusion might easily have become chaos, for matériel in transit was at all times difficult to keep track of and supply lines were long. In time, the Army Service Forces evolved a supply control system under which Ordnance and all other technical services operated, but a foolproof scheme of accounting and method of maintaining a balanced supply of the thousands of components, component assemblies, and complete items was never wholly achieved. Experience, as the war progressed, dictated establishment of four types of depot—bulk storage depots, master depots to handle selected types of ordnance, distribution depots to serve as retail distributors, and filler depots for ports of embarkation.

Packaging ordnance matériel had never been recognized as a major problem before World War II. Neither private industry nor government agencies had anticipated its importance. But when arms and ammunition, sensitive electronic devices, and expensive engine parts were found to be unusable on the combat fronts because of improper packing for shipment or outdoor storage, Field Service and Industrial Service jointly undertook a careful study of packaging. Design of sturdy, compact containers, use of desiccants and protective surface coatings, exact labeling of boxes, and application of engineering principles to loading freight cars and trucks had to be worked out in detailed procedures for shipping.

A still more exacting assignment for Field Service was maintenance of ordnance matériel. In peacetime, periodic inspection of items in storage, cleaning, overhaul, and reconditioning at depot or arsenal were more or less routine tasks. In wartime, maintenance of equipment being used by an army was a job of major proportions. For cleaning and minor repairs, the combat soldier was usually responsible. But spare parts had to be available so that he could replace a broken firing pin in his rifle or put new spark plugs in his tank engine. Having the right number of replacement parts at the spots where they were needed and at the time when they were needed was a constant logistical problem. Mobile ordnance supply and maintenance units, serving immediately in the rear of combat operations, repaired equipment that could be restored to serviceable condition promptly. Jobs more time consuming, or beyond the capabilities of mobile shops, were sent to Ordnance units in the communications zone. Ordnance troops salvaged matériel both to rebuild and to ship back as scrap to the zone of interior. Maintenance, a trying job in this country, was an even more difficult task overseas.

To make proper maintenance possible, Field Service, in the office of the Chief of

Ordnance, prepared a long series of technical manuals and bulletins for use in training both Ordnance units and using troops in the care of equipment. On special maintenance problems technical assistance was also furnished to commands responsible for matériel used by their troops. Of utmost importance were the Ordnance catalogs, popularly called SNL's, which provided complete information on spare parts stockage and identification data—name, number, and photograph of each part or assembly.[9] In all, Ordnance required about 1,700 different technical publications and 2,000 different supply catalogues. Preparing and distributing these and then keeping this huge publication system up to date, in order to cover improvements and new information, was a never-ending job.

Ordnance Department responsibility for supply did not end with the issue of matériel to troops or with consignment at depots to the Transportation Corps for overseas shipment; it endured until items received the "death certificate" and salvage began. Yet the Chief of Ordnance had no command responsibility outside this country. Overseas commanders had full authority over men and equipment in theatres of operations. Thus Ordnance units assigned to divisions outside the zone of interior were not under the control of the Chief of Ordnance, and Ordnance officers attached to the staffs of commanders in the field could not officially communicate directly with the Ordnance Department in Washington save on strictly technical matters. Technical missions to observe functioning of American munitions, to further the development and use of new items, and to note particular problems to be met served to keep some contact, while publications and confidential reports abetted translation of field experience into action in this country. Moreover, personal letters from Ordnance officers in the theatres to the Chief of Ordnance in Washington kept the headquarters informed of ordnance problems overseas.

Ordnance equipment is specialized. Its construction and maintenance require technical skills. Training Ordnance personnel, therefore, is a final, or perhaps more logically a first, duty of the Department. Civil Service employees to man the arsenals and depots, to administer the Ordnance districts, to inspect contractors' output, and to carry on much of the paper work in the Office, Chief of Ordnance, fall into one category, and Army officers and enlisted men into another. War Department ceilings on officers forced the Ordnance Department in World War II to use civilians on some jobs that officers might otherwise have filled, though, like other services, the Department commissioned a number of men straight from civilian life in order to avoid losing them to the draft. At the peak, in February 1943, 262,772 civilian employees, 6,500 officers, and 13,750 enlisted men were employed by the Department's operating missions in the continental United States. Over 14,000 Ordnance officers were assigned by the end of March 1945 to overseas commands.[10]

During World War II most of the key men in the arsenals, depots, and administrative offices brought to their war jobs their skills from civilian life. The Ordnance Department carried on a large training program for inspectors and also trained a

[9] SNL stands for "Standard Nomenclature List," the name used years ago.

[10] (1) ASF Monthly Progress Report, Personnel, Sec. 5. (2) Strength of the Army, prepared for WDGS by Machine Records Br, AGO, under direction of Stat Br, GS, STM-30, 1 Apr 45 (hereafter cited as Strength of the Army, STM-30), DRB AGO.

good many men for depot work. But the bulk of operators on production lines in war plants were schooled not by the Ordnance Department itself but by Ordnance contractors and by the War Manpower Commission's Training Within Industry Service.

Ordnance training for officers and enlisted men, though necessarily brief, was fairly intensive. To a degree never before considered necessary, the Ordnance Department had to teach raw recruits to be soldiers as well as technicians, for in World War II Ordnance troops had to function close to the front lines and be prepared to fight in case of an enemy break-through. Technical training itself embraced many specialties. Instruction in maintenance and repair of automotive and fire control equipment, of small arms, and of artillery constituted one kind of training. To prepare men to handle distribution of ordnance there were courses in ammunition supply, vehicle assembly, spare parts handling, and general depot work with its infinite detail of receipt, issue, and record-keeping. Units were trained in such diverse tasks as methods of disposing of unexploded enemy bombs and waterproofing vehicles for amphibious operations. All told, between 1942 and V-J Day some forty basic types of Ordnance military units, ranging from squads to battalions, were activated and trained—units for ammunition supply, for light, medium, and heavy maintenance, for automotive repair, and for armament and automotive repair in base shops. Because enlistment of men already possessed of experience in maintaining heavy machinery and automotive transport promised to ease the problems of training specialists, the Ordnance Department early in 1942 persuaded the National Automobile Dealers Association to organize a large-scale recruiting drive for Ordnance "Affiliated Units." The association, later assisted by other business organizations, supplied some 1,200 officers and 30,000 enlisted men in a few months' time. These men needed relatively little technical schooling and rather brief indoctrination in Ordnance procedures. As new trainees poured into the training centers, courses were repeated again and again. Several additional training centers had to be opened in 1942 as well as "continuation" schools at some of the depots. The 334 Ordnance officers and 3,950 enlisted men of mid-1940 grew by D Day in June 1944 to nearly 24,000 officers and nearly 325,000 men.[11]

The task of the Ordnance Department, difficult in any war, was far harder in World War II than ever before. Since the fighting of the U.S. Army in World War I was concentrated on the battlefields of northern France and Flanders, in 1917 and 1918 supplies had to be sent only to the Continent and distributed within a relatively small area. In World War II American forces were scattered almost literally "from Greenland's icy mountains to India's coral strand," and Allied nations, in part equipped by the United States, were fighting in every quarter of the globe. Supply lines had to extend in all directions. Weapons, ammunition, and vehicles had to be designed with the factors of weight and bulk constantly in mind so that equipment could be transported easily. The distance from factory to depot in the United States, to overseas ammunition dump, or to repair shop spelled a costly lapse of time for delivery of any replacement item not

[11] (1) *Annual Report of the Secretary of War to the President, 1940* (Washington, 1940) (hereafter cited as *Ann Rpt SW*), pp. 28–29. (2) Strength of the Army, STM–30, 1 Jun 44, DRB AGO.

shipped with the troops in the first place. And time might determine the success or failure of any tactical operation. Global warfare created a nearly overwhelming logistical problem for Ordnance, as for all the supply services.

The sheer quantity of ordnance matériel required constituted another problem. In the Civil War the Ordnance Department had furnished arms for somewhat over 1,500,000 Union soldiers, and in World War I for perhaps 4,000,000 men.[12] In April 1945 the United States Army totaled over 8,290,000 men.[13] Add to the individual equipment for these men the machine guns, mortars, artillery, ammunition of all types, mines, tanks, transport and combat vehicles, and the magnitude of the Ordnance task begins to emerge. Some items were also made for the Navy and the Marine Corps. Furthermore, the United States as the "Arsenal of Democracy" had to supply much matériel to the British, Russians, Free French, Chinese, and other allies. Plans to meet these demands were nursed by Assistant Secretary of War Louis Johnson before 1940 and by his successor, Robert Patterson, but most of the responsibility for carrying out this gargantuan undertaking fell upon the Ordnance Department. "From Pearl Harbor to V-J Day the Industry-Ordnance team furnished to the Army and 43 foreign nations 47 billion rounds of small arms ammunition, approximately 11 million tons of artillery ammunition, more than 12 million rifles and carbines, approximately 750,000 artillery pieces, and 3½ million military vehicles."[14]

The job would have been enormous even had American industry been prepared in 1940 to produce munitions on a large scale. Many Americans, and particularly isolationists, were opposed. A considerable public still branded munitions makers as merchants of death. Neither the will to participate in an armament program nor the machine tools and shops with which to carry it out existed. The "Industry-Ordnance Team" had to be built up from a skeleton organization. Enlisting the interest of American manufacturers in making munitions was easy in 1942, but in 1940 and 1941 was difficult. Only recently out from the shadow of a business depression, industrialists before Pearl Harbor were reluctant to forego opportunities to enlarge their civilian markets. Moreover, even if and when companies were willing to accept Ordnance orders, they faced a technological problem. To manu-

[12] The official figure for the total number of Civil War enlistments, Army and Navy, is 2,400,000, though what proportion was Navy is not certain. The discrepancy may be accounted for by short-term enlistments, which permitted the Ordnance Department in some cases to reissue used arms. Thomas L. Livermore considered these figures high and computed the total number of men who served for three years as 1,500,000. See (1) John D. Hicks, *The Federal Union* (Boston, 1937), p. 657, citing Thomas L. Livermore, *Numbers and Losses in the Civil War in America, 1861-1865* (Boston, 1901); and (2) Col. Leonard P. Ayres, *The War With Germany, A Statistical Summary* (Washington, 1919), p. 13.

The exact number of men actually equipped by the Ordnance Department in World War I is nowhere stated. The British and French supplied a great deal of the artillery the U.S. Army used in combat, but, on the other hand, America furnished the British with some small arms. Some 2,086,000 American soldiers served in the AEF. Troops in training in this country are estimated as bringing the total number to the 4,000,000 cited here. (1) Ayres, *op. cit.*, p. 11; (2) Benedict Crowell, *America's Munitions, 1917-1918* (Washington, 1919), p. 16.

[13] Kent R. Greenfield, Robert R. Palmer, and Bell I. Wiley, *The Organization of Ground Combat Troops* (Washington, 1947), p. 210.

[14] Lt. Gen. Levin H. Campbell, Jr., *The Industry-Ordnance Team* (McGraw-Hill Book Company, Inc., New York, 1946), p. 33. The official Army figures differ somewhat from those given by General Campbell. See Theodore E. Whiting *et al.*, Statistics, a volume in preparation for the series UNITED STATES ARMY IN WORLD WAR II.

facture intricate weapons and ammunition, tanks and cargo carriers markedly different from vehicles for civilian use, requires time—time to assemble machines, tools, and gages, time to teach workmen how to turn out parts made to exacting tolerances. Precision work as it was known in many American factories of 1940 was inexact when measured by the ten-thousandth-inch limits permitted for gun mechanisms and delicate fuze assemblies. It was the mission of the Ordnance Department to help industry learn how to produce ordnance and produce it quickly enough to turn out quantities in time to serve. The so-called technological time lag in manufacturing matériel was a problem shared in some measure by all the technical services of the armed forces, but was particularly acute for the Ordnance Department.

World War II was as different from World War I as a future war will be from World War II if the predictions of the Cassandras of the atomic age be fulfilled. The trench warfare of 1915–18 had few counterparts in the 1940's. Planes, combat vehicles, and cargo carriers made a war of movement. Mobility and maneuverability were prime requisites for an efficient army. Equipment that could not readily be shifted about even in the thick of combat was of limited use. The batteries of field artillery, in World War I solidly emplaced behind the front lines, had either to be mounted on self-propelled gun carriages or supplied with motorized tractors to tow them. Towed artillery, though extensively used, tended to slow the advance. Enemy planes and fast-moving tanks in turn necessitated more rapid and accurate sighting and fire. Motorization, while militating against the miseries of trench warfare, created its own supply problems, and maintenance of vehicles became a never-ending job. Furthermore, use of tanks called for countermeasures—fields of land mines. To met this hazard Army Ordnance had to develop mine exploders, as well as mines to sow against an enemy advance.

Still more far reaching were the changes brought about by aerial warfare. Planes flying at unheard of altitudes and at speeds unobtainable in the 1930's created new puzzles for Ordnance. Fire control instruments, new types of ammunition, higher velocity guns for both aircraft and antiaircraft became essential to survival. Employment of airborne troops was another innovation calling for redesign of equipment. Men must be supplied with weapons light in weight, sturdy enough to withstand parachuting, and powerful and reliable enough to protect the parachutists in encounters with the enemy behind his own lines. Later in the war German guided missiles, particularly the celebrated V–2 rocket, challenged American and British brains to find countermeasures. During the war no effective answer to the powerful German V–2 was found.

Indeed the complexities of munitions increased steadily. Trained soldiers and experts in ballistics no longer alone sufficed for the jobs of designing weapons to anticipate enemy developments. Scientists in a dozen fields were needed to evolve intricate devices which a generation before would have seemed fantastically remote from any application to arms for fighting men. Not all physicists were engaged on the MANHATTAN Project. Men trained in research laboratories, authorities in electronics, chemistry, metallurgy, meteorology, mathematics, and physics were called upon to contribute to ordnance. When workable applications of involved scientific formulae were completed, men of the Ordnance Department had still to locate facilities to produce the items and had still to train men properly in handling and maintaining them. Though the fruits of scientific research undoubtedly shortened the war by many months, the problems imposed by scientific developments in fighting equipment added to the immediate task of Army Ordnance.

Finally, supplying weapons and the means of keeping them in usable condition was complicated by unforeseen circumstances of combat. Extremes of climate, unexpected difficulties of terrain, and the demands of amphibious warfare presented new problems. From 1941 on, the Ordnance Department tested equipment under the arctic conditions of Alaska, the tropical of the Canal Zone, in the California desert, the swamps of Louisiana, and the mountains of Colorado. Yet neither these experiments nor imagination served to anticipate many situations that American soldiers later met. Fungus and corrosion from even short exposure to the humidity of jungle islands in the Pacific, wear on piston rings resulting from driving combat vehicles over 800 miles of Australian desert from ports in the south to camps on the northern coast, brittleness of steel armor plate and congealing of lubricants in the subzero temperatures of winter in Alaska might theoretically have been foreseen. But the most farsighted still could not realize how greatly these factors on the scale on which they were encountered around the globe would complicate the Ordnance task.

Despite the late start, American ordnance had overtaken and outdistanced enemy ordnance by 1945. Unflattering comparisons of some American weapons with those of the enemy, Ordnance officers were convinced, grew out of American soldiers' tendency to regard only the deadly effectiveness of an enemy arm without taking into consideration its weaknesses. Unquestionably, particular items of German design and make were superior in at least some particulars to the corresponding American pieces—simpler to operate, easier to repair, lighter to carry, cheaper to manufacture, or better killers. The dreaded German "Panthers" were more heavily armored and had more fire power than any American tanks that saw action. We now know that ever since 1933 Nazi Germany had been applying most of her science and productive capacity to preparing for war. Her head start put the United States at a nearly insuperable disadvantage. Nevertheless, by the last year of the war American fighting equipment in general was sturdier and better functioning than that of the enemy. And the U.S. Army had far more of it. The British, the Canadians, and the Russians held the lines while the United States got its vast armament production under way. But it is abundantly clear that in any future crisis better preparedness would be essential.

CHAPTER I

Origins and Growth to 1919

Early History

The immediate antecedents of the Ordnance Department of the United States Army date back to the first days of the American Revolution. The Ordnance Department is first mentioned by name in a resolution of the Continental Congress in 1778 that assigned to certain artillery officers responsibility for issue of ordnance supplies to troops in the field. Throughout the Revolutionary War the Congress kept final control of munitions procurement in its own hands but gradually delegated considerable authority to particular officers: to a Board of War and Ordnance, which in turn appointed a Surveyor of Ordnance to inspect matériel; to a Commissary General of Military Stores to keep record of purchases and of stocks on hand; and to the commanding artillery officer of the Army as the officer in charge of ordnance field activities.[1]

Little provision could be made for design of weapons since a large part of the arms with which the Continental Army fought the war was imported from France and the West Indies, confiscated on the high seas by American privateers, or captured from British stores in America. British-made muskets owned by colonial militiamen and rifles and muskets produced by local gunsmiths supplemented supply. Cartridges, ball, and powder were made in small shops scattered through the countryside. Yet while the urgency of getting usable field pieces, muskets, and ammunition was too great to permit of elaborate plans for improving ordnance, the commanding artillery officer was empowered to recommend alterations; if these proposed changes were approved by the Board of War and Ordnance, the board passed on instructions to the "artificers and laboratory men." [2] Thus the functions of the Ordnance Department of World War II were also those of the "Ordnance Department" of the Continental Army.

For nearly thirty years following the end of hostilities in 1782, the Ordnance Department as a distinct unit of the United States Army ceased to exist. In that interim ordnance supplies were first entrusted to the Keeper of Military Stores, and then in 1792 the Congress created the office of Purveyor of Public Supplies whose duties extended to purchase of arms and ammunition for the Army. To release the new republic from dependence upon foreign armsmakers, the Congress, moreover, in 1794 empowered the President to establish two national armories. Thus the Springfield Armory, the first federal arms factory, was erected and by 1795 had completed its first 245 muskets. Harpers Ferry, the south-

[1] *Journals of the Continental Congress, 1774-1789* (Library of Congress edition, Washington, 1904–1937), Feb 11, 1778, X, 144; Feb 18, 1779, XIII, 201–06.

[2] See (1) James E. Hicks, *Notes on United States Ordnance: II, Ordnance Correspondence* (Mount Vernon, New York, 1940), 11–13; and (2) Felicia J. Deyrup, *Arms Makers of the Connecticut Valley* (Smith College Studies in History, XXXIII, 1948), pp. 33–36.

SPRINGFIELD ARMORY. *The main arsenal as it appeared in 1852.*

ern armory, began operations in 1796. Additional arms for the State Militia and the United States Army were supplied by private contractors, most notable of whom was Eli Whitney.[3] It was Whitney's demonstration to officials of the War Department that first convinced doubting Thomases of the feasibility of making firearms on an interchangeable basis. Whitney's performance was as dramatic as its effects were revolutionizing. At the invitation of Capt. Decius Wadsworth, later the first Chief of Ordnance, Whitney in 1801 brought to Washington ten sets of the components of musket locks. These he dumped in piles upon a table and then selecting parts at random he assembled ten complete firing mechanisms. Initial disbelief of his audience gave way before this proof that use of jigs and machine tools could make components so identical that filing and special fitting in assembly were needless. Official objections to Whitney's delay in deliveries on his contract for muskets were thus stilled.[4] Shortly thereafter, the government armories adopted the new system of manu-

[3] Deyrup, *op. cit.*, p. 233. The correspondence of Tench Coxe, Purveyor of Public Supplies from 1803 to 1812, gives an illuminating picture of the difficulties of organizing supply of arms from domestic sources.

[4] See Joseph Roe, *English and American Tool Builders* (New Haven, 1916), p. 133. For full explanation of the consequences of acceptance of the principle of interchangeability, see also Deyrup, *op. cit.*, pp. 87–99.

291064 O—55——3

facturing and, by improvement in machine tools, gradually extended and perfected it.

The approach of war with Great Britain in 1812 stresssed the wisdom of placing responsibility for munitions upon the Army. Accordingly, the Congress on 14 May 1812 formally created an Ordnance Department and appropriated $20,000 for its expenses. The Commissary-General of Ordnance was charged with inspection, storage and issue, and supervision of the government "laboratories" or workshops; where gun carriages, muskets and other arms were made.[5] Elaboration of the duties of the Ordnance Department followed in 1815. The Chief of Ordnance thereafter was responsible for contracting for arms and ammunition, for supervision of the government armories and storage depots, and for recruitment and training of "artificers" to be attached to regiments, corps, and garrisons.[6] By 1816 the federal arsenals numbered five: Springfield and Harpers Ferry making small arms; Watervliet, "the arsenal near Troy," artillery equipment and ammunition; Watertown, in Massachusetts, small arms ammunition and gun carriages; and Frankford, near Philadelphia, ammunition. Only two more, Rock Island and Picatinny, were added after mid-century, while Harpers Ferry was destroyed early in the Civil War.

The importance of the role of the Ordnance Department was recognized from its beginning. Thus, the Secretary of War urged the Congress in carrying out proposed reductions in the size of the Army to exclude the Engineer Corps and Ordnance Department. "Their duties," he wrote in 1818, "are connected with the permanent preparation and defense of the country, and have so little reference to the existing military establishment, that if the army were reduced to a single regiment, no reduction could safely be made in either of them."[7] Nevertheless, the reduction effected in 1821 officially merged the Ordnance Department with the Artillery. The arrangement endured for eleven years, but, inasmuch as the officers who were transferred to the Artillery continued to perform the duties assigned to Ordnance by the Act of 1815, the change was more apparent than real. At the end of the 1820's the Ordnance Department was spending about $1,000,000 a year for equipment.[8] In 1830 the colonel on Ordnance service reported:

> . . . extensive operations are conducted at . . . two national armories, nine private armories, four cannon foundries, fourteen national arsenals, four ordnance depots, and an extensive region of public lead mines.
>
> These establishments are situated in different parts of the Union, and they employ more than one thousand men, consisting chiefly of artificers and mechanics. They are all conducted under the general supervision, and, with the exception of the private armories, under the immediate and special direction of the Ordnance Department.[9]

Officers trained as artillerymen soon proved less qualified to handle this business than ordnance specialists. The upshot was the re-establishment of the Ordnance Department as a separate unit in 1832 with 14 officers and 250 enlisted men assigned to it.[10] Occasionally in the course of the next century efforts were repeated to re-

[5] Adjutant and Inspector General's Office, *Military Laws and Rules and Regulations for the Armies of the United States* (Washington, May 1, 1813), pp. 104–09.

[6] *U.S. Statutes at Large,* III, Ch. 38, Feb 8, 1815.

[7] *American State Papers,* Military Affairs, I, 780.

[8] *A Collection of Annual Reports and other Important Papers, Relating to the Ordnance Department,* prepared under the direction of Brig. Gen. Stephen V. Benet (Washington, 1889), I, 209. (Hereafter cited as *Ordnance Reports.*)

[9] *Ordnance Reports,* I, 219.

[10] (1) *Ibid.,* 138–45, 147–49. (2) *U.S. Statutes at Large,* IV, Ch. 504, 1832.

assign the control of Ordnance. Wider civilian superintendence, renewed merging of the Department with the artillery, supervision by officers of the line, consolidation of all Army supply under one War Department supply service—all were urged, all discarded.[11] After 1832 the structure of the Ordnance Department remained unshaken; its functions continue today as they were established then.

Design of weapons had not originally been included specifically in the duties of the Ordnance Department, though Col. Decius Wadsworth, the first Chief of Ordnance, and his successor, Col. George Bomford, each played an active part in determining American ordnance designs and specifications. Colonel Bomford had in fact himself designed a "bomb-cannon," the "Columbiad," the first heavy shell-firing gun the United States Army ever employed.[12] The Regulations of 1834 first officially placed responsibility for design upon the Ordnance Department. This did not mean either then or later that Ordnance officers or arsenal employees originated designs. Usually new models were tendered for trial by independent inventors or commercial companies sponsoring them. The Ordnance Department selected, adapted when necessary, and then standardized, that is, officially accepted models for government use. To ensure having modern types of equipment, in 1840 and again in 1848 the Department sent officers to Europe to study foreign design and production methods. Utilization of ideas acquired abroad, together with development of techniques originating in America, placed United States artillery in mid-century more nearly on a par with that of other nations than had been possible in the Republic's infancy.[13] But American aversion to preoccupation with military affairs obstructed ordnance developments after, as before, the Civil War.

Design of small arms was a somewhat different story. The westward movement across the continent, with its accompaniment of Indian warfare and frontier violence, kept Americans immediately concerned with the adequacy of shoulder arms. In the forties the Ordnance Department replaced the old smooth bore, muzzle-loading flintlock with the percussion musket and the cumbersome pistol with the revolver invented by Samuel Colt. Notable improvements in rifles, pistols, and particularly ammunition, as well as in methods of production, occurred in the 1850's as the beginning of an independent machine-tool industry and of precision gage making nourished the growth of a series of private companies engaged in small arms manufacture. In this work the government arsenals collaborated.[14] Yet the conservatism of the Army was clearly

[11] Civilian superintendents, in charge of the national armories up to 1841, were supplanted for somewhat over a decade by Ordnance officers, and were then again put in charge until the outbreak of the Civil War. Since 1861 officers have always been in charge. Attempts to reorganize the whole Ordnance Department occurred in 1851, 1859, 1872, and 1919. New proposals for a centralized Army supply service were tendered as late as 1948.

[12] (1) Col. C. Wingate Reed, "Decius Wadsworth, First Chief of Ordnance, U.S. Army, 1812–1821," *Army Ordnance*, XXV, 139 (1943), 114–16. (2) *Cullum's Biographical Register of the Officers and Graduates of the United States Military Academy* (Boston, 1891), p. 59.

[13] (1) *Regulations for the Government of the Ordnance Department* (Washington, 1834). (2) *Ordnance Reports*, I, 381; II, 290–336; III, 229. (3) W. E. Birkhimer, *Historical Sketch of the Artillery, U. S. Army* (Washington, 1884), pp. 255ff.

[14] Government policy at this period permitted inventors to have the pilot models of their inventions built by government armorers in arsenal shops for Ordnance Department test. Thus in 1858, shortly before his Harpers Ferry raid, John Brown was having the Springfield Armory make a pistol of his design. See (1) Deyrup, *op. cit.*, p. 128, and (2) Hist of Springfield Armory, I, 1777–1865, 97–99, OHF.

manifested in the decision at the outbreak of the Civil War to drop the plans to manufacture breech-loading rifles using metallic rim cartridges. Government armorers, considering the models still experimental, feared the delays that always retard mass production of any new weapon. Thus, while American manufacturers were outstripping European in the speed and accuracy of their production techniques, the Ordnance Department was supplying the U.S. Army with rifles of a type that European manufacturers would have dubbed antiquated. Not until 1866 did the Ordnance Department succeed in converting its muzzle-loaders to breechloaders, and not until 1892 did the Army get bolt action rifles, modern by the standards of that day.[15] Widespread interest in small arms design largely subsided about 1890, partly because the possible improvements in rifles had by then been pretty much achieved and partly because the settlement of the West and disappearance of the frontier turned public attention to other problems.

In the eighties the Congress authorized creation of a permanent Ordnance Board to serve as final judge of the utility of proposed new models of weapons. Before the end of the century the Gatling gun and heavy machine guns had been adopted; research upon semiautomatic rifles, which would fire eight shots without reloading, and upon more powerful machine guns was inaugurated in 1901, and the new Springfield rifle, elaborated from the Krag-Jörgensen and the German Mauser, appeared in 1903. Meanwhile, artillery design was a subject of much debate. Adoption of the Crozier-Buffington recoil mechanism for heavy gun carriages was heralded as a great advance and perhaps served to strengthen Americans' belief in American technological superiority.[16] Though the volunteer regiments of the U.S. Army, supplied with black powder, fought the Spanish-American War against troops equipped with the newer smokeless powder, the speedy American victory quieted criticism. Confidence in American ordnance mounted steadily in spite of the discernible evidence that American equipment was consistently some years behind that of the European powers. On occasion the sharply revealed need of new models brought action. Just as Civil War combat proved the inferiority of the government-manufactured muzzle-loaders to the breechloaders of private manufacture that were purchased and issued in small numbers, so experience in the Philippine insurrection following the war with Spain impelled the Ordnance Department to seek a larger caliber side arm. Testimony of soldiers that their revolver shots failed to stop fanatical Moros from rushing to attack with their bolos led to adoption of .45-caliber instead of .38-caliber for the new automatic pistol M1911.[17]

Unlike design, responsibility for which was somewhat belatedly assigned to the Department, procurement was a major part of the Ordnance mission almost from the Department's beginning. Purchase of matériel or manufacture in government arsenals became one of its stated functions in 1815. Attempt to curtail government manufacture of arms in the interest of

[15] (1) Deyrup, *op. cit.*, pp. 23–32. (2) Hist of Springfield Armory, I, 1777–1865, pp. 101–02, OHF.

[16] (1) James E. Hicks, *Notes on United States Ordnance: I, Small Arms, 1776 to 1940* (Mount Vernon, New York, 1940), *passim.* (2) Springfield Armory Tests and Developments of Semi-Automatic Shoulder Arms, 1900 to 1914, OHF. (3) *Ordnance Reports,* III, 281. (4) Seventh Report of the Board of Ordnance and Fortification, 1897, p. 11.

[17] Record of Army Ord R&D, Vol. II, Small Arms and Small Arms Ammunition, Book 1, p. 79, OHF.

turning the business over to private industry was defeated in the fifties by the vigorous opposition of the Ordnance Department and the Secretary of War, Jefferson Davis, and was never seriously urged again. Davis argued that government manufacture as well as government design guaranteed constant improvement in models and enabled the Ordnance Department to check not only on the quality of contractors' output but also on their prices.[18] Thus the Congress, backed by public opinion, quashed the development in this country of a private munitions industry comparable to those in Europe. The enduring consequences for the Ordnance Department have been of signal importance.

Government inspection of arms before acceptance imposed the necessity of supplying gages to both government inspectors and, after 1840, to government contractors. Before that date a contractor could check his work only by comparing it with a model weapon lent as a pattern by the government. Not until after the Civil War did the Ordnance Department evolve any reasonably satisfactory system of furnishing gages and not until World War I was it applied on any scale. From the 1880's to 1916 the Master Armorer at each government arsenal was responsible for all gages needed in manufacture of the arms for which his arsenal had "technical responsibility." Under his eye, skilled workmen, rather than gage-checkers trained in mathematics, verified the accuracy of each gage. The artisan's experience largely offset the paucity of the precision measurement devices then available.[19] A separate gage unit within the Ordnance Inspection Division was a creation of World War I.

Contracting with commercial producers fell off somewhat toward the end of the nineteenth century. During the Civil War the impossibility of equipping the Union armies from stores on hand or by running the government arsenals at capacity had forced reliance upon private firms, but dependence upon inexperienced manufacturers whose output had to be reworked or assembled in government shops was expensive. All powder had to be purchased until 1907 when a plant was built at Picatinny Arsenal. After the standardization of the famous Springfield rifle M1903, government manufacture of small arms as well as most artillery became the general rule, and up to 1915 the art of ordnance-making in America was chiefly contained within the government establishments.[20]

While manufacture of arms on an interchangeable basis was achieved after a fashion long before the Civil War, in the nineteenth century it was still too little developed to enable the Ordnance Department to supply spare parts to maintenance companies in the field. Maintenance of his equipment was the user's job; repair work went back to the government arsenals.

[18] *Ordnance Reports*, II, 523–26. From time to time right down to the present, commercial producers or their congressmen have protested government manufacture of munitions, but since 1854 the matter has always been dismissed without prolonged debate. See, for example, Memorial of the Association of Manufacturers of Arms, Ammunition, and Equipments presented to the Congressional Joint Committee on the Reorganization of the Army in 1878, 45th Cong, 3d Sess, S Exec Doc 16, pp. 65–72.

[19] Interv with Theodore Fletcher, Supt Milling Div, Springfield Armory, and John Callahan, Chief of Gage Sec, Springfield Armory, Feb 45. Mr. Fletcher began his services at the armory in 1896, Mr. Callahan in 1903.

[20] (1) Hist of Springfield Armory, I, 1777–1865, OHF. (2) War Department Annual Reports, Report of the Chief of Ordnance, 1902, pp. 43, 48, 56, 63–66; 1907, pp. 46–71; 1912, p. 916; 1918–19, pp. 926–27. (Hereafter, regardless of variations of title, these reports are cited as Ann Rpt CofOrd.)

Hence, one of the knottiest recent problems of Ordnance Field Service was unknown in earlier years. During the Mexican War Ordnance rocket and mountain howitzer companies commanded by Ordnance officers served as combat troops, but thereafter Ordnance units in the field were assigned only to supply.[21] Ordnance officers commanding depots or arsenals were responsible for storing and issuing arms and ammunition and, after troop demobilization, for collecting repairable weapons for arsenal overhaul and reconditioning. Periodic inspection of matériel stored in depots or at the arsenals obtained all through the years. But Field Service, as such, was not established until after World War I.

The Ordnance Department enjoyed wide public confidence during its first hundred years. Occasional criticisms of American military equipment were usually forgotten as soon as the Ordnance Department had remedied a particular weakness. As American industrial genius began to emerge just before mid-century, America's faith in its own capacities, military and other, began to grow. Belief that American ordnance was equal to any demands that might be made upon it encouraged an unconcern over European munitions developments. What matter that foreign powers adopted machine guns a decade before the United States? If this country lagged behind a little in one field or another, when need arose American ingenuity could be counted on to overcome the handicap quickly. Entrenched on the North American continent with a friendly neighbor to the north and relatively feeble, even if troublesome, neighbors to the south, the United States felt no call to devote thought and money to making instruments of war. National energies were directed toward exploiting the natural resources of the continent and building up industrial might for peaceful ends. The Army had always fought through to victory in the past, so Americans reasoned, and, were ill chance to plunge the country into another war, again American arms would triumph. No one was troubled about deficiencies in American ordnance.

World War I

When war broke out on the continent of Europe in 1914, the American public refused to consider the possibility of United States involvement. The Ordnance Department in the preceding decades had developed orderly routines for supply of the small standing Army and as late as the fall of 1916 gave few signs of alarm at having the Congress make only moderate increases in appropriations.[22] In fact, not the Congress, but the Chief of Ordnance himself in the prewar years recommended reduction of proposed appropriations for some items of equipment.[23] The Chief of Ordnance, Brig. Gen. William B. Crozier,

[21] Apparently the violent protest of artillery officers after the Mexican War put an end to using "artisans" as soldiers. The rivalry between the artillery and the Ordnance Department in the 1840's and 1850's achieved an acrimony beside which the present-day differences among the branches of the armed services seem amicable. See *Ordnance Reports*, II, 462–67.

Probably during the Civil War, as again eighty years later, Ordnance units occasionally fought in the line when a battle became desperate, but such action was not according to the rules.

[22] (1) Ann Rpt CofOrd, 1916. (2) Army Appropriations Bill, 1918, *Hearings Before the Committee on Military Affairs, House of Representatives*, pp. 860–917. (Hereafter Congressional Hearings on Army appropriation bills will be cited as WDAB, S or HR.)

[23] The total appropriations for Ordnance increased, but the readiness of the Chief of Ordnance to curtail some expenditures below those of former years and the failure of the Department to spend all monies granted combined to create the impression that Con-

included in his annual reports for 1915 and 1916 recommendations based upon observation of the form the war in Europe was taking, particularly urging the need of more powerful artillery and armored motor cars. He protested the continued insistence of Congress that government arsenals manufacture practically all ordnance material unless private concerns could compete on price, a condition rarely realizable; he pointed out that pursuit of this policy would delay expansion of manufacturing capacity badly needed in any future emergency.[24] But he found reassurance in the number of American manufacturers that had undertaken large orders for munitions for European governments, although he recognized that plants set up to make foreign models could not immediately produce American arms and ammunition. "The time required for an unprepared adaptation of this kind is sometimes surprising, and in case of emergency would be serious." [25] Still, planning was unhurried. New designs for field and seacoast gun carriages were begun in 1916 and that summer, in order to equip and train militia in the use of machine guns, the War Department bought a few Lewis guns to supplement the meagre supply in the hands of troops on the Mexican border. Yet little more than six months before the United States was to declare war upon a major military power, the Department was just reaching a decision about how to spend the newly appropriated $12,000,000 earmarked for procurement of machine guns.[26]

Before 1918 determination of design and types of weapons for the United States Army lay chiefly with Ordnance officers. Although an Engineer officer, a Signal Corps officer, and usually both a Coast Artillery and a Field Artillery officer served on the Board of Ordnance and Fortification and so outnumbered the one Ordnance member, the Ordnance Department itself dominated this body whose recommendation was virtually fiat. Indeed, the authority exercised by the Chief of Ordnance over decisions as to what weapons the U.S. Army should have seems to have grown during General Crozier's regime. In the summer of 1901 the board had protested to the Secretary of War the Ordnance Department's arrogation unto itself of the authority and functions vested by law in the board. The Secretary of War apparently ignored the complaint. In December General Crozier, newly appointed Chief of Ordnance, won a skirmish over the question of Ordnance Department power to direct field gun tests. The rest of the board had to back down when Crozier presented a message from the Secretary of War declaring that it was his intention "to have the test of field guns conducted by the Ordnance Department, through the instrumentality of Ordnance officers by the methods of the Ordnance Department, and at the Ordnance Department's place." [27] Thereafter General Crozier, triply fortified by his position as Chief of

gress had been liberal, that the Ordnance Department had usually got what it asked for, and that Ordnance weaknesses later revealed were not traceable to Congressional parsimony. See, for example, WDAB 1916, HR, pp. 666–67, 676–77, 688–90.

[24] Ann Rpt CofOrd, 1915, pp. 23–26, 29–30; 1916, pp. 20–21, 26–28. The National Defense Act of 1916 had recognized the wisdom of placing educational orders by permitting public funds to be spent for procuring special tooling for private manufacturers willing to accept orders. But this provision and the lifting of the requirement of competitive bidding were so hedged about with other restrictions that the so-called mobilization of industry was theoretical only.

[25] Ann Rpt CofOrd, 1915, p. 25.

[26] *Ibid.*, 1916, p. 25.

[27] Proceedings of the Board of Ordnance and Fortification, 6 Dec 01, p. 103, OHF.

Ordnance, by his recognized stature as an engineer, and by his contributions in the field of artillery design, went through the motions of deferring to the board and of heeding reports of special Artillery committees or of Infantry Board members. But Ordnance Department influence was paramount. Crozier believed that the technician knew best what combat troops required.[28] While occasionally the Secretary of War appointed special boards to pass upon the respective merits of models offered by rival inventors, ordinarily the services had little say about what equipment they would fight with. The Infantry could request a more effective service revolver, the Artillery longer range guns, the Cavalry improved saddles and holsters.[29] But not until the 1920's were the using arms to play a primary part in determining military characteristics desired or in judging which model best met requirements.

The fact of the military unpreparedness of the United States in the spring of 1917 is familiar to all the generation that lived through that era and to all students of its history. The steps belatedly taken to overcome the shortages of trained men and equipment are less well known. Decision to adopt French artillery design in order to speed procurement for the U.S. Army was made before the Ordnance Department discovered the inescapable problems of adapting French drawings to American manufacturing processes. Locating facilities to produce more familiar items such as propellants, rifles, and pistols, was accomplished more successfully. The first and continuing difficulty was finding enough men competent to cope with the task.

The Chief of Ordnance had long insisted that at least two years were needed to prepare an officer for Ordnance duty. Ordnance before 1917, as after, was a technician's job. In April 1917, the Department numbered 97 officers; 11,000 Ordnance officers were needed for the projected 5,000,000-man army; in actuality 5,800 were commissioned from civilian life before the Armistice.[30] While two Ordnance schools for training officers had been organized early in the century, both were closed in the summer of 1917, presumably because they could not accommodate enough students to warrant assignments of teachers. Officer training then became sheer improvisation.[31] Candidates recruited by combing the training camps for men with some industrial engineering experience were hurried through special courses, commissioned, and assigned to work where it was hoped their civilian experience would count. So gas engine designers and manufacturers after a few weeks' instruc-

---

[28] (1) *Ibid.*, 1902–10, 1911–17, *passim.* (2) Memo, Col James H. Burns, sub: Procurement of Munitions, 14 Jan 19, OO 023/424, NA. Testimony to the undisputed character of General Crozier's authority comes also from two men attached to the Office, Chief of Ordnance, for over forty years, Arthur Adelman, from 1905 to 1916 gun designer, and L. M. Church, personal messenger for General Crozier from 1907 to 1909. Intervs with Arthur Adelman and L. M. Church, 27 Jan 49.

[29] See, for example: (1) WD SO 227, 1916; (2) WDAB 1918, HR, pp. 915–16; and (3) Ann Rpt CofOrd, 1916, pp. 17–18. See also below, Ch. VII.

[30] Sevellon Brown, *The Story of Ordnance in the World War* (Washington, 1920), pp. 35, 153–84.

All together the Ordnance Department on Armistice Day had 5,954 officers, 62,043 enlisted men, and 80,181 civilians. See Rpt D–1 (153), U.S. General Staff, Stat Br, cited in Harvey A. DeWeerd, Production Lag in the American Ordnance Program, 1917–1918, pp. 20–21. This is an unpublished doctoral dissertation, based upon thorough examination of most of the available material, both manuscript and published. Copy in OHF.

[31] Capt. William M. Spinrad, "Early History of the Ordnance School," *The Ordnance Sergeant,* III, 1 (1942), 1.

tion became the Ordnance Department's machine gun "experts,"[32] while men familiar with materials or products somewhat analogous to those of Ordnance were converted into "specialists" on other weapons and equipment. Nor were all the men commissioned as Ordnance officers possessed of engineering knowledge. Many came from fields as remote from Ordnance as bookselling, law, and the teaching of the humanities. The resulting difficulties affected all aspects of the Ordnance mission from design to inspection. In production and procurement, for example, the difference between the tools and production methods of the arsenals and those of commercial industry had to be harmonized, but the first step had to be the education or re-education alike of Regular Army Ordnance officers and officers brought in from civilian jobs. That the hasty and inevitably superficial training turned out a corps of officers even moderately effective is the miracle.[33]

Whereas provision for officer training was insufficient, no plans for enlisted men's training existed at all. In years past, troops in the line had themselves been expected to keep their equipment in serviceable condition; since equipment needing more extensive repairs had been sent to the government arsenals where workers as civilians were not subject to any Army training, the Ordnance Department had made no effort to develop courses of instruction for men in the ranks. Yet in a modern army the high degree of mechanization made special schooling for enlisted men essential, especially in techniques of maintenance. In September 1917 the Secretary of War authorized establishment of the first schools for "enlisted specialists," where in manufacturing centers in America and later in France nearly 11,000 men were trained.[34] Many times that number were needed.

But field maintenance depended upon more than trained officers and men back of the front lines; it depended upon an orderly flow of spare parts. Want of parts for automotive vehicles, in the judgment of one observer, came close to disrupting completely the AEF supply and transport system: ". . . it is generally conceded by those who were in authority and by those who were in a position to understand the situation that the Armistice came just in time to prevent this major catastrophe."[35] Exaggerated though this statement may be, the fact remains that a serious future problem was here foreshadowed. Lack of experience prevented sound guesses of what parts would be needed in what quantity, while improper numbering, a baffling multiplicity of parts, and, finally, faulty organization of handling contributed to the chaos. From the disastrous confusion over maintenance and supply, the Army learned that planned procedures must be evolved. Creation of the Division of Purchase, Storage, and Traffic in August 1918 eased matters for the last months of the war, and in 1919 the Ordnance Department was to organize its Field Service Division.

Even more alarming than the threatened breakdown in overseas maintenance was the initial lag in production of major

[32] "Before the war, a single Ordnance officer . . . had served as the expert 'staff' on automatic weapons. . . . Certainly not more than four other officers of the Ordnance Department in the field could have qualified as machine-gun Experts." Brown, *The Story of Ordnance in the World War,* p. 34.

[33] *Ibid.,* pp. 32–36.

[34] (1) *Ibid.,* pp. 153–84. (2) Spinrad, *op. cit.,* pp. 2–4.

[35] W. G. Burgan, The Spare Parts Problem and a Plan, incl to ltr, Department of the Army (AGAM-PM 451.9 (30 Mar 48) CSGSP/D7), 6 Apr 48, OHF.

items—artillery, artillery ammunition, and, to a lesser extent, trench warfare matériel. The number of field guns manufactured in this country after 1 April 1917 and shipped to France before 11 November 1918 was only 815, and the AEF was almost entirely dependent upon the French and the British through 1917 and 1918 for everything except rifles and small arms ammunition.[36] The large orders for American artillery in 1917 indicate not only fears lest foreign supply not suffice but also national pride in having the U.S. Army equipped with American guns. The reasons for the production lag deserve scrutiny.

First, time was necessary for tooling up for any big production job. The Chief of Ordnance had repeatedly pointed out that eighteen months must be allowed from the placing of orders to the beginning of large-scale production, a warning that had fallen on deaf ears. The Council of National Defense, created in August 1916, and its subsidiary Advisory Commission formed in December, had evolved some sound general ideas of procurement procedures but, before the declaration of war, had barely begun to act upon them. Next was the slowness with which the War Department arrived at decisions about what weapons it wanted.[37] It was two full months after the declaration of war before higher authority decided to adopt French artillery calibers and put in motion the plan to obtain drawings from the French Government for 75-mm. guns and 105-mm. and 155-mm. howitzers and ammunition. Six months after that the French drawings arrived, only to prove not immediately adaptable to American production processes. Indeed, the drawings for French shells were found to contain so many errors that the standard joke among the engineers of the Ordnance Department described these drawings as the ones the French had intended the German Government to obtain through secret sources. For manufacture of machine guns large orders were not placed until 20 June 1917; the special board had first to submit its recommendations and then wait for War Department red tape to unwind. Congressional adherence to peacetime restrictions on government spending further hampered negotiation of contracts; insistence on competitive bidding and allocation of funds for specified purposes were the chief sources of complications.[38]

The most frequently cited reason for the delays in producing complete ordnance items was the Department's handicap in the race for facilities. War Department acquiescence in allowing the Navy first chance to contract with established industrial firms and the decision to permit companies with foreign orders to complete them left the Ordnance Department with

[36] Crowell, *America's Munitions 1917-1918,* p. 90.

Unless otherwise noted, the data in the paragraphs that follow are derived from the careful study of DeWeerd, Production Lag in the American Ordnance Program, 1917-1918. Copy in OHF.

[37] Sharp criticism was hurled at the War Department in general and the Ordnance Department in particular for not having profited from reports of observers sent overseas. The accusations were that Ordnance Department failure to make use of descriptions of foreign matériel had needlessly delayed design and procurement of weapons proved in modern combat. Ltrs, Col Spencer Colby to Army War College, 26 Feb 15, OO 321.12/193 and 29 Dec 15, OO 231.12/121, cited in Edmund Littell, Procurement Problems of World War I, p. 9, OHF.

[38] See discussion by F. A. Scott, in 1917 chairman of the General Munitions Board and later of the War Industries Board, "Plans for an Unplanned Conflict," *Army Ordnance,* XVI, 91 (1935), 8.

Explicit permission to procure gages without competitive bidding was an exception introduced by the National Defense Act of 1916. But as late as January 1917 the Ordnance Department had placed few orders for gages. WDAB 1918, HR, pp. 865-66.

little choice but to build new facilities from the ground up.[39] Competition within the Army accentuated the problem, as the Coast Artillery, Signal Corps, Corps of Engineers, and Medical Department also had huge procurement programs to meet, and, whenever possible, pre-empted factories, materials, and labor that the Ordnance Department needed desperately.[40] Every service fended for itself as best it could. Before March 1918 when the President bestowed large powers on the War Industries Board, no clear scheme of priorities obtained and vital Ordnance orders got sidetracked. While it is a moot question whether or not the Department's inability to commandeer plants for ordnance manufacture was the primary cause of the production lag, it was unquestionably one major contributing factor.

In addition to difficulties imposed from above, Ordnance suffered from some circumstances beyond the control of any government agency in 1917. Labor shortages in many areas impeded contractors. Facilities found, materials delivered, labor recruited, producers were still seriously handicapped by a dearth of men with industrial managerial experience. Less obvious than many elements in the procurement situation, this lack of experienced men at key points created much confusion otherwise avoidable.

On the other hand, the procurement program had some weaknesses that greater foresight within the Ordnance Department might have minimized, if not wholly eliminated. Most important was the lack of information on where bottlenecks were most likely to crop up and of planned procedures to anticipate them. Obviously, the number of weapons completed must hinge on the number of components shortest in supply, usually those most difficult to make. Thousands of rifle barrels could be of no use without thousands of receivers. Yet the Ordnance Department operated for over a year without any system for checking on balanced production of matériel. In late May 1918 a Progress Section in the Estimates and Requirements Division was set up. Thereafter, repetition of earlier mistakes whereby there were more guns than gun carriages, more gun carriages than recuperators, more machined shell bodies than booster assemblies was halted. But it was too late to have effect upon deliveries of completed weapons.[41]

Hence, some of the errors derived from policy made at higher levels and some were the fault of the Ordnance Department itself. False confidence in the adequacy of American production capacity at first encouraged the Department in a complacency later paralleled only by that of the American public in prophesying quick victory over Japan immediately after Pearl Harbor. The exaggerated assurance of April 1917 that everything was ready was in turn succeeded by belief that production was hopelessly behind requirements even in November 1918. General John J. Pershing had doubled General Crozier's

[39] The Council of National Defense in April 1917 decreed "that as between the Army and the Navy priority should be given to such needs of the Navy as are intended to be completed within the period of one year." Minutes of the Council of National Defense, I, 163, cited in DeWeerd, *op. cit.*, p. 69.

[40] For fuller discussion of this situation, see Grosvenor B. Clarkson, *Industrial America in the World War* (New York, 1923), pp. 111–12, and B. Crowell and R. F. Wilson, *How America Went to War, The Armies of Industry* (New Haven, 1921), I, 2–9.

[41] On 75-mm. shells, in fact, the imbalance of completed components lasted till after the Armistice. On 1 December 1918 the totals of completed components were 30,600,000 primers, 26,800,000 cartridge cases, 12,000,000 fuzes, 13,900,000 shell bodies, 10,900,000 boosters. See Rpt 5, The Production of 75-mm H. E. Shell, p. 24, U.S. General Staff, Stat Br, cited in DeWeerd, *op. cit.*, p. 197.

MAJ. GEN. WILLIAM B. CROZIER,
Chief of Ordnance, 1901–18.

original estimates of quantities needed, and scheduling that increase had further delayed the first deliveries. Out of the confusion came one clear fact: regardless of any mistakes the General Staff or Secretary of War might make, the Ordnance Department itself must have a more efficient scheme of action. It must reappraise its organization, plan industrial mobilization of the future, and train more men and officers more fully.

Experiments in departmental reorganization had begun early in 1918, immediately after General Crozier's transfer to the War Council. But the new arrangement, based on a functional division of responsibility, heightened rather than lessened confusion because operating under separate divisions for procurement, manufacturing, inspection, and supply prevented anyone from knowing the exact status of any order or any equipment at any exact moment. A Control Bureau at the top, intended to co-ordinate activities, was unable to assemble necessary information quickly enough to apply it. Consequently upon Brig. Gen. Clarence C. Williams' appointment as Acting Chief of Ordnance in May 1918, he substituted an Estimates and Requirements Division for the Control Bureau and introduced weekly conferences between division heads, which cut through much of the administrative tangle. More sweeping changes had to wait till after the war.[42]

Meanwhile, one significant change took place: the decentralization of procurement. The delays and complexities of having every Ordnance contract go through the office of the Chief of Ordnance led to the decision to delegate authority to district offices in eleven sections of the country. This innovation, later heralded as revolutionizing, lay less in the creation of geographically scattered offices with considerable independence of action than in the fact that civilians were put in charge. For the former, the federal system of local and national government offered precedent, while the regional Federal Reserve banks set a more explicit pattern. But the effectiveness of the new arrangement derived from turning over to local industrial leaders responsibility for mobilizing local civilian industry for war production. "The purpose of this unusual arrangement," the Chief of Ordnance wrote after the war, "was to secure a measure of elasticity and a degree of discretion for the district chiefs which they could not obtain if they were

[42] Ordnance Department Office Orders 8, 31 May 17; 104, 4 Jan 18; 222, 25 May 18; 297, 10 Aug 18. All in OHF. (Hereafter Office Orders will be cited as ODO.) For further discussion, see below, Ch. IV.

under military discipline; to inspire among manufacturers the sense of cooperation and reciprocal understanding the presence of a civilian chief was calculated to arouse. . . . These objects were attained."[43]

Responsibility placed upon district chiefs was coupled with authority. Because Col. Guy E. Tripp, who organized the districts, succeeded in finding unusually able men to head the districts, the delays in placing contracts and getting ordnance production started began to diminish immediately. Colonel Tripp, in civilian life chairman of the board of directors of the Westinghouse Electrical and Manufacturing Company, encouraged short cuts. Business procedures, direct and informal, superseded military. Although actual negotiation and execution of formal contracts remained in Washington, the preliminaries to the legal work, the later supervision of fulfilling the contracts, and finally the all-important inspections for acceptance of matériel fell to the district staffs. The pronounced rise in the production curve after the districts began to function cannot, of course, be attributed solely to their work.[44] Yet Ordnance officers were so impressed with the value of the system that as the war went on the scope of district operations was widened and two more districts were added. Decentralization in Ordnance procurement was thus proceeding at the very time that centralization of controls at higher levels was being contrived by vesting power more largely in the War Industries Board. Though the Ordnance district offices disappeared after winding up their affairs in 1919, they were re-established in 1922 because they were believed to be the most effective agencies for industrial mobilization.

Published versions of what happened in

MAJ. GEN. CLARENCE C. WILLIAMS, *Chief of Ordnance, 1918–30.*

1917–18 have taken one or the other of two lines: violent criticism of the Ordnance Department for its slowness in meeting the Army's needs, or extravagant eulogies of the efficiency that converted a cabbage patch into a munitions factory in eight months. Both are partly justified. Had France and Great Britain not supplied the

[43] Ann Rpt CofOrd, 1919, p. 28.

[44] Figures giving exactly comparable data before and after the creation of the districts are not obtainable. Statistics showing the rise in volume of contracts placed, though not of orders completed, offer only partial evidence. Thus, of contracts totaling $1,073,305,731 entered into by the Ordnance Department before mid-December 1917, only $28,715,779 worth had been delivered—less than 3 percent. By 1 November 1918, the value of contracts let was $3,185,559,623. No computation of the percentage filled is possible, for manufacturers of many items apparently were paid for deliveries made in 1919. See Clark B. Firestone, *The Ordnance Districts, 1918-19* (Washington, 1920).

U.S. Army with arms and ammunition almost to the end of the fighting, the achievement of United States readiness for full-scale production nineteen months after declaration of war would not have mattered. Defeat or victory would have been already determined. Yet, given time, the Ordnance Department proved it could organize a colossal production program. During the next twenty years, the Army was to apply many of the lessons of World War I. The assumption that the United States always could meet any emergency was never again to induce such far-flung, fateful complacency within the Ordnance Department.

In one realm, unhappily, the Ordnance Department failed to profit fully from experience. It failed to follow the work of foreign munitions makers closely enough to keep American ordnance abreast of significant new developments. Little use was made of information brought back by officers sent abroad. After the appearance of the important report submitted in 1919 by a carefully chosen group of Army officers, usually called the Westervelt Board, no similar bodies were created empowered to explore the whole field of ordnance design, foreign as well as American. Money to build American weapons incorporating European improvements would, to be sure, not have been forthcoming from the Congresses of the 1920's and 1930's—the nation was intent on forgetting about war—but the Army would at least have comprehended more clearly what it had to compete against. Military observers in London and Berlin in the 1930's were to tender numerous reports on changes in British and German equipment, but if officers in Washington gave weight to the information, they took no steps to establish an efficient routine that would permit Ordnance designers to adopt useful European innovations.[45] Yet American ignorance of any details of German and French munitions developments preceding 1917 had admittedly had grave consequences. Realization that in twentieth century Europe a full-blown industry was giving constant attention to devising new weapons and refining old did not sink in sufficiently upon the War Department. Inattention to what competitors had available was eventually to prove extremely costly. Whether it stemmed from overconfidence in American technological genius or from apathy deriving from conviction that the Congress would not grant money for military research, this disregard of foreign developments after the early twenties must constitute a serious charge against the Ordnance Department.

In other fields Ordnance officers were to put their hard-won experience to effective use. Out of World War I came several important changes, changes in methods and planning and, still more basic, changes in thinking. The Ordnance Department had learned that it could not operate efficiently without a considerable body of trained men. Enlisted men as well as officers must be taught Ordnance techniques of supply and maintenance and be familiarized with some of the problems of design and production. The upshot was the launching, in the summer of 1919, of a school for enlisted men which in one form or another has carried on without break to the present. The Ordnance Department, like all other units of the Army and Navy, had

[45] See Ch. VII, below. Some officers had long appreciated the importance of having U.S. Army Ordnance experts in Europe. In 1901 the Secretary of War authorized the Department to send two officers to study special problems. Ann Rpt CofOrd, 1901, p. 10.

also discovered that careful plans for wartime use of private industry must be so complete that loss of time and waste effort in mass production would be reduced to a minimum. Much of the twenty years that followed the 1918 Armistice was to be dedicated, consequently, to producing blueprints for industrial mobilization. Establishment of the Army Industrial College in 1924 grew out of recognition that military procurement planning must have specialists trained for just that. A third lesson of World War I was the need for a staff within the Ordnance Department assigned to the sole task of organizing storage and issue of matériel and qualified to supervise maintenance of equipment. The creation of Field Service was the answer.

The final change in the workings of the Ordnance Department was the least immediately apparent but, in long-term effects, the most fundamental. The Chief of Ordnance ceased to be the Czar whose dictates on military characteristics and design of weapons the using arms accepted without demur. No General Crozier was ever again to issue to the Infantry or the Field Artillery or the Cavalry equipment that the Ordnance Department had decided was suitable. Partly because General Crozier's prestige had been badly shaken by the Senate Investigating Committee in December 1917,[46] and partly because General Williams, Chief of Ordnance from May 1918 to 1930, had himself seen overseas service, the combat arms thereafter were to have a constantly growing share in deciding what type and what model of weapons they would employ. General Williams is reported to have declared upon his return from Europe in the spring of 1918: "If the fighting men want elephants, we get them elephants."[47] Ordnance officers in Washington would no longer exercise their technicians' prerogative to insist that mice or mules would suffice. How far General Williams' influence counted in inaugurating the change whereby the Infantry Board and other service boards stipulated their requirements and passed judgment upon what the Ordnance Department produced to meet them may be a question. Certainly his attitude, born of personal observation of combat, made infinitely easier the transition to the new order. The Ordnance Department became to an ever greater degree the skilled servant, not the master, of the using arms.

[46] See *Hearings Before the Committee on Military Affairs*, Pt. I, S, 65th Cong, 2d Sess.

[47] Quoted by Arthur Adelman, Chief of Artillery Ammunition Branch, Industrial Division, OCO, in an interview with the author, 27 Jan 49. For a similar pronouncement made by General Williams in the summer of 1917 in France, see History of the Services of Supply, The Ordnance Department, A.E.F., OO 023/423, NA.

CHAPTER II

The Ordnance Department: 1919–40

The nearly twenty years between the Armistice of November 1918 and the German *Anschluss* with Austria in March 1938 saw the American public gradually shift from hope in the possibility of enduring peace to uneasy perception that aggressive force was again taking command of the international scene. For the Army, and for the Ordnance Department in particular, changes in public opinion, expressed through Congressional appropriations, set the pattern of activity; the amount of money available for maintenance, development, and manufacture of fighting equipment always imposed the limits within which the Ordnance Department could work. Had judgment invariably been faultless in interpreting the importance of foreign arms developments, had the Army evolved the most comprehensive, sound doctrine of what weapons were needed for mechanized warfare and how an army in the field should use them, and had the Ordnance Department devised an ideal scheme of procurement and maintenance of munitions, all this must still have been useless without money enough to turn ideas into matériel. Hence, funds voted by the Congress, generally adhering to the dictates of American public opinion, determined the scope of Ordnance work.

At the end of World War I the United States, shocked by recent discovery of its military weakness, appeared to be ready to support an army large enough and sufficiently well armed to prevent a repetition of the unpreparedness of 1917. The Ordnance Department was instructed to assemble, store, and maintain the equipment that had belatedly been manufactured in the United States or had been captured from the enemy. These stores alone might serve, so the Congress could believe, to guarantee American military strength for some years. Belief in the need of a sizable military establishment endured only long enough to put on the statute books the National Defense Act of June 1920 before a reaction swept away all idea of American participation in international affairs and, at the same time, interest in the Army. The slogan "Back to Normalcy," which carried Warren G. Harding into the White House, spelled not only repudiation of the League of Nations but rejection of plans to build a strong peacetime Army. Budget cuts for the War Department soon made unattainable the Army of 280,000 men and 18,000 officers authorized by the National Defense Act and reduced the Ordnance Department program to a shadow of the substance hoped for.

Meanwhile, despite American refusal to

join the League of Nations, a steadily mounting pressure to work for permanent peace began to make itself felt. This pressure somewhat altered the temper of the Congress, encouraging small appropriations for national defense. The naval building truce of 1922, followed by the Locarno Pact in 1925, and the high point of faith in world peace reached with the signing of the Kellogg-Briand Pact in 1928, made reasonable the hope that the Army need be only a police force. If war could be outlawed, Ordnance equipment could be kept at a minimum.

The depression of the thirties called a sudden halt to America's efforts to play a leading role in establishing permanent world peace. The general attitude now became: "Attend to problems at home and let other nations take care of themselves." Appropriations for the Ordnance Department in the early thirties were reduced to save money, apparently without regard to achieving any purely moral goal. Temporarily, additional funds from PWA and WPA bolstered the Ordnance Department. The public could view the later, larger allocations of money for Ordnance as part of a make-work program, primarily a means of shoring up the whole economy. Absorbed in domestic troubles, the United States turned its back upon Europe and Asia. The Italo-Ethiopian war, the German occupation of the Rhineland, the "dress rehearsal" of the Spanish Civil War, and the Japanese "incident" in Manchuria failed to rouse profound apprehensions in the United States. Conscientious military observers could report upon German rearmament and append data on new weapons, but the Ordnance Department, even if it digested the information, could not act upon it.

A partial awakening to the new aggressive spirit abroad that might involve the United States, rigid isolation notwithstanding, came with the German march into Austria in March 1938. It is reasonable to believe that this move helped the passage of the first act permitting the War Department to place "educational orders" with private industry. Antedating by over two years President Franklin D. Roosevelt's proclamation of a national emergency, the permission to spend money to give commercial concerns experience in manufacturing munitions marked the beginning of a new era. The next eighteen months, while public opinion veered steadily toward acceptance of national rearmament, saw greatly increased activity in the Ordnance Department. Yet by 1940 the task was just begun.

Because ordnance matériel takes years to design, test, and manufacture, and because it takes years to teach troops to use the finished product, full understanding of the Ordnance situation in 1940 calls for examination of the problems, achievements, and shortcomings of the Ordnance Department in the preceding twenty years. From 1920 to 1940 plans had always to be shaved down, operations were always restricted, projects were frequently stopped short of completion, all for lack of money. This fact must be borne in mind, but it cannot in itself explain 1940. Hence it is necessary to explore the evolution of careful industrial mobilization plans; the performance of the newly created Field Service Division; the mapping and partial execution of a comprehensive artillery development program; the experimentation with tank design; the difficulties besetting Ordnance designers in developing weapons that would satisfy the using arms, yet, if possible, anticipate the emergence of Army doctrine adapted to

291064 O—55——4

modern mechanized warfare; and finally, the consequences of faulty use of technical intelligence about new foreign equipment. Inasmuch as ordnance cannot be hastily improvised, the ideas that took shape during the peace years demand attention. Activities long established and conducted along accepted lines warrant no discussion here, for they represent no new facet of Ordnance Department problems. The organization of the Department must be described briefly in order to supply the framework within which operations were carried on. Some analysis of the budget and yearly appropriations must, of course, be included. But though ever-present financial considerations, be it repeated, and the earmarking of sums for particular projects limited Ordnance activities between wars, the pattern was not determined by money alone.

Organization, 1919–39

World War I proved to the War Department and all its branches that its administrative machinery must be revamped; what had sufficed for the tiny standing Army of the early years of the century could not bear the load that emergency put upon it.[1] The National Defense Act of 1920, which established the new over-all organization of the War Department, affected the Ordnance Department immediately in two respects. The first was the increase in the number of officers and enlisted men assigned to Ordnance. Before 1917 the Ordnance Department had been limited to 97 officers; after 1920 it was allotted a major general, two brigadier generals, 350 other officers, and 4,500 enlisted men. Notable though this increase would appear, it was only 1.9 and 1.6 percent, respectively, of the maximum officer and enlisted strength allowed the whole Army, and in actuality for twenty years it was never achieved. The second and greater consequence of the act for the Ordnance Department lay in the provision of Section 5a, which gave the Assistant Secretary of War "supervision of the procurement of all military supplies and other business of the War Department pertaining thereto and the assurance of adequate provision for the mobilization of matériel and industrial organizations essential to wartime needs."[2] Co-ordination of purchasing activities through the Assistant Secretary was intended to prevent a repetition of the World War I competition for facilities among separate supply bureaus within the Army. It meant that all the services of supply henceforward were to operate both through military channels by way of the General Staff and through civilian via the Assistant Secretary of War.

The Chief of Ordnance did not wait for Congressional action before reorganizing his own Department. Because he believed that the 1918 experience proved the inherent weaknesses of any purely functional plan of organization, General Williams early in 1919 realigned responsibilities, setting up a simple, logical scheme which, with minor changes, served as the basic pattern within the Ordnance Department all through the peace years. In describing his plan and the slight revisions he put into effect in the fall of 1920, he told a group at the General Staff College: "There is no question in the minds of all of us who have had experience in the Ordnance Department but that the subjective system of

[1] See, for example: (1) memo, Brig Gen J. H. Rice, Chief Ord Off AEF, for CofOrd, 21 Jun 19, sub: Fundamental Relations Between the General Staff and Other Branches of the Military Service, OO 320/100, NA; and (2) memo, Brig Gen W. S. Peirce, Actg CofOrd, for CofS, 18 Apr 19, sub: Organization of the Army on a Peace Footing, OO 320/83, NA.

[2] *U.S. Statutes at Large,* XLI, 764–65.

organization is far superior to the functional."[3] "Subjective" meant categories of weapons, artillery for example, and artillery ammunition, small arms, and combat vehicles. The board of officers he had appointed in 1920 to study alternatives worked out the details of the organization charts only after careful consideration of the relative merits of other systems. The result was a division of responsibility by function only at the top level. This made three main units. Design and manufacture were assigned to one division, maintenance and distribution to another, while the general administrative work that implemented the other two fell to the third. Within the two operating divisions, lines of responsibility were drawn "vertically" according to type of commodity, a subjective or product system.[4]

Administration was assigned to a General Office, and for a time to an Administration Division as well, which handled fiscal and legal matters for the whole Department, hired and trained civilian employees, supervised military training and personnel, and maintained records. Indicative of the new postwar awareness of problems of industrial mobilization, a War Planning unit was always included as one subdivision of the General Office. Though the Ordnance district offices, re-established in 1922, undertook some local planning, most administrative business of the Department between 1920 and 1940 was concentrated in Washington under the immediate eye of the Chief of Ordnance and his staff.

To the three main divisions of the Department, the Chief of Ordnance added a staff group to serve as general liaison on technical questions. The Technical Staff was composed of officers and civilians, each a specialist in a particular field of ordnance design or manufacture—field artillery, coast artillery, ammunition, small arms, tank and automotive equipment, or air ordnance. Primarily advisory, the Technical Staff was charged with the responsibility "to keep informed of the trend and progress of ordnance development at home and abroad," and, in keeping with this assignment, to act as a clearing house for information on technical engineering problems and to build up a technical library in the Ordnance Office.[5] Members of the Technical Staff did not themselves do the creative design work at the drawing boards and in the shops where pilot models were built. This was the function of the engineers of Manufacturing Service. But the Technical Staff was authorized to recommend research projects and to pass upon designs of the Manufacturing Service engineers.

Advisory to the chief of the Technical Staff was an Ordnance Committee. Creation of this committee marked a true innovation, for it included representatives of the using arms and services. It was the successor to the Ordnance Board of prewar days but was expressly aimed at giving "the line of the army a greater influence over the design and development of Ordnance than it ever possessed in the past. . . ."[6] The chief of the Technical Staff explained: "The line members of the Ordnance Committee will, therefore, be inti-

[3] Maj. Gen. C. C. Williams, Organization and Duties of the Ordnance Department, lecture, General Staff College, 21 Feb 21, OHF.

[4] ODO 13, 12 Jan 20; 164, 20 Nov 20, OHF. The first postwar scheme included a Nitrates Division to manage the nitrates plants acquired during the war. Later this unit was absorbed into the Manufacturing Division.

[5] ODO 164, 20 Nov 20, p. 4, OHF.

[6] Memo, Col Colden L'H. Ruggles, Chief of Tech Staff, OD, for Maj Gen William L. Kenly, Dir Mil Aeronautics, 21 Jan 19, sub: Assignment of Qualified Officers of Line to Tech Staff, OD T-210.313/2, Authority and Organization, Ordnance Committee Minutes, Ord Tech Committee Secretariat files.

mately concerned in establishing the type to be developed, in passing upon and approving the preliminary studies and the final drawings thereof and, lastly, in making and witnessing the actual test of the material and passing final judgment upon its satisfactoriness for use by the service."[7] Not until General George C. Marshall became Chief of Staff in 1939 did higher authority insist upon reviewing proposed military characteristics. Thus, for twenty years it was the Ordnance Committee that put the formal seal of approval upon specifications and designs after satisfactory trials of pilot models were completed, and who, after service tests, issued the minutes that in effect standardized or rendered obsolete each item of ordnance. As final approval of the General Staff and Secretary of War on matters of standardization soon became practically automatic, Ordnance Committee minutes in time constituted the orthodox "Bible of Ordnance." From the committee stemmed the *Book of Standards, Ordnance Department*—the listing of equipment, type by type and model by model, accepted for issue to troops.[8]

On the operating level, responsibility was divided between the Manufacturing Service and the Field Service. The Manufacturing Service designed, developed, produced or procured, and inspected all matériel and ran the manufacturing arsenals and acceptance proving grounds. The tests of experimental models, usually held at Aberdeen Proving Ground, were conducted by Manufacturing Service engineers, although the Technical Staff was in charge and prepared the formal reports of tests. When the district offices were reconstituted in 1922, Manufacturing Service directed their activities also. Within the Manufacturing Service, the breakdown of duties of lower echelons was by commodity—ammunition, artillery, aircraft armament, and small arms. Field Service had charge of all storage depots, maintenance and issue of equipment to troops, and all salvage operations. With the appearance of the more detailed organization orders of 1931, Field Service was assigned preparation of standard nomenclature lists, technical regulations, firing tables, and the tables of organization and basic allowances whereby distribution of Ordnance supplies was to be made. Field Service, like Manufacturing Service, set up separate operating units, during most of the period before 1940 consisting of four divisions, Executive, General Supply, Ammunition, and Maintenance. Although there was some shifting of particular duties from one major division of the Ordnance Department to another and some redistribution of tasks and titles within a division, this general pattern remained intact for twenty years. It was endorsed by the General Staff after a thorough survey of the Department in 1929.[9]

[7] (1) *Ibid.* (2) Memo, Gen Williams for CofS, 5 Feb 19, sub: Assignment of Qualified Officers of the Line to the Technical Staff, OO 023/428, NA. (3) ODO 815, 23 Jul 19, OHF.

[8] (1) AR 850-25, 15 Dec 24; 15 Jun 27; 15 Jul 31; 23 Jul 36. (2) Tech Staff General Instructions 7, 27 Sep 24, sub: *Book of Standards, Ordnance Department*, Authority and Organization, Ordnance Committee Minutes, Ord Tech Committee Secretariat files.

See also discussion in Mark Skinner Watson, *Chief of Staff, Prewar Plans and Preparations* (Washington, 1950), pp. 54–55.

[9] (1) ODO 412, 22 Jun 22; ODO 425, 28 Aug 22; ODO 573, 1 Dec 24; ODO 10, 20 Jan 31; ODO 27, 4 Jun 32; ODO 37, 20 Jun 33; ODO 43, 14 Oct 33; and ODO 112, 3 Jun 38, OHF. (2) Survey of Ord Dept, 20 Sep 29, OO 320/377, NA.

A good example of a reshuffling of labels without fundamental change in assignment of duties was the order of 1938 placing both the Technical Staff and the Field Service under a "Chief of Military Service." Both groups carried on their independent activities as before. See ODO 112, 3 Jun 38, and ODO 122, 31 Jul 39, OHF.

The orders of 1931 made more explicit allocation of duties in the Office, Chief of Ordnance, than had earlier organization orders. Issued shortly before the announcement of the first War Department Industrial Mobilization Plan, the new organization was "intended basically for either peace or war," a scheme that would enable changes in time of emergency to be confined to expansion by elevating branches to sections and sections to divisions.[10] The only significant change was the assignment to Field Service of responsibility for depots attached to arsenals and for Ordnance sections of Army general depots.

Revision in the summer of 1939 in turn reflected the reviving importance of the Ordnance Department, as the Congress, viewing the troubled world situation, appropriated money for educational orders and over-all Army expansion. While the 1939 organization plan of the Department was in essentials identical with the earlier, the order clearly specified new lines of activity. For example, the Technical Staff was charged with arranging to furnish qualified men to represent Ordnance on the technical committees of other branches of the War Department and was to review technical and training regulations, supervise training of Reserve officers assigned to Technical Staff work, and pass upon requests for loans and sales under the American Designers Act and upon applications for patents to determine their status regarding military secrecy. In the Industrial Service, as the Manufacturing Service was relabeled in 1938, a new Procurement Planning Division was created to expedite execution of educational orders placed with commercial producers and to prepare the path for greater co-operation with private industry. Training of Reserve officers here was also specifically directed. Field Service similarly added a unit, a War Plans and Training Division, and was instructed to so organize its General Supply Division that it could handle sales to foreign governments and other authorized purchasers.[11] In almost every particular the new enumeration of duties bespoke a comprehension of emergency needs, though war in Europe had not yet broken out. As far as paper organization went, the Office of the Chief of Ordnance had girded its loins in advance.

The arsenals, manufacturing installations long antedating World War I, were not profoundly affected by reassignments of responsibility in Washington. At the head of each arsenal was an officer of the Department who combined the roles of commanding officer of the installation as a military post and manager of a large industrial plant. His dual position was a small-scale replica of that of the Chief of Ordnance in relation to the Army as a whole. The commanding officers of the arsenals were allowed small staffs of lower ranking officers, in the lean days of the mid-twenties about four each, later seven or eight. One officer was usually assigned to the arsenal experimental unit, one as Works Manager or Production Manager, and one to head the Field Service depot after the Field Service installation at the arsenal was set up separately. Most of the administrative personnel and all the production workers in the shops were civilian. Many of them were Civil Service career men with long years of arsenal service; it was not unusual to find foremen who had been employees at one arsenal for thirty or forty years. These men supplied the continuity in operations that the officers, transferred after, at most, a four-year tour

[10] ODO 10, 20 Jan 31, p. 1, OHF.
[11] ODO 122, 31 Jul 39, OHF.

of duty at any one station, could not give. The old-timers, possessed of the know-how of ordnance manufacture, were the men who perpetuated the art. Though this superimposition of a perpetual succession of relatively inexperienced officers upon civilian administrators and workmen long expert in their own fields might appear to presage conflict, relations between the military and civilians in the peace years were as a rule easy to the point of cordiality.

Design or redesign of any piece of equipment might be undertaken by engineers in the Office, Chief of Ordnance, in Washington or might be assigned to men at one of the arsenals. Before 1940, regardless of the birthplace of a design, the first pilot was always built at an arsenal. The arsenal chosen depended on the article, since the postwar reorganization allotted each establishment particular items for which it alone had "technical responsibility." Thus, one or another of the six manufacturing arsenals filed and kept up to date the drawings and specifications for every article made or purchased by the Department. Rock Island, for example, assembled and kept all data on the manufacture of tanks; Frankford the drawings and specifications on optical and fire control instruments; and Springfield Armory the data on rifles and aircraft armament.[12] No two arsenals necessarily had the same internal organization at any given moment. The commanding officer could align his staff as he saw fit as long as the arsenal mission was achieved.[13] Basic research laboratories were maintained at every arsenal save Springfield and Watervliet; every one had an experimental unit, whether within or outside an engineering department, and each had its shops and its administrative division. When arsenal employees numbered only a few hundred, arsenal organization was simple; it was elaborated somewhat when, toward the end of the thirties, activity increased. War planning sections were established in 1935 and charged with maintaining liaison with district offices and with commercial producers who had to be furnished blueprints and descriptions of processes of manufacture of the weapons or parts they might contract to make.[14] Training inspectors for accepting the products of contracting firms was always an arsenal duty.

After the Armistice the district offices were closed one after the other, as contracts were terminated and salvage operations neared completion, until only Chicago and Philadelphia survived.[15] When surplus matériel, raw materials, and machine tools still undisposed of had been turned over to the arsenals or field depots, no function appeared to remain for procurement districts. But by 1922 War Department stress on planning industrial mobilization pointed to the wisdom of recreating a skeleton organization of district offices. Establishing these offices in peacetime to prepare for wartime procurement was a totally new departure. It showed how fully the War Department had learned that ordnance manufacture demands a skill not to be acquired overnight. Thirteen districts were formed covering the same areas as in the war, except that a San Francisco office was split off from the St. Louis District. Like the arsenals, the districts were a responsibility of the Manu-

[12] Aircraft armament immediately after World War I had constituted a separate division of Manufacturing Service with an office at Wright Field in Dayton, Ohio, but the reduction of staff in the summer of 1921 led to the transfer of this activity to Springfield Armory. (1) ODO 847, 15 Aug 19, OHF. (2) Hist of Springfield Armory, 1918–41, OHF.

[13] ODO 854, 14 Aug 19, OHF.

[14] See arsenal histories, MSs in OHF.

[15] ODO 207, 29 Jan 21, OHF.

facturing Service. The civilian district chiefs were leading businessmen familiar with the industrial facilities of their regions. Each was assigned a Regular Army officer as an assistant and each had a clerk. Before 1939 this was the whole staff. The chiefs assembled records of companies' war performance, made surveys of potential ordnance manufacturing capacity, and kept alive in their districts some understanding of Ordnance procurement problems. The value of the districts lay less in what they accomplished during the peace years than in their maintaining in standby condition the administrative machinery for procurement.[16] Meanwhile, probably the best public relations device of these years in nourishing the interest of American industry in Ordnance manufacture was the Army Ordnance Association, founded in 1920, together with its magazine, *Army Ordnance*.

Apart from the proving grounds, manufacturing arsenals, loading plants, and district offices, all field installations were the responsibility of Field Service. This new postwar service found itself obliged to organize and expand simultaneously. Manifestly, the handful of depots and repair arsenals that had existed before 1917 were totally insufficient to handle the storage and maintenance of the vast quantities of matériel accumulated at the end of the war. Nor did earlier experience offer any pattern of permanent organization and procedure. In September 1919 the Provisional Manual for Ordnance Field Service appeared, embodying the principles that had proved sound in overseas operations; upon this basis Field Service proceeded to organize the details of its work in this country.[17] Meanwhile, though makeshift arrangements were necessary to provide temporary storage for the tons of matériel that had accumulated in the United States immediately after the Armistice and that were soon augmented by shipments of supplies returned from overseas, common sense dictated formulation of some settled policy on what stocks of munitions as well as what manufacturing facilities were to be maintained for the future. The reports of the so-called Munitions Board, appointed by the Chief of Ordnance in the summer of 1919 to wrestle with this problem, formed the basis upon which plans for storage and maintenance were built. Yet it is worth noting that the failure of the General Staff and the Secretary of War to act upon some of the board's recommendations imposed upon the Ordnance Department obligation to store and maintain far larger quantities of munitions than the board believed could reasonably be marked as primary reserve. This reserve affected scheduling for the manufacture of new ammunition.[18]

The decision approved by the Secretary of War was to create a network of depots, some reserved for ammunition, the rest for other ordnance supplies. The five depots built during World War I along the Atlantic seaboard to serve as forwarding centers for overseas shipments were designated as

[16] (1) *Ann Rpt SW,* 1921, p. 172; 1922, pp. 249–50. (2) ODO 404, 17 May 22, OHF. (3) Wayne W. Cowan, "Ordnance District Operation in War," *Army Ordnance*, XIV, 80 (1933), 96–99.

[17] (1) Provisional Manual for Ordnance Field Service, September 1919 (Washington, 1920), NA. (2) Field Service, . . . General Duties and Functions, 1 May 1921 (Washington, 1921), pp. 8–9, NA.

[18] (1) Memo, CofOrd for CofS, 29 Jan 21, sub: Development of a Munitions Policy, and incl, memo, Board of Officers, appointed by Ord Office Order 798, for CofOrd, 14 Jan 21, sub: Final Rpt of Bd, OKD 470/135.1, Ord Tech Intel files. (2) Memo, Stat and Ind War Planning Sec for ASW, 30 Nov 22, sub: Introduction to 1922 Ord War Plan, OO 381, NA. (3) Statement of Maj Gen C. M. Wesson before the Truman Committee, U.S. Senate, April 1941, p. 3, OHF. (4) See below, "Field Service," pp. 59ff.

ammunition depots where 25 percent of the permanent reserve was to be stored. A new depot near Ogden, Utah, was to take 15 percent and one at Savanna, Illinois, the rest.[19] Four establishments combined supply functions with repair work: Augusta Arsenal in Georgia, Benicia Arsenal in California, San Antonio Arsenal in Texas, and Raritan Arsenal built at Metuchen, New Jersey, during the war. The first three dated from before the Civil War and had long operated machine shops for overhaul, repair, and modification work. But differentiation between ammunition and general storage or repair depots was never complete. Raritan, after 1919 by far the largest of the Field Service depots, became not only an ammunition depot and a repair arsenal but also the seat of the Ordnance Enlisted Specialist School and, in 1921, the office responsible for publication of the standard nomenclature lists.

By 1923 the twenty-two storage depots that existed in 1920 had shrunk to sixteen—seven ammunition, two reserve, and seven general supply depots. These were Raritan Arsenal; Delaware General Ordnance Depot, located near Wilmington; Curtis Bay near Baltimore; Nansemond near Norfolk, Virginia; Charleston in South Carolina; Ogden; Savanna in Illinois; Augusta; Benicia; San Antonio; Rock Island; Wingate in New Mexico; Erie Proving Ground and Columbus General Supply Depot in Ohio; New Cumberland General Depot in Pennsylvania; and the Schenectady General Depot in New York State. General depots were those where more than one Army supply service maintained sections. Overseas, technically outside the command of the Chief of Ordnance, Field Service had three depots, in Hawaii, Panama, and the Philippines; and after 1923 the depots at the manufacturing arsenals were turned over to Field Service.[20]

Command of each of these installations was usually assigned to an Ordnance officer who reported to the Chief of Field Service in the Office, Chief of Ordnance, in Washington. As at the manufacturing arsenals, subordinate officers, enlisted men, and civilians made up the rosters, numbers depending on the size and complexity of operations at the depot. Ideal execution of the multiple functions of Ordnance depots—reception, classification, storage, inspection, maintenance, and issue—would have required more personnel than the Ordnance Department could muster through the peace years. But to Field Service was assigned the largest number of the Department's military personnel. The value of the property to be accounted for was about $1,311,949,000 in the spring of 1921.[21] Although in time this valuation dropped as ammunition stores deteriorated and weapons, even when serviceable, approached obsolescence, the property accountability of Field Service continued to be heavy. This routine accounting, the necessarily complicated perpetual check on inventories through the Ordnance Provision System, and the specialized nature of the matériel repair and maintenance work conducted at depots demanded trained men. Hence, Field Service was at first charged with training all Ordnance troops except proving ground companies. While later the special

[19] Charles Baxter, "Ogden Arsenal," *Army Ordnance*, I, 1 (1920), 23–24.

[20] Field Service, . . . General Duties and Functions, 1 May 21, NA. In the case of the depots at the manufacturing arsenals, the arsenal commanding officer often acted as chief of the depot, in order to save officers for other assignment.

[21] Computed from data in Directory of Ordnance Establishments, 26 Apr 21, Ord Library, U294 XOM.

service schools became the responsibility of the General Office of the Office, Chief of Ordnance, enlisted men gained practical experience in such essential operations as stock-record-keeping chiefly at Field Service depots.[22]

Storage depots were classified as reserve, intermediate, embarkation, area, and station storage. The first were what the name implied, depots for war reserve matériel; the second were for supplies to be issued in bulk to territorial commands and theatres of operations; embarkation storage depots were bases for overseas shipments; area storage for storage and issue within particular territorial commands; and station storage for items to be issued locally to troops at Army posts and camps. Ammunition depots, recognized as constituting a special problem, were organized differently. Classification of ammunition for storage was sixfold: finished ammunition and loaded components; smokeless powder; fuzes and primers; high explosives; sodium nitrate; and inert components such as empty shell, metallic components of fuses, and also small arms ammunition. To safeguard against deterioration, careful provision was made for "surveillance" with a "Surveillance Inspector" responsible for periodic testing of explosives at each large ammunition depot.[23] Maintenance of other matériel was a responsibility divided between repair arsenals servicing designated Army corps areas and the Ordnance officers assigned to the staff of each of the nine corps area commanders and commanders of foreign departments. The position and duties of officers responsible for maintenance of equipment in the hands of troops were analogous to those of Ordnance officers of armies operating in the field.[24]

MAJ. GEN. WILLIAM H. TSCHAPPAT, *Chief of Ordnance, 1934–38.*

The organization of the Ordnance Department during the "twenty-year Armistice" was thus orderly and well suited to the scale of operations the Department was allowed. Restriction to fewer than 270 officers before 1939 automatically limited what the Department could accomplish. That all gaps and overlappings of duties were not provided for was fully admitted. The Chief of Ordnance stated flatly in January 1931: "Whereas this order is intended to indicate division of responsibility and lines of authority within the Office, Chief of Ordnance, it is obvious that hard and fast lines cannot be drawn. Lapses and overlaps are bound to occur. With

[22] ODO 425, 28 Aug 22; 573, 5 Dec 24, OHF. See below, "Field Service," pp. 59ff.

[23] Field Service, . . . General Duties and Functions, 1 May 21, pp. 18–23, 29–38, NA.

[24] (1) *Ibid.*, pp. 51–52. (2) WD GO 80, 1919, and WD GO 21, 1920.

this order as a guide, all are enjoined to co-operate in the effort to best perform the functions as a whole." [25] In the field installations, as in the Washington office, on the whole the machinery worked.

Four chiefs of Ordnance served the Department during the years between world wars: General Williams, 1918–30; Maj. Gen. Samuel Hof, 1930–34; Maj. Gen. William H. Tschappat, 1934–38; and Maj. Gen. Charles M. Wesson, 1938–42. General Williams, an officer whose conception of the Ordnance mission had been profoundly affected by his overseas service in 1917–18, combined openmindedness with unusual administrative ability. His vigorous pursuit of the Westervelt Board recommendations on new equipment, his encouragement of industrial mobilization planning, and his judicious selection of officers to carry out these basic policies earned him universal respect. Department morale during his term of office was exceptionally high. His successor, General Hof, was handicapped by the curtailment of Ordnance funds, a result of the countrywide depression of the early thirties. Hof's greatest contribution to the Department lay in preserving the gains it had already made. General Tschappat, known to his associates as the greatest ballistician of all time, was pre-eminently concerned with the scientific aspects of ordnance and, by his insistence upon the importance of this field, laid the groundwork for much of the later research and development program. General Wesson began his tour as chief shortly before the Congress and the American public discovered the necessity of extensive re-equipping of the Army. To this problem General Wesson dedicated his considerable experience. As a former assistant military attaché in London, for four years the chief of the Technical Staff in the office of the Chief of Ordnance, and for the next four years the commanding officer at Aberdeen Proving Ground, he had a wide knowledge of Ordnance matériel and Army needs. Methodically, and with unfaltering confidence in the ability of the Ordnance Department to meet the new demands, General Wesson laid and executed his plans for the war ahead.

MAJ. GEN. SAMUEL HOF, *Chief of Ordnance, 1930–34.*

The Budget

Ordnance Appropriations, 1919–37

In 1919 the Ordnance Department expected the Congress to cut its appropriations sharply, but it failed to envisage the extreme economy wave of the mid-twenties that reduced Ordnance funds far below even those of prewar years. No one

[25] ODO 10, 20 Jan 31, OHF.

TABLE 1—TOTAL APPROPRIATIONS FOR THE ORDNANCE DEPARTMENT COMPARED WITH TOTAL APPROPRIATIONS FOR THE MILITARY ACTIVITIES OF THE WAR DEPARTMENT

Fiscal Year	Ordnance	War Department	Percent
1910	$10, 093, 856. 00	$115, 696, 518. 61	8. 72
1911	9, 210, 554. 60	109, 971, 367. 17	8. 37
1912	8, 794, 475. 00	104, 845, 810. 52	8. 38
1913	9, 001, 733. 30	115, 561, 920. 10	7. 78
1914	9, 503, 641. 00	112, 859, 212. 59	8. 42
1915	12, 353, 432. 00	125, 514, 560. 95	9. 84
1916	14, 947, 110. 00	113, 505, 383. 29	13. 10
1920	20, 805, 634. 79	813, 304, 262. 20	2. 55
1921	22, 880, 186. 06	495, 122, 339. 55	4. 62
1922	13, 425, 960. 00	373, 019, 831. 22	3. 59
1923	6, 859, 030. 00	270, 184, 805. 19	2. 52
1924	5, 812, 180. 00	256, 669, 118. 00	2. 26
1925	7, 751, 272. 00	260, 246, 731. 67	2. 97
1926	7, 543. 802. 00	260, 757, 250. 00	2. 89
1927	9, 549, 827. 00	270, 872, 055. 16	3. 52
1928	12, 179, 856. 00	300, 781, 710. 93	4. 04
1929	12, 549, 877. 00	317, 378, 294. 00	3. 95
1930	11, 858, 981. 00	331, 748, 443. 50	3. 57
1931	12, 422, 466. 00	347, 379, 178. 61	3. 57
1932	11, 121, 567. 00	335, 505, 965. 00	3. 31
1933	11, 588, 737. 00	299, 993, 920. 00	3. 86
1934	7, 048, 455. 00	277, 126, 281. 00	2. 54
1935	11, 049, 829. 00	263, 640, 736. 00	4. 19
1936	17, 110, 301. 00	312, 235, 811. 00	5. 47
1937[a]	18, 376, 606. 00	394, 047, 936. 33	4. 66
1938	24, 949, 075. 00	415, 508, 009. 94	6. 00
1939	112, 226, 412. 00	462, 252, 552. 89	24. 27
1940	176, 546. 788. 00	813, 816, 590. 74	21. 69

[a] For the years 1937–40 the figures are those of the Ordnance Budget and Fiscal Branch.
Source: Ord Fiscal Bull 2, p. 30, NA.

could think the United States a militaristic country in 1910, yet the ten million dollars allotted for that year was nearly twice the figure for 1924. Ordnance appropriations for 1924 were set at $5,812,180. In the entire 1920–40 period this figure was the nadir not only absolutely but also relatively, as it constituted only 2.26 percent of the entire War Department appropriations, whereas the average from 1910 through 1915 had been 8.58 percent. Not until 1939 did the ratio again equal that of pre-World War I years.[26] *(See Table 1.)* The cuts in appropriations precipitated a struggle to keep activities going at all. The reduction in funds was not paralleled by an appreciable sloughing off of Ordnance responsibilities at arsenals, depots, laboratories, and testing grounds, yet necessitated reduction of force, both military and civilian.

Heavy maintenance expenses obtained

[26] WDAB 1922, HR, p. 1020.

through all these years. Col. David M. King, Ordnance Department, early explained the situation to a Congressional committee: "whether the Army is to have 175,000, 200,000 or 225,000 men has little to do with the size of the appropriation 'Ordnance Service.' The Ordnance Department has the enormous quantities of property to be guarded, protected, and cared for, regardless of any other consideration."[27] In 1920, 1,580 guards and firemen were required to protect the vastly increased postwar establishment and matériel, whereas 100 or less had sufficed before the war. Not only were labor and supplies more expensive, but plants and depots were more widely scattered, and often larger. In 1916, with only fourteen small plants, the Department had received $290,000 for repairs. In 1929 with twenty-four plants and ten times the capital investment, it got less than $800,000. The 1929 War Department survey recommended an immediate increase of over 50 percent "to preserve the Government property from serious deterioration." And in a later paragraph the survey stated: "To carry out the mission of the Ordnance Department in accordance with programs approved by the War Department would require annual appropriations of $54,000,000."[28]

In spite of the collapse of the stock market and the beginning of the country-wide depression, in the late twenties and early thirties appropriations picked up somewhat and in 1931 were over $12,000,000. Then, as the Congress realized the severity of the depression, it again cut Ordnance funds, for 1934 appropriating only $7,048,455. At this point only Navy orders placed with the Army Ordnance Department saved Watertown and Watervliet Arsenals from being closed down altogether. Had this occurred, it is doubtful whether they could have been resuscitated later. By 1936 at Watervliet Arsenal 85 percent of the year's work was for the Navy and at Watertown more than half.[29]

Fortunately, the financial picture after 1932 was less somber than the official figures of Ordnance appropriations would suggest. The extensive emergency relief program that the Roosevelt administration launched in 1933 benefited the Department greatly. During the Hoover administration the Congress had set the precedent in the First Deficiency Act of 6 February 1931 by which Ordnance obtained a grant of $471,005 for repairs to arsenals. In 1934–35 relief funds for Ordnance purposes were sizable:[30]

Procurement and preservation of ammunition	$ 6,000,000
Procurement of motor vehicles	1,163,200
Procurement of machine guns	349,204
Seacoast defenses	1,007,660
Procurement of machinery for modernization	2,309,491
Repair and preservation of Ordnance matériel, storehouses, water mains, and roads at Rock Island	370,000
Repairs to buildings at Watertown Arsenal	89,000
TOTAL	$11,288,555

[27] WDAB 1921, HR, p. 536.

[28] Survey of WD, 1929, pp. 6–7, 18, NA.

[29] (1) Intervs with Col George Outland, and with August Dabrasky, 7 Dec 49. Dabrasky was an OD designer who had formerly been with Navy Ordnance. Dabrasky, Maj. Thomas K. Vincent, and Col. Edwin D. Bricker, of Watervliet, through personal friendship with Navy Ordnance men, contrived this deal, which saved the arsenals. (2) Memo, CofOrd for ACofS G–4, 7 Jan 37, sub: Steps Taken by OD to Effect Economies. . . , OO 111.3/6310, NA.

[30] Ord Fisc Bull 1, p. 6, and Bull 5, p. 4, NA. Except for $370,000 from PWA funds, this money came from funds appropriated in the National Recovery Act.

The total amount, spread over two years, roughly equaled normal appropriations for one year. The Roosevelt administration stressed projects that employed large numbers of men rather than expensive equipment, and much of the repair work at Ordnance installations fitted admirably into that category. From the Civil Works Administration, Ordnance received about $1,390,000, mostly for the pay of laborers to spray and paint buildings and to clean and reslush machinery. Though this labor force taken from the rolls of the unemployed was usually unaccustomed to Ordnance assignments and suffered many physical handicaps, it accomplished valuable work that must otherwise have been delayed or left undone.[31]

Every Ordnance establishment inevitably felt the pinch of economy, especially in the years from 1923 to 1936. At Springfield Armory, for example, the civilian staff of the Ordnance Laboratory in 1923 was cut from sixteen to four persons,[32] and over-all cuts in personnel were proportionate. *(See Table 2.)* The story at Springfield was typical. At Watervliet when Lt. Col. William I. Westervelt assumed command on 31 May 1921 he supervised 550 employees; on 1 September 1923, the date of his transfer, only 220 employees. Under his successor, Col. Edwin D. Bricker, Watervliet touched a low of 198 employees.[33] Secretary of War John W. Weeks in the fall of 1922 noted that on 1 January 1923 there would be a smaller force employed in the government arsenals than at any time in the previous twenty years.[34] The close correlation between Ordnance appropriations and Ordnance payrolls meant that as funds in the mid-twenties dipped below the levels of the 1910–15 period, so also did total personnel.[35]

From 1919 on, the Chief of Ordnance, General Williams, protested vigorously against the small quota of officers allotted to the Department. He submitted in 1919 a figure of 494 officers as "a bona fide minimum estimate . . . not subject to discount." Instead, the Ordnance Department was allotted 258 officers, a number

TABLE 2—EMPLOYEES AND PAYROLL AT SPRINGFIELD ARMORY

Fiscal Year Ending 30 June	Civilian Employees Average for Year	Average Monthly Payroll
1920	2,451	$331,162
1921	1,000	154,509
1922	514	61,903
1923	300	35,176
1924	257	33,365
1925	236	31,525
1926	253	34,385
1927	321	43,258
1928	353	47,646
1929	427	57,058
1930	471	63,236
1931	478	63,498
1932	475	62,217
1933	466	61,430
1934	580	79,856
1935	966	115,565
1936	905	112,652
1937	930	115,817
1938	1,285	154,645
1939	1,594	192,140
1940	2,362	272,207

Source: Hist of Springfield Armory, Vol. II, OHF.

[31] WDAB 1935, HR, pp. 265–66.

[32] The Ord Lab at Springfield, p. 1, OHF.

[33] Hist of Watervliet Arsenal, 1813–1946, pp. 101–02, OHF. This was the General Westervelt who had headed the Westervelt Board and was now reduced to permanent grade.

[34] John W. Weeks, "Industrial Mobilization," *Army Ordnance* III, 15 (1922), 134.

[35] (1) Ord Civ Pers Br notebook containing Statement of Ord Pers in Field, 1910 to 1933, NA. (2) Ord Fisc Bull 2, p. 30, NA.

TABLE 3—ORDNANCE DEPARTMENT MILITARY AND CIVILIAN STRENGTH: 1919–41

30 June	Military Strength [a]				Civilians Employed
	Total Military	Officers	Enlisted Personnel		
			Total	Philippine Scouts	
1919	10,597	1,885	8,712	0	(b)
1920	4,081	368	3,713	0	(b)
1921	4,009	281	3,728	0	14,569
1922	3,087	288	2,799	0	8,119
1923	2,557	266	2,291	48	6,340
1924	2,747	248	2,499	0	4,561
1925	2,570	251	2,319	48	4,378
1926	2,571	267	2,304	49	4,754
1927	2,540	271	2,269	49	5,207
1928	2,665	271	2,394	48	5,899
1929	2,676	278	2,398	48	6,461
1930	2,576	277	2,299	49	6,852
1931	2,498	275	2,223	44	8,378
1932	2,500	271	2,229	49	7,707
1933	2,382	270	2,112	47	6,751
1934	2,348	271	2,077	45	8,986
1935	2,401	266	2,135	45	9,315
1936	2,631	269	2,362	47	10,005
1937	2,990	270	2,720	46	10,921
1938	3,040	269	2,771	47	12,656
1939	3,063	287	2,776	47	16,213
1940	4,330	334	3,996	46	27,088
1941	27,073	3,024	24,049	137	67,612

[a] Represents military personnel in all Army commands whose duty branch was reported as Ordnance Department; does not include personnel assigned to the Chief of Ordnance whose duty branch was reported as an arm or service other than Ordnance Department.
[b] Data not available.

Source: Stat Div, Office of Army Comptroller, 1949. Military: Ann Rpts SW. Civilian: 1921 from Special Rpt 158, 12 Nov 21, Stat Br, WDGS; 1922 from Regular Rpt 195, 10 Aug 22, Stat Br, WDGS; 1923 and 1924 from Special Rpt 182, 9 Oct 24, Stat Br, WDGS; 1925–38 from records of Civ Pers Div, Office Secy Army; 1939 from Special Rpt 264, 1 Dec 39, Stat Br, WDGS; 1940 and 1941 from tabulations in Stat Div, Office of Army Comptroller.

which General Williams considered entirely out of line with totals assigned to other departments. The average property responsibility per Ordnance officer, he pointed out, was some $7,000,000, far above that of officers in any other branch of the Army.[36] Despite this plea, Ordnance officers on active duty as of 30 June 1921 numbered only 281, and even in 1939, a mere 287.[37] (*See Table 3.*) What the figures do not reveal is the excessive reductions in rank and the stagnation in promotion that stemmed largely from the paring down of officer strength. In 1923 reductions for noncommissioned officers ran from 2.44 percent in one grade to 100 percent in

[36] Memo, CofOrd for Dir of Opns and Pers, 2 Oct 19, sub: Allotment of Personnel, OO 023/735, NA.
[37] Strength of Army tables in *Ann Rpt SW*, 1921, p. 157; 1939, facing p. 56.

TABLE 4—PROPOSED TEN-YEAR ORDNANCE PROGRAM

Weapon	Quantity	Units To Be Equipped	Cost	Ammunition for 1-year Period
Infantry				
Cal. .30 semiautomatic shoulder rifle	2,000	3 divisions	$1,000,000	$168,000
Cal. .276 semiautomatic shoulder rifles	2,000	3 divisions	1,000,000	200,000
37-mm. infantry-accompanying gun	22	1 division	350,000	16,500
75-mm. infantry mortar	24	1 division	320,000	100,000
Divisional				
75-mm. pack howitzer	48	2 regiments	2,000,000	180,000
75-mm. field gun	24	1 regiment	1,300,000	100,000
105-mm. howitzer	72	3 regiments	4,110,000	390,000
Corps				
4.7″ gun	24	1 regiment	3,285,000	168,000
155-mm. howitzer	24	1 regiment	3,285,000	150,000
Army				
155-mm. gun	16	2 battalions	2,920,000	90,000
8″ howitzer	16	2 battalions	2,920,000	72,000
8″ railway matériel	2	(a)	420,000	10,000
tanks (23-ton, medium)	64	4 companies	5,200,000	(a)
Antiaircraft				
Cal. .50 Browning machine gun	1,000	(a)	1,400,000	500,000
37-mm. cannon	200	(a)	1,000,000	650,000
3″ antiaircraft gun	36	3 regiments	1,050,000	225,000
105-mm. antiaircraft gun	20	(a)	800,000	100,000
Aircraft				
Cal. .50 aircraft machine gun	continue as at present	(a)	covered	(a)
37-mm. automatic gun	50	(a)	250,000	(a)
Bombs	continue as at present	(a)	covered	(a)
TOTAL			$32,610,000	$3,119,500
GRAND TOTAL			$35,729,500	

[a] Unknown.

Source: Memo, CofOrd for ACofS G–4, 8 May 25, sub: Extended Service Test and Limited Rearmament with Improved Types of Ordnance Weapons in the Next Ten-Year Period, OO 400.11/51, NA.

another, action that seriously hurt morale.[38] At no time did military personnel approach the figure of 350 officers and 4,500 enlisted men, set in the National Defense Act of 1920 as a reasonable peacetime level, or the recommendation of 373 officers in the War Department survey of 1929. Since of the small staff about 87 percent was assigned to the Field Service, the Chief of Ordnance had only some 35 offi-

[38] Ann Rpt CofOrd, 1923, p. 2. Annual reports for later years frequently comment on the same problem. Promotions stagnated also because of the "hump" left by World War I.

cers for all other duties, except in so far as officers from other branches of the service were detailed to special Ordnance duty. This circumstance goes far to explain the Department's inability to assign a number of officers as military observers abroad.[39]

Lack of money similarly limited planning and execution of plans. With the experience of World War I to give perspective, the Ordnance Department in 1922 prepared a comprehensive munitions policy aimed at procuring for and supplying to the Army at all times munitions that would "at the minimum be equal in quality and quantity to those available to our enemy." Achievement of this aim called for a development program, a reserve stock program, and a manufacturing, replacement, and rearmament program.[40] Three days after its submission, the Ordnance statement of basic policy, with a few modifications, obtained the approval of General of the Armies John J. Pershing and the Secretary of War. The story of the rearmament plan will suffice to illustrate the effects of the budget cuts.

To implement the rearmament portion of the munitions policy, the Ordnance Department on 8 May 1925 submitted to the Secretary of War a detailed ten-year program of "Extended Service Test and Limited Rearmament." (*See Table 4.*) The program was critically studied by the Chief of Staff and the General Staff, and by the Cavalry, Coast Artillery, Air Service, Field Artillery, and Infantry. It received enthusiastic approval as a whole, though modifications and reductions were recommended. General Williams explained that unit cost for many of these items was high because, as they were new, the expense of dies, jigs, tools, and gages had to be added to the necessarily high cost of small-scale production.

The Ordnance limited rearmament program of 1925 thus proposed merely a modest scale of re-equipment for a part of the Regular Army. The Adjutant General informed the Chief of Ordnance that the program would be subject to annual revision, and, after lengthy study, the Secretary of War in April 1926 approved the plan with the proviso: "the extent to which it is carried out to be dependent upon funds appropriated for the purpose."[41] But the moderate character of the program failed to protect it from large reductions. Cuts were made in nearly all items so that the $35,729,500 program of 1925 was scaled down to the $21,798,500 program of 1928.[42] Unfortunately, and ironically, the maximum production was scheduled for 1932–36, with the peak in 1935. From the start, funds available remained below the amounts scheduled even in the reduced program. At the Congressional hearings in December 1928 for the fiscal year 1930, for example, General Williams stated that financial limitations had forced reductions of $500,000 in the 75-mm. and 105-mm. howitzer and 3-inch antiaircraft phases of the rearmament program.[43]

By June 1933, more than seven years after the ten-year program had been approved, Ordnance production of major artillery items stood as follows:[44]

[39] Survey of WD, 1929, p. 5, NA. Interv, 20 Sep 49, with Col John C. Raaen, exec off to CofOrd, Jun 42–Feb 46.

[40] Memo, CofOrd for Gen Pershing, 6 Jun 22, sub: Recommendations as to a Munitions Policy, OO 023/1553, NA.

[41] Ltr, TAG to CofOrd, 12 Apr 25; 3d Ind, 28 Oct 25; and 5th Ind, 12 Apr 26, all in OO 400.11/51, NA.

[42] Memo, TAG for CofOrd, 24 Feb 28, sub: Alteration of the Ten Year Ord Program . . . , OO 400.11/111, NA.

[43] WDAB 1929, HR, p. 517; 1930, p. 699.

[44] Ann Rpt CofOrd, 1933, par. 15.

Item	Produced or Appropriated For	Ten-Year Goal	Percentage Achieved
75-mm. pack howitzer	32	58	55
3-inch AA gun	62	110	56
75-mm. mortar	16	48	33
75-mm. field gun	4	12	33
105-mm. howitzer	14	48	29
155-mm. howitzer	0	12	0
155-mm. gun	0	12	0
8-inch howitzer	0	12	0
8-inch railway gun	0	2	0
105-mm. AA gun	0	20	0

In no category had progress been rapid, and in the larger caliber matériel, army, corps, and seacoast artillery, not a single weapon had been completed. Nor did items completed in the next few years brighten the picture. Only a few guns and mortars came off the production line at the arsenals and, apart from three 155-mm. guns, there was still no heavy artillery.[45] Yet The Inspector General's reports consistently commended the efficiency of the arsenals. By and large the program was too small to keep the arsenals busy, much less to give selected private firms production experience.[46]

Meanwhile, in line with a War Department attempt to integrate the numerous, and often overlapping, programs that had been started since the end of the war, the Ordnance Department submitted a rearmament and re-equipment program for the six-year period, 1935 through 1940. The objective was to equip the units involved in initial mobilization under the 1933 mobilization plan.[47] The original Ordnance six-year re-equipment program as submitted in 1932, although considerably revised later, offered an excellent picture of the most pressing needs of the Department in supplying the Army. The program called for only $1,400,000 yearly. For the six years the chief items, in order of cost, ranked: (1) antiaircraft guns, $1,240,800; (2) tanks, $1,000,000; (3) combat cars $837,000; (4) semiautomatic rifles, $900,000; (5) railway artillery, $610,000; and (6) antitank guns, $442,400. Yet budget cuts prevented full execution of these plans. For example, in estimates for the fiscal year 1938 under its re-equipment program the Ordnance Department asked for $7,849,536. G–4 reduced this to $5,395,363, and the Bureau of the Budget forced it down to about $5,000,000.[48] The Ordnance Department did well when in any one year it could proceed at more than half the pace envisioned in the six-year program.

If the entire rearmament program had been carried out, by 30 June 1940 the results would have comprised: mechanizing one cavalry regiment, equipping the 1st Cavalry Division with standard armored cars, supplying active units of the Field Artillery with high-speed artillery, new or modernized, supplying antiaircraft units with standard matériel including fire

[45] Ann Rpt CofOrd, 1934, pars. 15–16; 1935, pars. 16–18; 1936, pars. 14–15; 1937, pars. 17–18; 1938, pars. 21–22. By 1938 one 8-inch howitzer T3 was under manufacture.

[46] For example, see: (1) rpt to TIG, Ann Inspection Springfield Armory, 19 Nov 34, OO 333.1/4102; (2) rpt to TIG, Ann Inspection Rock Island Arsenal, 4 Dec 35, OO 333.1/4366 RIA; (3) rpt to TIG, Ann Inspection Frankford Arsenal, 25 Mar 36, OO 333.1/4484; (4) rpt to TIG, Ann Inspection Picatinny Arsenal, 18 Jun 36, OO 333.1/4541. All in NA IG files.

[47] Memo, ACofS for DCofS, 7 Sep 34, sub: Rearmament and Reequipment Program, G–4/29552, P&E file, Sec 1, NA. For background see in same file, (1) memo, ACofS G–4 for TAG, 16 Sep 32; and (2) ltr, TAG to Chiefs of WD Arms and Services, 24 Mar 34, sub: Revision of Six-Year WD Programs, OO 400.11/165, NA. The letter repeats that the objective of the programs was the re-equipment of all units to be included in the initial mobilization under the 1933 mobilization plan.

[48] (1) See OO 111.3/6101–6750 and OO 111.3 files for this period for data illustrative of the constant difficulties. (2) Memo, CofOrd for ACofS G–4, 25 Nov 36, OO 111.3/6285 and Incl 1. All in NA.

291064 O—55——5

control, and the beginning of supply to the Infantry of new tanks, rifles, mortars, and guns. That would have been all.[49]

The consequences of the meagre appropriations year after year, limiting operations and narrowing down planning to the conceivably attainable, are so clear in retrospect that the layman must wonder whether the Ordnance Department could not have staged a successful fight for more money. Could the Chief of Ordnance not have persuaded the General Staff to allot to him a larger share of the War Department budget? Or, failing that, could he not enter a special plea for urgent projects when he appeared at hearings of the House Appropriations Committee? To the second question the answer is an emphatic *no.* The budget law of 1924 expressly prohibited any government official from appealing to the Congress for more money than the President's budget had allotted his department, and Army officers were further bound by military discipline to accept the decision of the Commander in Chief, once it had been formulated.[50] The most a service chief dared hope to accomplish before the Congress was to present his needs so convincingly that the Appropriations Committee would not slice his part of the budget. The answer to the first question, on the other hand, might theoretically be yes. It was always possible for the Chief of Ordnance to protest to the General Staff any proposed budget cuts before G–4 approved them. But each service had to compete with every other for its share. The War Department had to consider the Army as a whole, and the supply branches were not likely to get special favors. Still, protocol permitted each chief to convince the General Staff, if he could, that the needs of his service exceeded those of any other, and Ordnance representatives frequently tried their powers of persuasion. But skillful salesmanship, Ordnance officers agree, was not a strong point in the Department during the twenties and thirties. Furthermore, military tradition precluded protracted argument with one's superior officers. There was simply never enough money to go round. Each Chief of Ordnance in turn was obliged to accept his allowance and then stretch it as far as he could.

The Upturn, 1938–40

Fortunately, after 1935 Ordnance appropriations increased steadily. Up through fiscal year 1938 the gains were in line with those for the War Department as a whole. For the fiscal year 1939 the Ordnance Department's share showed a pronounced proportional gain, from 6 percent of the War Department total of 1938 to 24 percent. The Ordnance appropriation for 1939 was 4.5 times that for 1938 and 16 times that for 1934. (*See Table 1.*) As the situation abroad darkened, President Roosevelt's interest in the deficiencies of the armed forces grew. A special message to the Congress on 28 January 1938 asked for $16,880,000 for antiaircraft matériel, manufacture of gages, dies, and the like, and a start on making up the ammunition deficiency. The Congress promptly authorized this expenditure. The $112,226,412

[49] Memo, CofOrd for TAG, 2 May 34, sub: Revision of Six Year WD Program, OO 400.11/165, NA. The using arms submitted suggestions. Typical were (1) memo, CofCA for CofOrd, 9 Nov 32, sub: Rearmament Program, 1935–1940, OO 400.11/158; (2) ltr, CofInf to CofOrd, 7 Nov 32, sub: Suggested Six-Year Rearmament Program, OO 400.11/156 and ind. In general, folders OO 400.11/101–150 and OO 400.11/28–257 contain much of interest on the re-equipment programs. All in NA.

[50] See Watson, *Chief of Staff: Prewar Plans and Preparations,* pp. 21–22.

available for Ordnance in that summer of 1938 permitted planning and operations on so enlarged a scale that an Assistant Chief of Ordnance later declared that for the Ordnance Department the war began in 1938.[51]

By October descriptions of conditions in Europe, particularly information brought back by William C. Bullitt, U.S. Ambassador to France, so alarmed the President that he called for immediate reports on what was most needed to strengthen the Army.[52] The Chief of Ordnance on 20 October 1938 presented an itemized bill for $125,000,000 as the minimum price for meeting Ordnance deficiencies and, one day later, an estimate of $349,000,000 as the cost of matériel to equip a 4,000,000-man Army to be called up under the Protective Mobilization Plan.[53] On 12 January 1939 President Roosevelt, armed with detailed figures, forcefully urged upon the Congress the appropriation of some $477,000,000, of which the Air Corps would get the largest amount, and the ground forces $110,000,000 for new equipment. In April the Congress passed the regular appropriation act granting the Ordnance Department $62,000,000. But the President's plea for full rearmament asked for much more: the proposed bill gave Ordnance $55,366,362 in cash for expenditures for "Ordnance Service and Supplies, Army," plus authorization to place contracts with commercial companies up to $44,000,000.[54] The Second Deficiency Appropriation Act, when passed, carried the exact amounts requested. The general breakdown for Ordnance read:

Project	*Item*	*Amount*
4	Renovation of ammunition. .	$10,000,000
11	Maintenance and overhaul of matériel in storage.	4,891,052
11	Augmentation of stocks of ammunition.	37,506,505
11	Augmentation of critical items of antiaircraft equipment. .	7,581,500
11	Augmentation of other critical ordnance items.	39,387,305
		$99,366,362

"Other critical ordnance items" signified chiefly semiautomatic rifles, antitank guns, 60-mm. and 81-mm. mortars, ground machine guns, trucks, tanks, 8-inch railway artillery guns, 155-mm. howitzers, and modernization of 75-mm. guns.[55] "Critical" items were defined as those essential to effective combat but for which the maximum procurement rate fell short of war requirements.[56] These appropriations, Ordnance officers declared, would enable industry to get ready for production and be somewhat prepared in case of real emergency. On 1 July 1939 another $11,500,000 was appropriated for Ordnance. Thus, all together the Ordnance Department got $176,546,788 for the year ahead, $62,000,000 additional in May, and approximately $11,500,000 on 1 July.[57] The total constituted a 58 percent increase over the appropriations for 1939. The lean years were over, but their legacy

[51] Interv with Brig Gen Earl McFarland, 28 Feb 50.

[52] See Mark S. Watson, "First Vigorous Steps," *Military Affairs*, XII, 2 (1948), 70.

[53] (1) Memo, CofOrd for DCofS G–4, 20 Oct 38, sub: Deficiencies in Ordnance Equipment. (2) Memo, CofOrd for ACofS G–4, 21 Oct 38, sub: Deficiencies in Ordnance Equipment for the Protective Mobilization Plan. Both in Ord Study Folder 69, War Plans and Requirements files, DRB AGO. See also below, "The Protective Mobilization Plan," pp. 53–54.

[54] Cash for settlement of contracts authorized in one fiscal year was usually appropriated in the next fiscal year.

[55] *Hearings*, Second Deficiency Appropriation Bill, 1939, HR, pp. 454–72.

[56] AR 700-10, 24 Oct 42.

[57] PL 44, PL 61, and PL 164, 76th Cong, 1st Sess.

was an accumulated deficiency of desperately needed matériel.

Industrial Mobilization Plans

One immediate consequence of the supply tangle of World War I was the War Department's decision thenceforward to plan in advance. From 1920 on, industrial mobilization planning was a task to which the Ordnance Department gave constant thought. The planning involved two stages: preparation of cost estimates and schedules of items and quantities needed to fit the over-all Army mobilization plans; and plans for allocating manufacture of the matériel to commercial companies and government arsenals. The War Plans Staff in the Office, Chief of Ordnance, was in charge of the first, but the Manufacturing Division, because it supervised the district offices and the arsenals, had a large part in the second, the actual procurement planning. The considerable labor expended on both phases of planning was a clear reflection of the Ordnance Department's conviction that careful preparation for industrial mobilization was essential if the disasters of supply in 1917–18 were not to be repeated.

Three steps taken in the first years after the war indicated the constructive thinking of Ordnance officers on this whole subject. The Ordnance Munitions Board reports, submitted in twenty-four separate papers between 1919 and 1921, mapped out an intelligent, comprehensive policy for keeping the United States Army equipped and industry prepared to meet military emergency demands. That higher authority disregarded many of these recommendations in no way invalidates their soundness, as later events proved.[58] The second measure was the drafting of Section 5a of the National Defense Act of 1920. While this was the work of a number of men besides Ordnance officers, several high-ranking men in the Department played a considerable part in bringing about the creation of a War Department office specifically charged with responsibility for procurement and industrial mobilization planning.[59] The third move was the founding of the Army Industrial College to which officers were assigned to study problems of industrial mobilization. This project, like the National Defense Act, was the fruit of many men's efforts, but Ordnance officers conceived the idea and by skillful persuasion contributed to its realization.[60] Through the years of discouragement that lay ahead, the Ordnance Department constantly worked at the problem of preparing the nation's industry for the moment when the nation must rearm. Though, as World War II approached, Navy and Air Force priorities obliged the Department to recast some of its plans, Ordnance officers believed that their work had been sound and the surveys and production studies valuable.[61] To understand the character of this work, review of Army mobilization planning and

[58] Interv with Maj Gen Charles T. Harris, 1 Dec 49. The Munitions Board report was largely the work of Maj. James H. Burns. See memo, CofOrd for CofS, 29 Jan 21, sub: Development of a Munition Policy, OKD 470/135.1.

[59] For full discussion of the origins, content, and implications of Section 5a, see Troyer Anderson's manuscript history of the Office of the Under Secretary of War, Ch. III, pp. 2–5, in OCMH files.

[60] The idea was again more Major Burns' than that of any other one person. He was also chiefly responsible for converting the Under Secretary, Dwight F. Davis, and the Secretary of War, John W. Weeks, to faith in the proposal. See (1) Anderson MS, Ch. III, pp. 30–31, OCMH; and (2) pamphlet, The Industrial College of the Armed Forces, 1924–1949, Twenty-fifth Anniversary, 25 Feb 49, OHF.

[61] Interv with Gen Harris, 2 Dec 49.

brief examination of district procurement planning is necessary.

Early Mobilization Plans

Preparation of over-all Army mobilization plans was a nearly continuous process throughout the peace years. The blueprint for American rearmament—the elaborate Protective Mobilization Plan of the late 1930's—had its beginnings in the simpler plans of the early 1920's. When the National Defense Act of 1920 made the Assistant Secretary of War responsible for industrial mobilization planning and procurement, he organized his office to include a Planning Branch. This staff, together with the Army and Navy Munitions Board, was charged with co-ordinating Army and Navy procurement programs and exerted strong influence upon the Ordnance Department's planning between world wars. For two decades these two groups, in the face of public indifference, struggled to devise comprehensive programs of industrial mobilization.

The 1920's saw the completion of several editions of mobilization plans. As soon as one version was finished, modification began, and usually within four years a new one appeared. The earlier plans, especially those of 1921 and 1922, tended to be chiefly munitions plans for the Army instead of all-around industrial mobilization plans.[62] Ordnance experts who drafted the extensive Ordnance annex of the 1922 plan noted that the 1921 plans were absurd in that they set impossible requirements for Ordnance. The 1922 over-all Ordnance plan ran to about fifty mimeographed pages. In addition, the Ordnance unit in each corps area had branch plans, while Field Service and other divisions, as well as all field establishments, each had a unit plan prepared by the individual installation and submitted to the Chief of Ordnance for approval.[63] In 1924 a new mobilization plan superseded the less detailed scheme of 1922. The Ordnance Department took its part in the planning with such seriousness that it ran an elaborate test on a mythical M Day to ascertain the quality of its plans. Analysis of this test revealed manifold complications and numerous deficiencies.[64] By decision of the General Staff, the Army's still more exhaustively detailed plan of 1928 was based entirely upon manpower potential, rather than upon reasonable procurement capacity. The result was a schedule of procurement objectives that the supply services considered impossible of attainment.[65] The special survey of the Army made in 1929 called attention to several basic defects. One serious weakness was the failure to apply one of the fundamental lessons of World War I—that it takes at least a year longer to arm men for fighting than to mobilize and train them for actual combat. The survey stated: ". . . it will be noted that in all munition phases there is a wide gap between the exhaustion of the present reserve and the receipt of munition[s] from new production." [66] The Ordnance Department could not meet the requirements of the plan under its budgetary

[62] Anderson MS, Ch. III, p. 38, OCMH. The 1921–22 plans assumed that the peacetime economic life of the nation could carry the load without serious derangement. A true industrial mobilization plan involves far-reaching controls over national economic institutions.

[63] Introduction to the 1922 Ordnance War Plan, pp. 6–8, filed in DRB AGO with OO 381 material. Unclassified unit plans are in the National Archives OO 381 files.

[64] Memo, CofOrd for CofS, 9 Sep 24, sub: Test of Ord War Plans, OO 370.01/520, NA.

[65] Anderson MS, Ch. III, pp. 40, 45–48, OCMH.

[66] Survey of Ord Dept, 20 Sep 29, pp. 28–29, OO 320/365, NA.

limitations, and indeed as late as 1930 execution of the 1924 procurement program was still far behind schedule. Nevertheless, the 1928 plan for a four-field-army, 4,000,000-man mobilization formed the basis of all Ordnance computations of requirements right down to 1940. It constituted what Maj. Gen. Charles T. Harris, one of the key men of the Ordnance Manufacturing Service, called the "Position of Readiness Plan." If goals set seemed in the thirties too unrealizable to achieve with funds that the Department dared hope for, at least Ordnance officers were ready with detailed estimates of quantities of each type of munitions needed and a planned procedure for getting them.[67]

The over-all Army and Ordnance mobilization planning of the twenties, defects notwithstanding, marked a great forward step simply because it was the first extensive peacetime planning the United States had ever undertaken. It was experimental and flexible. The plans, although not considered secret in broad outlines, were shielded from public view because the War Department feared an unfavorable public reaction. Probably the chief drawback of the top-level planning effort was its superficial, generalized nature. It failed to envision the extreme complexity and the enormous scale of operations another war would entail.[68]

The 1930's saw a pronounced broadening of perspective in mobilization planning. In part this was brought about by the work of the War Policies Commission, a body created by the Congress to consider how best "to promote peace and to equalize the burdens and to minimize the profits of war." [69] The commission, composed of six cabinet officers and eight congressmen, made a painstaking survey and submitted reports in December 1931 and March 1932. It pronounced the Army procurement program excellent and recommended Congressional review of the plans every two years. The Congress took no action.[70]

While earlier plans had been confined to a narrowly interpreted scheme for producing munitions, a plan worked out in 1930–31 dealt with the problem of over-all mobilization of national industry. This took a new approach based on the premise that Army procurement plans could not be made workable unless the entire economy of the nation was subject to governmental controls.[71] A revision in 1933 made more explicit provision for these controls and for administrative organization.[72] But in the Ordnance Department the 1933 plan was not popular because it called for equipping a large force faster than Ordnance could possibly effect it, particularly in view of the fact that most of the World War I stocks of matériel by then were obsolete and approaching uselessness. If troops were supplied at the rate at which they were called up, the heaviest procurement load would come in the first few months and then taper off—obviously an impossible arrangement. A revision of 1936, primarily important because issued jointly by the Army and Navy, took a somewhat wider view of the problems of

[67] (1) Inspection of OCO, 1930, par. 13(c), NA. (2) Interv with Gen Harris, 2 Dec 49. The 1928 plan, like the versions of the early thirties, followed out Maj. Gen. Douglas MacArthur's views. See *Hearings*, War Policies Commission, 13–14 May, 1931, Pt. II, pp. 354–78.

[68] QMC Historical Study 4, Harold W. Thatcher, *Planning for Industrial Mobilization, 1920-1940* (August, 1943, reprinted 1948), pp. 82, 133–34.

[69] Pub Res 98, 71st Cong.

[70] John D. Millett, *The Organization and Role of the Army Service Forces* (Washington, 1954).

[71] (1) Thatcher, *op. cit.*, pp. 82–83. (2) Anderson MS, Ch. III, pp. 52, 54, OCMH.

[72] Industrial Mobilization Plan, 1933, p. xi, NA.

mobilization.[73] In the next two years study of British industrial mobilization procedures produced a series of informing articles in *Army Ordnance,*[74] but public interest in preparedness remained almost nil. The Neutrality Act had become law in 1935, the Nye Committee investigations were pillorying Army officers advocating any planning for war, and a series of magazine articles and books, under suggestive titles such as *The Merchants of Death,* were fanning public hostility to such measures. The Congress before 1938 made no move to legislate for industrial mobilization.

The Protective Mobilization Plan

In spite of public opposition to any preparations for war, in 1937 the Protective Mobilization Plan was born. The 1938 annual report of the Secretary of War, Harry H. Woodring, describes its genesis:

> During my tenure of office as Assistant Secretary of War from 1933 to 1936 I became convinced that the then current War Department plan for mobilization in the event of major emergency contained discrepancies between the programs for procurement of personnel and procurement of supplies which were so incompatible that the plan would prove ineffective in war time. . . . It became evident to me that the War Department mobilization plan then current was gravely defective in that supplies required during the first months of a major war could not be procured from industry in sufficient quantities to meet the requirements of the mobilization program. . . . My conviction of the inadequacy of the initial plan from the supply procurement standpoint was so strong that one of the first directives issued by me as Secretary of War was that the General Staff restudy the whole intricate problem of emergency mobilization with a view to complete replacement of the then current War Department mobilization plan. . . . The result of that study is now found in what we term the protective mobilization plan of 1937. The 1937 plan has not been perfected; details remain to be worked out and are being worked out thoroughly and diligently. But we have every reason to believe that the protective mobilization plan is feasible and will meet our national defense requirements.[75]

The name Protective Mobilization Plan, usually abbreviated to PMP, was designed to reassure the average American. The plan underwent steady amplification and refinement for the next two years.[76] Unlike its forerunners, it set only attainable goals for the Ordnance Department. It called for an Initial Protective Force of 400,000 men within three months after mobilization, far fewer than demanded in earlier plans; eight months after M Day, 800,000 men were to be ready for combat, and in one year, 1,000,000 men. The maximum-size Army envisioned was 3,750,000 men. Ordnance leaders felt reasonably confident that the Department could equip the new quotas on time.[77]

From mid-1937 on, Ordnance plans in large part revolved around the PMP. Endless computations and recomputations were requested by the Secretary of War,

[73] (1) Millett, *op. cit.*, pp. 17, 77. (2) Thatcher, *op. cit.*, p. 231.

[74] Maj. L. A. Codd, "Preparedness in England," *Army Ordnance*, XVIII, 105 (1937), 143–46; 106 (1938), 210–13; 107 (1938), 285–88; 108 (1938), 347–50.

In 1936 the Assistant Secretary of War called for a survey of mobilization plans of several of the Great Powers. (1) Ltr to ACofS G–2, 29 Aug 38, OO 321.12/4279, NA. (2) Ltr, CofOrd thru ACofS G–2, 29 May [?] 36, directed that the same questions asked the French be given to the British. The directive for the survey is in letter from ASW in 1936. OO 381/17061 Misc, NA.

[75] *Ann Rpt SW*, 1938, p. 1.

[76] Ltr, TAG to CofOrd, 17 Jul 39, sub: Chief of Ordnance PMP, 1939, OO 381/25782, NA.

[77] Maj. Gen. Charles M. Wesson, The Operations of the Ordnance Department, lecture, Army War College, 16 Nov 39, p. 18.

the Assistant Secretary of War, and the General Staff.[78] Calculation of war reserves, for example, in August 1937 resulted in scheduling expenditures of funds by priorities up to $50,000,000.[79] When the worsening international situation led President Roosevelt in October 1938 to confer with his top military advisers on stepping up defense expenditures, the Deputy Chief of Staff asked the Chief of Ordnance to prepare a program to plug the biggest holes in Ordnance supply. Twenty-four hours later General Wesson turned in an estimate of $125,000,000, an amount that would "supply the deficiencies in essential equipment required for the Initial Protective Force." Only the existence of plans already well worked out under the PMP enabled the Department to complete a tabulation so speedily. One day later, 21 October, following a telephone conversation with G-4, General Wesson submitted a supplemental plan calling for $349,000,000 to meet the additional requirements for the PMP as a whole, in contrast to coverage of the Initial Protective Force only.[80] A conviction that the White House mood favored a bold program, plus the readiness of the Department's plans, help explain this move. Actually the translation of such a program into action had to wait many months till more decisive events abroad crystallized American public opinion in favor of large expenditures for arms.

Just before the outbreak of war in Europe, the Office of the Assistant Secretary of War requested the Chief of Ordnance to provide in forty-eight hours a detailed outline of Ordnance action in case of war in Europe. The reply listed funds needed under three headings: those to equip completely the forces under PMP, those for PMP requirements with augmentation for one year, and those for PMP requirements with augmentation for two years.[81] Soon after, the Ordnance Department estimated the cost of the munitions procurement program under PMP augmented for two years to be $6,076,750,000 and declared that its computations were up to date for all items under PMP.[82]

The Ordnance sections of PMP were thus subjected to careful revision over a period of more than two years. The 132-page document, which became effective 30 November 1939, was entitled "Ordnance Protective Mobilization Plan, 1939." [83] Ordnance corps areas and field installations prepared their individual plans. All these were the bases upon which the Department built its program of preparation for war.

Procurement Planning

Procurement planning, the step that followed over-all industrial mobilization planning, was mapped out in the Office, Chief of Ordnance, but the arsenals and

[78] Typical examples are: (1) ltr, ACofS G-4 to all chiefs, 14 May 37, and (2) follow-up ltr, 18 Aug, both in AG 381.4 (5-14-37)-G-4 13765-103, DRB AGO.

[79] *Ibid.*

[80] (1) Memo, CofOrd for CofS, 20 Oct 38, sub: Deficiencies in Ord Equipment, and incl, OO 111.3/6877. (2) Memo, CofOrd for ACofS G-4, 21 Oct 38, sub: Deficiencies in Ord Equipment for PMP, and incl, OO 111.3/6878. (3) By December 1938 General Wesson was talking in terms of a $420,000,000 program. Memo, CofOrd for ACofS G-4, 19 Dec 38, sub: Breakdown of PMP Requirements into Increments, OO 111.3/6916. All in NA.

[81] Min, Wesson Conferences, 19 and 21 Aug 39, OHF. The report went to President Roosevelt for study.

[82] Memo, CofOrd for Dir of Planning Br, OASW, 8 Sep 39, sub: Measures to be Taken by War Department in the Event of War in Europe, OO 381/27496 Misc, NA.

[83] The PMP as printed for public sale at ten cents a copy under the title *Protective Mobilization Plan, Revision of 1939* was a slim document of only eighteen pages. The appendices were omitted, both because of their confidential nature and because of the need for constant revision.

the Ordnance districts supplied the data. The districts were re-established in 1922 for the express purpose of keeping contacts the country over with industrial concerns that might one day serve as sources of supply. A group of Ordnance officers had already evolved a careful scheme of procedures upon which district operations thereafter were based.[84] While orders for matériel down into the late 1930's were scarcely enough to keep the government arsenals in operation, and contracts with commercial producers were rarely negotiated, every district office had the job of determining its area's industrial potential for manufacture of each type of ordnance item. Analysis of this information from all the districts permitted the Manufacturing Division in Washington to allocate particular items to particular districts. Thereupon the district staffs made plant surveys. A complete survey called for a large amount of detailed information:

> . . . the location, construction, and equipment of the plant; the availability of power, materials, and labor; the examination of the manufacturing processes involved to determine the readiness with which the facility can adapt itself to the proposed task of manufacture, and the extent to which variations from the Ordnance prescribed routine may be permitted; the new equipment and new construction which will be needed for conversion, the sources from which this equipment and the construction material must come, and the time within which they can be secured.[85]

With staffs of only three or four people through most of the peace years, district offices could not undertake any such thorough job. The partial surveys first completed merely produced lists of companies arranged according to the type of ordnance they were capable of manufacturing. The early industrial mobilization records in one district consisted of a few reference cards filed in shoe boxes. During the depression, economy necessitated abandoning even the yearly meetings of district chiefs. These were resumed in 1935. Over the years some districts succeeded better than others in keeping interest in planning alive, for some were able to enlist the co-operation of a greater number of Reserve officers. In this the New York District was particularly successful; every winter from 1923 on a group of Reserve officers met once a week with the district officials to discuss district problems, to hear lectures on Ordnance developments, and occasionally to rehearse the steps in negotiating contracts. Where district officers had less help of this sort, keeping in readiness the machinery for large-scale procurement was more difficult, but all districts maintained some activity.[86]

In spite of meagre budgets and limited personnel, the districts succeeded from time to time in obtaining from manufacturers gentlemen's agreements, known as Accepted Schedules of Production, which specified quantities and rates of future war production. Upon request, the Assistant Secretary of War then allocated their plants to Ordnance. This arrangement was designed to eliminate competition among the Army and Navy supply services for particular facilities. By 1937 the districts had in hand some 2,500 accepted schedules representing 645 different commercial facilities. When any company had thus pledged itself to ordnance manufac-

[84] The three men primarily responsible for this first planning were Major Harris, Maj. Richard H. Somers, and Capt. Edward E. MacMorland.

[85] Hist of Pittsburgh Ord Dist 66, OHF.

[86] (1) The Ordnance District System, Its Growth and Development, January 1918–June 1945, prepared under the direction of Brig. Gen. A. B. Quinton, Jr., p. 6, OHF. (2) Chester Mueller, *The New York Ordnance District in World War II* (New York, 1947), pp. 8–10.

ture in case of emergency, the district executive assistant worked out with the management fairly detailed production plans—plant layouts, machine tool requirements, gages, raw materials, power and manpower needs to convert rapidly to manufacture of the unfamiliar Ordnance item. The government arsenals' blueprints and data on production methods were always available for this purpose. Ordnance officers regarded these as manufacturing aids, not mandatory instructions.[87] In view of public apathy and industrialists' reluctance to be involved in government munitions making, it is hard to see what more the Ordnance Department could have done in these years toward planning procurement from private companies.

Special mention must be made of the machine tool surveys. Though neither the Ordnance districts nor the Office, Chief of Ordnance, conducted these alone, their participation was of importance. The over-all studies were the responsibility of the Assistant Secretary of War; the Army and Navy Munitions Board also played a part. The urgency of having an adequate supply of machine tools suitable for munitions manufacture was well understood, but the problems involved were as complex as they were vital. The industry was always relatively small and except in boom periods operated below capacity. From the mid-thirties on, through a special committee of the National Machine Tool Builders Association, the industry cooperated with the government in an effort to forestall the shortages a national emergency might bring. The questions were: What did the armed forces require? and then, Could the industry meet the requirements? [88] In a computation of Army machine-tool requirements prepared in 1937, the needs of the Ordnance Department comprised a big percentage of the total. Out of 20,613 lathes needed for the whole Army, Ordnance required 16,220.[89] In spite of efforts to anticipate these needs, 1939 and 1940 found machine-tool supply the principal bottleneck in the rearmament program. Indeed, to stretch the supply early in 1940 it became necessary to resurrect obsolete or incomplete machine tools from arsenal storehouses.[90]

In 1938 conditions in Europe brought an upward turn in district activities. In every district Army inspectors were appointed to inspect items under current commercial procurement, a scheme that was later of great help because it provided a nucleus of trained inspectors qualified to train others when war came. Col. A. B. Quinton, Jr., Chief of the District Control Division, was directed to conduct more extensive industrial surveys and, as soon as funds were available, to enlarge the district organizations.[91] Louis Johnson, Assistant Secretary of War, in December 1938 at a conference of district chiefs, urged them to bring their surveys up to

---

[87] (1) Campbell, *Industry-Ordnance Team,* p. 20. (2) Ann Rpt CofOrd, 1937, par. 10. Post-World War II comments of some industrialists have implied that the Ordnance Department expected to show industry how to manufacture what private industry unguided could produce most efficiently without military interference. The Ordnance Department, on the other hand, contends that it offered help only where help was needed.

[88] Progress Report on Machine Tool Plan, 20 Jun 39, pp. 2–4, Exhibits, C, D, E, F, G, OO 381/26423 ASW, NA. Early in 1938 the Tool Builder's Association sent a questionnaire to all machine-tool builders to be returned directly to the ANMB.

[89] (1) Rpt cited n. 88, Exhibits C and D. (2) Ltr, OASW to all Supply Arms and Services, 1 Oct 36, sub: Planning for Procurement of Machine Tools, OO 381/26423 ASW, NA.

[90] (1) Ltr, B. A. Franklin, Hartford Dist Chief, to CofOrd, 19 Jun 39, OO 381/26757 Hartford, NA. (2) Ltr, CofOrd to Hartford Ord Dist, 7 Mar 40, and 1st Ind, 3 Apr 40, OO 381/33149 Hartford, DRB AGO. (3) Ord Digest, Mar 40, Minton file, OHF.

[91] (1) Hist of Boston Ord Dist, p. 40, OHF. (2) Ann Rpt CofOrd, 1938, par. 10.

date so that "you are familiar with every potential war-producing facility in your District."[92] The money was appropriated early in 1939. Accordingly, as soon as procurement planning engineers, more inspectors, and more clerks could be hired, district office personnel increased. The Pittsburgh District, which in 1930 had had only two full-time workers, by mid-1939 had twenty-three; Philadelphia jumped to fifty-one. Even teletype systems were installed that summer. To prepare for the "accelerated Procurement Planning Program" every district submitted lists of machine-tool shortages.[93]

That this work was effective is proven by the report made by the Chief of Industrial Service a few days before war broke out in Europe. On 29 August 1939 General Harris stated that out of 133 orders placed under the $50,000,000 procurement program for 1939, 50 were completed, 70 were on schedule, and only 13 were delayed because of hold ups on deliveries of forgings. Whereas on 1 January, 119 orders had been waiting for drawings, only 44 were now wanting detailed blueprints, and of a January backlog of 319 orders deficient in specifications, only 90 remained. By May 1940, on the 1940 program 870 contracts for matériel totaling over $66,000,000 had been placed with commercial firms, and procurement of raw materials and parts at the government arsenals amounted to $29,000,000.[94]

Educational Orders: The First Step in Industrial Mobilization

Meanwhile, on 16 June 1938, nearly eighteen months before the appearance of the "Ordnance Protective Mobilization Plan, 1939," the Educational Orders Act became law. This enabled the Ordnance Department to make its first definite move toward industrial mobilization. The funds voted were not large, but Congressional appropriation of any money at all for this purpose three and a half years before Pearl Harbor was a minor triumph and by 1941 proved to be of significance.

The Ordnance Department's campaign for permission to place orders with private industrial firms to give them experience in munitions manufacture had stretched over more than twenty years.[95] An abortive effort before World War I preceded a series of attempts in the 1920's to obtain such legislation. In 1922 Secretary of War Weeks had advocated it, as did his successor, Dwight Davis. General Williams in 1925 had suggested to the Assistant Secretary of War that educational orders be employed as an instrument to speed up progress on each item of the new ten-year Ordnance program and, to back up this idea, attached the text of a proposed law.[96] One of the main purposes of the ten-year program was to set up facilities for manufacture of the new matériel so that in event of war long delays would be avoided. Without authorization to place educational orders with suitable firms—and not necessarily with those submitting the lowest bids—only the government arsenals with their limited capacity would be ready in emergency. In 1926 Guy E. Tripp, Chairman of the Westinghouse Company, as head of a national committee on industrial preparedness, brought in a compre-

[92] Campbell, *op. cit.*, p. 21.

[93] (1) Hist of Pittsburgh Ord Dist, I, 17, OHF. (2) Hist of Philadelphia Ord Dist, Vol. I, Pt. I, p. 2, OHF. (3) Ord Digest, Jul 34, Aug 39, Folder Educational Orders, OHF.

[94] (1) Min, Wesson Conference, 29 Aug 39, OHF. (2) Memo, CofOrd for Stat Br, OASW, 15 May 40, sub: Weekly Report of Ordnance Procurement and Production as of May 11, 1940, OO 400.12/5904, NA.

[95] See n. 24, p. 21, above.

[96] Memo, CofOrd for ASW, 11 Nov 25, sub: Ten-Year Program, OO 400.11/35, NA.

hensive report vigorously recommending legislation for educational orders, but a bill introduced in Congress the next year and reintroduced in 1929 failed to pass.[97] A new bill in 1933, proposing expenditure of $2,000,000 yearly for five years, was pigeonholed without debate, although advocates in the worst period of the depression pointed out that educational orders would help "prime the industrial pump." Yet the second recovery appropriation act specifically banned "munitions." Furthermore, the opprobrium attached to the term munitions maker before 1937 led most industrialists to avoid any risk of estranging public good will, especially since probable profits looked slim.[98] Hence enactment of legislation for educational orders in June 1938 marked a considerable victory.

The act of June 1938 authorized the Secretary of War to place educational orders with commercial firms to familiarize them with the techniques of manufacturing "munitions of war of special or technical design . . . non-commercial in character." He was to solicit bids only from firms that from their records appeared competent to handle large wartime contracts for the items bid on. This meant elimination of the usual competitive bidding. As a check upon the Secretary's judgment, every contract had to have the approval of the President. No concern could receive more than one order within any three consecutive years. To carry out the provisions the Congress appropriated $2,000,000.[99] Seven months later, in the famous defense message of 12 January 1939, President Roosevelt called for $32,500,000 more in educational orders, and $1,762,000 for both procurement planning and production orders. An act of 3 April 1939 authorized $32,500,000 to be available until 30 June 1941, and $2,000,000 in each of the four ensuing years. It also authorized funds for purchase of production studies and provided for storage of the special aids to manufacture—gages, jigs, dies, and the like—which became government property.[100] At the last minute the Congress appropriated an additional $14,250,000 for 1940. Thus in reality a seven-year program was mapped out.

A special board of officers met in the summer of 1938 to define specific objectives and work out procedures. They drew up a list of fifty-five critical items, and selected six for orders in 1939: recoil mechanisms for the 3-inch antiaircraft gun, semiautomatic rifles, forging 75-mm. shells, machining 75-mm. shells, searchlights, and gas masks. Four of these six were Ordnance items; aircraft matériel was excluded because a growing number of military orders from foreign countries obviated the need of American orders. Ordnance's allotment for 1939 amounted to $1,600,000; for 1940, $8,800,000. In the first year four educational orders were placed:[101]

Company	*Item*	*Amount*
Winchester Repeating Arms Co. (New Haven)	Rifle M1, Cal. .30	$1,382,000
R. Hoe & Co. (New York)	3″ AA recoil mechanism	110,000
S. A. Woods Co. (Boston)	Machining 75-mm. shell	83,000
American Forge Co. (Chicago)	Forging 75-mm. shell	20,000

In retrospect, question might arise as to why, in view of Springfield Armory's ac-

[97] The Secretary of War in urging Congressional action cited the new types of guns and gun carriages and rifle ammunition as categories for which educational orders would be most valuable. Ltr, SW to Chairman of House Military Affairs Committee, 24 Sep 27, OO 400.11/104, NA.

[98] Wesson lecture cited n. 77, above, pp. 11–12.

[99] PL 639, Ch. 458, 75th Cong, 3d Sess, HR 6246.

[100] See memo, ASW for CofOrd, 25 Oct 39, sub: Procurement Planning, OO 381.28767 Misc, NA.

[101] Wesson lecture cited n. 77, p. 12.

tual and large future potential production, the M1 rifle was chosen for an educational order when the shortage of medium and heavy artillery was so great.[102] The justification was that Winchester's added capacity was essential to speed achievement of the PMP requirement of 149,000 M1 rifles for the Initial Protective Force. The Infantry listed the semiautomatic rifle as priority "1" in the rearmament program.[103]

The program started off auspiciously. To ensure careful check on progress, Louis Johnson on 15 July 1939 appointed a committee on Review of the Program of Educational Orders, headed by Brig. Gen. Benedict Crowell. Ten other eminent industrialists, including William S. Knudsen, President of General Motors Corporation, and J. L. Perry, President of Carnegie Illinois Steel Company, also served. Their report, submitted early in August, commended the previous handling of educational orders and made recommendations for future procedures.[104] In the course of the next ten months seventy-six additional educational orders were placed, most of them for ammunition items. While the question arose as to whether and when these should be converted to production orders, the decision in September was to continue the program as it was "on the premise of educating more firms and in some instances providing complete rather than partial tooling."[105] After February 1940 a number of contracts for production studies were inaugurated. These studies, though not so useful ultimately as educational orders, had the advantage of requiring less time to complete and therefore enabled a larger number of manufacturers in diverse fields to study the problems of making Ordnance matériel than were willing at this time to accept educational orders.[106]

Field Service

However much budgetary limitations cut the operations of the Manufacturing Service before 1939 and curtailed planning and research, economy itself demanded that the matériel accumulated during World War I be preserved in usable condition. Consequently, money for storage and maintenance depots was always forthcoming, although Field Service, the unit responsible, like the other divisions of the Ordnance Department, never had enough.

After the signing of the Armistice in November 1918, the newly created Field Service faced peculiarly urgent problems. The sudden collapse of the enemy put upon Field Service the obligation of taking immediate measures to deal with the immense stores of arms, ammunition, and other ordnance matériel piled high in American factories and depots, on trains, docks, and ships, and in supply depots in France. Of the persistent and significant problems Field Service encountered in the

[102] Springfield Armory produced 3,519,471 M1 rifles by the end of the war, Winchester only 513,880. See Hist of Springfield Armory, Vol. II, Book 2, Ch. VI, p. 10, OHF.

[103] (1) See Pt. I, Annex 7, PMP, 1 Jan 38, and OO 472.41/1749, NA, for 1936 requirements of 148,832 rifles. (2) Ltr, CofInf to CofOrd, 9 Mar 39, sub: Rearmament and Reequipment Program, FY 1941, OO 111.3/7023, NA.

[104] See text of report in *Army Ordnance*, XX, 117 (1939), 167–68. Working in close co-operation was the Army board on educational orders which, under the chairmanship of General Harris, had the chief voice in selection of items for orders. Memo, TAG thru CofOrd for Gen Harris, 15 Mar 39, OO 381/24300, NA.

[105] (1) Memo, Gen Harris for Dist Planning Bd, OASW, 8 Sep 39, sub: Measures to be Taken by the WD in the Event of War in Europe, OO 381/27496 Misc, NA. (2) Memo, CofOrd for ASW, 20 Sep 39, sub: Readiness of the OD to Meet the Requirements of a Major Emergency, OO 381/278000 ASW, NA.

[106] Ord Digest, Mar–May 40, Folder, Educational Orders, OHF.

years between world wars, none had greater importance for the future than provision of storage facilities for both ammunition and general supplies. Solution of the problem involved immediate temporary disposition of the large, scattered stocks, determination of a long-range peacetime policy, and finally, plans and facilities for storing the greatly increased stocks needed in a future emergency.

The first step was of necessity accomplished quickly. From mid-1919 to mid-1920 the Supply Division of Field Service increased its storage space from about 3,500,000 to 8,700,000 square feet, a total that did not include space in general Army storage depots, posts, cantonments, and camps. In these twelve months the Division received and stored some 1,000,000 rifles, 58,000 automatic rifles, 118,000 machine guns, 1,500 37-mm. guns, 11,000 guns and howitzers, and 12,000 automotive vehicles, trailers, and accessories. Most of this matériel went into storage at Rock Island, the rest at Aberdeen, Erie, Savanna, Middletown, San Antonio, Fort Bliss in Texas, and Augusta. Before storage every item needed overhaul, cleaning, and reconditioning. A small sampling of the task of the Maintenance Division shows by midsummer of 1920 overhaul of 3,099 75-mm. guns, 2,567 155-mm. howitzers, 1,849 10-ton tractors, 826 6-ton tanks, 2,216,448 .30-caliber rifles, 25,604 Browning machine guns, and 140,814 automatic pistols. And these items were only a fraction of 119 types of artillery and small arms handled.[107]

Some ammunition was left for a brief time in manufacturing plants, but factory owners soon demanded the space for their reconversion operations. A less temporary expedient lay in using the ammunition depots built as forwarding points during the war. On the problem of long-range strategic storage, the Department made a special study which the Secretary of War approved 29 August 1919. The plan provided that about one fourth of the ammunition be stored at five permanent depots already built in the East, and the remainder at new facilities near Ogden in Utah, Sparta in Wisconsin, and Savanna. The second deficiency bill of 6 March 1920 allotted $5,000,000 for part of this construction program. Like general supplies, ammunition required thorough inspection and repacking before storing. This job occupied depot personnel all through 1919 and 1920.[108]

Another important storage problem was the preservation of jigs, gages, and dies. The munitions plants shipped these items to Springfield Armory for verification and storage. Since about 125,000 gages were processed, the task ran well into 1921.[109]

Meanwhile an Ordnance Salvage Board, created on 19 November 1918, was engaged in disposing of all government-owned surplus manufacturing equipment, materials, and buildings. Wherever possible the work was decentralized through the salvage boards of Ordnance districts. By 30 June 1920 the board had disposed of materials valued at $174,000,000 and property at $84,000,000. The disposal work underwent careful scrutiny by House of Representatives committees, inasmuch as the project was costly, with some 3,500 civilian workers on the staff at one time. The Congress permitted continuation of the organization for several years, but on a steadily contracting scale. Sales in the fis-

[107] Ann Rpt CofOrd, 1920, pp. 40–42, 45–46.

[108] (1) *Ibid.*, pp. 42–44. (2) *Ann Rpt SW*, 1921, p. 171.

[109] Ann Rpt CofOrd, 1920, p. 37.

cal year 1922 netted only about $15,000,-000 and the next year slightly less.[110]

By June 1922 a comprehensive Ordnance munitions policy was established. It decreed the rapid sale of surplus ammunition; abandonment of temporary storage places and removal of reserve ammunition to permanent depots; halting of all expenditures at temporary installations and the least possible investment at permanent ones; reduction of nitrates reserves; and retention of only a limited number of experts at each arsenal.[111] To reduce overhead the Department had disposed of two wartime depots in 1919, Sandy Hook and Tobyhanna, and in 1922 dispensed with Mays Landing and nine temporary depots: Amatol, Middletown, Morgan, Penniman, Seven Pines, Sparta, Toledo, Tullytown, and Woodbury. The matériel stored in these went to other depots or to salvage.[112]

After the readjustments of the immediate postwar years, depot activities subsided for more than a decade. Ogden Arsenal, for instance, reverted to an inactive, caretaker status. From 1926 to 1935 a sergeant commanded the post, and usually only one other sergeant was on duty. Part of the magazine and the lower area were leased for grazing.[113] Other depots carried on the routine duties of maintenance and renovation of matériel, surveillance, protection, supply of troops for occasional maneuvers, and keeping stock records of issue and shipment. Administration of the depots was competent. Inspectors from The Inspector General's Department in the peacetime years usually directed criticism only at the run-down physical condition of facilities. At Wingate Depot, for example, the old wooden magazines offered a serious fire hazard in a region noted for electrical storms, and personnel was too limited to guard the magazines. At Curtis Bay Depot, on the other hand, physical facilities were in excellent shape. At Raritan Arsenal, while administration of both the Field Service School and maintenance and storage activities was pronounced efficient, the inspector noted that fifty-four temporary buildings unfit for habitation were still in use and that many of the tools and equipment used in World War I were obsolete.[114]

Curtailed appropriations during the depression limited operations both at depots and at arsenals, but the threatened reduction to stand-by status was obviated by use of federal relief funds.[115] The relief funds for individual depots assumed sizable proportions. In the fiscal year 1938 Augusta Arsenal received $106,354; Delaware Ordnance Depot, $133,011; Savanna, $20,959; and Ogden $321,477. The money was spent on such work as improving roads, railroad tracks, barracks, and officers' quarters, and for constructing loading plants and magazines.[116]

[110] (1) *Ibid.*, 1920, pp. 56–60; 1922, p. 18; 1923, p. 21. (2) WDAB 1921, HR, pp. 533–34, 540. Large amounts of surplus property were transferred to other government departments, for example, $41,650,656.32 in 1922–23.

[111] (1) Memo, CofOrd for all Ord Offs, 14 Jun 22, sub: Ordnance Department Policies, OO 023/1549, NA. (2) Memo, CofOrd for General Pershing, 6 Jan 22, sub: Recommendations as to a Munitions Policy, OO 023/1553, NA.

[112] (1) Hist of FS Exec Div, 1919 to 30 June 39, I, 8, OHF. (2) Ann Rpt CofOrd, 1923, pp. 17–18.

[113] Hist of Ogden Arsenal, Vol. I, Pt. 1, p. 12, OHF.

[114] (1) Rpt to CG 8th Corps Area, 9 May 35, sub: Inspection of Wingate Ord Depot, OO 333.1/4237 IG. (2) Rpt to TIG, 15 Aug 35, sub: Ann General Inspection of Curtis Bay Ord Depot, OO 333.1/4336 IG. (3) Rpt to TIG, sub: Ann Inspection of Raritan Arsenal and Ord Field Service School, 8 May 36, OO 333.1/4522 IG. All in NA.

[115] (1) WDAB 1935, HR, pp. 262–63. Watervliet, for example, operated on a skeleton basis during the period 1932–34. (2) Ann Rpt CofOrd, 1934, par. 71ff. See also Hist of Watervliet Arsenal, p. 106, OHF.

[116] Ann Rpt CofOrd, 1938, par. 102.

Ammunition storage and maintenance caused the most trouble during these years. More money than for any other one purpose was earmarked for maintenance of the War Reserve; and of the total sum, annually about three fifths was for preservation of ammunition. To maintain a usable War Reserve, periodic surveillance of stocks was necessary, a careful testing of representative lots to detect incipient deterioration; lots that were no longer good must be renovated or replaced. In 1926 Public Law 318 authorized exchange of deteriorated ammunition for new, but adequate funds for renovation continued to be hard to get from congressmen who, despite the yearly attempts of Ordnance Department spokesmen to explain the chemistry of ammunition deterioration, found the argument unconvincing.[117] A special program of surveillance and renovation was started in 1928, when the Department not only exchanged some 4,000,000 pounds of unserviceable powder for 360,000 pounds of new flashless, nonhygroscopic powder, but also opened its first special renovation plants. By 1931 the Charleston, Nansemond, Delaware, Raritan, and Hawaiian depots were operating renovating plants on 75-mm. shell, Curtis Bay on 75-mm. shrapnel, and Savanna on 155-mm. shell.[118] While the 1929 Army survey and the 1930 inspections of Ordnance depots showed that storage depots contained seriously deteriorated stock "far in excess of quantities which [could] be properly maintained with available maintenance funds,"[119] by 1933 the Department was able to draw upon public works funds for some of its renovation work.[120] Surveillance inspectors, trained in the use of new as well as old techniques of testing, functioned at various depots and the absence of any great conflagrations and explosions at Ordnance depots in these years indicates the success of their work. The only heavy loss was caused by a great wind, hail, and rainstorm at Ogden in June 1929 where thirty of the thirty-five magazines were destroyed at an estimated loss of more than $781,000.[121]

Yet up to the outbreak of World War II, the question was ever recurring whether it was better to renovate old stocks than to buy all new ammunition. The Ammunition Supply Division of Field Service estimated in October 1938 that it would cost $19,373,734 to renovate the ammunition items required to meet the war reserve for the Initial Protective Force.[122] But when careful study showed that renovation would cost only one fourth as much as new ammunition, the Chief of Ordnance and his aides concluded that renovated artillery ammunition would provide "the best means of having immediately available a reasonable supply of ammunition."[123] Large sums were earmarked for renovation work at depots; by the summer of 1939 some $10,000,000 was available for a two-year program.[124]

Issue of ammunition for troop training

[117] (1) Ann Rpt CofOrd, 1925, pp. 5–6, 33–34; 1930, par. 61. (2) Hist of FS Exec Div, 1919–30 June 1939, I, pp. 4–5, OHF. (3) WDAB 1927, HR, pp. 272–78; 1928, HR, pp. 406–408; 1936, HR, pp. 326–27; 1938, HR, pp. 341–45; 1938, S, pp. 94–95; 1939, HR, pp. 363, 370.

[118] Ann Rpt CofOrd, 1928, pars. 155, 156; 1931, par. 17.

[119] (1) Inspection of OD, 1930, p. 20, OO 333.1/2870, NA. (2) Survey of WD, 1929, p. 20, NA.

[120] Ann Rpt CofOrd, 1934, Sec. 4, War Reserves, par. 12 (2)b.

[121] (1) Ann Rpt CofOrd, 1928, par. 159; 1931, par. 17c; 1935, par. 13c. (2) For further details, see correspondence in OO 600.913/2611–2638 Ogden, NA.

[122] Intraoffice memo, Chief of Ammo Supply Div, FS, for Chief of Ord War Plans Div, General Office, 20 Oct 38, Folder 69, WPD General Office files, NA.

[123] Min, Wesson Conference, 13 Dec 38, OHF.

[124] *Ibid.*, 29 Aug 39.

was guided by the War Department's pay-as-you-go policy. Under this plan allowances were fitted to the available appropriations so that the War Reserve would not be depleted by use of ammunition for training purposes. The Ordnance Department made one exception. Because of the rapid deterioration of the .30-caliber ball ammunition of World War I vintage, great quantities of this type were issued "free" to get some value out of it before the stock became useless. In 1932 alone, $2,339,000 worth was issued. But in spite of all precautions, 1931 found approximately 20 percent of the World War I ammunition unusable because of visible defects, and some additional spoilage because of powder decomposition. The replacement policy was to order items low in stock in quantity, rather than to replace round-for-round the types actually fired in training. This lowered unit cost.[125]

With the rapid expansion of the Air Corps in the 1930's, Field Service faced problems of handling, storing, and maintaining quantities of specialized matériel at regular Ordnance depots and at air bases as well. A large Ordnance detachment was stationed at Langley Field, attached to General Headquarters Air Force. Its duties were to provide and maintain all ordnance items used by the GHQ Air Force, operate GHQ Air Force Ordnance depots and distributing points, dispose of "duds" on ranges, and compile and distribute technical information on the use and defects of matériel issued to personnel of the air arm. The growing shortage of Ordnance storage facilities at air bases, the specialized demands of the air ammunition supply system, and the field assembly of demolition bombs made special difficulties. Thus, for example, development and subsequent maintenance of tractors and trucks with cranes and trailers for loading heavy bombs became an arduous task.[126] In 1938 Ogden, Savanna, and Delaware Ordnance Depots were named the ammunition storage bases for Air Corps storage. This meant that funds for constructing the necessary igloos could be sought under the Wilcox Act.[127] Early in 1938 Ordnance proposed a $5,000,000 program for construction of additional igloos for air ammunition storage at the three depots, a plan that received support from the General Staff.[128] Subsequently the Congress voted money for this purpose.

Meanwhile the whole question of location of munitions plants and storage depots had been subject to some study. Increasingly aware of the dangers of air attack, several groups in the War Department had urged adoption of a definite policy that would determine the choice of sites for new manufacturing facilities and additional storage depots. When a War Department policy statement appeared in February 1936, it was confined to recommendations on sites for storage depots only.[129] Nevertheless, at the request of the Assistant Chief of Staff, G–4, the Chief of Ordnance appointed a board of officers "to prepare a secret plan embodying an ideal setup for

[125] Ann Rpt CofOrd, 1931, par. 17.

[126] (1) Ann Rpt CofOrd, 1938, par. 89J. (2) OCM 13180, 22 Oct 36.

[127] PL 263, 74th Cong.

[128] (1) Ltr, CofOrd to WD Budget Off, 21 Jan 38, sub: Authorizing Legislation for Additional Ammunition Storage Facilities, and incl, OO 111.3/6623 NA. (2) Ltr, CofOrd to TQMG, 21 May 38, sub: Construction of Additional Ammunition Storage Facilities, OO 111.3/6812, NA.

Public Law 164, approved 3 April 1939, carried an item for additional Ordnance storage facilities under the aviation expansion program. Acts and Res relating to WD, XLVI, 462.

[129] Office, Chief of Ordnance, title: WD Policy Concerning Sites for New Ordnance Depots, Approved Site Board Reports, 1 Dec 44 (hereafter cited as Approved Site Bd Rpts), Rpts 1, 3, 5, and 15, OHF.

Ordnance manufacturing and storage facilities in the United States." The study projected was to consider five points in order of importance: strategic location, proximity to strategic raw materials, transportation facilities to probable theatres of war, economy of operation, and climate. The report submitted in April 1937 included a map marked "Reasonably Safe Area for Arsenals and Depots," upon which the western line of safety ran along the crest of the Cascades and Sierra Nevadas, the eastern line along the Appalachian ridge. To a number of the board's findings, the Chief of Ordnance took exception. Regarding storage, he questioned the wisdom of abandoning three depots on the Atlantic seaboard in spite of the proposal to erect a new depot in eastern Pennsylvania.[130] No action was taken.

As Ordnance appropriations mounted in 1938 and 1939, the Department gave new attention to storage facilities, but less with an eye to safe strategic location than to total available cubic footage. As late as 15 December 1938 an Ordnance Department study confidently reported that there was enough unoccupied storage space—over 700,000 square feet—to care for all needs under the Initial Protective Force mobilization; by eliminating obsolete matériel, much additional space could be released. Beyond construction of a few warehouses at Ogden Arsenal, the study envisaged little need for more space, even under complete PMP mobilization. At Ogden 115 igloos and 8 smokeless powder magazines had been built between 1935 and 1939.[131] But soon after, when the General Staff, evincing new anxiety over the exposed location of some Ordnance supply depots, requested the Department to prepare an "integrated plan of Ordnance depots," the Chief of Ordnance admitted that eventually new construction would be necessary.[132] Though exploration of a stopgap measure of more complete utilization of existing facilities revealed considerable unused space at several depots such as Erie and Curtis Bay, in the Great Salt Lake area alone the Department listed as primary needs under PMP eight warehouses for general supplies, twenty-eight standard ammunition magazines, thirty standard underground magazines, and four standard primer and fuze magazines.[133] Still, neither the higher echelons of the War Department nor the Ordnance Department in 1939 had a clear conception of the dimensions that the storage problem would assume in the next two years. The Ordnance annex to PMP of November 1939 merely stated: "Details as to the amount of expansion required cannot be definitely stated until the stock levels to be maintained at the several levels have been determined." The plan proposed construction at Ogden for both ammunition and general supplies, and at Savanna for ammunition only.[134] Later events were to dwarf the PMP calculations.

---

[130] Rpt of Bd of Offs to Prepare a Secret Plan Embodying an Ideal Setup for Ord Manufacturing and Storage Facilities in U.S., 13 Apr 37, and 2d Ind, 2 May 37, OO 682/1499, NA.

[131] (1) Memo, Col William E. Larned for Gen McFarland, 15 Dec 38, sub: Storage Requirements for IPF and the PMP Plan, Folder 69, WPD General Office files, NA. (2) Hist of Ogden Arsenal, Vol. I, Pt. 2, p. 51, OHF.

[132] (1) Approved Site Bd Rpts, Rpt 27, OHF. (2) CofOrd for ACofS, G-4, 20 Jan 39, sub: New Construction Facilities, FY 1940, OO 600.1/1386½, NA.

[133] (1) Min, Wesson Conferences, 22 and 23 Jun 39, OHF. (2) Ltr, OCO to TAG, 26 Aug 39, sub: Supply Facilities under PMP and 1st Ind, OO 381/25469, NA.

[134] CofOrd, PMP,1939, No. 42, NA. This edition of PMP was dated 30 Nov 39.

CHAPTER III

Finances and the Effects of Lend-Lease

Upon the outbreak of war in Europe the problems of the War Department became more acute. General apprehension solidified into clear realization that American rearmament was not merely desirable but was now necessary. A summary of the developments of the twenty-seven months when America was not wholly at peace but was not acknowledgedly at war should serve to illuminate the over-all problems that later chapters will explore in some detail. The financial story and the beginnings of the foreign aid program can hereafter be dismissed, since the Ordnance Department's work under the Lend-Lease Act became part and parcel of its activities in behalf of the United States Army, and since after Pearl Harbor money ceased to be a controlling factor.

The Period of Limited Emergency

On 8 September 1939, a week after the German armies swept across the border into Poland and five days after Great Britain and France declared war, President Roosevelt proclaimed a state of limited national emergency and authorized the Army to take steps to bring itself up to full statutory strength. The greatly enlarged War Department appropriations voted earlier in the year had already set machinery in motion to hasten American rearmament. In August, at the President's request, the Assistant Secretaries of War and Navy had appointed the members to the War Resources Board to assist in planning industrial mobilization. Early in September the Ordnance Department had ready a $6,300,000,000 over-all plan for carrying out its responsibilities under the Protective Mobilization Plan augmented for two years. The Ordnance Department completed an annex to PMP in November, showing schedules for increased production and tentative plans for additional storage space; district officers with constantly augmented staffs were expanding their procurement activities, contracting for production studies and new educational orders, while the government arsenals hurried through detailed blueprints of essential matériel and trained the inspectors for work in private manufacturing plants that were to undertake orders.

Time for industrial mobilization was of particular importance to the Ordnance Department because of the peculiar nature of ordnance matériel. Much of it was heavy, complex, and hard to manufacture. Since American industry produced no commercial counterparts of the big guns, the tanks, the high-explosive shells, and the bombs, special tooling up was necessary. The six government arsenals, Ordnance officers estimated, could turn out about 5 percent of what the Army would need; hence, private industrial plants must be converted to munitions manufacture, and new facilities built. Under the most favorable circumstances that would take time.

The initial expansion of munitions production had come from orders placed with American industrial firms not by the United States Government but by France and Great Britain. Beginning in 1938, and increasing sharply after the outbreak of war in Europe, foreign orders had been placed with American companies for guns, rifles, ammunition, airplanes, and other military equipment, with the result that during 1939 and 1940 more munitions were produced in this country for the British and French Armies than for the United States Army.[1] In December 1939 the President appointed an interdepartmental committee to co-ordinate foreign and domestic military purchases, and soon afterward the Anglo-French Purchasing Board was formed. Multiplying foreign orders by no means committed American industry as a whole to "all-out" war production. On the contrary, for many months after fighting began in Europe, the belief was widely held in America that the United States could and should avoid entanglement in the European war. In November 1939 the Congress amended the neutrality legislation to permit the sale of munitions to warring nations, but only on a cash-and-carry basis designed to keep America free from financial involvement in the conflict. During the winter of 1939–40, inaction on the Western Front was interpreted as a stalemate, and the conviction took hold in the minds of many Americans that this was a "phony war." Many businessmen were reluctant to enter into agreements with the United States Government for the manufacture of military equipment because of the uncertainty of the outlook and because of the vigorous criticism the public had leveled at munitions makers during the 1930's. These and other factors deterred rapid mobilization of American industry for war production and directly affected Ordnance Department operations.

While, difficulties notwithstanding, the tempo of preparation had quickened during 1939 and the early months of 1940, it was laggardly in the light of the events of late spring 1940. In February General Marshall had presented to the Congress the War Department's budgetary requests in figures that the House subcommittee promptly cut by about 10 percent. Early in April the House passed a bill for the reduced amount. Before the Senate could act came the German conquest of Denmark and Norway. During May, while discussion of large increases in War Department appropriations proceeded feverishly on Capitol Hill, the Nazi armies moved into the Low Countries and then into France. The changes in War Department concepts of need and in Congressional sentiment between September 1939 and mid-May 1940 plainly show in the tabulation of requests and sums voted. *(See Table 5.)* After February 1940 these figures include money authorized for contract obligations, the payment of which would not fall within the fiscal year. Sen. Henry Cabot Lodge of Massachusetts expressed the new attitude of the Congress: ". . . it is the general feeling of Congress, and as far as I can gather, among public opinion throughout the country, to provide all the

[1] Civilian Production Administration, *Industrial Mobilization for War* (Washington, 1947), I, 51.

TABLE 5—REQUESTS AND APPROPRIATIONS: SEPTEMBER 1939–MAY 1940

Date	Title	War Department Total	Ordnance Total
September–October 1939	Tentative War Department program	$317,000,000	$139,200,000
February 1940	War Department budget	941,137,254	119,641,358
4 April 1940	House appropriation bill	828,999,094	118,067,993
29 April 1940 and early May	Additions recommended by Secretary of War and partial restoration of cuts made by House.	103,878,630	11,199,700
16 May 1940	War Department supplementary budget	733,000,000	306,897,576
22 May 1940	Passed by Senate	1,823,554,624	436,296,991

money necessary for the National Defense, and so all you have to do is ask for it."[2] The limited emergency was over. Recognition of full emergency was written into the appropriations act of June.

The Period of Unlimited Emergency

Peacetime procedures for obtaining Ordnance appropriations had always been time consuming; a lapse of eighteen months to two years was usual between preparation of fiscal estimates and receipt of funds voted by the Congress. The fall of France on 17 June 1940 necessitated a faster system. The annual appropriation for the War Department voted four days earlier would obviously not be enough. The process therefore adopted, and kept in operation for the next two years, was to pass supplemental acts. To form a basis for each request for supplemental funds, the General Staff prepared documents known as Expenditure Programs, giving detailed summaries of the specific quantities of items to be procured with the money to be voted in each act. It was a piecemeal system, a series of procurement demands and additions to appropriations. Not until the spring of 1942 was longer-range planning effected in the Army Supply Program stating requirements in terms of two or three calendar years.[3]

The Military Appropriation Act, approved 13 June 1940, and the supplemental acts that followed at brief intervals through the summer and fall, plus the supplemental act of 5 April 1941, brought the 1941 fiscal year figure for the Ordnance Department up to $2,977,913,998. Another $46,000,000 for liquidating 1939 contracts raised the total to $3,023,913,998. Table 1 shows the apportionment of money for various purposes. For the mechanized units alone, an Ordnance estimate in June called for $89,719,000 to purchase 1,690 medium tanks, 200 scout cars, 744 personnel carriers, 527 75-mm. howitzers, and 72 105-mm. howitzers.[4] But, for all its readiness to provide necessary funds, the Congress did not accept Ordnance estimates without questioning how the money was to be spent. The regular appropriation and first supplemental funds were to equip the

[2] WDAB 1941, S, p. 126.

[3] See Harry C. Thomson and Lida Mayo, Procurement and Supply of Munitions, the second volume of this subseries, now in preparation for the series UNITED STATES ARMY IN WORLD WAR II. MS, OHF (copy in OCMH).

[4] Ltr, TAG to CofOrd, 26 Jun 40, sub: Additional Expenditure Authorization, OO 112.5/1600, DRB AGO.

TABLE 6—APPROPRIATIONS FOR ORDNANCE SERVICE AND SUPPLIES ARMY, BY TYPE OF FUNDS AND BY PROJECT: FISCAL YEAR 1941

Item	Total	Regular Appropriation 18 Jun 40	National Defense Act Supplements			
			First	Second	Third	Fifth
Type of Funds						
Total	$3,023,913,998	$436,196,991	$193,915,085	$1,442,162,645	$38,441,426	$913,197,851
Contract authorization	1,956,925,950	133,774,679	90,085,520	902,000,000	0	831,065,751
Cash	1,066,988,048	302,422,312	103,829,565	540,162,645	[a] 38,441,426	82,132,100
Project						
Total	3,023,913,998	436,196,991	193,915,085	1,442,162,645	38,441,426	913,197,851
1939 Contract authorization, not distributed by project	46,000,000	46,000,000	0	0	0	0
Sub-total	2,977,913,998	390,196,991	193,915,085	1,442,162,645	[a] 38,441,426	913,197,851
Procurement of training ammunition	41,556,458	9,685,777	3,106,500	0	28,764,181	0
Procurement of Ordnance matériel	325,953,890	42,454,343	107,118,585	103,637,940	3,403,001	69,340,021
Preservation of Ordnance matériel	31,410,293	6,108,640	1,250,000	0	5,644,553	18,407,100
Preservation of ammunition	9,772,710	9,772,710	0	0	0	0
Research and development	6,173,000	2,673,000	3,500,000	0	0	0
Current expenses	2,433,901	1,804,210	200,000	0	429,691	0
Procurement planning	2,955,080	2,955,080	0	0	0	0
Ordnance schools for training	241,100	41,100	0	0	200,000	0
Gages	290,500	290,500	0	0	0	0
Preservation and augmentation of reserve for defense projects	2,557,127,066	314,411,631	78,740,000	1,338,524,705	0	825,450,730

[a] Includes $2,000,000 reappropriated from National Guard.

full-strength Regular Army and the first 750,000 men enlisted through PMP. Money had to be spent in building powder plants, an ammunition loading plant, new storage facilities, a new Garand rifle plant, and in repairing arsenals. The Ordnance Department's allotment under the Second Supplemental National Defense Appropriation Act was designed to provide for the entire PMP force plus critical items of reserve for a force of 2,000,000 men, and to supply armament for the aircraft program. Most of the Third Supplemental Act fund was assigned to ammunition procurement. Of the $913,197,851 of the Fifth Supplemental Act, about $800,000,000 represented critical items deferred from the Second Supplemental Act. Money for ammunition plants was the chief item of cash expenditure, but antiaircraft guns, fire control equipment, mortars, tank guns, tanks, tractors, and personnel carriers also were covered.[5]

From July 1941 to Pearl Harbor, the Congress continued to vote large Ordnance appropriations at fairly close intervals to cover increases in equipment, acquisition of facilities to produce that equipment, and additional manpower. In preparing the regular appropriation bill for the War Department for the fiscal year 1942, neither the Bureau of the Budget nor the Congress attempted to cut back the Ordnance Department's requests. General Wesson found not a single item challenged.[6] The largest part of the $1,339,390,595 allotted for Ordnance was cash for liquidating the preceding year's contract authorizations, that is, paying for critical items contracted for in the 30 June 1940 program.[7]

When the German forces invaded the Soviet Union on 22 June 1941 and advanced rapidly, the considered judgment of competent observers was that Germany would conquer the USSR in six weeks or two months. Consequently, American political and military leaders were eager to speed industrial and military mobilization. On 11 July 1941 officers of the War Department again appeared before the House subcommittee, this time to explain the first supplemental requests for the fiscal year 1942. The $4,770,065,588 asked for the Army would procure critical equipment and ammunition for a 3,000,000-man force as well as large amounts of essential items. Some $84,000,000 was allotted to new storage facilities, including six ammunition storage depots.[8]

The First Supplemental National Defense Appropriation Act for 1942, passed on 25 August 1941, allowed the Ordnance Department $2,888,980,486—nearly as much as the total of all appropriations for Ordnance for the fiscal year 1941. (*See Tables 2 and 3.*) Yet a month later President Roosevelt wrote the Secretary of War that it was "perfectly clear that there should be a very substantial increase in ordnance items other than tanks," and requested prompt submission of "proposals of the Army relative to increasing these ordnance items." [9] After five days of intensive work at all levels, the War Department on 2 October sent a list to the White House. The program proposed an expenditure of $320,000,000 for antiaircraft weapons, $222,000,000 for antitank weapons and artillery, and $1,408,000,000 for tanks and

[5] WDAB 1941, S, p. 406; WDAB, Second Supp 1941, S, pp. 96–97; WDAB, Fifth Supp 1941, HR, pp. 247–48, S, p. 158; WDAB 1942, S, p. 30.

[6] WDAB 1942, HR, pp. 524–40.

[7] WDAB, First Supp 1942, HR, p. 2.

[8] WDAB, First Supp 1942, HR, pp. 1–7, 56–60.

[9] Ltr, President to SW, 27 Sep 41, sub: Procurement of Additional Ord Items, AG 111 (8–9–39) Sec 2, NA.

TABLE 7—APPROPRIATIONS FOR ORDNANCE SERVICE AND SUPPLIES ARMY, BY TYPE OF FUNDS AND BY PROJECT: FISCAL YEAR 1942

Item	Regular Appropriation 30 June 1941	First Supplemental 25 Aug 1941	Third Supplemental 17 Dec 1941	Fourth Supplemental 2 Feb 1942	Fifth Supplemental 5 Mar 1942
CASH APPROPRIATED					
Total	$1, 339, 390, 595	$2, 888, 980, 486	$3, 719, 883, 246	$1, 547, 948, 529	$13, 252, 200, 000
Cash for obligation in FY 1942	235, 464, 645	2, 888, 980, 486	3, 719, 883, 246	1, 547, 948, 529	12, 332, 200, 000
Cash to liquidate prior year obligational authority	1, 103, 925, 950	0	0	0	920, 000, 000
NEW OBLIGATIONAL AUTHORITY					
Type of funds					
Total	292, 464, 645	2, 888, 980, 486	3, 719, 883, 246	1, 547, 948, 529	12, 332, 200, 000
FY 1942 contract authorization	57, 000, 000	0	0	0	0
Cash for obligation in FY 1942	235, 464, 645	2, 888, 980, 486	3, 719, 883, 246	1, 547, 948, 529	12, 332, 200, 000
Project					
Total	292, 464, 645	2, 888, 980, 486	3, 719, 883, 246	1, 547, 948, 529	12, 332, 200, 000
Procurement of training ammunition and target matériel	73, 587, 087	0	23, 173, 992	0	0
Procurement of Ordnance matériel	147, 304, 189	2, 684, 407	3, 407, 283	0	0
Preservation of Ordnance matériel	31, 797, 680	0	3, 193, 360	0	0
Preservation of ammunition	9, 085, 000	0	0	0	0
Research and development	9, 563, 000	0	0	0	0
Current expenses	8, 000, 000	0	0	0	0
Procurement planning	864, 080	0	0	0	0
Ordnance schools for training	250, 000	0	0	0	0
Gages	1, 509, 750	0	0	0	0
Preservation and augmentation of reserve for defense projects	10, 503, 859	2, 886, 296, 079	3, 690, 108, 611	1, 547, 948, 529	12, 332, 200, 000

Item	Sixth Supplemental 28 Apr 1942	Total Appropriations	Transfers Between Projects	Transfers From Ordnance Funds	As Apportioned by Project 30 April 1942
CASH APPROPRIATED					
Total	$543, 721, 283	$23, 292, 124, 139	0	−$4, 436, 000	$23, 287, 688, 139
Cash for obligation in FY 1942	543, 721, 283	21, 268, 198, 189	0	−4, 436, 000	21, 263, 762, 189
Cash to liquidate prior year obligational authority	0	2, 023, 925, 950	0	0	2, 023, 925, 950
NEW OBLIGATIONAL AUTHORITY					
Type of funds					
Total	543, 721, 283	21, 325, 198, 189	0	−4, 436, 000	21, 320, 762, 189
FY 1942 contract authorization	0	57, 000, 000	0	0	57, 000, 000
Cash for obligation in FY 1942	543, 721, 283	21, 268, 198, 189	0	−4, 436, 000	21, 263, 762, 189
Project					
Total	543, 721, 283	21, 325, 198, 189	0	−4, 436, 000	21, 320, 762, 189
Procurement of training ammunition and target matériel	69, 088, 338	165, 849, 417	−$44, 936, 248	0	120, 913, 169
Procurement of Ordnance matériel	0	153, 395, 879	+52, 144, 520	0	205, 540, 399
Preservation of Ordnance matériel	87, 267, 199	122, 258, 239	+2, 244, 343	0	124, 502, 582
Preservation of ammunition	0	9, 085, 000	−349, 250	0	8, 735, 750
Research and development	0	9, 563, 000	+27, 003, 000	−36, 000	36, 530, 000
Current expenses	15, 883, 481	23, 883, 481	+35, 253, 417	0	59, 136, 898
Procurement planning	0	864, 080	0	0	864, 080
Ordnance schools for training	150, 698	400, 698	+594, 000	0	994, 698
Gages	1, 500, 000	3, 009, 750	+7, 500, 000	0	10, 509, 750
Preservation and augmentation of reserve for defense projects	369, 831, 567	20, 836, 888, 645	−79, 453, 782	−4, 400, 000	20, 753, 034, 863

TABLE 8—APPROPRIATIONS FOR ORDNANCE SERVICE AND SUPPLIES: FISCAL YEAR 1943

Project	Regular 2 Jul 42	War Dept. Reserve	Net Total
Procurement and Production			
Procurement Planning	$864, 080	0	$864, 080
Procurement of Ammunition	2, 706, 763, 472	$270, 643, 000	2, 436, 120, 472
Procurement of Ordnance Materiel	6, 850, 295, 085	677, 056, 030	6, 173, 239, 055
Procurement of Gages and Gage Laboratory Equipment	3, 763, 000	376, 000	3, 387, 000
Operating (Including Maintenance and Repair of Chattels)			
Preservation of O. S. & S. A. Materiel	108, 971, 690	4, 102, 300	104, 869, 390
Preservation of Ammunition	3, 840, 725	419, 000	3, 421, 725
Current Expenses of the Ordnance Dept	211, 489, 497	26, 894, 280	[a] 181, 345, 217
Education and Training			
Ordnance Schools and Training	912, 688	0	912, 688
Research and Development			
Research and Development	46, 419, 000	0	46, 419, 000
Departmental Overhead			
Departmental Overhead Chief of Ordnance	15, 000, 000	15, 000, 000	0
Total	$9, 948, 319, 237	$994, 490, 610	$8, 953, 828, 627

[a] Excludes $3,250,000 transferred to General Depots, SOS.

tank guns.[10] This high-speed planning typified the preparation of the 1942 financial and rearmament programs under way when the attack on Pearl Harbor came.

From June 1940 to 7 December 1941 Ordnance appropriations were:[11]

Over-all, fiscal year 1941	$2,977,913,998
"Regular" 1942 appropriation	1,339,390,595
First Supplemental, 1942	2,888,980,486
TOTAL	$7,206,285,079

After America's entrance into the war, seven billion dollars for munitions ceased to be a staggering figure. Once the nation was actually at war, money was no major consideration. The Ordnance Department could count on having as much as it needed. But before Pearl Harbor the United States was formally at peace. In the seventeen months of the unlimited emergency, the Congress voted the Ordnance Department fourteen times the total given the Department in the preceding twenty years.

Shipment of Ordnance "Surplus" After Dunkerque and Its Consequences[12]

Preliminaries of Lend-Lease

While the Congress was preparing to vote the first huge defense budgets in late

[10] Incl to memo, SW for President, 2 Oct 41, sub: Procurement of Additional Ord Items of Equipment, AG 111 (9-27-41), DRB AGO.

[11] Ord Budget and Fiscal Br.

[12] For fuller discussion of many aspects of this topic and lend-lease operations, see Richard M. Leighton and Robert W. Coakley, Global Logistics and Strategy, 1940-1943, a volume in preparation for the series UNITED STATES ARMY IN WORLD WAR II, MS, OCMH.

May 1940, American leaders took one of the greatest peacetime gambles in American history. As Belgian and French resistance gave way before the German attack and the British Expeditionary Force suffered staggering losses, the War Department faced the question of whether the United States should send large quantities of American reserve stocks to bolster the English and French. Several weeks before the fall of France the President, after careful study of the complex problem and upon advice of military and civilian advisers, decided to gamble upon the survival of Great Britain and France and to send them American equipment.[13] It required a ruling of The Attorney General to clear the way for this transfer of matériel. By legislation enacted in 1919 and 1926, military supplies declared to be surplus to needs of the War Department could be sold, and unserviceable or deteriorated ammunition could be exchanged for new. These laws The Attorney General declared applicable to the transfer, but the "surplus" stocks must be sold to private citizens, who in turn could sell to foreign governments. The United States Steel Corporation agreed to have one of its subsidiary companies be the agent in the deal. This roundabout procedure thus acquired some color of legality.

Determining exactly what military supplies could best be spared fell mainly to the Ordnance Department. The German Army reached Abbeville on the Channel on 21 May. Early on the morning of 22 May General Marshall called General Wesson to his office, outlined the problems of determining "surplus," and asked for a list of ordnance items and quantities that could be shipped to England. The Chief of Ordnance straightway called his top aides into conference to draw up the list of equipment that "could be released without prejudice to the United States National Defense." Tentative agreement came quickly, and General Wesson later the same day carried the resulting memorandum to General Marshall's office.[14]

During the next two weeks the Nazi troops rolled on to other spots along the Channel. The British, mustering 600 ships, yachts, and small river craft, succeeded in evacuating about 335,000 men from Dunkerque, but left behind most of their arms and all their heavy ordnance. In Washington frequent conferences were held to iron out the details of transfer of American "surplus." To complicate matters an Allied commission kept raising its demands. For example, early in June it requested 250,000,000 additional rounds of .30-caliber rifle ammunition; General Wesson considered 100,000,000 the limit. As a compromise, 130,000,000 rounds was finally settled upon. Decisions involving a wide range of ordnance matériel were necessary, but by 4 June the program for shipment was virtually complete and had General Marshall's approval. That day the Equipment Division of the Ordnance Department Field Service sent its first batch of telegrams to field installations ordering immediate shipment of the listed items to Raritan for overseas transit.[15]

The capitulation of France later in June meant that all ordnance "surplus" maté-

---

[13] This decision was made over the violent protests of many of the top presidential advisers and legislative leaders of the government. They believed that Great Britain was finished and that the matériel would simply fall into Nazi hands to be used against America. Robert E. Sherwood, *Roosevelt and Hopkins, An Intimate History* (New York, 1948), p. 149.

[14] Min, Wesson Conference, 22 May 40, OHF.

[15] Min, Wesson Conferences, 3–6 Jun 40, OHF.

riel would go to England. Within the next two months the British received 615,000 Enfield rifles, 25,000 Browning automatic rifles, BAR's, with 1,000,000 20-round BAR magazines, 86,000 machine guns, 895 75-mm. guns, 138,000,000 rounds of .30-caliber ammunition, 1,075,000 rounds for the 75's, and lesser amounts of smokeless powder and TNT. This matériel comprised a very important accretion to British defensive powers at a most critical period.[16]

However wise the transfer of this matériel proved to be ultimately, the immediate consequences were a loss of equipment available to the United States Army. The value of the munitions first shipped was set at $37,100,000, of which nearly $22,000,000 was in ammunition. Later, as additional matériel was sent, the total reached $41,289,130. Though the purchase money would go into replacements, production could not be contrived overnight. The tanks that were shipped were obsolete; it is true the Enfield rifles could have been used in the United States only for training; and some of the 75-mm. guns and 76,000 of the machine guns, an assortment of British Marlin, Vickers, and Lewis models stored away and practically forgotten after World War I, would not have been issued to the U.S. Army in any case. But the Browning automatic rifles were badly needed. Shipping 25,000 BAR's reduced the supply of the U.S. Army by nearly 30 percent, and the 895 75-mm. guns came from a total of 5,131. The ammunition sent was officially labeled deteriorated but was still usable.[17]

After subtracting the "surplus," ordnance matériel on hand at the end of June 1940 looked meagre. Exclusive of a few big guns mounted for seacoast defense, computation showed twelve types of artillery available in the following quantities:

Artillery [18]	
Antiaircraft guns:	
37-mm.	8
3-inch	807
105-mm.	13
Howitzers:	
75-mm.	91
105-mm.	14
155-mm.	[a] 2,971
8-inch	475
240-mm.	320
Tank and antitank guns:	
37-mm. antitank	228
37-mm. tank	184
Field guns:	
75-mm. (all models)	4,236
155-mm. (all models)	973
Mortars	
81-mm.	150
3-inch trench	1,226

[a] Includes 599 HiSpeeded

Small arms were in better supply: about 67,000 .30-caliber Browning machine guns of all types, 4,421 .50-caliber of all types, 62,430 Browning automatic rifles, 895,738 Springfield rifles, 44,170 semiautomatic rifles, and 371 submachine guns. There were 468 tanks, 511 scout cars, and just over 1,200 tractors and auxiliary vehicles.

[16] ANMB Clearance Committee, Summary of British Orders as of 28 Dec 40 in Clearance Committee file, Rpts to ASW, 1941, DRB AGO. For fuller discussion, see Leighton and Coakley, Global Logistics and Strategy, 1940–1943, Ch. I, MS, OCMH.

[17] Interv, 13 Mar 50, with Col Burnett R. Olmsted, officer in charge of figuring requirements, 1940–46.

[18] Computations are based on: Consolidated Supply Report, Status of Principal Items of Ordnance General Supply as of 1 November 1939, and figures as of 29 June 1940 requested by the Chief of Staff in Weekly Materiel Report. Both in General Supply Div, ODFS files. Sources of figures for artillery differ sharply from tabulations in G–4 files. For example, the 155-mm. field guns according to the General Staff record numbered only 641. The 973 listed above include pieces apparently not available for modernization. See Production Rates which must be Attained to get Initial Equipment for PMP, G–4/31773, 6 Sep 40, DRB AGO.

The ammunition situation was particularly acute. On 5 June 1940 there were 588,000,000 rounds of .30-caliber ball ammunition in existence; the shipment of 130,000,000 rounds to Great Britain cut that figure by 22 percent. By September additional shipments and Army consumption reduced the rounds on hand to 370,000,000. No .50-caliber ammunition was sent. The 1,075,000 75-mm. shells shipped left the United States Army with 3,625,000 rounds, though there were also about one and a half million unloaded cases. There were 124,108 loaded bombs of all types, 27,972,979 pounds of smokeless powder for guns smaller than 10-inch, and bulk explosives in greater quantity. But the 17,716,000 pounds of TNT released to Great Britain came out of a manufacturing surplus of only about 20,000,000 pounds.[19]

In the fall of 1940, 329 obsolete tanks were turned over to Canada and 212 to Britain to be used for training, and some months later an additional 50,000,000 rounds of .30-caliber ammunition and most of the remaining stock of Enfield rifles went to the United Kingdom. Some equipment was released to other countries in the course of these months, but the quantities were comparatively small. Between June 1940 and February 1941 about 1,135,000 Enfields and 188,000,000 rounds of .30-caliber ammunition were sent Great Britain. Except for the rifles, the transfer cost the United States much matériel that could be called "surplus" only by a long stretch of the imagination.

Nevertheless, apart from the long-term advantage of strengthening British defense, the Ordnance Department did benefit somewhat from the transfer. Of some importance was the effect of the agreement to have British .30-caliber ammunition production released to the Ordnance Department till the 50,000,000 rounds shipped in February was replaced.

This arrangement gave the U.S. Army new Remington ammunition at an earlier date than would otherwise have been possible. Furthermore, the revelation of the paucity of all ammunition reserves hastened action to expand manufacturing capacity. And finally, the Field Service learned in this first small-scale dress rehearsal that it must strengthen its system of distribution and maintenance. While packaging and shipping the equipment to Britain was officially handled by the United States Steel Export Company, this agent employed Field Service depot workmen. The experience thus gained was useful.[20]

Subsequent Foreign Aid: Procurement

By the end of 1940 munitions orders placed with American companies by the British Purchasing Commission amounted to some 3.2 billion dollars, of which the largest sums were for machine tools, aircraft, and ordnance.[21] Though these orders were invaluable in creating new plant capacity and initiating American firms into ordnance manufacture, they posed fresh problems to officers responsible for re-equipping the United States Army. Companies that had contracted with for-

---

[19] (1) Computed from Consolidated Ammunition Rpt, Status of Principal Items of Ammunition, 31 Dec 39, ODFS files, supplemented by data in memo, ACofS G-4 for CofOrd, 6 Jun 40, sub: Exchange of Deteriorated Ammo, G-4/16110-6, DRB AGO. (2) Memo, ACofS G-4 for CofOrd, 23 Sep 40, sub: Production of S.A. Ammo, G-4/31773, DRB AGO.

[20] Interv, 2 Sep 42, Capt Paul Olejar with E. H. Meyers, Chief Clerk FS Div, 1940-41.

[21] ANMB Clearance Committee, Summary of British Orders as of 28 Dec 40, in CC file, Rpts to ASW, 1941, DRB AGO.

eign governments usually could not accept large Ordnance Department contracts. The plant allocation system worked out during the peace years therefore threatened to fall apart before industrial mobilization was well started.[22] Unfilled British orders, amounting to some 90 million dollars, at the end of June 1940 pre-empted very considerable capacity of the producers of forgings and tank transmissions, machine guns, ammunition, and explosives. Still more difficult was the problem of equipping new facilities because of large foreign machine-tool orders. British policy before mid-1940 deliberately aimed at obtaining tools to use in plants in the United Kingdom rather than at purchasing matériel manufactured in the United States.[23] When the Ordnance Department at last had money to launch a big procurement program, the 114 unfilled machine-tool orders placed earlier by the British Purchasing Commission constituted a stumbling block. The creation of the National Defense Advisory Committee with power to veto all production contracts of more than $150,000 somewhat eased this problem for the Ordnance Department after midsummer 1940, although the Army and Navy Munitions Board Clearance Committee had for months scrutinized foreign orders in an attempt to prevent interference with the American military procurement program.[24] "The creation of additional production capacity to meet the desired program," wrote Maj. Gen. James H. Burns in September, "is controlled primarily by the available production of machine tools. The output of machine tools analysis shows demand of the United States and Great Britain about twice the present yearly supply." [25] A priorities system eventually worked reasonably well, but not until the Chief of Ordnance vigorously protested the allocations to Ordnance.[26] In the last analysis the most serious problems of equipping the U.S. Army stemmed from the delays in developing new production facilities. For small arms ammunition these delays were particularly costly.[27]

As long as foreign orders were for matériel differing in design from standardized American equipment, the Ordnance Department could consider the experience American producers were gaining only partially helpful. But when late in the fall of 1940 the "battle of the types" was won and the British agreed to accept American-type equipment, American firms tooling up for munitions work were preparing for production that could be immediately switched to the United States Army. In a very few cases the United States was persuaded to adopt British weapons, but exasperating delays grew out of the failure

[22] Memo, OASW for Chiefs of Supply Armies and Services, 31 Dec 40, sub: Earmarking Industrial Facilities for Specialized Production, OO 381 Key Industrial Facilities, DRB AGO.

[23] (1) Memo, Secy ANMB for CofOrd, 23 Jul 40, sub: Status of British Orders in U.S. as of 29 Jun 40, OO 400.3295/136, Eng, DRB AGO. (2) W. K. Hancock and M. M. Gowing, *British War Economy* (London, 1949), pp. 106, 229–30.

[24] See, for example, memo, 1st Ind, CofOrd for ANMB Clearance Committee, 2 Aug 40, sub: Use of Government Owned Machinery in Production of 75mm. Ammunition for British Orders, OO 400.3295/177, Eng, DRB AGO.

[25] Ltr, Gen Burns to ASW, 16 Sep 40, cited in memo, Brig Gen George V. Strong for CofS, 25 Sep 40, WPD 4321-9, DRB AGO.

[26] (1) Memo, CofOrd for USW, 12 Mar 41, sub: Probable Failure of Ord Program, OO 400.12/2085, DRB AGO. (2) Memo, CofOrd for USW, 2 Jun 41, sub: Necessary Measures to Prevent Failure of Ord Prod Program, OO 400.12/3480, DRB AGO. The conflict lay between the Ordnance Department and the Air Forces and Navy to whose orders machine tools were diverted.

[27] Memo, Brig Gen Richard C. Moore, DCofS, for CofOrd, 23 Sep 40, sub: Production of Small Arms Ammunition, G–4/31773.

of the British to send complete drawings and specifications.[28] Only a few "noncommon" items were to be made to British specifications.[29] In fact, the Anglophile in 1940 might have contended that this arrangement left the British to pay the bill for tooling up for American military production. Meanwhile, by agreement of officials in higher echelons than the Ordnance Department Industrial Service, foreign orders placed before the passage of the Lend-Lease Act of 1941 were ordinarily not to be set aside for Ordnance Department work. Formal provisos guaranteeing priority to PMP critical items were not invoked.[30]

Passage of the Lend-Lease Act in March 1941 brought a new administrative system.[31] Foreign procurement programs were henceforward to be financed by the United States Government and carried on by its departments and agencies. After the United States entered the war, lend-lease money was included in Army appropriations, and consequently the Ordnance Department contracted for, inspected, and shipped matériel for foreign aid by the same procedures that it employed in supplying the United States armed forces. But before Pearl Harbor the Congress made special appropriations for lend-lease and the Ordnance Department found itself in the awkward position of having to run two production programs. Inasmuch as Army matériel was mostly for use in training the American forces now expanding under Selective Service whereas lend-lease equipment had to be shipped overseas, the twofold distribution was complicated. Keeping two simultaneous production schedules separate soon proved so wasteful of time in getting items completed that the Ordnance Department resorted to juggling United States Army and lend-lease contracts on items common to both and to making the allocation of money a matter of accounting. For a time the Defense Aid Requirements Committee, established to deal with ordnance matériel, reviewed foreign requests and attempted to co-ordinate them with American requirements, but after October 1941 a special unit under Maj. Paul M. Seleen was added to the Executive Branch of the Office, Chief of Ordnance, to handle these.[32] Because the Ordnance Department was more concerned than any other service with procurement of machine tools, throughout the war all foreign requests for machine tools went through the Ordnance Department War Aid Section.[33] While planning lend-lease production programs so they would dovetail with the United States PMP was the responsibility of the General Staff and

[28] For example, inability to obtain a single drawing for the Kerrison director and power control for the British Bofors 40-mm. gun obliged Frankford Arsenal to disassemble the model completely, measure each gear, and then make some 600 drawings before production could be started. (General Barnes Diary, 14 Jan 41, OHF.) Besides the Bofors the principal British weapon adopted by the U.S. Army was the 6-pounder (57-mm.), though the American 4.7-inch gun was rechambered to take British 4.5-inch ammunition. See below, Ch. IX.

[29] (1) Hancock and Gowing, *British War Economy*, p. 231. (2) Memo, Arthur E. Palmer, Jr., Special Asst to SW, for Secy GS, 6 Nov 40, AG 400.3295, DRB AGO.

[30] (1) International Aid, Ordnance Lend-Lease Activities (hereafter cited as Intn'tl Aid, Ord I), Vol. I, Ch. 1, p. 9, OHF. (2) Memo, CofS for ACofS WPD, 2 Dec 40, sub: Material Assistance to Gt Brit under the Brit "B" Program, OO 400.3295/1460 Eng, DRB AGO.

In 1939 the Chief of Ordnance had announced a policy of noninterference with French Government orders unless the United States itself became involved in war. Min, Wesson Conference, 11 Apr 39.

[31] For fuller discussion, see Leighton and Coakley, Global Logistics and Strategy, 1940–1943, Ch. I, MS, OCMH.

[32] See Ch. IV, below.

[33] This was variously entitled Defense Aid, War Aid, and finally International Aid Section.

Under Secretary of War, detailed information and advice on proposed ordnance schedules had to come from the Ordnance Department. Ordnance recommendations might be overruled for political or other reasons, but they carried great weight.

The expansion of munitions production and rapid increase in facilities to achieve it were the most urgent parts of the task the Ordnance Department faced in 1940 and 1941. Industrial mobilization planning in the preceding twenty years had laid the ground carefully so that Ordnance officers and civilian chiefs were ready to start the machinery of large-scale procurement as soon as the money for it was appropriated. But peacetime planning had not included any program of foreign aid, and lend-lease commitments in the months before the United States became a belligerent consequently imposed particular procurement problems. The four most important were establishing balanced production, contriving manufacture of items not used by the U.S. Army, handling "bits and pieces" requisitions, and administering the program of shipments sanctioned in the Lend-Lease Act.

Keeping production in balance so that all component parts are ready for assembly at the same moment is difficult under any circumstances. The complications of this procedure that arose after the passage of the Lend-Lease Act are well illustrated by the situation in tank production. Early in 1941 the Baldwin Locomotive Company and the American Locomotive Company each had contracts from the Ordnance Department for 685 medium tanks and from the British Tank Commission for a like number. The American Locomotive Company, moreover, had agreed to build in Canada an additional number for the British, and the Pullman-Standard Company and the Pressed Steel Car Company had each accepted British orders for 500. The Ordnance Department's policy was to buy complete tanks and supply as "free issue" only government-made radio equipment, guns, and engines. The British, on the other hand, negotiated separate contracts for armor plate, suspension wheels, and other major components. Unhappily, the British Tank Commission had failed to place a contract for engine transmissions.[34] Without transmissions no tanks could be assembled.

As noted above, when the confusions and delays became inescapable, the Ordnance Department abandoned the attempt to keep foreign orders and Army orders separate. With all the prime contractors using subcontractors for parts, manufacture of components was under way in many different plants and localities. Output of complete tanks could only be speeded if assembly could proceed as soon as parts were ready, irrespective of whether they were made for lend-lease or Ordnance Department orders. Presidential approval of this procedure was announced in September 1941.[35]

The second problem confronting the Ordnance Department on lend-lease orders concerned manufacture of noncommon items. The volume of these was not large because of British acceptance of American types of most equipment, but the exceptions to the general rule created difficulties of procurement out of all proportion to either volume or money value.

[34] Rpt, Lt Col W. W. Knight, Jr., for Brig Gen John K. Christmas, 16 May 45, sub: Informal Rpt on Early Phases of Tank Program, OHF.

[35] Ltr, President Roosevelt to SW, 18 Aug 41, quoted in memo, Lt Col John B. Franks, QMC, Defense Aid Div, for Chiefs of all Supply Arms and Services, 4 Sep 41, sub: Defense Aid. . . . Intn'tl Aid, Ord, I, OHF.

Furthermore, upon the recognition of China and later the USSR as lend-lease countries, their wishes for munitions meeting their own special specifications had to be considered. The Ordnance Department Defense Aid Branch assembled for the War Department Defense Aid office the information bearing upon the requests for noncommon items. If procuring these severely threatened schedules for common items, the Ordnance Department recommended refusal of the requests. Higher authority made the decision. When requisitions for noncommon items were accepted, the Ordnance Department undertook to find contractors for the jobs. Foreign blueprints of design and specifications had to be obtained, and sometimes special gages. The Ordnance Department had to see that light tanks for the British were built with special British-designed turrets, that tanks for Russia had diesel instead of gasoline engines; the Chinese wanted 7.92-mm. ammunition, the Russians a special nitroglycerine powder. All this at best was time consuming, and time was short. When the nonstandard items requested constituted an order, placing the order where it would not interfere with the execution of larger orders was particularly difficult.

"Bits and pieces" requisitions for standard matériel also created problems in 1941. Tiny orders made wholesale purchase impossible. An extreme example was a foreign government's request for ten yards of cheesecloth. On that occasion Col. A. B. Quinton, Jr., reached into his pocket, pulled out a dollar bill and offered it to anyone who would go to a local department store to make the purchase direct.[36] Unfortunately, more specialized matériel was a different matter. Representatives of foreign governments, on learning from depot officers that certain items were on hand, were prone to submit urgent requests for all or part of the supply. Refusal of such requests was often not possible for political reasons, but piecemeal replacement of the supplies released was uneconomical. The solution finally reached was twofold: first, to reduce the frequency of these requests by forbidding American officers to divulge to foreign agents any information about the stocks available, and, second, when "bits and pieces" requisitions were authorized, to divert from existing Army stores or current production the quantities requested but to wait till total "diversions" mounted to a sizable lot before placing a production order for replacement.[37]

The fourth complication arose out of the continued shipment of "surplus" equipment to lend-lease nations. The Lend-Lease Act expressly sanctioned transfers of supplies produced on appropriations antedating 11 March 1941, provided the Chief of Staff declared them surplus to the defense needs of the United States and provided the total value did not exceed 1.3 billion dollars. The "Billion Three" shipments, as they came to be called, covered almost all the first lots of matériel sent to the Soviet Union. The First (Moscow) Protocol putting the terms of the agreement on paper was endorsed by President Roosevelt on 1 October 1941. The United Kingdom not only received supplies direct from United States stocks

[36] Interv with Maj Gen A. B. Quinton, Jr., 1 Jun 49.

[37] (1) Memo, 1st Lt John G. Detwiler for Maj Paul M. Seleen, 17 Oct 41, sub: Possible Elimination of Small Requisitions. (2) Memo, Brig Gen James K. Crain for Chief of Equipment Div and Chief of Ammo Supply Div, 21 Oct 41. (3) Memo, Col Hugh C. Minton for WD DA Administrator, 27 Oct 41, sub: DA Requisitions for Small Quantities. All in Intn'tl Aid, Ord, I, OHF.

291064 O—55——7

immediately after enactment of lend-lease but also, following the British withdrawal from Greece in May, a second large consignment of "surplus," sent to augment British matériel in the Mediterranean and Middle East.[38] No one who knew the facts of the strategic situation doubted the wisdom of the new transfers, but the Ordnance Department was obliged to recast hastily its procurement schedules whenever fresh disasters on the battlefronts or sinkings of vessels carrying machine tools, machinery, and munitions occurred. This virtual commandeering of American matériel for foreign aid was, of course, to endure through much of the war,[39] but replacement was less difficult after the United States' entry into the war enlisted the whole-hearted co-operation of all American industry in the fight to keep supply lines full. The release of "surplus" military supplies just after Dunkerque was more dramatic than the subsequent transfers; on the first occasion the need arose more unexpectedly, and the response of the United States was then unprecedented. Still, the effect of later transfers was similar. Indeed, difficulties for the Ordnance Department in the later pre-Pearl Harbor transactions were greater, as manufacturing facilities ready to accept munitions orders became glutted with work and many peacetime procedures of procurement still obtained. Considering that over nine billion dollars in ordnance matériel was shipped to lend-lease nations before 1945, the miracle is not that troubles developed but that military procurement for the United States could proceed at all.

Field Service and Foreign Aid

While vigorous endeavors to expand production went forward, research and development work and the storage problem received relatively little attention. Because development of new weapons was less important than having adequate supplies of matériel already standardized ready at the earliest possible moment, all through 1940 and 1941 effort was deliberately concentrated upon expediting output of standard items. Work upon new experimental models was not canceled, but its priority was not high.[40] Field Service responsibilities, on the other hand, expanded at once. As the training camps opened after the inauguration of the Selective Service Act, depot operations became active and the mounting tasks of preparing shipments to foreign governments both before and after the passage of the Lend-Lease Act required many more people to handle them. The corresponding need for a series of new depots to store the matériel that the enlarged procurement program must accumulate was not immediately understood. General Staff strategic planning through 1940 was based solely upon defense of the American continent, not upon overseas offensives. Depot operations accordingly were mapped out without regard to supplying armies overseas.[41] When the foreign aid program was superimposed upon this scheme, a number of changes became imperative.

[38] International Div, Hq ASF, A Guide to International Supply, 31 Dec 45, pp. 5, 7, 21, 31, DRB AGO. Later legislation removed most of the limitations on date of appropriation and amounts transferable. See Budgetary Methods and Financing of Lend-Lease Activities, 17 Oct 44, in Intn'tl Aid, Ord I, OHF.

[39] See, for example, memo, OD Fiscal Br for Brig Gen Harry R. Kutz, Contracting Off, 27 Sep 43, sub: Audit Rpt on York Safe & Lock Co, Exchange Contract W-ORD-489.00160/13032 York Safe & Lock Co. Intn'tl Aid, Ord I, OHF.

[40] The Assistant Secretary of War in fact warned emphatically of the dangerous delays in production that must result from failure to freeze designs. ASW for CofOrd, 26 Aug 40, sub: Freezing of Designs, OO 400.114/752 Misc, DRB AGO.

[41] Approved Site Bd Rpts, Rpt 42, OHF.

In the fall of 1939 plans for increasing Ordnance storage facilities had called for new buildings at Ogden, Utah, for both ammunition and general supplies, and at Savanna, Illinois, for ammunition. Six months later additional storage and repairs for Field Service installations still stood sixteenth on the list of undertakings deemed essential to prepare the Ordnance Department for emergency, and even after the June 1940 Munitions Program was launched, the General Staff was proposing to rent commercial warehouses rather than construct new government depots.[42] That this procedure was unwise was by then clear to Ordnance Field Service. Strong representations made by the Ordnance Department persuaded G–4 of the General Staff that new depots were a necessity. War Department policy, decreed in 1937, limited location of depots and new munitions plants to sites within areas considered strategically safe from bombing, though the Chief of Ordnance succeeded in getting approval for placing some depots nearer the seaboard than the General Staff was originally willing to sanction. The result was selection of eight sites in the fall of 1940 for the Ordnance Department's "A" Program, creating a ring of permanent depots, none placed nearer than 200 miles to the country's borders.[43]

Construction began in February 1941 on the Umatilla, Oregon, depot, and on the other seven depots that summer. First to be activated were Umatilla, in the northwest corner of the "safe" zone; Wingate, New Mexico, in the southwest; Portage, Ohio, in the northeast; and Anniston, Alabama, in the southeast. While not completed, these four were ready for use by the time of the attack on Pearl Harbor, thereby providing some 8,000,000 additional square feet of space, over 5,000,000 of it for ammunition. Furthermore, the construction and layout of the new depots, modern in every respect, permitted concentration of large quantities of matériel and far more efficient operations than when stocks were scattered among twenty or thirty depots. These facilities doubled ammunition storage capacity, but adequate storage for general supplies had not as yet been provided. For these the General Staff in the summer of 1941 was still expecting to use commercial facilities. Again the Ordnance Department protested. During the second half of 1941 Field Service worked out its "B" plan for eight more depots. G–4 approved, and construction began early in 1942.[44]

The first plans for expanding storage capacity had thus been conceived before foreign aid shipments were a consideration. Yet before the building program actually got started, assembling matériel to be sent to the British was beginning to complicate operations at Ordnance depots. After lend-lease was enacted these complications multiplied. Question arose in the late spring of 1941 of the legality of storing in U.S. Army depots packaged supplies bought by the British from commercial concerns. Temporarily, the Ordnance Department arranged to lease to the British some depot space, but this was no perma-

[42] (1) 2d Ind to memo, Col Minton for OASW, 22 May 40, OO 381/29669. DRB AGO. (2) Min, Wesson Conference, 15 Jul 40, OHF.

[43] (1) Min, Wesson Conference, 16 Jul 40, OHF. (2) Pers ltr, Gen Crain to CofOrd, 25 Jul 50, OHF. (3) 1st ind to ltr, OCO to TAG, 17 Jul 40, OO 633/34 Misc, DRB AGO. (4) Approved Site Bd Rpts, Rpts 33–41, OHF. These contain background information about the bases of selection of depot sites.

[44] (1) Pers ltr, Gen Crain to CofOrd, 25 Jul 50. (2) Min, Wesson Conference, 2 Jul 41, OHF. (3) OCO, FS Storage Div, Hist of Depot System, Jul 39 to 7 Dec 41, Exhibits 1–3, OHF. For fuller discussion of Field Service problems, see Thomson and Mayo, Procurement and Supply of Munitions, MS, OHF.

nent solution of the problem.[45] Submarine warfare made shipping schedules so irregular that transport of completed items direct from factory to the docks would have created intolerable congestion at the ports. Furthermore, some equipment required assembly of complementary items. Consequently, "intransit" storage was unavoidable, either in regular Army depots or occasionally at commercial warehouses that the British had acquired. In May 1941 the Chief of Ordnance described the situation:

> Theoretically at least a shipload of tanks should, as far as practicable, be by organization. The shipment should include not only tanks but all accessories, essential extra parts and all allied equipment. It has been necessary for the Ordnance Department to utilize in a manner . . . far from ideal available storage space. At Raritan Arsenal, for example, nowhere is there available a covered floor space essential to the gradually increasing task of receiving, sorting and checking equipment to see that ships can be loaded from the standpoint of organization equipment so that as promptly as possible after reaching the other side the equipment can be put to use.[46]

The congestion at British ports on the west coast of Great Britain during this period necessitated taking every possible measure in the United States to expedite unloading in the United Kingdom.[47] The result was a decision ordinarily to exclude lend-lease matériel from regular Army depots in order to prevent clogging of operations there, and to establish intransit storage depots for lend-lease. The first intransit storage depot opened in midsummer of 1941. Here lend-lease as well as some United States Army matériel waiting for shipping space was stored, and Ordnance personnel assisted a British contingent in assembling equipment. Eventually the Treasury Department allotted lend-lease money to building eleven depots for lend-lease supplies. Five of these were in time turned over to the Ordnance Department to run without special differentiation between Army and lend-lease matériel.[48]

That the depot programs of 1939 and 1940 were inadequate by 1941 was due far less to the scheduling of large-scale foreign aid than to the General Staff concept of continental defense.[49] As realization grew that the United States would almost surely be drawn into the war, earlier plans were revised, but not before Ordnance Field Service was beginning to suffer from lack of depot facilities. Storage was only one of many Ordnance responsibilities for maintenance and distribution of fighting equipment, but within the zone of the interior during the defense period and, indeed, long after, storage constituted a peculiarly acute problem. Foreign aid added to, but did not create, these difficulties. In fact, the prewar experience gained in handling foreign aid matériel was invaluable later.

---

[45] (1) Memo, Lt Col Henry S. Aurand for Gen Eugene Reybold, 3 Jun 41, sub: Storage for Defense Aid, Exhibit 48, Approved Site Rpts, Rpt 48, OHF. (2) Memo, Brig Gen George R. Spaulding for G-4, 29 Jun 41, Folder Correspondence Lend-Lease 4, DRB AGO.

[46] Memo, CofOrd for TAG, 14 May 41, sub: Storage Space under LL Act, AG 400.242 (5-14-41) (1), DRB AGO.

[47] Bombings and sinkings along the east coast where the bulk of British imports was ordinarily handled had mounted to a pitch that had led the British Government to route all cargos to west coast ports. These were insufficiently equipped with dock storage or rail transport facilities. See discussion in Hancock and Gowing, *British War Economy*, pp. 250-65.

[48] (1) OCT, Hist Br, Monograph 6, pp. 338-39. (2) Ltr, TAG to Chiefs of Arms and Services and Chief of AAF, 20 Aug 41, sub: DA Storage and Transportation, AG 681 (8-14-41), DRB AGO. For fuller discussion, see Chester Wardlow, *The Transportation Corps: Responsibilities, Organization, and Operations* (Washington, 1951).

[49] See Stetson Conn and Byron Fairchild, The Framework of Hemisphere Defense, a volume in preparation for the series UNITED STATES ARMY IN WORLD WAR II. MS, OCMH.

CHAPTER IV

Organization of the Ordnance Department: 1940–45

The Early Months of 1940

In the early months of 1940 the Office, Chief of Ordnance, in Washington was still housed in the Munitions Building, which had been its home since World War I. General Wesson's staff at the end of May numbered 400—56 Regular Army officers, 3 Reserve officers, and 341 civilians.[1] All the other supply services also had their headquarters in the Munitions Building, and overcrowding was becoming a serious problem. By the end of the summer the Ordnance Department had outgrown its peacetime quarters and in December moved to larger, more modern offices in the Social Security Building on Independence Avenue.

No essential change in the Ordnance mission or organizational pattern had been made for nearly twenty years, but the complexity and variety of the Army's weapons had increased and by 1940 plans were well under way for their production in enormous quantities. With $176,000,000 allotted to the Department for the fiscal year 1940, and many times that amount for the following year, the procurement and distribution of munitions was becoming "big business." General Wesson's staff in 1940 was divided, as it had been since 1920, into four main groups—the General Office, the Technical Staff, the Industrial Service, and the Field Service.[2] *(Chart 1)* The General Office performed administrative duties under direction of the executive officer, Brig. Gen. Hugh C. Minton. The Technical Staff supervised tests of experimental equipment and collaborated, through the Ordnance Committee, with the using arms. The two main operating units of the Ordnance office were the Industrial Service, with broad responsibility for production and procurement, and the Field Service, which handled supply.

To aid in administering the Department, the Chief of Ordnance was authorized by law to have two assistants with the rank of brigadier general.[3] During General Wesson's term of office the assistants were Brig. Gen. Earl McFarland and General Harris. In 1940 General McFarland was chief of the Military Service, with jurisdiction over both the Field Service and the

[1] On 30 January 1940 the chief of the Military Personnel and Training Branch reported that the total military strength of the Ordnance Department was 376 officers and 3,280 enlisted men. Min, Wesson Conference, 30 Jan 40, OHF.

[2] ODO 122, 31 Jul 39, OHF. These four units were officially called "groups" and were subdivided into divisions, sections, and branches. The term "headquarters" was seldom used to refer to the Office, Chief of Ordnance. General Wesson felt that "headquarters" was properly applied only to a military organization, and he looked upon his staff as primarily a business office.

[3] National Defense Act, 4 June 1920, PL 242, 66th Cong.

CHART 1—ORGANIZATION OF THE ORDNANCE DEPARTMENT: 31 JULY 1939

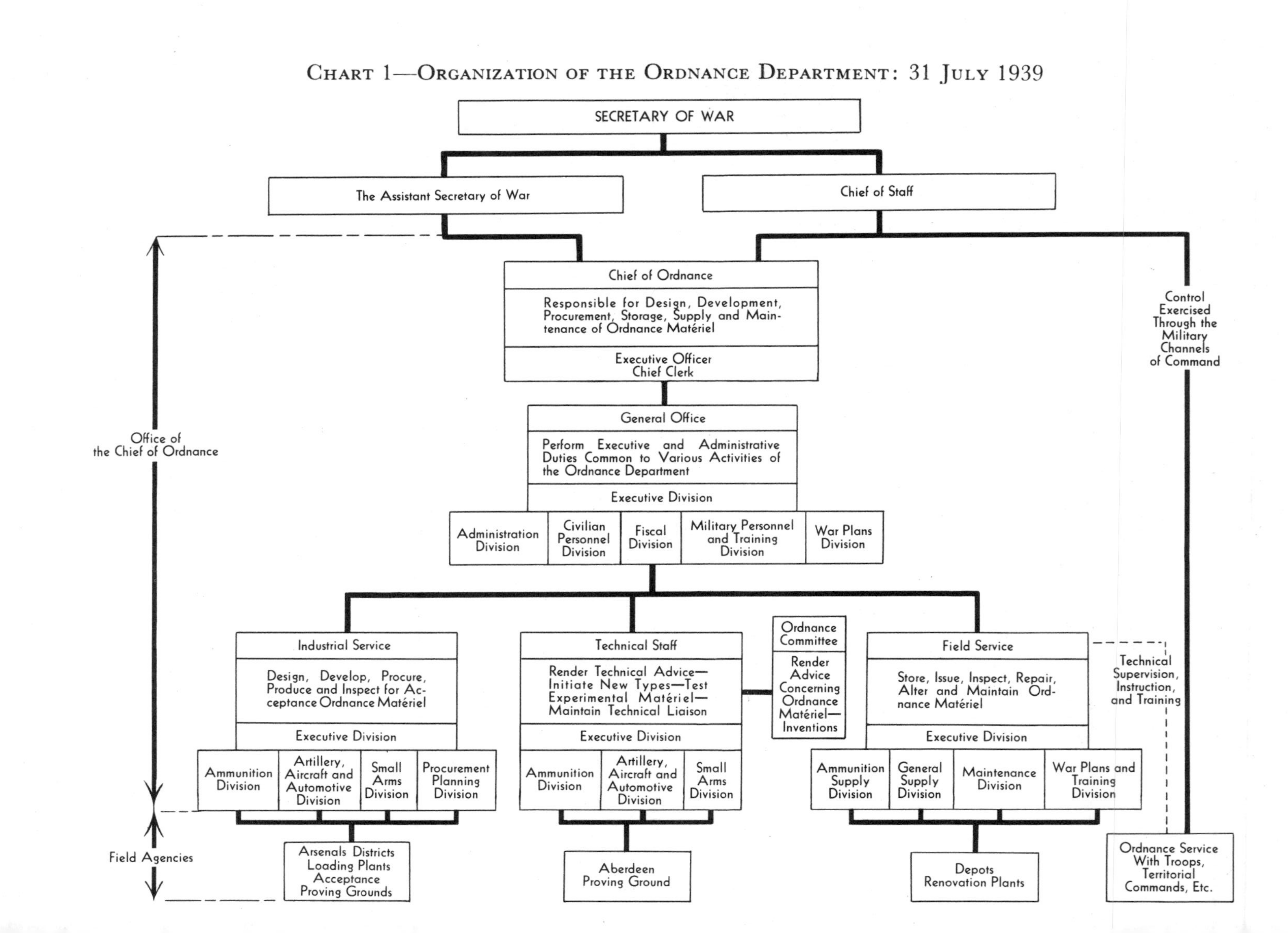

Technical Staff, while General Harris was chief of the Industrial Service. This arrangement gave emphasis to the distinction between the military duties of the Chief of Ordnance, for which he was responsible to the Chief of Staff of the Army, and his industrial duties, for which he was responsible to the Assistant Secretary of War.

By far the largest of the four groups was the Industrial Service which, in addition to its procurement and production functions, had responsibility for designing and developing new and improved weapons, since Ordnance at the time had no Research and Development Division.[4] During the spring of 1940, when interest in the rearmament program was growing, Col. Gladeon M. Barnes, chief of the Technical Staff, urged General Wesson to separate the research function from production and procurement by establishing a research division independent of the Industrial Service. Colonel Barnes argued that this would give the research experts freedom to carry on their investigations and experiments without being constantly hampered by production problems.[5] But General Wesson decided that the most pressing need at the moment was not for more time-consuming research and experimentation with new weapons but for the preparation of blueprints and specifications for equipment already approved. He chose to keep design and development within the Industrial Service and, at the same time, to strengthen that service by adding three experienced officers as assistants to General Harris. He named Col. Burton O. Lewis as assistant chief for production and procurement; transferred Colonel Barnes from the Technical Staff to the Industrial Service as assistant chief for engineering; and a short time later ordered Lt. Col.

MAJ. GEN. CHARLES M. WESSON, *Chief of Ordnance, 1938–42.*

Levin H. Campbell, Jr., from Frankford Arsenal to Washington to become assistant chief for facilities.[6]

These three "vice presidents," as they were familiarly known in the Department, assumed their duties while Ordnance was being tooled up for the big job ahead. In the summer of 1940 the Industrial Service was suddenly called upon to negotiate contracts amounting to hundreds of millions of dollars for a great variety of complex

[4] ODO 122, 31 Jul 39, OHF.

[5] Memo, Col Barnes for Gen Wesson, 13 May 40, sub: Expansion of Research and Development Activities, OHF. For further discussion of the problem of organizing research and development activities, see Ch. VIII, below.

[6] (1) Intervs with Gen Harris and Brig Gen Burton O. Lewis, Jun 49. (2) General Instructions 1, 2, 3, 4, Ind Serv, Jun–Jul 40, OHF. See also Brig. Gen. Levin H. Campbell, Jr., "Ordnance Facilities," *Army Ordnance*, XXI, 124 (1941), 369.

CHART 2—ORGANIZATION OF THE INDUSTRIAL SERVICE

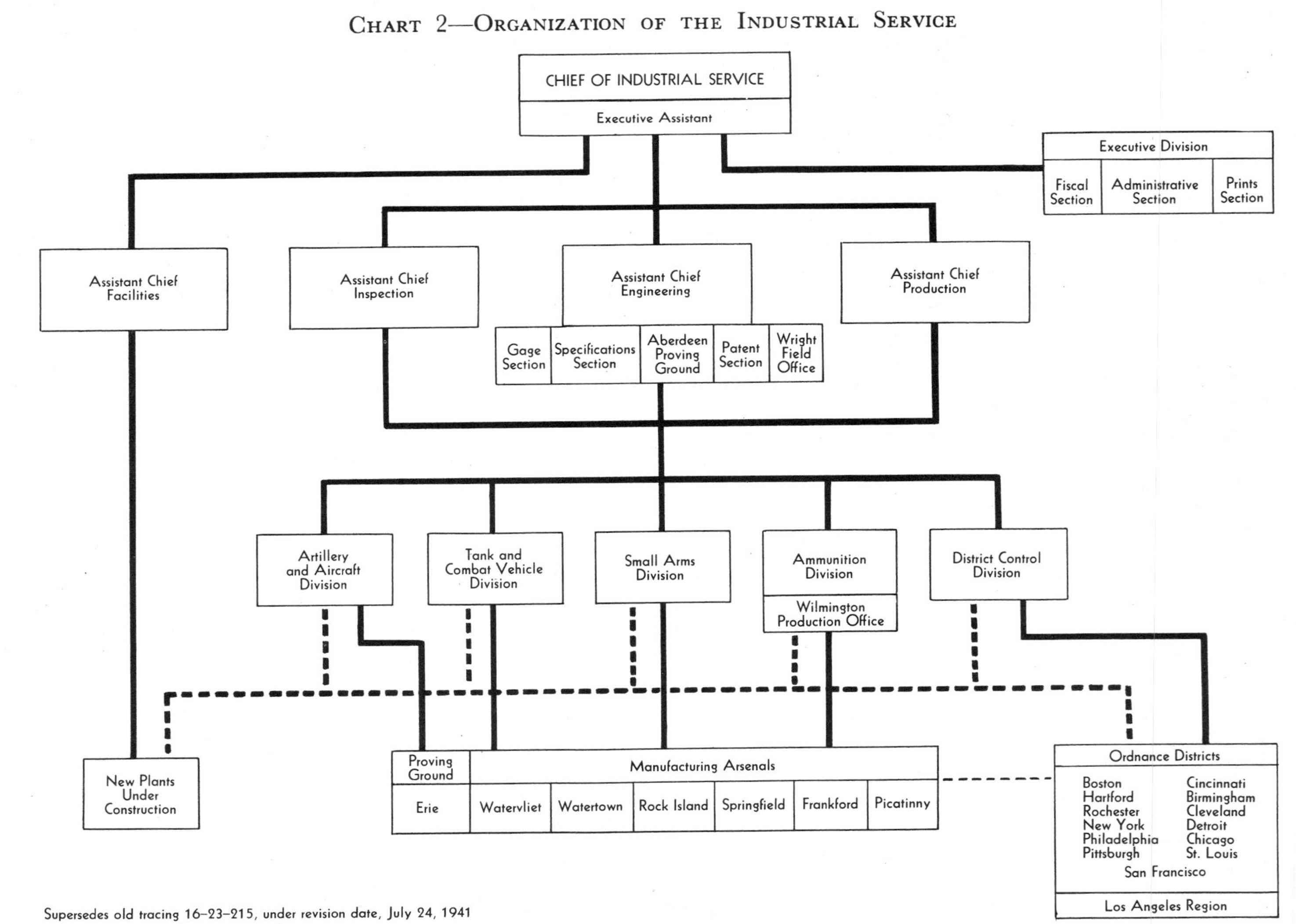

Supersedes old tracing 16–23–215, under revision date, July 24, 1941

weapons. The district offices were expanding their small peacetime organizations as quickly as possible and were preparing to handle procurement assignments on a grand scale. The three assistant chiefs aided General Harris in exercising effective supervision over the operating divisions of the Industrial Service during this period of rapid growth.

Management of supply activities was the responsibility of Field Service. It stored and issued matériel; inspected, repaired, and maintained ordnance equipment, whether in storage or in the hands of troops; and administered storage depots, renovation plants, and other field establishments. The growing importance of supply operations early in 1940 led to the assignment of the executive officer for Field Service, Col. James K. Crain, as chief of the Field Service, under the supervision of General McFarland, chief of the Military Service.[7] The Field Service at that time was organized into an Executive Division, a War Plans and Training Division (later renamed Military Organization and Publications Division), and three operating divisions—Ammunition Supply, General Supply, and Maintenance. In April the Maintenance and General Supply Divisions were placed under the direction of Col. Everett S. Hughes, then designated chief of the Equipment Division, to bring about closer co-ordination of their activities, particularly as they concerned spare parts.[8] Under Colonel Crain's supervision, specially trained Ordnance companies and battalions were organized to administer Field Service depots and maintain Ordnance equipment in the hands of troops. Construction of new storage facilities was begun during 1940, and in midsummer the Field Service handled its first big prewar assignment—the transfer of over 50,000 tons of Ordnance supplies to the British Army.

From the Office, Chief of Ordnance, control was exercised over an increasing number of field establishments. These were divided into four main groups, with the General Office administering the schools, the Technical Staff the laboratories and proving grounds, the Industrial Service the arsenals and district offices, and the Field Service the storage depots and renovation plants. General Wesson delegated full authority to the commanding officers to carry on day-to-day operations, subject only to broad policies determined by the Washington headquarters. This practice was based on the traditional Ordnance policy of "centralized control from the Washington office with operations decentralized to field agencies."[9]

At General Wesson's 11 o'clock conferences, held virtually every day, members of the staff reported on progress and difficulties and threshed out common problems. Sometimes only two or three officers attended and at other times the heads of all the groups and staff branches were present. On several occasions the Chief of Staff and other representatives of the War Department high command attended. Under General Wesson's leadership, the "11 o'clocks" served as the central policy-making agency for the Ordnance Department.[10]

---

[7] (1) Ord SO 76, par. 5, 30 Mar 40, OHF. (2) Intervs with Gen McFarland and Maj Gen James K. Crain, 30 Jun 49.

[8] (1) Change 2, ODO 122, 1 Apr 40, OHF. (2) Interv with Gen Crain, 30 Jun 49.

[9] Ordnance Department Reply to Questionnaire No. 2, House Committee on Military Affairs, 14 Jul 41, OO 400.12/4454, DRB AGO.

[10] (1) Interv with Gen McFarland, 28 Feb 50. (2) Min, Wesson Conferences, 21 Dec 38–18 May 42, OHF.

Organizational Developments, June 1940 to June 1942

Most of the changes in the organization of the Department between June 1940 and June 1942 resulted from the swift expansion of Ordnance operations, beginning with the Munitions Program of 30 June 1940 and culminating in the multibillion-dollar arms appropriations of early 1942. The extent of this expansion is indicated by the rise in the number of people in the Washington office—from 400 in May 1940 to 5,000 in June 1942. Between these two dates nearly 100,000 civilian workers throughout the nation were added to the Ordnance Department payroll, not counting hundreds of thousands employed by contractors holding Ordnance contracts.

In spite of this rapid growth, few changes were made in the organization of the Department until June 1942 when Maj. Gen. Levin H. Campbell, Jr., became Chief of Ordnance. General Wesson's hope, expressed in early 1940, that "the machine is so designed and planned that it can meet the load imposed on it without breaking down," was largely realized.[11] The changes in the headquarters organization were mostly additions to the staff, such as the establishment of a Lend-Lease Section in the Fiscal Division after the passage of the Lend-Lease Act in March 1941. Similarly, because of the pressure for increased tank production in the spring of 1941, a separate Tank and Combat Vehicle Division was split off from the Artillery Division of the Industrial Service.[12]

In July 1941 General Wesson made one major organizational change when he abolished the Technical Staff and transferred its functions and personnel to various branches of the Industrial Service.[13] He assigned most of the former Technical Staff functions to Brig. Gen. Gladeon M. Barnes, who then became the assistant chief for research and engineering in the Industrial Service. General Wesson's purpose was to eliminate duplication of effort between the Technical Staff and the Industrial Service. This change, coupled with the increasing independence of the Field Service under the leadership of Brig. Gen. James K. Crain, led to dropping the position of chief of the Military Service in the summer of 1941. General McFarland, who had filled this position since 1938, was assigned to continue as chairman of the Ordnance Committee and to supervise and investigate various activities pertaining directly to the Office, Chief of Ordnance.[14]

A fourth "vice president" was added to the Industrial Service in July 1941, when Brig. Gen. Richard H. Somers, former chief of the Technical Staff, was appointed assistant chief for inspection.[15] General Somers was responsible for testing new matériel at Ordnance proving grounds and for co-ordinating all inspection activities within the Industrial Service. As the munitions production curve began to rise, and as plans for a tremendous procurement program matured, inspection assumed huge proportions.

In December 1941, a few days after the attack on Pearl Harbor, Brig. Gen. Burton O. Lewis, assistant chief for production and procurement, was named deputy chief to General Harris. General Lewis' respon-

[11] Gen. C. M. Wesson, "Ordnance Department Procurement," lecture, Army Industrial College, 15 Jan 40.

[12] Change 4, ODO 156, 18 Jul 41, OHF.

[13] (1) Changes 1–5, ODO 156, 22 Jul 41. (2) ODO 183, 29 Jul 41, OHF. For a discussion of the Technical Staff and its position in the Ordnance organization, see Ch. VIII, below.

[14] Interv with Gen McFarland, 28 Feb 50.

[15] (1) General Instructions 22, Ind Serv, 24 Jul 41, OHF. (2) ODO 183, 29 Jul 41, OHF.

CHART 3—ORGANIZATION OF THE ORDNANCE DEPARTMENT: 1 FEBRUARY 1942

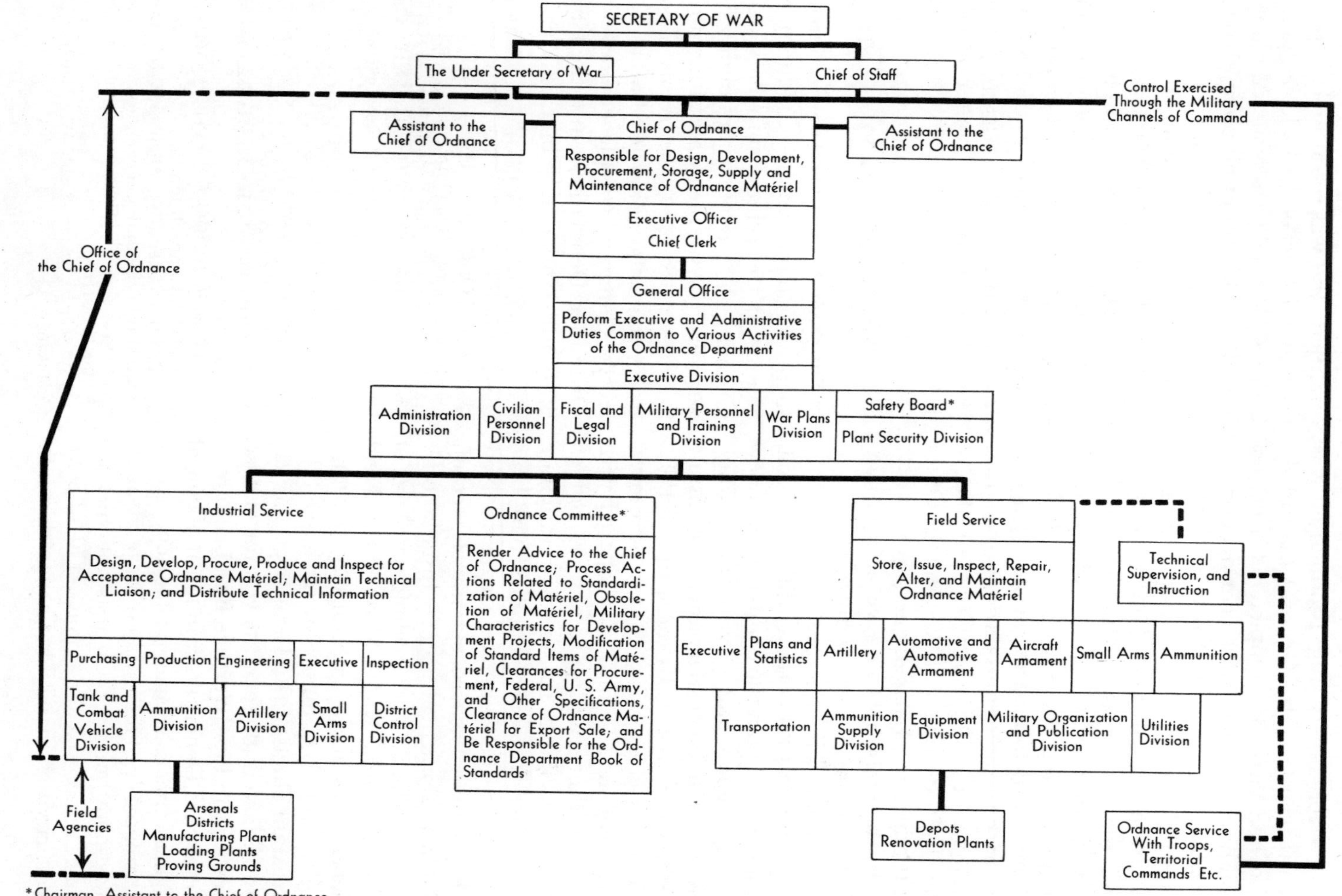

*Chairman, Assistant to the Chief of Ordnance.
Source: Ordnance Department Order No. 215, 1-1-42; Change No. 1, 2-1-42.

sibility for supervising production was then taken over by General Campbell, who had virtually completed his earlier assignment by getting the construction of new facilities well under way.[16] At the same time, the Department's procurement program was turned over to Colonel Quinton, former chief of the District Control Division, who became assistant chief for purchasing. In this capacity Colonel Quinton supervised the purchasing activities of the arsenals and Ordnance districts and maintained liaison with the Office of the Under Secretary of War and the Office of Production Management.[17]

In the Field Service several organizational changes occurred during 1941 and early 1942. The first was the establishment in July 1941 of the Utilities Division, which was to plan the construction of new storage depots and provide for maintenance and new construction at all existing Ordnance depots.[18] By the spring of 1942, Field Service exercised control over forty-two field installations as compared with twenty-seven two years earlier. Fifteen new depots for the storage of ammunition and other ordnance supplies had been built, and the Wingate Depot in New Mexico had been so extensively rebuilt that it was practically a new installation.[19]

In February 1942 a whole new level of administration was added to the Field Service when six positions of assistant chief, roughly comparable to those of the assistant chiefs of the Industrial Service, were created. By then the volume of business in the Field Service had become so great that General Crain felt it essential to have the assistance of experienced officers capable of assuming a large measure of responsibility.[20] Each assistant chief was made responsible for a phase of Field Service activities in which he was specially qualified, and was required to report directly to the chief of the Field Service. Col. Charles M. Steese was assigned plans and statistics, and ammunition and bombs; Colonel Hughes, artillery; Col. Morris K. Barroll, automotive equipment and armament; Col. Stephen MacGregor, small arms; and Col. James L. Hatcher, aircraft armament. The new appointees also maintained close contact with the appropriate assistant chiefs of the Industrial Service in order to expedite deliveries of ordnance from factory to training center or fighting front.[21]

Relations with Army Service Forces

The 9 March 1942 reorganization of the Army brought about a fundamental change in the relationship between the Ordnance Department and higher headquarters.[22] With the establishment of the Services of Supply, the Army Ground Forces, and the Army Air Forces, a new level of command was placed between the Ordnance Department and the Chief of Staff and Under Secretary of War. The

[16] (1) Interv with Gen Lewis, summer 1949. (2) General Instructions 29, Ind Serv, 16 Dec 41, OHF. (3) Change 8, ODO 183, 15 Dec 41, OHF.

[17] (1) Interv with Gen Quinton, 1 Jun 49. (2) General Instructions 29, Ind Serv, 16 Dec 41, OHF. (3) Change 8, ODO 183, 15 Dec 41, OHF. General Quinton was on duty in the Office of the Under Secretary of War during February and March 1942.

[18] ODO 183, 29 Jul 41, OHF. For a general description of the Field Service, see Brig. Gen. James K. Crain, "Ordnance Service in Our New Army," *Army Ordnance*, XXI, 125 (1941), 464.

[19] See ODO 250, 31 Mar 42, OHF, for list of field installations.

[20] (1) Change 1, ODO 215, 4 Feb 42, OHF. (2) Interv with Gen Crain, 30 Jun 49.

[21] FS Office Memo 32, 5 Feb 42, OHF. Detailed statements of the duties of each assistant chief appeared in various FS office memos and in ODO 250, 31 Mar 42, OHF.

[22] WD Cir 59, 2 Mar 42, sub: War Department Reorganization.

commanding general of the Services of Supply, Lt. Gen. Brehon B. Somervell, was given broad powers over all the supply services.[23] He and his staff not only took a large part of the administrative burden off the shoulders of General Marshall and Under Secretary Patterson, but also worked out the Army Supply Program to guide procurement activities of the supply services.

The new headquarters combined in one organization all elements of supervision formerly divided between G-4 of the General Staff and the Office of the Under Secretary of War. The March 1942 reorganization did not abolish the Office, Chief of Ordnance, or the offices of any of the other supply chiefs as it abolished the offices of the Chiefs of Infantry, Cavalry, Field Artillery, and Coast Artillery when those arms were united to form the Army Ground Forces. As a result each supply service continued to have some measure of independence. The Ordnance Department, for one, vigorously resisted further moves to limit its prerogatives and to interfere with its methods of operation.

In the relations between Ordnance and ASF friction gradually developed and eventually increased to such a degree that it had a marked effect upon the functioning of the two organizations.[24] The Ordnance Department, with its century-old tradition of independence and technical competence, looked upon the new headquarters with suspicion and resentment, while a few of the officers in ASF considered the Ordnance Department rather stiff-necked and imbued with an uncooperative spirit bordering at times on insubordination. Some ASF officers regarded Ordnance not only as being too conservative and unimaginative but also as being so intent upon protecting its own interests that it sometimes placed them above the interests of the Army as a whole.[25] Col. Clinton F. Robinson, director of the ASF Control Division, commented in April 1942:

> There appears to be a decided fraternity or clique feeling among the majority of Ordnance officers. . . . There is apparently a belief that there is something "mysterious" about the design and production of Ordnance munitions; Ordnance officers are specialists in this—no one else knows anything about it, and no one should interfere. Apparently there is the feeling that the way the organization should operate is to give the Ordnance Department the job, and complete authority for production of Ordnance munitions, and then for any higher headquarters to forget about it and assume that the job is being done. . . .[26]

Ordnance officers believed that there was a great deal about the production and maintenance of munitions that the uninitiated could not readily comprehend, and many who had specialized in their chosen fields for years resented supervision by officers on General Somervell's staff who

[23] In April 1942 the term "supply services" was adopted by the Services of Supply, in place of the older term "supply arms and services," to describe Ordnance, Quartermaster Corps, Corps of Engineers, Signal Corps, Chemical Warfare Service, Transportation Corps, and Medical Corps. A year later the term "technical services" was officially introduced as more accurately descriptive. SOS GO 4, 9 Apr 42; ASF Cir 30, 15 May 43, DRB AGO. The Services of Supply was redesignated Army Service Forces by WD GO 14, 12 May 43. To avoid confusion, the latter title is used throughout the rest of this chapter.

[24] The following paragraphs are based on numerous interviews with officers who served in ASF and in Ordnance during the war period, and upon many scattered fragments found in the correspondence files of both agencies. For a statement of the situation from the ASF point of view, see Millett, *Organization and Role of the Army Service Forces*.

[25] Interv, 10 Aug 49, with Col Kilbourne Johnston, ASF Control Div.

[26] Memo, Col Robinson for Gen Somervell, 12 Apr 42, ASF Control Div File 321 (Ord), DRB AGO.

CHART 4—ORDNANCE IN THE ORGANIZATION OF THE ARMY: 1942–45

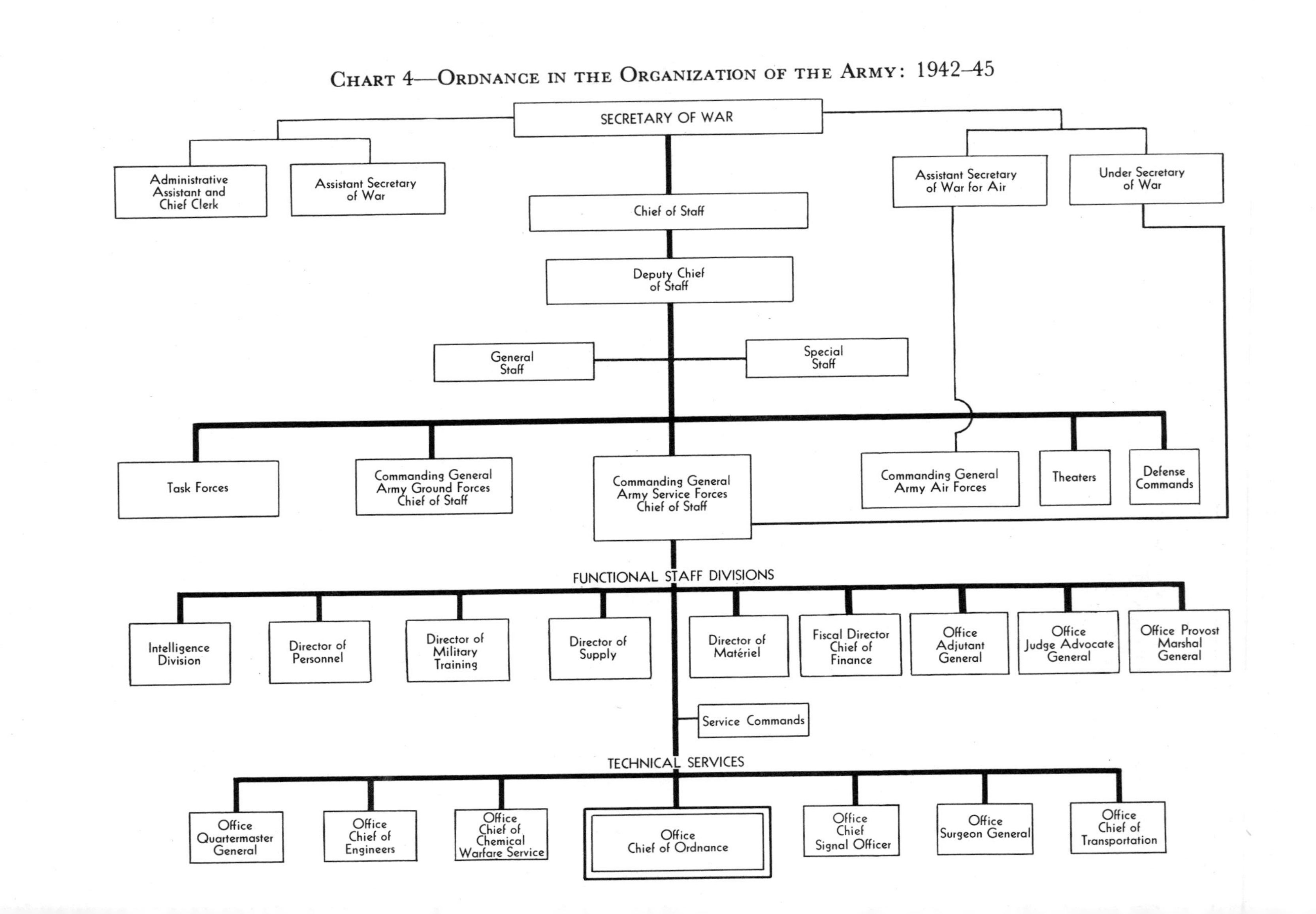

were not familiar with the nature of Ordnance problems. They complained that they were forced again and again to waste valuable time explaining to a succession of ASF officers why existing Ordnance procedures were necessary, why munitions production "could not be turned on and off like a water spigot," and why proposals for achieving greater efficiency would not work. One top-ranking Ordnance officer summarized the Department's point of view:

> The Ordnance Department had been a procuring service over a period of some 130 years. During that time it had developed a certain know-how concerning procurement and manufacture. Very few of the members of the ASF headquarters had any experience in the procurement or manufacture of ordnance items. . . . There was a group of some two or three thousand in the ASF headquarters with little or no experience along our specialized line who were continually telling us just how to do our job in the minutest details. We resented this, and I think rightly so.[27]

The Ordnance Department fully recognized the need for control of the Army's procurement program by an agency such as the General Staff, the Office of the Under Secretary of War, or the ASF, but it strongly objected to attempts by any such agency to take on direct operating functions or to supervise its activities too closely. As General Harris once expressed it, "The higher headquarters should chart the course, but not keep a hand on the wheel." In accord with this policy, the Ordnance Department, during 1941 and early 1942 when it was directly responsible to the Under Secretary of War, had arranged frequent production conferences to which Mr. Patterson, members of the General Staff, and representatives of the civilian production control agencies were invited. "At these meetings," said General Lewis, "the Ordnance Department took the initiative in laying its cards on the table. We said to Judge Patterson and to all the others present, 'Here is what we are doing, and here is what we plan to do. Look over our production schedules and our program for the future and tell us if we are on the right track.' " These conferences, carried on in a spirit of co-operation and mutual confidence, promoted understanding, but were discontinued soon after the creation of the ASF.[28]

The new headquarters introduced impersonal supervision and reporting. In its efforts to harness the supply services and to keep them all pulling in the same direction at the same speed, it standardized procedures wherever possible and minimized the differences among the services. At the same time, the ASF staff exercised much closer supervision over the services than had the Under Secretary of War. Inspections of various activities and requests for statistical reports on many phases of the supply program became the order of the day and, as time went on, Ordnance officers felt that ASF interfered more and more in the details of Ordnance operations.

General Somervell recognized in the summer of 1942 that some members of his staff had gone too far. At a conference of the commanding generals of the Service Commands in August, he declared: "I know that you have been plagued with a lot of parachute jumpers from Washington. They drop in on you every day, in great numbers, and inspect you from hell to breakfast. We want to cut that out to a very considerable extent. I notice that here

[27] Ltr, Col Raaen, exec off to Gen Campbell, 1942–45, to author, 15 Aug 49, OHF.

[28] Intervs with Gen Lewis, during summer of 1949.

in Chicago alone, for example, in the Ordnance District office, one month they had 151 inspectors come here . . . 151. Well, how in the world they ever had a chance to do anything, I don't know." [29] These comments suggest that many of the difficulties that arose in Ordnance-ASF relations could have been avoided if supervision by ASF had been more effectively co-ordinated and controlled. Particularly during 1942, while ASF was building up its organization and working out its internal plans of operation, friction frequently occurred as a result of inexpert implementation of ASF policies.

Other difficulties in Ordnance-ASF relations stemmed from the fact that in 1942 and 1943 only one high-ranking Ordnance officer, General Minton, held an important position in the ASF. The lack of Ordnance representation within ASF was due in large part to General Campbell's reluctance to release badly needed Ordnance officers, but it nevertheless aggravated the Ordnance Department's irritation over close staff supervision, and made difficult the development of mutual confidence. Many Ordnance officers agreed with General Somervell's objectives, but they felt that ASF staff officers were defeating their own ends and delaying the Ordnance program by issuing directives that took little account of the Department's problems. The presence of even two or three Ordnance officers in the councils of the ASF in 1942 might have served the dual purpose of allaying the resentment aroused by the very existence of the new headquarters and of adjusting ASF policies to fit Ordnance needs.[30]

Underlying the structure of Ordnance-ASF relations was the fear, shared in varying degrees by all the technical services, that the ultimate objective of ASF was to abolish the technical services. They feared they might some day meet the fate of the combat arms, which lost their identities at the creation of the AGF. General Somervell never reassured them on this point, and throughout the war the services saw the ASF as a constant threat to their independent existence. This feeling became particularly strong after a detailed ASF plan for abolishing the services was actually made public in the summer of 1943.[31]

Upon the Department's internal organization also, ASF had important effects. Though ASF policy was to leave the commanding general of each technical service free to organize his own command as he saw fit, ASF in the course of the war directed a number of specific changes in the organization of the Ordnance Department. Moreover, the mere existence of ASF exerted an indirect effect on Ordnance organization. After General Somervell's headquarters achieved a relatively stable organization, it urged the technical services to copy its pattern so that each ASF staff division would have a counterpart in each technical service. At the same time, the chiefs of the technical services were required to conform to certain broad principles set forth in the ASF Control

[29] Rpt of Conference of CG's Service Commands, 5th Session, 1 Aug 42, p. 250, OHF.

[30] This view has been expressed by many Ordnance officers in conversations with the author. When asked to comment on it in June 1952, General Somervell stated that there were many Ordnance colonels in ASF and that, because of the urgent need for capable officers to manage the Ordnance program, he acceded to General Campbell's request not to take more officers out of the Department. Ltr, Gen Somervell to author, 17 Jun 52, OHF.

[31] For a description of this plan see Millett, *op. cit.* The attitude of the Secretary of War toward the plan is expressed in Henry L. Stimson and McGeorge Bundy, *On Active Service in Peace and War* (New York, 1948), p. 452. See copy of a similar plan, dated 15 Jul 44, ASF Control Div file 020, DRB AGO.

Manual and the ASF Organization Manual, and to submit all proposals for major organizational changes to the ASF Control Division for approval.[32]

The Latter Half of 1942

On 1 April 1942 President Roosevelt sent the name of Maj. Gen. James H. Burns to the Senate for confirmation as Chief of Ordnance to succeed General Wesson, whose term of office was to expire in June.[33] General Burns, at that time executive officer to Mr. Harry L. Hopkins, chairman of the Munitions Assignments Board, was an outstanding Ordnance officer with a distinguished record. His nomination was promptly confirmed.[34] But on 20 May the President nominated General Campbell to be Chief of Ordnance, explaining that General Burns had declined to accept the nomination.[35] On the same day the War Department announced that General Burns had acted at the request of Mr. Hopkins who felt that an "urgent necessity" existed for General Burns to continue his work with the Munitions Assignments Board.[36] In the summer of 1949 General Burns stated that he requested withdrawal of his nomination primarily because it had become apparent to him that the differences between his and General Somervell's views on the management of the Ordnance Department were too sharp to be reconciled.[37] On the morning of 1 June General Campbell took the oath of office in the new Pentagon Building, into which the Department—the first war agency to occupy quarters in the still unfinished structure—had moved a few weeks earlier.[38]

General Campbell had graduated from the United States Naval Academy in June 1909, and shortly thereafter resigned to enter industry. He was commissioned in the Army as a second lieutenant, Coast Artillery Corps, in December 1911. During World War I, while assigned to the Office, Chief of Ordnance, he worked on the engineering development of railway gun mounts. He served at various Ordnance installations during the 1920's and 1930's, devoting his attention primarily to the production of artillery, tanks, and ammunition. In 1939 and 1940 he won wide recognition for his success in introducing new automatic machinery for the assembly-line production of artillery ammunition at Frankford Arsenal. After being ordered to Washington in June 1940 to become assistant chief of the Industrial Service for facilities, he planned and supervised the construction of new plants needed by the Industrial Service and then succeeded General Lewis as assistant chief of the Industrial Service for production.

[32] The Ordnance Department had close relations with the various civilian agencies created to promote effective co-ordination of the national war production program. The activities of all these agencies are considered in detail in the account of Ordnance production and procurement in Thomson and Mayo, Procurement and Supply of Munitions, MS, OHF. For discussion of Ordnance relations with civilian research agencies, see Ch. VIII, below.

[33] *Congressional Record,* Vol. 88, Pt. 3, 77th Cong, 2d Sess, pp. 3282–83. Announcement of the nomination was made by the White House and by the War Department on 1 April 1942, and appeared in the *The New York Times,* April 2, 1942, p. 15, and in *Army Ordnance,* XXII, 132 (1942), 965, 970.

[34] *Congressional Record,* Vol. 88, Pt. 3, p. 3328.

[35] (1) *Ibid.,* p. 4410. (2) Executive Proceedings of the Senate, 77th Cong, 2d Sess, Vol. 84, p. 276.

[36] (1) WD press release, 20 May 42. (2) *The New York Times,* May 21, 1942, p. 11. (3) *Army Ordnance,* XXIII, 133 (1942) 106.

[37] Interv with Gen Burns, 12 Sep 49. When questioned about the incident by the author in 1952, General Somervell disclaimed any recollection of it. Ltr, Somervell to author, 17 Jun 52, OHF.

[38] For an account of the ceremony attending General Campbell's induction into office, see *Army and Navy Journal,* 6 June 1942, p. 1114.

Immediately after General Campbell became Chief of Ordnance, the Department experienced more changes in organization and personnel than it had known during the preceding two and a half years. In the summer of 1942 there was not only the reshuffling of key men that normally accompanies a change in command, but also a series of changes in the structure of the Department. General Campbell, an energetic administrator, became Chief of Ordnance just as the full influence of the newly formed ASF was being felt and the Department was reaching the peak of its expansion.

The two most important organizational changes were the formation of new divisions in the Washington office and the further decentralization of the Department's operations to field offices. General Campbell immediately created three new divisions—Military Training, Technical, and Parts Control—and placed them on the same administrative level as the Industrial Service and the Field Service.[39] He changed the internal organization of the two latter divisions by abolishing the positions of assistant chiefs and decentralized the Department's operations by establishing the Office of Field Director of Ammunition Plants at St. Louis, seven Field Service zone headquarters, the Tank-Automotive Center in Detroit, and other suboffices in the field.

General Campbell also appointed a special advisory staff of four prominent businessmen to consult with him on problems of industrial production. The members of this staff were Bernard Baruch, chairman of the War Industries Board during the first World War; K. T. Keller, president of the Chrysler Corporation; Benjamin F. Fairless, president of U.S. Steel Corporation; and Lewis H. Brown, president of the Johns-Manville Corporation. The creation of this staff, General Campbell wrote at the end of the war, "was intended to underscore again and to reaffirm in the most emphatic way the tremendous importance of Industry's role in the great, bewildering, onrushing armament program." [40] Contrary to Campbell's wishes, however, the two statutory positions of assistant chief of Ordnance were virtually abolished for the duration of the war by ASF headquarters in May 1942.

LT. GEN. LEVIN H. CAMPBELL, Jr., *Chief of Ordnance, 1942–46.*

[39] By direction of ASF headquarters, the term "division" was now applied to the major units formerly known as "services" to avoid confusion with the use of the word "services" to describe all the elements within Army Service Forces, the "supply services" or the "technical services."

[40] Campbell, *Industry-Ordnance Team*, p. 10. For a contemporary account of the creation of the special advisory staff, see *Army Ordnance*, XXIII, 134 (1942), 266–67.

CHART 5—ORGANIZATION OF THE ORDNANCE DEPARTMENT: 1 SEPTEMBER 1942

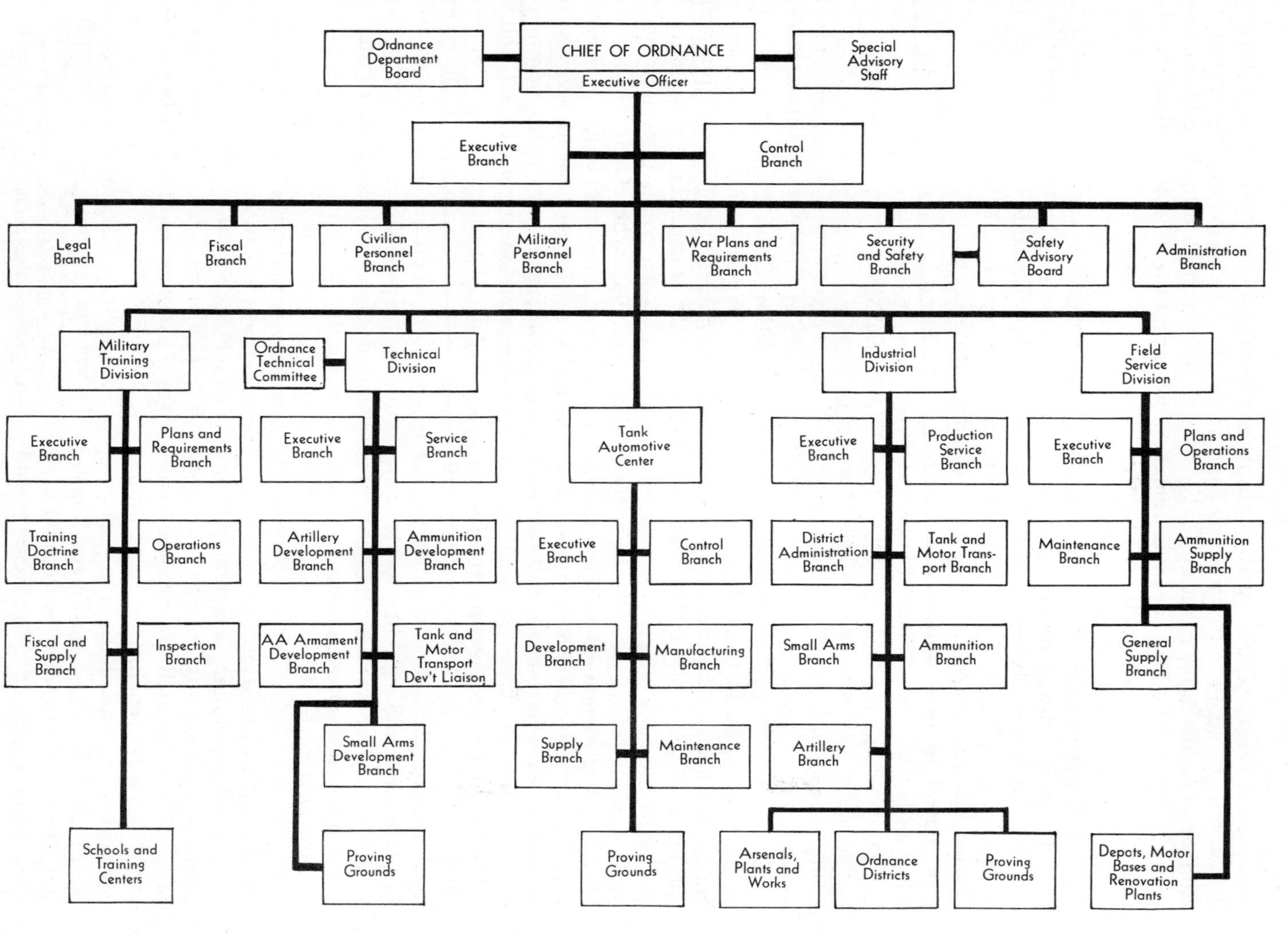

When their terms expired at the end of that month, Generals Harris and McFarland were transferred to other duties.[41]

In addition to these organizational changes, General Campbell ordered the reassignment of nearly all the top-ranking officers within the Department headquarters. To an increasing degree, authority was delegated directly from the Chief of Ordnance to the heads of the operating divisions, and control of all these divisions was placed in new hands. Maj. Gen. Thomas J. Hayes, an officer of outstanding production ability and experience who had served in the Office of the Under Secretary of War during 1941 and then briefly as chief of the Production Branch of ASF headquarters, succeeded General Harris as chief of the Industrial Division. Col. Harry R. Kutz, who had served as chief of the Fiscal Division since 1938, was promoted to the rank of brigadier general and appointed chief of the Field Service Division, succeeding General Crain. General Barnes, who had served for two years as assistant chief for research and engineering in the Industrial Service, became chief of the newly formed Technical Division. Of the other two new divisions, the Military Training Division was headed by Brig. Gen. Julian S. Hatcher, former commanding general of the Ordnance Training Center at Aberdeen, and the Parts Control Division by Brig. Gen. Rolland W. Case, former commanding general of Aberdeen Proving Ground.

This brief summary suggests that the changes made during the first few weeks of General Campbell's term were so numerous and far reaching as to be almost revolutionary. The changes in personnel were indeed almost revolutionary, but the structural changes were less radical than they at first appeared. Most were the end products of a long evolutionary development. To persons intimately acquainted with the gradual unfolding of the Ordnance program for war production, they came as no surprise. General Campbell even felt that "reorganization" was too strong a word to use in describing the steps taken during his first few weeks in office, and preferred to say that it was simply a matter of "making additions to the organization."[42]

Abolition of Assistant Chiefs of Industrial Service

The evolutionary character of the events of June 1942 is well illustrated by the abolition of the positions of assistant chief that had been created in the Industrial Service in 1940. This apparently sudden and drastic step was actually the culmination of a gradual development. In the fall of 1941, when General Campbell was serving as assistant chief for facilities, he had seen the need for his services decline as the job of constructing new manufacturing and loading plants got well under way. In December this position was abolished, on Campbell's own recommendation, when he was appointed assistant chief for production. A short time later General Campbell concluded that the need for this position had also lessened because the operating divisions of the Industrial Service had succeeded in building up competent staffs and were able to manage their jobs without the supervision of an assistant chief. Substantially the same was true of Colonel Quinton's duties as assist-

[41] General Harris became commanding general of Aberdeen Proving Ground. General McFarland reverted to his permanent rank of colonel and became commanding officer of the Springfield Armory.

[42] Ltr, Campbell to author, 29 Apr 49, OHF.

ant chief for purchasing and General Somers' duties as assistant chief for inspection.[43]

The decisive factor that brought the "Assistant Chiefs Era" to an end was General Campbell's conviction—shared by General Hayes, the new chief of the Industrial Division—that the positions of assistant chief violated fundamental principles of sound organization. "I did not want in the organization any 'Vice Presidents'—men who were without real authority and responsibility," General Campbell wrote, "I wanted the organization to be one of direct responsibility. If performance was lacking, then I could accurately and quickly assess responsibility for non-performance." [44]

After the elimination of the assistant chiefs, a Production Service Branch was formed to absorb the remaining functions of the assistant chief for production and, later on, to assume responsibility for administration of the Controlled Materials Plan for the Department.[45] The remaining functions of the assistant chief for purchasing were taken over by the various staff branches, particularly by the Legal Branch. Supervision of inspection activities was assigned to inspection sections within the operating branches of the Industrial Division, and these branches were placed on the same organizational level as the production and engineering sections to guard against the danger that quality would be sacrificed to achieve quantity production.

Field Service Division

The Field Service Division also experienced an organizational overhauling during June and July of 1942. General Campbell ended the six-months-old experiment with the assistant chiefs of the Field Service and eliminated two of the divisions that had been created during the preceding two years—the Military Organization and Publications Division, which became a part of the Executive Branch, and the Bomb Disposal Division, which was combined with the Ammunition Supply Branch. The number of main divisions of the service was thus reduced to five—an Executive Branch, a newly created Plans and Operations Branch, and the three operating branches, Ammunition Supply, General Supply, and Maintenance.[46]

This reshuffling of responsibility occurred to a large extent because the new Plans and Operations Branch took over depot administration and other overhead duties affecting more than one branch. It absorbed the responsibilities and personnel formerly assigned to the Transportation and Facilities Divisions and consolidated them with duties that had been performed by the assistant chief for plans and statistics, Colonel Steese, who became chief of the new branch. In this way, all phases of depot administration including the construction and maintenance of buildings, the supervision of personnel, the control of shipments to and from the depots, and the gathering of statistics on available stocks were co-ordinated through a single staff branch.[47]

[43] The statements in this paragraph are based on interviews with Generals Hayes, Lewis, and Quinton, and correspondence with Generals Campbell and Somers. For discussion of the elimination of General Barnes' position as assistant chief for research and engineering, see Ch. VIII, below.

[44] (1) Ltr, Campbell to author, 7 Sep 49, OHF. (2) Intervs with Gen Hayes, summer of 1949.

[45] Campbell, *op. cit.*, p. 177.

[46] (1) ODO 291, 8 Jul 42, OHF. (2) FS Office Memo 55, 25 Jun 42, OHF.

[47] Hist of FS, Plans and Opns Br, Vol. I, Pt. 1, OHF.

Military Training Division

Because of the rapid expansion of the Ordnance training mission, General Campbell established a separate Military Training Division in June 1942. Since enactment of the Selective Service Act in September 1940, the Department had been called upon to train an ever increasing number of officers and enlisted men at the Ordnance school at Aberdeen Proving Ground. Two additional training organizations were established at Aberdeen to carry on a well-rounded program—the Ordnance Replacement Training Center and the Ordnance Unit Training Center. To administer the three training units, and to supervise the training of military personnel at various civilian institutions, the Ordnance Training Center had been formed on New Year's Day, 1941, with headquarters at Aberdeen.[48] In establishing the Military Training Division, General Campbell converted the Ordnance Training Center into a full-fledged division on a par with the Industrial, Field Service, and other divisions of the headquarters.[49] To avoid any break in the continuity of command, the Military Training Division was placed under the direction of the former chief of the Ordnance Training Center, General Hatcher. The organization of the new division was patterned closely after that of the training directorate at ASF headquarters.

Unlike the other divisions in the Office, Chief of Ordnance, all of which had their headquarters in the Pentagon, the Military Training Division at first had its headquarters at Aberdeen Proving Ground, where most of the training was carried on. To maintain contact with the other divisions of the Department and with ASF headquarters, a Liaison Branch was established in Washington. Placing the Military Training Division headquarters at Aberdeen was the first major attempt to decentralize the Ordnance Department, but it proved unsuccessful and it was abandoned within a few weeks. It soon became apparent, for example, that the large volume of directives and requests for information from ASF could never be handled fast enough through the Liaison Branch to satisfy ASF headquarters. The announcement in July that the Quartermaster Motor Transport Service was soon to be transferred to the Ordnance Department, along with a large-scale training program for automotive mechanics, further complicated the situation. The training section of the Motor Transport Service was in Washington—as, in fact, were the training sections of all the other supply services—and its schools were widely scattered. In mid-August General Campbell therefore ordered the Military Training Division to move its headquarters to the Pentagon. From that vantage point it directed the training of thousands of officers and enlisted men at training centers in all parts of the country.[50]

Parts Control Division

The importance of administrative machinery for handling matters relating to spare parts had been recognized early in the defense period by the Ordnance Department. In November 1940 General Wesson had appointed a permanent board of officers to determine the types and quan-

[48] (1) ODO 151, 26 Dec 40, OHF. (2) Interv with Gen Hatcher, 11 Jul 49. See also Gen J. S. Hatcher, "The Ordnance Training Center," *Army Ordnance*, XXI, 126 (1941), 625.

[49] ODO 285, 26 Jun 42, OHF.

[50] Intervs with Gen Hatcher and Col Herman U. Wagner, summer 1949.

tities of spare parts to be ordered when large-scale production contracts were let.[51] The board consisted of the chiefs of the Field Service, the Fiscal Division, the War Plans Division, and the assistant chief of Industrial Service for engineering. Within the various subdivisions of Field Service and Industrial Service spare parts sections were created to maintain lists of essential spare parts, arrange for the distribution of parts among the depots, and generally supervise spare-parts production and procurement.

Toward the end of 1941 it became apparent that this arrangement had not yielded altogether satisfactory results. By the very nature of their activities, the Industrial and Field Services were constantly at loggerheads on the subject of spare parts. The primary concern of the Industrial Service was to produce completed items of equipment, and it was under constant pressure from higher headquarters to get maximum production. The primary concern of the Field Service, on the other hand, was to build up stocks of replacement parts for maintenance work in the field. Any reconciliation of these two missions involved compromise, and there was no recognized objective standard of spare-parts requirements on which to base such a compromise.[52] The problem finally became so serious that the Control Division of ASF headquarters made a special study of it, and the Ordnance Department on its own initiative called in experts from the General Motors Overseas Operations to investigate the matter and make recommendations.[53] The reports of both groups emphasized the inadequacy of the co-ordination effected by the Spare Parts Board and the various spare parts sections. "The major problem," the ASF Control Division reported, "is that ten separate offices deal with various aspects of Spare Parts, and no one is effectively coordinating the entire operation."[54] To remedy this situation, the General Motors group recommended that the Spare Parts Board be abolished and that a "Spare Parts Service" be established in the Ordnance Department on the same level as the Industrial Service and Field Service. This recommendation was in accord with the spare parts organizations that prevailed in industry. The proposed service was to formulate spare parts policies and, when they were approved by the Chief of Ordnance, to be responsible for their execution. Acting on this recommendation, General Campbell on 26 June ordered the formation of a Parts Control Division as one of the six main units of the Ordnance Department.[55] General Case, formerly commanding general of Aberdeen Proving Ground, was brought in to

[51] Ord SO 263, 7 Nov 40, DRB AGO. The organization and functions of the board were described in detail in Ordnance Office Memo 510, 21 Jan 41, which remained in effect, with minor changes, until rescinded by Ordnance Office Memo 618, 30 Apr 42, DRB AGO.

[52] Intervs with Gen Harris, Gen Crain, and other officers, summer 1950.

[53] (1) ASF Control Div Rpt 26, Notes on Organization and Operation of the Tank and Combat Vehicle Division of the Ordnance Department, ASF Control Div files, DRB AGO. (2) General Motors Overseas Operations, May 1942, General Survey of the Organization, Functions and Operations of the Ordnance Department (3 vols.), OHF.

See also Lawrence S. Barroll, Study of U. S. Army Ordnance Department Spare Parts Procedure, 8 Oct 40, PSP 63, Exhibit 1; and Lawrence S. Barroll, Survey of Ordnance Spare Parts Supply, 26 Dec 42, PSP 63, Exhibit 2. Both in OHF.

[54] ASF Control Div Rpt. 26, cited n. 53(1).

The report of the General Motors survey included an organization chart that illustrated this dispersion of spare-part functions throughout the Department. General Survey of the Organization . . . , Vol. II, p. 31, OHF.

[55] ODO 285, 26 Jun 42, OHF. The new division was established in June on verbal orders from General Campbell.

be chief of the new division. Some of his staff came from the spare parts sections that were to be taken over by the Parts Control Division, while others came from among the General Motors experts who had made the survey.

Neither the order creating the new division nor the General Motors report went into any detail as to how the new division was to function. General Case and his staff were therefore at once faced with the task of determining their operating procedures. A difference of opinion soon emerged among the personnel of the new division as to whether it should take over all operations bearing on spare parts or should merely set up controls to see that those responsible for such operations actually produced the desired results. Further, the General Motors people, who were experienced in peacetime supply problems of the automobile industry, did not see eye to eye with Ordnance officers who were familiar with the much different problems of wartime military supply.[56] In the many conferences on these subjects held during the month of July, the wisdom of creating a Parts Control Division was seriously questioned.

General Case finally came to the conclusion toward the end of the month that the establishment of the division had been a mistake. Feeling that he had been put in the position of having responsibility without full authority, he recommended that the division be abolished, and that the spare parts problem be given to the Field Service.[57] General Campbell reluctantly accepted General Case's recommendation and abolished the Parts Control Division on 28 July—just four weeks after its creation. Responsibility for parts control was then turned over to the Field Service Division. The Spare Parts Board was re-established with essentially the same responsibilities it had had before the creation of the Parts Control Division, but its membership was now limited to two officers—the chiefs of the Industrial and the Field Service Divisions.[58]

With the elimination of Parts Control, the number of divisions was reduced to four—Industrial Service, Field Service, Technical, and Military Training. In terms of personnel and funds, every one of these divisions was many times larger than the entire Ordnance Department had been before the war. They had budgets running into the hundreds of millions of dollars and directed the activities of many thousands of officers, enlisted men, and civilian workers. Of their relationship to each other and to the Chief of Ordnance, General Campbell wrote:

> These divisions were largely autonomous. They were tied together as to the common policy and as to inter-division relations by me and my immediate personal staff. The heads of each of the divisions reported directly to me, as did also the heads of the Personnel, Fiscal, and Legal Branches. I tried to give each of them full authority, and I also tried to be completely frank with them at all times so that they, acting in a given situation, could have the maximum background on which to base an action. I tried to impress upon them that the more decisions they gave, within general broad policy limitations, the more value to me they were. They were at all times to keep me advised of matters which their common sense indicated I should know; equally, their common sense was exercised to

[56] (1) Intervs, Aug–Nov 49, with Gen Case, and Col W. F. Sadtler, Production Control Off Parts Control Div. (2) Key Pers Rpt, 1945, Col L. J. Meyns, Exec Off Parts Control Div, OHF.

[57] Interv with Gen Case, 22 Nov 49.

[58] Change 1, Ord Office Memo 618, 12 Aug 42. The Parts Control Div was abolished by Change 1, ODO 285, 28 Jul 42, OHF. For further discussion of the spare parts problem see Thomson and Mayo, Procurement and Supply of Munitions, MS, OHF.

keep unimportant things away from me . . . . My job as I saw it was to be the *Chief of Ordnance* and to be as free as time would permit, to think and to spend time in the selection of men. In practically every case I was able to fill the principal positions with men who could do the job far better than I could.[59]

The "Front Office Team"

In the new administration, General Campbell's right-hand man was Colonel Raaen, his executive officer, but there were also several assistants who handled special assignments. Lt. Col. Paul M. Seleen, who had served with General Wesson as assistant for matters pertaining to Field Service and research and development, continued in this position on General Campbell's staff, with the important additional duty of heading the War Aid Branch. Lt. Col. Everett P. Russell, a consulting engineer in civilian life, handled matters concerning the Industrial Service, and Col. Herbert R. White, a former General Motors executive, served as a "trouble shooter" on industrial production matters. Lt. Col. Leo A. Codd, the executive vice president of the Army Ordnance Association and editor of the magazine *Army Ordnance,* handled the public relations activities of the Department. These four officers, with Colonel Raaen and Lt. Col. Thomas Moore, aide to General Campbell, made up the "front office team" during nearly all of General Campbell's term.[60]

Staff Branches

In addition to the changes on the operating division level, several were made during June among the staff branches of the former General Office. A Control Branch, an Explosives Safety Branch, and a War Aid Branch were established, and the Fiscal and Legal Division was split into the Fiscal Branch and the Legal Branch. At the same time an Ordnance Department Board was created to study Field Service operations. Most of these changes were results of developments within the Department that had been gradually unfolding during the preceding months, but the establishment of the Control Branch and the War Aid Branch were specifically directed by ASF headquarters.

The Control Branch was a new and unfamiliar piece of administrative machinery that was virtually forced upon Ordnance by ASF, and was not welcomed by officers in the Department.[61] With the formation of ASF in March, a Control Division had been set up as a part of General Somervell's staff, and the proposal was advanced that corresponding control units be formed in all of the supply services. Because of the reluctance to accept this innovation, no final action was taken on the matter for over three months.

When the Ordnance Control Branch was finally established at the end of June, it was placed under the direction of Col. Clarence E. Davies, former executive officer to General Lewis in the Industrial

---

[59] Ltr, Campbell to author, 29 Apr 49, OHF.

[60] (1) Intervs with Cols Raaen, Seleen, and Codd, and other officers. (2) Correspondence with Campbell, 1949–50, OHF.

[61] See, for example, comments on the Ordnance Control Branch by O. A. Gottschalk, special assistant to the chief of the ASF Control Division, in November 1942: "The mission of the Control Branch is not fully understood and appreciated by heads of operating divisions. This is indicated by resistance to studies being made by the Control Branch." Rpt 54, ASF Control Div files, DRB AGO. The same view has also been expressed to the author by many officers of the Ordnance Department during interviews.

Service.[62] Steps were then taken to recruit a competent staff of officers and civilians, but progress was slow.[63] The new branch was charged with broad responsibilities for obtaining information regarding the efficiency of operation of all elements of the Department, recommending changes in organization, procedures, and policies, and managing statistical and reporting activities. Actually, the Control Branch seldom went beyond more or less routine functions and never achieved the position of influence that ASF wished it to have. In terms of initiative, rate of progress, and ability to get its recommendations put into effect, the Ordnance Control Branch was repeatedly given a low rating, as compared with similar branches in other services, by the ASF Control Division.[64]

Much of the difficulty ASF experienced with the Control Branch sprang from a misunderstanding within Ordnance of the functions of such a branch. The name itself was not accurately descriptive. General Somervell did not intend that the ASF Control Division should actually exercise control over day-to-day operations, but only that it should be an investigative and fact-finding agency to study organizational matters and help him keep informed about rates of progress, or lack of progress, in the many diverse activities of his command.[65] General Wesson, taking a literal interpretation of the name, had assumed that the Control Division was to be an agency that would actually exercise control over operating personnel. When first approached by ASF representatives on this matter in 1942, he is reported to have declared that Ordnance did not need any such unit because he himself exercised full control of the Department. Much of the friction that subsequently developed between ASF and Ordnance stemmed from this brusque refusal by General Wesson to consider the need for an Ordnance Control Branch. General Campbell, though less hostile toward the proposal, never had much enthusiasm for it except in terms of making organizational charts and preparing statistical studies.[66]

In September 1942, following a survey of the existing administrative machinery for handling lend-lease transactions, ASF directed that a war aid branch or division be established within each of the supply services.[67] A Defense Aid Section, headed by Colonel Seleen, was already in existence in Ordnance, as part of the Executive Branch. To comply with the ASF directive, this section was simply renamed the War Aid Branch and given status equal to that of the other staff branches. The War Aid Branch (later redesignated International Aid Division) always remained a staff unit and never grew to large proportions because the basic policy of the Ordnance Department was to handle war aid transactions through the existing organization—procurement through the Industrial Serv-

[62] (1) ODO 285, 26 Jun 42, OHF. (2) Hist of Control Div, OHF. (3) Correspondence and interv with Col Davies, OHF. In civilian life, Colonel Davies had been secretary of the American Society of Mechanical Engineers.

[63] A critical review of the Ordnance Control Branch, including the slowness of recruiting, appears in the ASF Control Division report cited in n. 61, above.

[64] Summary of Comparative Evaluations of Control Offices . . . , 15 Mar 43, Cabinet 12, ASF Control Div File 321 (Ord), DRB AGO.

[65] Memo, CG SOS to Staff Divisions, 27 Mar 42, sub: Control, OO 020/29, DRB AGO. See also Hist of ASF Control Div, ASF Control Div files, DRB AGO.

[66] Intervs with Gen Harris, Col Davies, and Col Johnston, summer of 1949.

[67] Memo, CG SOS for Chiefs of Supply Services, 8 Sep 42, sub: Responsibility of Supply Services for Accomplishing Aid to United Nations, SPX 400.3295 (9-6-42), DRB AGO.

ice and distribution and shipping through the Field Service.[68]

Before the summer of 1942 the legal functions of the Department had been performed in three separate sections created to serve special needs. General responsibility for advising the Chief of Ordnance on legal matters had traditionally been assigned to the Fiscal Division. Legal problems relating to patent applications had been handled separately by a section of the Technical Staff. A third legal section, formed by General Campbell in 1940 when he was assistant chief of the Industrial Service for facilities, had handled the work connected with the construction and operation of scores of government-owned, contractor-operated plants.[69] With the armament program in full swing by the summer of 1942, the volume and complexity of the legal work relating to contracts, patents, taxes, price ceilings, and renegotiation of contracts mounted steadily. General Campbell therefore named Lt. Col. Irving A. Duffy, former assistant chief of the Fiscal and Legal Division, chief of a separate Legal Branch and gave him full authority to handle all the legal work of the Department.

District Offices

Another phase of the June 1942 reorganization was the change in the administration of the district offices. The volume of business handled in the districts rose to tremendous proportions during the spring of 1942, and it became apparent that the civilian chiefs, most of whom were prominent industrialists serving on a volunteer basis, could not devote their full time and energy to district affairs. General Campbell therefore assigned experienced Ordnance officers to be chiefs of the districts and the former civilian heads, now relieved of the day-to-day operating responsibilities, became top-level policy advisers. Of the appointments to the larger districts, General Lewis was assigned to Boston, General Minton to Pittsburgh, Brig. Gen. Walter P. Boatwright to New York, Colonel Quinton to Detroit, Col. Guy H. Drewry to Springfield, Col. David N. Hauseman to Philadelphia, and Col. Merle H. Davis to St. Louis.[70] Later, as demands for Regular officers had to be met for service in the field and elsewhere, many of these men were replaced by Reserve officers or by leading local industrialists.

At the same time, a uniform organization for all districts was prescribed, a plan that had been under study for several months by a board of officers headed by Col. Fred A. McMahon. Before this time the districts had been developing rather diverse structures. In 1935, when most district offices were staffed by only a volunteer civilian chief, one Ordnance officer, and a secretary, Ordnance had published a model for district wartime organization, but it had not been made mandatory as its authors felt that each district chief should have broad discretionary powers in developing his organization. The prescribed pattern of June 1942 paralleled that of the Industrial Division and thus facilitated communication between the districts and the Washington headquarters.[71]

After he had been in office for eight months, General Campbell wrote to ASF

[68] (1) Interv with Col Seleen, 13 Sep 49. (2) Intern'tl Aid, Ord, I, Ch. 3, OHF.

[69] Leon Malman, Origin and Early History of the Legal Division, OHF. See also ODO 122, 31 Jul 39, and ODO 215, 10 Jan 42, OHF.

[70] Directory of Ordnance Establishments, 10 Aug 42, OHF.

[71] (1) Cir Ltr 496, Dist Control Div, 30 Jun 42, OO 381/81236, DRB AGO. (2) Ann Rpt CofOrd, 1943, p. 22.

describing the progress the Department had made since the start of the defense period, and the nature of the organizational problems that had been faced.[72] He pointed out that by December 1942 the dollar value of Ordnance production had risen to something over one billion dollars a month, and contrasted that figure with the meagre appropriations available to the Department during the 1920's and 1930's. He conceded that there had been mistakes, false starts, inefficiency, and some duplication of effort. No organization could have expanded as fast as Ordnance did in the hectic atmosphere of wartime Washington with anything like normal peacetime efficiency. But, wrote Campbell, the faults were not all within Ordnance—the top-heavy administrative structure of the War Department itself was a serious handicap to the operating agencies. He referred to the "multiplicity of layers above the Services" and cited, as one example, the large number of boards, offices, and commissions in the War Department that dealt with the single problem of personnel. "The result of this," he declared, "is confusion, uncertainty, and delay in putting our own organization on the efficient basis that the importance of our work demands. We welcome the opportunity to demonstrate how we can do a better job with less people. We have much yet to do. Much is being done. Our work will be materially aided if the multiplicity of reviewing and inspecting agencies can be reduced."[73]

Decentralization of the Ordnance Department

Throughout World War II the Ordnance Department followed its traditional policy of decentralization to reduce the volume of administrative work that had to flow through the office of the Chief of Ordnance. Long before Pearl Harbor General Wesson had delegated a large measure of responsibility to existing Ordnance field agencies, and had transferred various headquarters sections from Washington to other parts of the country. When General Campbell became Chief of Ordnance in June he entered enthusiastically into the task of further decentralizing the Department and soon made Ordnance the leader among the supply services in delegating responsibility to field headquarters and in moving units out of Washington.[74] In explaining his policy of decentralization to his staff, General Campbell frequently quoted the old adage, "If you want to eat an elephant, first cut him up into small pieces." It was his firm conviction that the multibillion-dollar Ordnance program was far too big and too complicated to be successfully administered from a single headquarters in Washington and that it had to be "cut up into small pieces."[75]

Field Director of Ammunition Plants

In applying this principle during the summer of 1942, General Campbell established the office of Field Director of Ammunition Plants (FDAP) in St. Louis to administer a group of about 60 government-owned, contractor-operated (GOCO) plants producing artillery ammunition under cost-plus-fixed-fee contracts.

[72] Pers ltr, Gen Campbell to Maj Gen Wilhelm D. Styer, 10 Feb 43, OO 230/7603, DRB AGO.

[73] *Ibid.*

[74] Memo, CofOrd for Gen Hayes, 7 Oct 42. This memo reports General Somervell's statement at a staff conference praising the Ordnance Department's decentralization. See also memo, Col Robinson for CG SOS, 28 Nov 42, sub: GOCO Ord Plants, ASF Control Div files, DRB AGO.

[75] Campbell, *Industry-Ordnance Team*, p. 56.

St. Louis was chosen as the location for the FDAP office because it had excellent railroad and airplane connections with the ammunition plants and was "the natural hub of this three-billion-dollar wheel."[76] Office space was leased in the basement of the Scottish Rite Cathedral on Lindell Boulevard, a convenient location next door to the office of the St. Louis Ordnance District.

To staff the new headquarters twenty-five officers and thirty civilians, who had served as contract negotiators and administrators in the Ammunition Division of the Industrial Service, were transferred to St. Louis. Col. Theodore C. Gerber, an Ordnance officer with extensive experience in commanding GOCO plants, was appointed field director and was made responsible to the chief of the Ammunition Branch of the Industrial Division.[77] The task of the FDAP was to analyze and co-ordinate the operations of the various ammunition plants under its jurisdiction, regulate the flow of raw material and parts to the plants, and help each contractor to benefit from the experience of the others. The type of cost-plus-fixed-fee contract under which the plants were operating was comparatively new and required close FDAP supervision to get all the contractors to adopt standard procedures for reporting costs, preparing statistical data, and using manpower efficiently. As the functions of the FDAP were gradually extended to include supervision of ammunition loading plants, the staff increased in size until it numbered more than 500 officers, including officers assigned to plants as well as those in the field director's office. In December 1943 Colonel Gerber was given the additional duty of serving as chief of the Safety and Security Branch, which had its headquarters in Chicago. This step brought about a closer co-ordination of the efforts of those who were responsible for production and those who were concerned with matters of safety and security.

The Industrial Division established four other suboffices during the latter half of 1942. The first of these was the Small Arms Ammunition Suboffice, formed by transferring the Ammunition unit of the Small Arms Branch to Philadelphia and assigning to it responsibility for administering the contracts at twelve GOCO plants manufacturing small arms ammunition.[78] A second suboffice was established in Philadelphia at the same time by transferring to that city the Inspection Gage Section of the Production Service Branch to handle all matters pertaining to the procurement of inspection gages and the expansion of gage facilities.[79] A third suboffice of the Industrial Division, established at Rock Island Arsenal late in August, was assigned engineering and inspection functions for all types of field carriages, and in December a suboffice for mobile artillery was also established at Rock Island.

[76] History of Field Director of Ammunition Plants (hereafter cited as Hist of FDAP), OHF. See also ODO 305, 16 Jul 42, OHF, and Campbell, *op. cit.*, pp. 58–69.

[77] Col. T. C. Gerber, "Ammunition Production," *Army Ordnance*, XXIV, 137 (1943), 305. This article, written by the field director, describes the origin and function of the FDAP and contains a chart showing the principal divisions of the office. A later article by Colonel Gerber on the FDAP appeared in *Army Ordnance*, XXVIII, 149 (1945), 237.

[78] (1) ODO 303, 14 Jul 42, OHF. (2) Memo, Col Robinson for CG SOS, 28 Nov 42, sub: GOCO Ordnance Plants, ASF Control Div files, DRB AGO. The Small Arms Ammunition Suboffice was located at Frankford Arsenal for a short time before being transferred to Philadelphia. See Hist of Small Arms Div, Ind Serv, Vol. I, OHF.

[79] ODO 303, 14 Jul 42, OHF. Both of the Philadelphia suboffices were attached to Frankford Arsenal for purposes of administration.

The Tank-Automotive Center

On 17 July 1942, the day the FDAP was established in St. Louis, General Somervell issued an order transferring to the Ordnance Department within six weeks all the automotive activities of the Quartermaster Corps except operating units.[80] This action was taken in order to centralize in the Ordnance Department control over the development, production, distribution, and maintenance of vehicles, which had many common elements—engines, transmissions, and axles—and was intended to eliminate duplication of effort by the two supply services in dealing with the automotive industry. To the Department's traditional responsibility for combat vehicles such as tanks and armored cars, was now added the responsibility for trucks, passenger cars, ambulances, jeeps, and other types of transport vehicles.

In terms of organization, the order of 17 July meant that the civilian and military personnel of the Motor Transport Service (MTS), and all Quartermaster motor bases, motor supply depots, and schools for automobile mechanics were to be transferred to the Ordnance Department. The administration of more than 4,000 contracts with a total value of nearly three billion dollars was taken over by Ordnance. It was by far the largest single addition to the Department made during the war and, because of its magnitude, was a gradual process of absorption.[81]

To manage this enormous automotive production and distribution program, the Department made a move that one observer called "the boldest stroke of decentralization the country has yet seen in this war."[82] The Tank-Automotive Center in Detroit was established in the heart of the automobile manufacturing industry, and to it was delegated a large degree of authority and responsibility. The new headquarters was formed during September and October by moving the Motor Transport Service and the Tank and Combat Vehicle Division from their Washington offices to the Union Guardian Building in Detroit, along with other branches of the Ordnance Department concerned with tank and automotive matters.

The main reasons for this action were General Campbell's concern lest there be too great a concentration of Ordnance functions in Washington and his desire to establish the closest possible relations with the automobile industry in the Detroit area. Office space in Washington was at a premium in 1942, as was housing for both military and civilian personnel. Agencies of the federal government had been urged to decentralize their operations wherever possible. General Somervell was keenly interested in decentralization within the technical services, and the Control Division of his headquarters had recommended transfer of the Tank and Combat Vehicle Division to Detroit or some other city. All of these factors had a bearing on the decision finally reached in August to establish the T-AC in Detroit.[83]

Brig. Gen. Donald Armstrong took the

[80] Ltr, CG SOS to CofOrd, 17 Jul 42, sub: Transfer of . . . Motor Transportation . . . , OO 020/47, DRB AGO. See also WD Cir 245, par. 10, 25 Jul 42, as amended by WD Cir 267, 8 Aug 42.

[81] ODO 315, 28 Jul 42, OHF. For a list of installations transferred, see ltr, CofOrd to CG SOS, 7 Aug 42, sub: Redesignation of Certain Installations, OO 029/69, DRB AGO.

[82] Brig. Gen. A. R. Glancy, "Integration for Production, Industrial Committees as an Aid to Manufacture," *Army Ordnance*, XXIV, 136 (1943), 72.

[83] (1) ASF Control Div Rpt 26, Notes on Organization and Operations of the Tank and Combat Vehicle Division of the Ordnance Department, ASF Control Div files, DRB AGO. (2) Intervs with Gens Christmas Glancy, Armstrong, and Hayes, summer 1949.

CHART 6—ORGANIZATION OF THE TANK-AUTOMOTIVE CENTER

As of January 2, 1943

- DEPUTY CHIEF OF ORDNANCE AND CHIEF OF CENTER
  - Assistant Chief of Center
  - Director Tanks and Combat Vehicles | Director Transport Vehicles | Director Parts and Supplies | Director Tools and Equipment | Director Rubber Products
  - Executive Officer
- Industry Integration Committees
- Liaison Representatives

STAFF BRANCHES

- LEGAL BRANCH: Chief; Executive Officer
- CONTROL BRANCH: Chief; Executive Officer
  - Policy Section: Chief
  - Organization Planning Section: Chief
  - Procedures and Methods Section: Chief
  - Statistics Section: Chief
  - Executive Personnel Section: Chief
- EXECUTIVE BRANCH: Chief; Asst Chief; Asst Chief
  - Publications Section: Chief
  - Security Section: Chief
  - Military Personnel Section: Chief
  - Civilian Personnel Section: Chief
  - Administration Section: Chief
  - Fiscal Section: Chief

OPERATING BRANCHES

- DEVELOPMENT BRANCH: Chief; Asst Chief; Asst Chief; Executive Officer; Assistants and Staff
  - STAFF SECTIONS
    - Planning and Control Section: Chief; Asst Chief
    - Simplification Section: Chief; Asst Chief
    - Engineering Operations Section: Chief; Asst Chief
    - Administrative Section: Chief; Asst Chief
  - OPERATING SECTIONS
    - Combat Vehicle Section: Chief; Asst Chief
    - Components Section: Chief; Asst Chief
    - Special Project Section: Chief; Asst Chief
    - Transport Vehicle Section: Chief; Asst Chief
    - Materials Section: Chief; Asst Chief
- ENGINEERING BRANCH: Chief; Asst Chief; Asst Chief; Executive Officer; Assistants and Staff
  - STAFF SECTIONS
    - Planning and Control Section: Chief; Asst Chief
    - Product Appraisal Section: Chief; Asst Chief
    - Drafting Section: Chief; Asst Chief
    - Engineering Records Section: Chief; Asst Chief
    - Engineering Specialists Section: Chief; Asst Chief
    - Administrative Section: Chief; Asst Chief
  - OPERATING SECTIONS
    - Light and Heavy Tank Section: Chief; Asst Chief
    - Misc Vehicles Section: Chief; Asst Chief
    - Medium Tank Section: Chief; Asst Chief
    - ½ Track, Armored and Scout Car Section: Chief; Asst Chief
    - Trucks and Trailers Section: Chief; Asst Chief
    - Special Maintenance Tools Section: Chief; Asst Chief
- MANUFACTURING BRANCH: Chief; Assistant Chief; Executive Officer; Assistants and Staff
  - Small War Plants: Chief
  - Washington Liaison: Chief
  - STAFF SECTIONS
    - Planning and Control Section: Chief; Asst Chief
    - Production Service Section: Chief; Asst Chief
    - Inspection Section: Chief; Asst Chief
    - Procurement Processing Section: Chief; Asst Chief
    - Statistics Section: Chief; Asst Chief
    - Administrative Section: Chief; Asst Chief
  - OPERATING SECTIONS
    - Tanks and Combat Vehicles Section: Chief; Asst Chief
    - Tools and Equipment Section: Chief; Asst Chief
    - Tank Depot Section: Chief; Asst Chief
    - Transport Vehicles Section: Chief; Asst Chief
    - Parts and Supplies Section: Chief; Asst Chief
    - Misc Products Section: Chief; Asst Chief
- SUPPLY BRANCH: Chief; Asst Chief; Asst Chief; Executive Officer; Assistants and Staff
  - STAFF SECTIONS
    - Planning and Control Section: Chief; Asst Chief
    - Statistics Section: Chief; Asst Chief
    - Packaging Section: Chief; Asst Chief
    - Administrative Section: Chief; Asst Chief
    - Machine Service Section: Chief; Asst Chief
    - Storage and Issue Section: Chief; Asst Chief
  - OPERATING SECTIONS
    - Parts and Supplies Section: Chief; Asst Chief
    - Tank and Vehicle Section: Chief; Asst Chief
    - Tools and Equipment Section: Chief; Asst Chief
- MAINTENANCE BRANCH: Chief; Assistant Chief; Executive Officer; Assistants and Staff
  - STAFF SECTIONS
    - Planning and Control Section: Chief; Asst Chief
    - Administrative Section: Chief; Asst Chief
  - OPERATING SECTIONS
    - Technical Section: Chief; Asst Chief
    - Parts Requirements Section: Chief; Asst Chief
    - Small Arms and Artillery Liaison Section: Chief; Asst Chief
    - Operations Section: Chief; Asst Chief
    - Allocations Section: Chief; Asst Chief

first steps to establish the T-AC in August, and was joined a short time later by Brig. Gen. John K. Christmas.[84] In September, Mr. A. R. Glancy accepted a reserve commission as brigadier general and became deputy chief of Ordnance in charge of the tank-automotive activities of the Department in Detroit.[85] General Campbell selected these three officers for the Detroit headquarters because each had special qualifications for the job, which was partly industrial and partly military in nature. General Glancy, the chief of the T-AC, was an industrialist with experience in military procurement and production problems. General Armstrong, deputy chief of the center, was a Regular Army officer with experience in procurement, distribution, and supply. General Christmas, who had devoted most of his military career to tank design and engineering, became the chief engineer of the T-AC. But this arrangement proved to be unsound and was soon abandoned. As one officer commented, it provided "too many chiefs and not enough Indians." The situation was further complicated by the fact that Generals Glancy and Armstrong were not suited by temperament and background to pull together in the same harness. Within a few months, General Armstrong was named chief of the Ordnance Training Center at Aberdeen Proving Ground and General Glancy was left in full command of the center, with General Christmas as his deputy.[86]

Under these circumstances, the T-AC was naturally beset with many administrative difficulties during the first few months of its existence. It was impossible to establish such a large headquarters, and at the same time integrate the Motor Transport Service with Ordnance, without going through a shakedown period. During these trying months, many criticisms of the organization and functioning of the T-AC came to General Campbell from ASF, particularly of the organizational structure and lines of authority. But by the first anniversary of Pearl Harbor—just three months after the creation of the T-AC—General Glancy was able to report: "Now that all our organization charts, manning charts, flow charts, and job sheets have been written, I doubt if there is another organization in the whole Army whose lines of authority and scope of activities are as clearly defined."[87]

One feature of the T-AC organization adopted by General Glancy was the staff of five directors who stood between the chiefs of the operating branches and the commanding general. Each director was assigned to a product specialty—tanks and combat vehicles, transport vehicles, parts and supplies, tools and equipment, and rubber products. Each was an expert in his own field, and each was given broad responsibility for supervising and co-ordinating the work of the appropriate sections of the operating branches. The Director of Transport Vehicles, for example, who was a Motor Transport Service officer of long experience, worked closely with the transport vehicle sections of the Development, Engineering, Manufacturing, Supply, and Maintenance

[84] (1) Intervs with Gen Armstrong and Gen Christmas, Oct–Nov 49. (2) Pers ltr, Gen Campbell to Gen Armstrong, 20 Aug 42, OO 020/84, DRB AGO.

[85] Intervs with Gen Glancy, Oct–Nov 49. For a detailed report on General Glancy's appointment, see "The Tank-Automotive Center," *Army Ordnance*, XXIII, 135 (1942), 501.

[86] (1) Ltr, Campbell to author, 15 Jul 49, OHF. (2) Intervs with Gens Glancy, Armstrong, and Christmas, summer 1949.

[87] 2d Ind, Glancy to Campbell, 7 Dec 42, on memo, Somervell for Campbell, 24 Nov 42, OO 023/144, DRB AGO.

Branches, while the Director of Tanks and Combat Vehicles supervised the combat vehicle sections of the branches.[88] Appointment of these directors was an attempt on General Glancy's part to create an executive committee for the T-AC. He felt that any organization as large as the Detroit center, or as large as the Office, Chief of Ordnance, in Washington, needed the kind of executive committee found in industry—a small group of mature, highly qualified men who would spend their full time watching the whole operation, advising on major policy decisions, and handling major problems as they came up. But, finding this concept foreign to traditional Army organization, he never put it into full operation in Detroit.[89]

By the end of June 1943 ill health forced General Glancy to relinquish his duties at the center, and General Boatwright, chief of the New York Ordnance District, was appointed to succeed him.[90] Within the following three months the new commanding general made a number of organizational changes, most important of which were the elimination of the directors and the establishment of an Operations Planning Branch headed by Col. Graeme K. Howard, a former General Motors executive. The new branch was given responsibility for co-ordinating projects common to two or more of the operating branches and thus assumed a large part of the job formerly handled by the directors.[91]

General Boatwright's tenure as chief of the center was marked by several important steps taken to strengthen the supply organization, for the year 1943 brought to the T-AC, as to the Ordnance Department and all the other supply services, the need for closer attention to stock control, storage, and distribution functions. Brig. Gen. Stewart E. Reimel was appointed assistant chief for supply and maintenance and was given a position in the organization on a par with that of General Christmas, who remained as assistant chief for development, engineering, and manufacturing. A short time later two new branches—Storage and Redistribution—were added to cope with the task of maintaining a constant flow of vehicles and spare parts to and from distant theaters of operations.[92]

The T-AC was not only the largest of all the decentralized offices established by the Ordnance Department during the war but, unlike the other suboffices which were agencies of particular divisions or branches of the Department, the T-AC represented all of the major divisions. It was, as its later title of Office, Chief of Ordnance–Detroit (OCO–D) indicated, a replica of the Office, Chief of Ordnance, in Washington.[93] The size and importance of the organization are indicated by the fact that during the course of the war it spent nearly 50 percent of all the funds allocated to the entire Ordnance Department. It directed the production of more than three million vehicles, ranging from bicycles to

[88] Interv with Col Edwin S. Van Deusen, 12 Aug 49.

[89] Intervs with Gen Glancy, Oct–Nov 49.

[90] T-AC GO 7, 12 Jul 43, OHF.

[91] T-AC Bull 96, 27 Sep 43, OHF.

[92] History, Office, Chief of Ordnance–Detroit (hereafter cited as Hist OCO–D), OHF.

[93] The change in name was made by ODO 113, 31 Dec 43, OHF. "The Ordnance automotive activity in Detroit was originally called the Tank-Automotive Center," General Campbell explained, "in order to identify to Industry the nature of its activities. Later I changed this name to Office, Chief of Ordnance–Detroit, as I found it desirable to give this decentralized part of my office the fullest recognition as an integral part of the Office, Chief of Ordnance, rather than as a subordinate agency." Lt. Gen. Levin H. Campbell, Jr., *The Industry-Ordnance Team* (McGraw-Hill Book Company, Inc., New York, 1946), p. 226.

70-ton tanks. Its personnel strength grew from 40 officers and 593 civilians in September 1942 to 500 officers and 3,800 civilians by February 1943.[94] These figures support the conclusion reached by Colonel Raaen, Ordnance executive officer, that "the establishment of the Tank-Automotive Center . . . was the greatest step taken toward decentralization since the Ordnance district offices were established during the last war."[95]

In the opinion of officers who served in the OCO–D, one of the major lessons learned from the experience was the need for clear-cut delegation of authority by the headquarters in Washington. Many of the difficulties experienced by the Detroit office during the war were due to the fact that not all of the division chiefs in Washington delegated full authority to their representatives in the OCO–D. It was General Campbell's intention that the Washington office should exercise only staff functions and that the Detroit office should be the operating level. But there were many different interpretations as to what was a staff and what was an operating function. "On the one hand," a Control Division report stated in 1944, "offices in Detroit believe that Washington exceeds the bounds of staff supervision and indulges in operations to the point of interference, while on the other hand, some officers in Washington feel that staff supervision properly may be carried to any point that the staff officers feel is necessary in order to achieve effective results and that, where Washington has gone into operating details, it has been justified by failure on the part of Detroit to take prompt and effective measures, or by other sufficient reasons."[96]

These difficulties were greater in supply and maintenance than in production and procurement. In general, there was more complete delegation of authority to the OCO–D by the Industrial Division in Washington than by the Field Service Division. Commenting after the war on this phase of Ordnance operations, General Boatwright stated that securing full co-operation between the various subordinate groups in Washington and Detroit was one of his most difficult problems in 1943. OCO–D was organized on a product basis well understood by the Industrial Service but not so well understood by the Field Service, which had an essentially functional organization.[97]

Other elements were also in the picture. The tank-automotive section of the Industrial Division, which became the manufacturing-engineering branch of the OCO–D, had been physically transferred to Detroit in the fall of 1942 as a going concern under General Christmas and had been given relatively free rein at the outset, but General Reimel only gradually built up the maintenance-supply organization after the Detroit headquarters was established. As a result, the Industrial Division in Washington tended to give greater freedom of action to the manufacturing branch in Detroit than the Field Service Division gave to the maintenance and supply branches. In addition, there was within the maintenance and supply branches a large proportion of former Quartermaster officers who had just recently been transferred to the Ordnance Department and who did not have close

[94] Statistical Summary of Accomplishments, T-AC, Dec 45, p. 51, OHF.

[95] "The Ordnance Reorganization," *Army Ordnance*, XXIV, 136 (1943), 66.

[96] Relationships Between the OCO–Washington and the OCO–D, 24 Aug 44, prepared by Control Div, OCO–Washington, OHF.

[97] Ltr, Gen Boatwright to author, 16 Nov 49, OHF.

personal ties, based on long years of association, with their opposite numbers in Washington. Finally, there was the feeling among some officers, both in Washington and Detroit, that the supply-maintenance functions should never have been assigned to the OCO-D at all but should have been kept within the Field Service Division or delegated to some other subordinate command.

When asked, after the war, to evaluate the Detroit experiment in decentralization on the basis of his experience, General Christmas summed up the matter in these words:

> Decentralization by General Campbell in 1942 of substantially half of his office (and substantially half of the money value of his program) to Detroit, was a bold and far-seeing move. I consider that it was highly successful and contributed greatly to the outstanding success of the Ordnance Department.
>
> But it is no secret that the operation of the OCO-D, employing some 500 officers and nearly 5,000 civilians, was not accomplished without some wear and tear on the people in charge (both in Detroit and Washington) nor without some inefficiency and error. These I lay to two factors: (a) The functional organization of the higher echelon of the Ordnance Department, which cut across the essentially commodity organization of the OCO-D, which had been given complete responsibility for all automotive vehicles under the Chief of Ordnance and his staff. (b) The fact that it takes a long time to get such a new idea across to most people. Hence, there were people in the Office, Chief of Ordnance-Washington, who either misunderstood the object of decentralization, were out of sympathy with it, or in some few cases, as so often happens, had personal reasons for opposing it.[98]

Field Service Zones

At the same time that the FDAP was being established in St. Louis, and the T-AC in Detroit, seven zone offices were established by the Field Service Division to decentralize the administration of its depots.[99] This step was taken largely because the Ordnance Department, following the transfer of transport vehicles from the Quartermaster Corps, had assumed responsibility for approximately 55,000,000 additional square feet of storage space, including eight motor bases, four motor supply depots, eleven motor supply sections, one motor reception park, and two training centers. This had brought to more than sixty the total number of depots and other field establishments under the jurisdiction of the Field Service, and had added to the mounting volume of administrative work in the Washington headquarters of the Field Service Division. To provide for decentralized administration and management of these widely scattered establishments, seven zones were marked out on the map, with headquarters at Albany, New York, Baltimore, Maryland, Indianapolis, Indiana, Augusta, Georgia (moved within a few weeks to Atlanta, Georgia), Shreveport, Louisiana, Pueblo, Colorado, and Salt Lake City, Utah.[100] Each zone office had from seven to twelve depots under its supervision, and served as an intermediate headquarters between these installations and the Office, Chief of Ordnance.

After six months the zones were abolished and the depots again came directly under the Field Service Division in Wash-

[98] Statement by Gen Christmas, 11 Oct 49, OHF.

[99] As early as May 1942 General Crain, then chief of the Field Service, had recommended that this be done, but no action had been taken before General Crain's departure from the office. Ltr, CofOrd to CG SOS, 29 May 42, sub: Plan to Place Experienced Ordnance Officers at Various Points . . . , Exhibit 35, Hist of FS Plans and Opns Br, OHF.

[100] (1) ODO 338, 25 Sep 42, and Rev 1, 29 Jan 43, and (2) FS Bull 1-15, 10 Dec 42, both in OHF.

ington. The zone offices were closed early in April 1943 because experience had shown that, instead of eliminating unnecessary administrative work, the zones had simply become "yet another channel through which reports and directives funneled." [101] General Campbell and the chief of the Field Service Division, General Hatcher, were in agreement that the zone offices had become bottlenecks that slowed up operations and that their discontinuance would result in a great saving of manpower.[102]

Developments, 1943–45

The organization of the Department remained relatively stable during the 1943–45 period. (See charts dated 6 July 1944 and 14 August 1945.) Changes occurred in the names of various units, and occasionally functions were reassigned, but there was no modification of the broad outlines of the organizational structure. In June 1944 the word "service" came back into use to replace "division" as the designation of the major units of the Department, and at the same time all the staff branches were renamed divisions.[103] The four main operating units—Industrial, Field Service, Technical, and Training—continued as the major elements of the Department, and, except in name, the eleven staff branches existing at the end of 1942 continued throughout the war. Early in 1943 the Department reached the peak of its wartime expansion, and after that time more and more attention was given to tightening up the existing organization, economizing in the use of manpower and essential raw materials, and carefully scrutinizing all production schedules and stock inventories.

Of all the major divisions of the Department, the Field Service experienced the greatest number of organizational changes during the 1943–45 period. This was chiefly because of a significant shift of emphasis in the operation of the Department that took place during the latter half of 1942. Throughout the preceding two years, first priority had necessarily been given to production, and the Industrial Service had occupied the center of the stage. At the end of 1942 the Field Service came to the front as munitions of all kinds came off the assembly lines in mountainous quantities and created serious problems in storage, distribution, maintenance, and stock control. As war production moved into high gear, and as large overseas movements of men and matériel got under way, the scale and complexity of supply operations reached unprecedented proportions and placed a severe strain on the Field Service Division.[104] The recommendations of a special advisory staff, combined with pressure from ASF headquarters to make the division correspond more closely to the pattern of ASF organization, accounted for the revisions made in the Field Service organization at this time.

In January 1943 General Hatcher replaced General Kutz as chief of the division. A short time later a Military Plans and Organizations Branch was formed to obtain information from higher headquarters on projected troop movements overseas and use it as a basis for scheduling

[101] Ann Rpt CofOrd, 1943, p. 28. The zone offices were officially abolished by ODO 37, 6 Apr 43, OHF.

[102] (1) Intervs with Gen Hatcher and Col Ray M. Hare, summer 1949. (2) Memo, Campbell for Hatcher, 8 Mar 43, Exhibit 37, Hist of FS Plans and Opns, Vol. I, Pt. 2, OHF.

[103] ODO 88-44, 27 Jun 44, OHF.

[104] (1) Interv with Gen Hatcher, summer 1949. (2) Key Pers Rpt, 1945, Gen Hatcher, OHF.

CHART 7—ORGANIZATION OF THE ORDNANCE DEPARTMENT: 6 JULY 1944

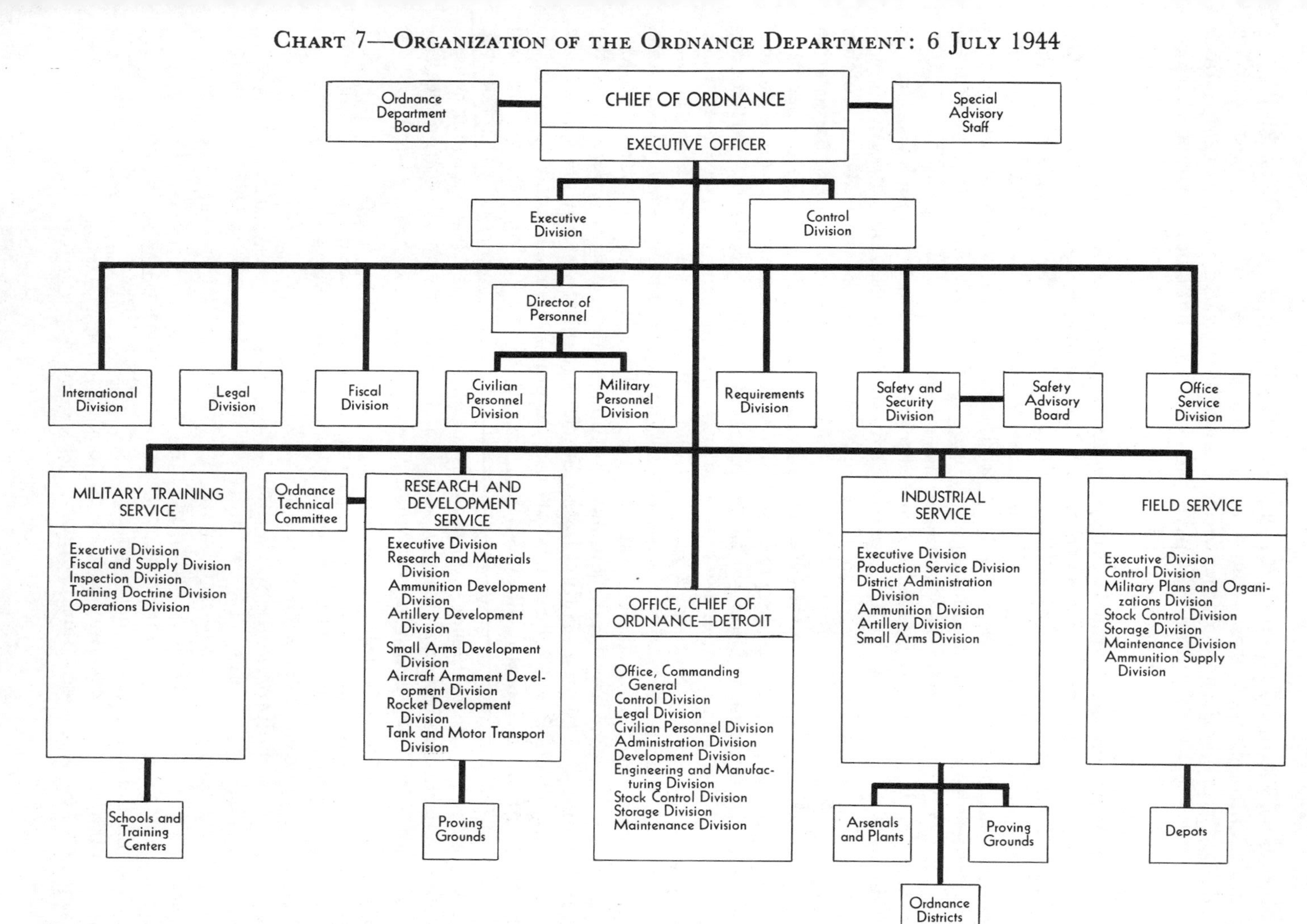

See Section 402.02 a and g, Army Service Forces Organization Manual.

operations within the Division.[105] A Field Service Control Branch was created in April to comply with orders from ASF headquarters that the Ordnance Department set up control branches in each of its main operating divisions.[106]

The most important change in the organization of the Field Service Division during 1943 was the creation of the Storage Branch and Stock Control Branch in August. This move came as a result of direct orders from ASF headquarters and was reluctantly accepted by the Ordnance Department. In organizing his staff at ASF headquarters, Maj. Gen. LeRoy Lutes, assistant chief of staff for operations, had established two separate divisions, one to deal with storage and the other with stock control. In April 1943 he directed the Ordnance Department to adopt the same type of functional organization in its Field Service Division.[107] Neither General Campbell nor General Hatcher favored taking such a step. Both believed that the traditional Ordnance practice of assigning supply responsibility on a product basis should be continued, with the Ammunition Supply Branch handling all phases of ammunition supply, including storage and stock control, and the General Supply Branch handling all other types of Ordnance supplies.[108] In the middle of May General Hatcher created a Supply Branch, made up of a Storage Section and a Stock Control Section. The Supply Branch, headed by Brig. Gen. R. S. Chavin, was a compromise between the ASF and Ordnance points of view, and did not last long. In August General Hatcher was forced to abolish the Supply Branch and to raise its two sections to the level of branches, on the same organizational plane as the existing Executive, Control, Maintenance, and Military Plans and Organizations Branches.[109]

During 1944 ASF ordered another change in the Field Service organization. To comply with the provisions of ASF Circular 67, General Hatcher appointed Colonel McMahon to serve as executive assistant for matériel control. Colonel McMahon was charged with responsibility for co-ordinating the activities of the Field Service Division, the Industrial Division, and the War Plans and Requirements Branch of the General Office on all matters relating to stock levels and distribution of supplies, and to maintain liaison for the Ordnance Department with ASF headquarters.[110] After V-E Day Colonel McMahon's title was changed to executive assistant for surplus military property, as increasing attention was given to the disposal of surplus matériel, particularly trucks and automotive parts for which there was a big demand in the civilian economy. A year later, when its functions were relatively routine, Colonel McMahon's office was transferred to the Stock Control Division where it became the Surplus Property Branch.

The Military Training Service gained new responsibilities in 1944 when both the Military Plans and Organizations Branch of the Field Service and the Ordnance De-

[105] (1) Change 2, Rev 2, ODO 291, 29 Mar 43, OHF. (2) Hist of FS Exec Div, Vol. III, Ch. 3, OHF. (3) Interv, summer 1949, with Col Harold J. Conway, Chief of FS Exec Br, 1943.

[106] (1) Memo, CofOrd for Chiefs of Divs, 8 Apr 43, sub: Establishment of Additional Control Offices, OO 023/489, DRB AGO. (2) FS Office Memo 116, 30 Apr 43, DRB AGO.

[107] Memo, CG ASF for CofOrd, 30 Apr 43, sub: Depot Operations, OO 400.24/3556, DRB AGO.

[108] Intervs with Gen Hatcher, summer 1950.

[109] FS Office Memo 142, 24 Aug 43, DRB AGO.

[110] ODO 45-44, 25 Mar 44, OHF. See also Key Pers Rpt, 1945, Col McMahon, and Hist of Exec Asst for Materiel Control, OHF.

partment Board were assigned to it.[111] Before this time the service had been exclusively a training organization. The follow-up on Ordnance troops after completion of their training had been a responsibility of the Field Service Military Plans and Organizations Branch. Similarly, studies of troop equipment and organization had been carried on by the Ordnance Department Board, which had been administratively independent although reporting through the Military Training Service. This separation of related staff functions was ended in October 1944 when General Campbell transferred both the Ordnance Department Board and the Military Plans and Organizations Branch of Field Service to the Military Training Service, and at the same time renamed it the Military Plans and Training Service, thus placing under one command the threefold responsibility for training, troop movement, and the study of equipment and organization of Ordnance units.

In the Technical Division the only organizational change of any importance during 1943 came in September when a Rocket Development Branch was added to the five existing development branches (Ammunition, Artillery, Tank, Small Arms, and Aircraft Armament) because of the growing importance of these new weapons.[112] Before this time rocket development work had been carried on within the Ammunition, Artillery, and Small Arms Branches. The new branch took over all rocket development work except that on the shoulder-type launcher, the "bazooka," which remained with the Small Arms Development Branch. In April 1944 a small Control Section was added to the Executive Branch in order to decentralize the control function within the Department, and in June 1944 the name of the Technical Division was changed to Research and Development Service.[113]

Among the staff branches the only noteworthy change was the creation of the office of director of personnel in March 1944 to co-ordinate the activities of the Civilian Personnel Branch and the Military Personnel Branch. Such a link between the two branches was necessary because ASF headquarters had adopted a system of bulk allotments of personnel, lumping together civilian and military manpower, and had itself established a single personnel branch. To bring the Ordnance organization into line with that of ASF headquarters and thus facilitate the transaction of business, General Campbell appointed the chief of the Military Personnel Branch, Col. C. Wingate Reed, as director of personnel and made him responsible for all Ordnance personnel matters.[114]

Throughout the war the leaders of the Ordnance Department were influenced by several more or less clearly defined principles of administration. The officers who held controlling positions in Ordnance were, for the most part, not men who had devoted much time to studying the theory of public administration, but were men with strong convictions on the subject, convictions that were the outgrowth of many years of experience with various

[111] (1) Change 1, Rev 1, ODO 6-44, 10 Oct 44. (2) Rev 2, ODO 6-44, 21 Oct 44. See also Hist of Ord Dept Bd, Vol. III, Ch. 13. All in OHF.

[112] Tech Div Memo 22, 23 Sep 43, OHF.

[113] (1) Rpt of Tech Div, 1943–44, OO 319.1/4303, DRB AGO. (2) ODO 88-44, 27 Jun 44, OHF.

[114] (1) Rev 1, ODO 4-44, 13 Mar 44, and ODO 5-44, 18 Mar 44, OHF. (2) ASF Ann Rpt, 1943, pp. 248–49, DRB AGO.

types of military and industrial organization. The fundamental concepts that these men had formulated during the twenty years between the two world wars were carried over into the period after 1941 and did much to determine the structure of the Department during World War II.

Perhaps the most important of these was the principle of decentralization. Since the creation of the Ordnance districts in World War I, decentralization of procurement functions had been a traditional Ordnance policy, while decentralization of manufacturing and related functions to the arsenals had been an established policy for over a century. During World War II the decentralization principle was applied on a much wider basis than ever before and was generally credited with making an important contribution to the success of the Ordnance program. Among all the technical services in the War Department, Ordnance took the lead in decentralizing its activities to subordinate headquarters in various parts of the country, both General Wesson and General Campbell strongly supporting the principle. Decentralization created certain problems, but the soundness of the principle was recognized by the ASF Control Division and by virtually all the leading officers in the Ordnance Department.

There was a sharp contrast between the type of decentralization represented by the districts and arsenals and that introduced when the Tank-Automotive Center was established. Each district covered a specific geographical area and was responsible for procurement and inspection of all types of products, although each district tended to specialize in certain types most commonly produced by the industries within its boundaries. The arsenals were primarily government-owned manufacturing establishments that served to keep alive the art of munitions making in time of peace, to develop new weapons and manufacturing techniques, and to serve as production centers and training grounds in time of war. The establishment of the Tank-Automotive Center in Detroit added a third type of geographical decentralization along product lines. The T-AC was not limited to procurement, inspection, and manufacture, but was created to manage all aspects of the tank-automotive program—development, test, procurement (through the districts), distribution, and maintenance. Its activities were chiefly concentrated within the Detroit area, but the center had no fixed geographical boundaries. The functions of the T-AC were so broad that it was considered to be a replica of the Office, Chief of Ordnance.

The existence of the Detroit office led many Ordnance officers to propose that the Department be organized after the war on the basis of similar decentralized "product centers," each of which would be responsible for one group of items from start to finish. This was perhaps the most significant new concept of organization developed within the Department during the war, and the one that resulted in the widest differences of opinion. Reorganization along these lines was the chief recommendation made by the Harris Board, appointed by General Campbell in 1944 to study the postwar organization of the Department.[115] This suggestion was not put into effect by Campbell's successor, Maj. Gen. Everett S. Hughes, during the years immediately following the war and remained one of the major questions on

[115] As it was concerned principally with production and storage, this proposal will be discussed in detail in Thomson and Mayo, Procurement and Supply of Munitions, MS, OHF.

which opinion within the Department was divided.

Another organizational issue that aroused a great deal of discussion and led to sharp differences of opinion was that of functional as opposed to product organization. Confusion often entered the picture when this issue was under discussion because the Ordnance Department, like most large organizations, combined the two types, with alternate levels of authority being organized on functional and product bases. The top-level division followed functional lines—the production and procurement functions to Industrial Service, the supply and distribution functions to Field Service, the research and development functions to the Technical Division, and so on. But, with the exception of the Field Service, the first level of authority below these top divisions was based on products rather than functions. Within the Industrial Division there were separate branches devoted to the major product groups such as artillery, small arms, and ammunition, rather than branches dealing with functions such as design, manufacture, procurement, and inspection. Within each of the product branches, in turn, there were sections organized on a functional basis.

Early in the war the Field Service was organized in similar fashion, dividing its activities between two product branches—ammunition supply and general supply. As time went on, the Field Service Division adopted an essentially functional organization with separate branches devoted to storage, stock control, and maintenance, but with ammunition remaining as a separate product-type branch.

General Campbell regretted that it was necessary for the Department to continue during the war on a partly functional-type and partly product-type of organization. Had he considered it feasible to make such a drastic change while the war was in progress, he would have rooted out "every last malingering vestige of functionalism." [116] He favored establishing a plan of definite product responsibility, with the chief of each product division given full responsibility for that product from design to obsolescence. And he gave his approval to the recommendation of the Harris Board on the postwar organization of the Department that decentralization be combined with product responsibility to form six "product centers."

In the minds of many Ordnance officers, functional organization was looked upon as the first step on the road to the merger of all technical services within a single Army supply agency, along the lines of General Somervell's proposals in the summer of 1943 and at the end of the war. This was in part due to the fact that the Somervell plans contemplated a functional organization for the proposed Army supply agency, with Ordnance handling only the procurement function, and other supply services handling research and development, storage and issue, and so on. There was virtually universal agreement among high-ranking Ordnance officers that such a plan of organization would have resulted in a dispersal of responsibility and would have made effective integration of the entire program of production and distribution impossible. The officers contended that a functional organization would have allowed too much opportunity for the production program to get out of balance—with too many guns of one caliber and not enough of another, insufficient ammunition for the guns on

[116] Campbell, *Industry-Ordnance Team*, p. 443.

hand, or more trucks than there were tires to equip them—because no one individual would have been responsible for any one product group.

Of all the organizational issues that arose during the war, the most important for the Ordnance Department was that of the position the Department was to occupy within the framework of the War Department. Ordnance leaders were convinced that the Department could function most effectively, and make its greatest contribution to the war effort, if it enjoyed a large measure of freedom in carrying out the production programs adopted by higher authority. Far from ever questioning the need for over-all direction of the war program, these officers, particularly in 1940 and 1941, consistently argued that the failure of the War Department to provide sufficient guidance by determining well in advance how large the Army was eventually to be and what equipment it was to have, was one of the gravest handicaps for the Ordnance Department in getting large-scale production of munitions under way. But they vigorously opposed any efforts by higher authority to go beyond the establishment of requirements and broad policies, feeling that top-level staff agencies should concern themselves only with questions of policy and should not interfere with operating details.

Many Ordnance officers felt that General Campbell's greatest service to the Ordnance Department—and to the cause of national security—was his successful resistance to proposals of the Army Service Forces to merge all the technical services into one Army-wide supply agency. With its century-old tradition of independent status and its high standards of technical competence, the Department felt that it was fully capable of completing its assigned mission without the constant supervision of any higher headquarters. It was also convinced that any proposal to assign Ordnance research and development, ammunition supply, or any other technical phase of Ordnance operations to a War Department agency such as the Quartermaster Corps or the Chemical Warfare Service, which had had no experience in that particular specialty, would have been foolhardy.

Although the Ordnance Department successfully opposed many of the ASF proposals advanced during World War II, the issue was not dead at the end of the war. The officers who had championed the Department's point of view gained some satisfaction in witnessing the abolition of the Army Service Forces in 1946 and the restoration of the technical services to substantially the same positions—as related to higher authority—they had held before 1942. But these officers remained on the alert to challenge any revival of proposals to abolish the separate product responsibilities of the technical services in favor of a consolidated supply agency based on a functional organization.

CHAPTER V

Military Personnel and Training

During the years between the two world wars the number of officers and enlisted men in the Ordnance Department was never large. The Department was limited by law to 350 Regular Army officers, and lack of funds kept its actual officer strength during those years to an average of only 275. By June 1940, in spite of the increased tempo of national defense activities, the total number of Regular Army officers in the Department had risen only to 375. There were, in addition, 3,000 Ordnance Reserve officers on the rolls, but nearly two thirds of these were earmarked for duty with troops or with other arms and services and were not under the jurisdiction of the Chief of Ordnance. The average number of enlisted men in the Department during the years between the wars was only about 2,200, and by June 1940 had not risen to much more than 3,500.[1] During the latter half of 1940, with larger appropriations available, the military strength of the Department rose rapidly and continued to rise throughout 1941. The ranks of the officer corps were filled at first by calling Reserve officers to active duty and by granting Reserve commissions to qualified civilians, and later by commissioning graduates of the Officer Candidate School.[2] At the time of the attack on Pearl Harbor the Department had 410 Regular Army officers and 3,338 Reserve officers on active duty, and approximately 30,000 enlisted men. A year later the number of officers and men had jumped to 235,000, a 700 percent increase within one year.[3]

During the prewar years the "regulars" who carried on the work of the Department were professional soldiers well trained in both military and technical subjects. The rapid expansion of the war period, however, brought in so many thousands of untrained or only partially trained officers and men that an intensive, large-scale training program became necessary. New schools and training centers were established to produce automotive mechanics, ammunition handlers, and experts in repairing small arms and artillery—the "fighting technicians" who were to supply and maintain the complicated weapons and vehicles used by the U.S. Army in World War II. Although many officers and some enlisted men were assigned to procurement, storage, and inspection functions at depots and district offices, the majority of Ordnance troops

[1] (1) *Ann Rpts SW*, 1920–40. (2) Ltr, CofOrd to TAG, 15 Jul 40, sub: Allotment of Officers . . . , AG 320.2 (7–19–40) (1) Sec 1, DRB AGO. (3) ASF Control Div, The Period of Military Preparedness, 1940–1941, MS hist, OCMH.

[2] By August 1940, Ordnance had called 800 Reserve officers to active duty on a voluntary basis. By the following summer, when the Officer Candidate School opened, there were nearly 1,500 Reserve officers on duty with the Department. Ordnance Administration, Ch. 14, Table I, MS hist, OHF.

[3] (1) Period of Military Preparedness, OCMH. (2) Greenfield, Palmer, and Wiley, *The Organization of Ground Combat Troops*, p. 203.

were assigned to duty with maintenance units in the field, and the Ordnance training program had to provide the skilled manpower needed. The number of officers engaged in training activities in 1943 far exceeded the total number of officers in the Department during the prewar years, and the number of Ordnance men trained during World War II was greater than the total of the peacetime Army.

Ordnance Schools, 1920–40

From 1920 to 1940 the Ordnance Department maintained two schools at which small groups of officers and enlisted men were given formal training. The Ordnance School at Watertown Arsenal offered a comprehensive two-year ordnance engineering course in which twenty officers were normally enrolled.[4] The Ordnance Specialist School at Raritan Arsenal offered a number of nine-month courses in the repair, maintenance, and storage of Ordnance matériel for groups of carefully selected enlisted men.

Enlisted students at Raritan were given no military training because they were all veterans of two or more years of active Army service. Each student enrolled for a period of from nine to twelve months in one of the specialized courses for armorers, artillery mechanics, automotive mechanics, carpenters, welders, or other specialists. In addition, each year a group of about twenty-five enlisted men took the noncommissioned officers course, which gave them a broad survey of all aspects of the Ordnance sergeant's duties. The Ordnance Field Service School, as it was renamed in 1931, was essentially a trade school for enlisted men with about 150 students normally enrolled, but in 1932 the curriculum was extended to include a three months' course for officers.[5]

The facilities at Raritan were never adequate. The buildings were of temporary World War I construction, and by the middle 1930's were in urgent need of repair.[6] There was no outdoor range on which students could fire weapons, no cross-country course for maneuvering vehicles, and only limited amounts of equipment for teaching repair of optical instruments. Further, since Raritan was principally an ammunition depot, it had on hand very little Ordnance equipment for the students to observe and study. When officers of both schools surveyed the situation during the summer of 1936, they reached the conclusion that Aberdeen Proving Ground, the center for Ordnance research and learning, was the most suitable location for all the educational activities of the Department. This conclusion was approved by the Secretary of War early in December, but funds were not made available for the needed construction at Aberdeen until nearly eighteen months later.

The final impetus for moving the enlisted men's school to Aberdeen came from the swift victories of the German armies in the early summer of 1940. In May of that year, while Lt. Col. Julian S. Hatcher, commandant of the officers' school, was en

[4] (1) Interv with Gen Lewis, Jan 50. (2) Capt. W. H. Spinrad, "Early History of The Ordnance School," *The Ordnance Sergeant*, III, 1 (1942), 1–4. (3) Hist of Ord School and appended docs, OHF.

[5] (1) Spinrad, *loc. cit.* (2) Interv, Oct 49, with Col George W. Outland, former commandant of FS School.

[6] (1) Memo, Gen Tschappat for ACofS G–3, 14 Nov 36, sub: Consolidation of the Ordnance Field Service School and the Ordnance School, OO 352/146, NA. (2) Memo, Lt Col Julian S. Hatcher for Capt Norris W. Osborn, Engr Sec, 11 Aug 37, sub: New Construction, OHF. (3) Hist of Ord School, App., pp. 2–7, OHF.

route to the Army maneuvers in Louisiana, he read in newspapers of the German invasion of the Low Countries. "Before proceeding further to the maneuvers," Major General Hatcher wrote later, "I dispatched an informal letter to Maj. Gen. C. M. Wesson, Chief of Ordnance, making the urgent personal recommendation that, without delay, the schools at Aberdeen and Raritan should be consolidated and suitable emergency facilities found at Aberdeen for a greatly expanded training program."[7] Although the new buildings were still incomplete, General Wesson approved the proposal to combine the two schools as soon as possible. Early in July the 40th Training Company, which had been stationed at Raritan Arsenal since World War I, moved to Aberdeen.[8] This step marked the end of relatively leisurely training of small groups at separate Ordnance schools and ushered in the period when tens of thousands of men arrived at Aberdeen every year for intensive, high-speed instruction.

1940 Plans for Training

As the possibility of American involvement in the war daily came closer during the summer of 1940, War Department plans for training troops were hastily revised and brought up to date, but they had to remain in the blueprint stage until the Congress enacted legislation to increase the size of the Army. During that summer legislation to draft men for military service was under protracted consideration by the House and Senate. Huge sums of money were voted in June for the procurement of military supplies, but it was not until 16 September that the Selective Service and Training Act was passed.

Anticipating enactment of this legislation, the G–3 Division of the General Staff in August completed a tentative plan for mobilization training and forwarded copies to all interested agencies.[9] This plan called for the establishment of a score of Replacement Centers to receive "enlistees" who volunteered for military service and "selectees" inducted under the Selective Service Act and give them thirteen weeks of training in basic military and basic technical subjects. The Replacement Center at Aberdeen Proving Ground was to be used to train Ordnance troops and was to have a capacity of 5,800. At the same time the G–3 Division approved an increase in the capacity of the Ordnance School to 2,200 and the establishment of three Ordnance Unit Training Centers (UTC's) with a combined capacity of 3,700.

Although these plans existed only on paper, they outlined a well-rounded program of Ordnance training. The Ordnance School, with its long experience and its competent staff, was designed to provide technical training for both officers and enlisted specialists. It was also to serve as the source of cadres for the new training centers. The Replacement Center, later renamed Replacement Training Center, was to teach newly inducted men their military ABC's and give them an elementary course in some phase of Ordnance service. The Unit Training Centers were to receive graduates, both officers and enlisted men, from the Replacement Center and Ordnance School, organize them as companies, and, with the aid of an

[7] Key Pers Rpt, 1945, Hatcher, OHF.

[8] Hist of Ord School, pp. 39–40, OHF. A detachment was left at Raritan to train a group of enlisted men who were to be transferred to Aberdeen later for specialized training as instructors.

[9] See ltr, CofOrd to QMG, 6 Sep 40, sub: Additional QMC Personnel . . . , OO 353/76, DRB AGO.

experienced cadre assigned to each unit, give them a thirteen-week course on working together as members of a team. The whole program of Army training in 1940 was geared to crowding as much instruction as possible into one year since the Selective Service Act provided that men would return to civilian life after twelve months of military training.

Actual establishment of the proposed training centers was not authorized by the War Department until several weeks after the enactment of Selective Service in mid-September.[10] Then began the long process of erecting barracks, shops, and buildings for classrooms, acquiring training equipment, and organizing staffs of instructors. Because the Ordnance School, Replacement Center, and Unit Training Center were all to be located at Aberdeen, an Ordnance Training Center was formed there to provide unified control of all training activities. The Ordnance Training Center was officially activated on New Year's Day 1941 with Colonel Hatcher in command.[11]

The Ordnance School at Aberdeen 1940–45

Within a few days of the transfer of the 40th Training Company to Aberdeen in July 1940, the Ordnance School was conducting classes for both officers and enlisted men at its new location. Instruction began while partitions, plumbing, heating, and lighting were still being installed. The unfinished barracks offered only cold showers, screenless windows, and beds without sheets or pillows. An old museum building provided makeshift classrooms and shops while new buildings were being erected. At the same time, preparations were being made for the future, although no definite long-range training objectives had yet been set by the War Department.

Streamlining the Curriculum

The pace of Ordnance training before 1940 had been slow, and the instruction had been thorough. Classes had normally been small and students had been specially selected, above-average, career soldiers.[12] The enlisted students who came to the Ordnance School after 1940 were not experienced Regular Army veterans, but young men who had been drafted for a year of military training under the Selective Service Act. There was not time to give them nine-month courses in various phases of ordnance. They had to be trained quickly—and in large numbers—and then be transferred to the field forces for additional training in large-unit operations. To meet this situation the Ordnance School streamlined its courses by eliminating all but the most essential material and reducing the time allotted for each subject.[13]

The first course given at Aberdeen was a shortened version of the former NCO course, lasting only twelve weeks instead

[10] Ltr, TAG to CG's major commands, 25 Oct 40, sub: Replacement Centers, AG 680.1 (7–11–40) (1) Sec 1, DRB AGO.

[11] (1) ODO 151, 26 Dec 40, OHF. (2) Col. J. S. Hatcher, "The Ordnance Training Center," *Army Ordnance*, XXI, 126 (1941), 625. (3) For comment on the difficulties encountered at Aberdeen, see memo, Col Outland for author, 31 Oct 50, OHF.

[12] Brig. Gen. Harry R. Kutz, "Military Education," *Army Ordnance*, XXVI, 144 (1944), 531–32. General Kutz was chief of the Military Training Division from 1943 to 1945. See also Capt. J. G. Smithwick, "Training Enlisted Specialists," *Army Ordnance*, XXIX, 152 (1945), 260–61.

[13] Col. G. W. Outland, "The Ordnance School," *The Ordnance Sergeant*, V, 1 (1943), 36–37. The same step was taken by the German Army in training its ordnance technicians. See manuscript study, MS D-175, *Die Technische Ausbildung des Waffenmeister*—Personals, GMDS DRB AGO.

of nine months. During July, a few days after the 40th Training Company had moved to Aberdeen, a group of two hundred enlisted men—eight times the number usually enrolled at Raritan—arrived at the school to take the NCO course.[14] Later in the year, as construction of more classrooms and shop buildings was completed, the specialist courses in artillery, small arms, automotive vehicles, fire control instruments, carpentry, and welding, formerly conducted at Raritan, were included in the curriculum at Aberdeen. Each course was given in three months instead of nine and, as time went on, other short courses were added for machinists, clerks, munitions workers, and antiaircraft fire control specialists. In addition to the courses for enlisted men, the Ordnance School also developed a streamlined program of officer training. In June 1940 the two-year course for officers was discontinued and several short, specialized courses, designed chiefly for the large number of Reserve officers who were being called to active duty, were substituted.[15]

In the summer of 1941 the demand for enlisted specialists became so great that the Ordnance School had to speed up its training process. The school authorities adopted the methods of industrial mass production, setting up many different production lines to turn out specialists just as factory production lines turned out interchangeable parts for a machine. In the automotive section, for example, the attempt to produce in thirteen weeks versatile automotive mechanics capable of repairing all types of vehicles was abandoned. Instead, students were divided into three groups—tank mechanics, tractor mechanics, and wheeled-vehicle and half-track mechanics—each group being given a short but intensive course in its special field. Meanwhile, the general-purpose NCO course was dropped because it proved to be less valuable than the specialized courses, particularly since it could no longer be restricted to highly qualified, experienced veterans. As General Kutz, who became chief of the Military Training Division in 1943, described this move: "We discarded the time-consuming endeavor of trying to train a Jack-of-all-trades and concentrated, instead, upon turning out highly skilled technicians in specialized fields."[16]

A new form of specialized training was added to the curriculum early in 1942 when the Base Shop School was opened. In 1940 it had generally been assumed that, in time of war, ordnance in need of major overhaul would be returned to the arsenals in the United States, as had been the procedure in World War I. Although several officers on the Ordnance School staff had dissented, and recommended that troop units be trained to operate Ordnance base maintenance shops overseas, no provision for such training was made during the first year of the school's operation at Aberdeen. In the fall of 1941, however, it became apparent that such instruction was needed, and a few weeks before Pearl Harbor General Wesson directed the Ordnance School to establish an organization to train personnel for overseas base shop units.[17]

---

[14] Hist of Ord School, p. 208, OHF.

[15] *Ibid.*, p. 137.

[16] Gen. H. R. Kutz, "Military Education," *Army Ordnance*, XXVI, 144 (1944), 532. See also the remarks of Dr. Robert E. Doherty in the same issue, p. 538.

[17] (1) Ltr, CofOrd to CG Ord Training Center, 22 Nov 41, sub: Base Shop Facilities at APG, copy in Hist of Ord School, App., OHF. (2) Intervs with Col Outland and Lt Col Keith T. O'Keefe, Apr 50. (3) Hist of MPTS, XI, 37-44, OHF.

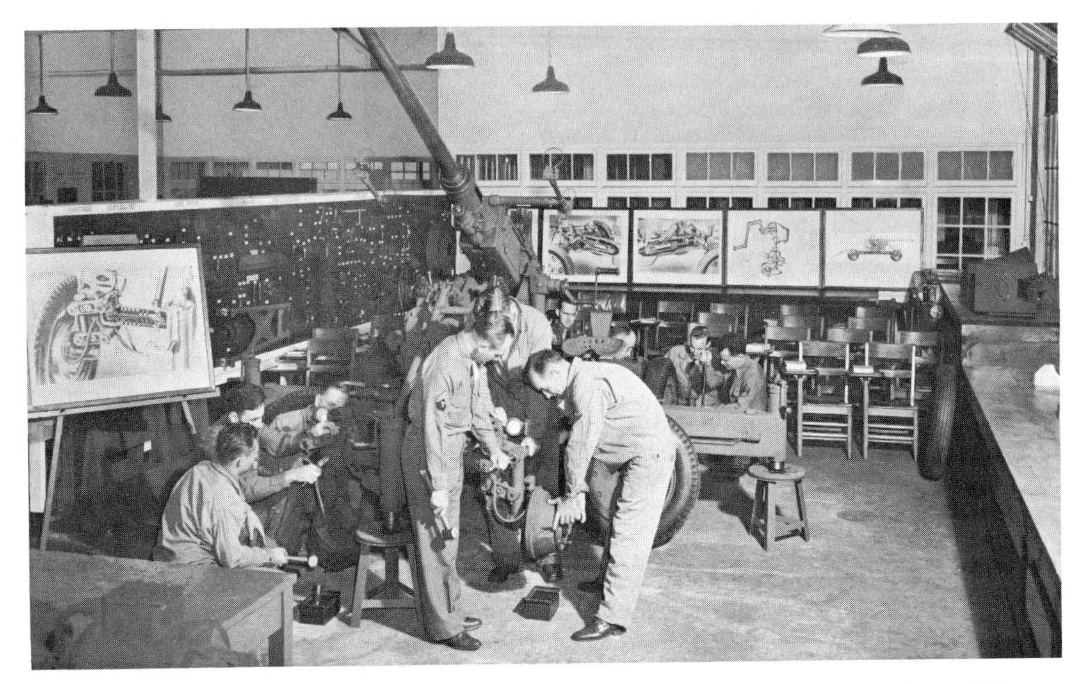

FACTORY TRAINING CLASS *at the Firestone Tire and Rubber Company, Akron, Ohio.*

Decentralization of Technical Training

The Ordnance School steadily increased in size during 1941, reaching a capacity of 1,500 by the end of the year.[18] After the outbreak of war in December the school area was extended until it eventually covered 275 acres, with more than 300 buildings, and, at the peak of the training load, the curriculum included more than 70 different technical courses. But even with this rapid growth, the school was not able to train all the Ordnance technicians required by the Army, and an elaborate program of decentralization was adopted. To supplement the facilities at Aberdeen, the Ordnance Department turned first to various civilian trade schools, then to specialized branches of the Ordnance School, and finally to factory schools.

As early as November 1940 the Ordnance School had adopted the practice of farming out a few of its students to civilian trade schools. At that time, a group of 50 student machinists had been enrolled at the Springfield Trade School in Massachusetts, and in July 1941 another group of students had been sent to a civilian trade school in Baltimore for training in electrical maintenance. Contracts for training Ordnance troops were made with several other civilian trade schools in 1942.[19] At the same time the Ordnance School established branches at Ordnance depots. In

[18] Ltr, CofOrd to ACofS G-3, 8 Jan 42, sub: The Ordnance Training Problem, OO 353.4/61, DRB AGO. The average number of graduates per month during fiscal year 1941 was 200; during 1942 it rose to 400, and during 1943 to over 1,000. See Hist of Ord School, Vol. I, App., pp. 2-55, OHF.

[19] Hist of MPTS, I, 56-60, OHF.

January 1942 after the UTC at Savanna had been closed, the clerical and ammunition courses at Aberdeen were transferred to Savanna to release facilities urgently needed for the expanding Officer Candidate School which had been opened at Aberdeen in July 1941. As the problems of distributing and keeping records of spare parts for all kinds of Ordnance equipment became critical during 1942, a school for training parts clerks was organized at the Rossford Ordnance Depot, Toledo, Ohio.

In 1942, as it became apparent that the Department would not be able to train all the technical specialists needed, the Military Training Division asked manufacturing concerns holding war contracts to train Ordnance personnel in their own shops and classrooms. In many instances these concerns were ideally prepared to train maintenance mechanics as they had staffs of expert instructors and ample supplies of tools, equipment, and technical literature. The manufacturers entered wholeheartedly into the task of producing "factory-trained soldiers" to maintain the weapons of war coming off the production lines.

The largest single addition to Ordnance training operations during World War II came in August 1942 when responsibility for Army trucks and other vehicles was transferred from The Quartermaster General to the Chief of Ordnance. Included in the transfer were a score of Quartermaster automotive schools, both military and civilian, with a combined capacity for nearly 15,000 students. Most of these schools were comparatively small, however, and were closed during the spring and summer of 1943 in an effort to consolidate automotive training in a few large centers.[20] By December 1943, when the automotive school at Holabird Ordnance Depot in Baltimore, Maryland, was closed, only four Ordnance automotive schools were still in operation—Atlanta, Georgia; Normoyle in San Antonio, Texas; Fort Crook, Nebraska; and Mt. Rainier in Tacoma, Washington. Normoyle was closed in March 1944 and Fort Crook in April 1945, leaving only Atlanta and Mt. Rainier in operation at the end of the war. For some months after the transfer of motor vehicles to Ordnance, the Quartermaster Corps trained men for the Ordnance Department at its two large replacement centers.

Ordnance school training expanded so rapidly during 1941 and 1942 that it was impossible to keep an accurate and detailed record of the number of students trained. "We were adding new schools so rapidly in 1942," Col. George W. Outland later remarked, "that I would have been hard pressed to tell you on any one day exactly how many we had."[21] New courses were added to the curriculum and old courses were revised and redesignated. Not all students assigned to the Ordnance School followed the simple pattern of completing a single course and then moving on to a new assignment. Some took several short courses in related fields before leaving the school while others, for one reason or another, were transferred before completing a single course. The courses varied so in length that statistical tabulations of courses completed are virtually meaningless. The following table of the number of men graduated from these courses is based on the best available estimates for the

[20] ASF Monthly Progress Rpt, 30 Apr 43, Sec. 9, p. 5, OHF. For discussion of Ordnance automotive UTC's, see below, p. 144.

[21] Interv with Col Outland, Jan 50.

period between January 1941 and September 1945:[22]

	Officers	*Officer Candidates*	*Enlisted Men*
1941	1,400	37	
1942	2,400	4,600	12,000[a]
1943	5,000	6,100	15,000
1944	3,500	1,800	12,000
1945 (to Sep)	2,300	700	5,000
	14,600	13,237	44,000

[a] Total for 1941 and 1942.

Teaching Methods and Training Aids

The veteran instructors on the faculty of the Ordnance School in 1940 had learned effective teaching methods through many years of experience, but most of the new members who joined the staff in 1941 needed instruction in the techniques of teaching. In September 1941, therefore, Colonel Outland created a Training Methods Branch and assigned as its head a senior instructor from the automotive section who had extensive civilian experience as a teacher of engineering subjects.[23] Beginning in September the new branch gave a thirty-hour course in teaching methods to all officer instructors. The course included discussion of lesson plans, the proper use of various techniques of teaching, the employment of visual aids, and a showing of the War Department film, "Military Training" (TF 7-295). Approximately half the course time was devoted to practice teaching, with each practice period followed by a critique of the student teacher's methods. "A Manual for Ordnance Instructors," prepared by the Training Methods Branch, was published in February 1942 and was used as the basic text until publication of TM 21-250 by the War Department a year later. The training methods course was later given to enlisted instructors of the Ordnance School, to bomb disposal officers, and in abbreviated form to students in the Officer Candidate School.

In accordance with War Department policy, Ordnance instructors were encouraged to use training aids of all types, ranging from books and blackboards to motion pictures and cut-away models. In the early days of the war period up-to-date publications were virtually nonexistent, and the only usable drawings were those made on the blackboard by the instructor.[24] Most of the printed manuals on hand had been prepared by the Field Service School in earlier years for Army extension courses. To bring these manuals up to date and to produce others as rapidly as possible, a small publications section was formed, and during the winter of 1940–41 a growing staff of writers, editors, and illustrators prepared texts, charts, scenarios for training films, and other instructional material. An impressive list of Ordnance School texts soon appeared, including separate manuals on telescopes, range finders, ammunition, and other subjects.[25] Thousands of charts, maps, and photographs were prepared and reproduced for classroom use,

[22] Computed from various tabulations in Hist of Ord School, OHF.

The Ordnance School at Santa Anita, California, closed in May 1944 after graduating 8,488 students. Hist of MPTS, XI, 97, OHF.

[23] Hist of Ord School, p. 85, OHF.

[24] "Ordnance training literature, thus far, is woefully insufficient," the Chief of Ordnance wrote in May 1941. "We have only one War Department approved Field Manual, which incidentally, is already out of date. Likewise, we have only one instructional type of Technical Manual which has been approved by the War Department." Ltr, CofOrd to CO OTC, 20 May 41, sub: Ordnance Training Literature, OO 353/395, DRB AGO.

[25] Hist of MPTS, XI, 16, OHF.

and models of many types of equipment were used in all sections of the school. Carburetors, for example, were made of transparent plastic to give the students a chance to see exactly how a carburetor functioned, and models of small items of equipment were made ten or twenty times their actual size for demonstration to large classes.[26]

One of the most important training aids originated within the Ordnance School was a monthly magazine, *The Ordnance Sergeant.* In the fall of 1940, Sgt. Hugh E. Martin, a graduate of the first NCO course at Aberdeen and chief of the publications section of the school, observed that, however effective the Ordnance School courses might be, something would be lacking in the instruction program if nothing were done to keep the enlisted specialists abreast of developments in ordnance after their graduation.[27] Sergeant Martin recommended that an "alumni magazine," containing descriptions of revised procedures and new matériel and answers to questions received from troops in the field, be prepared and distributed by the Ordnance School. This recommendation was promptly approved, and the first issue of *The Ordnance Sergeant* appeared in mimeographed form in January 1941, with Sergeant Martin as editor.[28] The first few issues had such a favorable reception that an improved reproduction process was adopted and the size of the magazine was increased to 100 pages. It was distributed free of charge to all Ordnance organizations, and its circulation eventually passed the 25,000 mark. Many officers reported that wherever copies of *The Ordnance Sergeant* were found in the dayrooms and libraries of Ordnance units, their smudged and dog-eared pages gave evidence of having been read and reread.

The Officer Candidate School

In the summer of 1940 Colonel Hatcher, foreseeing the need for hundreds of additional officers to carry out Ordnance Department responsibilities, urged that authority be granted to institute an officer candidate training program, erect school buildings, and organize a corps of instructors.[29] The War Department, however, was reluctant to approve the training of additional officers at that time because so many Reservists had not yet been called to active duty, and it was not until the spring of 1941 that the War Department authorized the various arms and services to establish Officer Candidate Schools (OCS). On 26 April 1941 Ordnance was directed to open its OCS at Aberdeen Proving Ground in July, but with an initial quota of only fifty students.[30]

The first class at Aberdeen was made up of candidates selected chiefly from the Regular Army and National Guard by

[26] Lt. E. D. Roberts, "Seeing Is Believing," *Army Ordnance,* XXIX, 153 (1945), 418–19. See also illustrated article in *Life,* XIX, 4 (1945), 42. Inspecting officers in January 1944 rated the training aids in use at the school "exceptionally good." Inspection Rpt on Ord School, 29 Jan 44, OO 353/6468, DRB AGO.

[27] Col. G. W. Outland, "The Birth of the Ordnance Sergeant," *The Ordnance Sergeant,* III, 1 (1942), 5–7.

[28] Sergeant Martin was awarded the Legion of Merit for his work as editor of *The Ordnance Sergeant.* WD GO 44, 30 May 44.

[29] Interview, January 1950, with Colonel Outland, first commandant of the Ordnance Officer Candidate School. Establishment of Officer Candidate Schools had been envisaged in the National Defense Act of 1920 and in Mobilization Regulations published by the War Department during the 1930's.

[30] Ltr, TAG to CG's all armies and others, 26 Apr 41, sub: Officer Candidate Schools, AG 352 (4-10-41), DRB AGO. For a discussion of War Department policy on officer candidate training in 1940 see Robert R. Palmer, Bell I. Wiley, and William R. Keast, *The Procurement and Training of Ground Combat Troops* (Washington, 1948), pp. 325–28.

OCS boards appointed by corps area or department commanders.[31] The group was housed on the second floor of the auxiliary barracks of the 40th Ordnance Company, and, for lack of better accommodations, classes were held in the basement of the barracks. The officer candidates were instructed by the faculty of the Ordnance School, the OCS actually being a section within the school. The first course of study, adopted in July 1941, provided a quick survey of both military and technical subjects, and allotted thirty-two hours to each of four technical specialties—small arms, artillery, ammunition, and automotive equipment.[32] Experience soon showed that this program needed elaboration and refinement. It made no provision for instruction in such essential subjects as camouflage, defense against aerial attack, and the use of weapons. It offered little opportunity for the candidates to become familiar with field operations, and the time allotted for the study of each category of Ordnance items was sufficient only for a sketchy orientation.

Beginning with the third class, which entered in January 1942, the course was revised to include more specialized instruction in technical subjects.[33] At the end of the eighth week of training each candidate chose one technical subject as his field of study for the remaining four weeks of the course. Toward the end of this period of specialization, the student went on an overnight bivouac and worked out a field problem that required him to apply his newly acquired knowledge. Throughout 1942, because of the necessity for crowding both military and technical training into such a short period, the Ordnance OCS was unable to train its officer candidates with the desired degree of thoroughness. A single overnight bivouac did little to prepare them for the realities of combat operations, and four weeks of technical instruction was not adequate preparation for dealing with practical problems of field maintenance.

After the landings in North Africa in November 1942, reports from overseas commanders indicated that many service troops, in addition to their technical proficiency, needed more thorough training in adapting themselves to field conditions.[34] Beginning in May 1943, therefore, a radical change was made in the Ordnance OCS course. The entire period was given over to basic military subjects including rifle marksmanship, first aid, convoy operations, sanitation, and field expedients. After completing this intensive course of military training and receiving their commissions, the students entered upon the second phase of their training—twelve weeks of technical instruction during which they spent four weeks on "basic ordnance" and eight weeks on the study of a specialty such as small arms, ammunition, or artillery.

In addition to basic military training and physical conditioning, the Ordnance OCS constantly emphasized the selection and training of men for leadership.[35] The War Department directive authorizing officer candidate schools had stated that demonstrated leadership ability was to be "the basic and predominant consideration governing selection to officer candidate

[31] WD Cir 245, 26 Nov 41, and AR 625-5 prescribed the procedures for selecting officer candidates.

[32] The Ordnance OCS, Hist of MPTS, Vol. 100, p. 2, OHF.

[33] *Ibid.*, p. 5.

[34] Ltr, CofOrd to CG ASF, 13 Apr 43, sub: Revision Ordnance OC Training, OO 352.11/16447, DRB AGO.

[35] For a description of leadership training of officer candidates in the Army Ground Forces, see Palmer, Wiley, and Keast, *op. cit.*, pp. 334–35.

schools,"[36] but experience soon showed that the various OCS boards were sending many poorly qualified candidates to the Ordnance OCS.[37] Thus, the school not only had to teach the principles of leadership but also to devise means of evaluating the leadership qualities of the students so that those who were not up to standard could be eliminated. The methods employed at Aberdeen to select and train students for military leadership were similar to those used throughout the Army. They included close-order drill, the "floor rating" system, and subjection of students to constant pressure. The day-by-day judgments of instructors—many of whom were themselves recent graduates of the course they were teaching—played an important part, as did the impressions made by the candidates on their classmates. Some candidates felt that in judging leadership ability, the emphasis placed on close-order drill was excessive and that too little weight was given to the individual's technical knowledge and experience. Others felt that "lack of leadership qualities" was simply a convenient catch-all used by instructors in lieu of more specific criticism. Rightly or wrongly, more candidates were eliminated from the Ordnance OCS for leadership deficiencies than for any other reason.[38]

One of the most pressing problems facing the school throughout its first two years was the need for more barracks, more classrooms, more instructors, and huge quantities of teaching materials. The first classes in 1941 were small and entered at intervals of several weeks, but soon the quotas were doubled and tripled, and a new class was formed every week. During the first six months of 1943 the peak enrollment was reached when over 1,000 students entered the school every month. Classes were then reduced to 200 each, beginning at intervals of two weeks, and late in the year the classes were limited to 50 candidates each, entering at intervals of eight weeks. This schedule continued in effect with only minor changes throughout 1944 and the first eight months of 1945. A total of 713 candidates received their commissions during 1945, bringing the number of graduates for the 1941–45 period to approximately 13,000.[39]

Replacement Training

The Ordnance Replacement Training Center (ORTC) was activated at Aberdeen Proving Ground on 1 January 1941 to train the Ordnance quota of men brought into the Army under the Selective Service Act. Its mission was to receive newly inducted men from reception centers, give them basic military and technical training, and then transfer them as individual replacements for existing units, as cadre for new units, or as specialist students for the Ordnance School.[40] After the peacetime "defense" training turned into

[36] See also WD Cir 126, 28 Apr 42, for further details on the selection of candidates.

[37] "The boards sent to the school," the OCS historians wrote, "a student body which ranged in qualifications from the brilliant to the dull-witted and from the born leaders to the uninspired followers." Hist of MPTS, Vol. 100, p. 9, OHF. This problem was not peculiar to the Ordnance OCS, but was Army wide.

[38] For a more detailed description of the leadership deficiencies of officer candidates, see Palmer, Wiley, and Keast, *op. cit.*, pp. 345–50.

[39] Hist of MPTS, XVI, Supplement 1, 16, OHF.

[40] The terminology applied to training activities in 1941 was sometimes confusing. "Replacements" were men assigned to organizations either to replace actual losses (loss replacements) or to bring the organization initially up to strength (filler replacements). A cadre was a small group of trained officers and men who formed the nucleus around which a new unit was organized.

actual war training in December 1941, the ORTC continued as the focal point for Ordnance replacement training throughout World War II.

Training Under MTP 9-1, 1941-42

The basic military and technical training given at the ORTC during the first half of 1941 was guided by Mobilization Training Program 9–1, dated 1 October 1940, which prescribed a course of instruction for all Ordnance enlisted replacements during their first four weeks in the Army.[41] Two weeks were devoted exclusively to basic military subjects and two weeks to a combination of basic military and basic technical instruction. In contrast to the more elaborate training programs developed in later years, this early 1941 schedule was sketchy. It allotted a disproportionate amount of time to close-order drill and made no provision for teaching subjects such as map reading and night operations. Nevertheless, it was considered adequate because the four weeks of basic training were intended to serve only as the first phase of a recruit's military education.

The original version of MTP 9-1 made no provision for keeping trainees in the ORTC itself for specialized technical training, but as the volume of recruits mounted in 1941 it became impractical to transfer all of them elsewhere for such training, and technical sections had to be hastily organized. The technical courses, ranging in length from six to eight weeks, were not designed to produce highly skilled specialists but to turn out men who could fit into Ordnance units as basic replacements and then gain greater proficiency through experience on the job. For this reason, the courses covered only the most essential data. Emphasis was placed on the nomenclature and function of each item, its assembly and disassembly, and the repairs normally made by an Ordnance maintenance company in the field. All the courses devoted as much time as possible to practical work, and all included at least one brief field exercise.

The technical sections faced a great many difficulties in getting started during the summer of 1941. There was a shortage of virtually everything except students. Barracks had to be used as classrooms until new shop buildings were completed, and many classes had to be held outdoors during the summer. There were practically no visual aids, and even items of equipment for observation and study were scarce. The automotive section, for example, opened in July with only one M3 tank, one scout car, and ten condemned trucks in its stock room.

Recognizing that instructors are the vitally important "machine tools" of a training center, the ORTC staff immediately took steps to train a corps of competent instructors for both technical and military subjects. Two hundred of the most promising men were withdrawn from the first contingents to arrive at Aberdeen, given an intensive course of instruction in basic military subjects, and then assigned to training battalions, where they filled all cadre positions from first sergeant to corporal. As time went on, more and more men were given "cadre training" and the instruction was broadened to cover technical as well as military subjects.[42] A related program of instructor training was launched early in 1942 to improve the

[41] Copy in AG 300.8 MTP (8 Feb 40) (1), DRB AGO.

[42] (1) Hist of MPTS, XIV, 216, OHF. (2) PSP 60, Ordnance Military Training, 1939–1944, Sec. V, OHF.

technique of teaching. All enlisted instructors in the technical sections were required to attend an evening class each week for six weeks to study the principles set forth in FM 21-5, "Military Training," to discuss examinations and visual aids, and to practice public speaking. This combined program of training in military subjects and teacher training eventually became a permanent feature of the ORTC curriculum and was made a requirement in all cadre training.[43]

Although Ordnance troops were given more military training during 1941 than had ever before been considered necessary, inspecting officers of G–3 found that the military training given at the ORTC in the summer of 1941 was not sufficiently thorough and was inferior to the technical training. The inspecting officers attributed this condition largely to the fact that most of the instructors were Reserve officers who had been schooled primarily in technical subjects rather than in the command of troops.[44] The Chief of Ordnance acknowledged the soundness of this criticism and replied that it was an unavoidable consequence since sufficient funds for training Ordnance Reserve officers had not been available during the prewar years. General Wesson immediately directed the ORTC officers to give constant attention to raising the level of military training. Steady progress resulted during the following months, and by the summer of 1942 an inspecting officer reported that the ORTC military training program was "exceptionally well conducted."[45]

A number of factors contributed to this improvement. One was the Congressional action in August 1941 extending the Selective Service Act for another year and lengthening the period of training from twelve to eighteen months. Another was the approval by the G–3 Division of a new Ordnance training program that more than doubled the number of hours allotted to basic military training—254 hours in contrast to 102 hours in the 1940 MTP. The new program also provided that some military training be given during the weeks of technical instruction so that the benefits of the initial training would not be lost. Most of the additional time for military training was devoted to close-order drill, physical training, marches and bivouacs, inspections, and running the obstacle course.[46]

The most important stimulus to improvement of training in 1941 was the outbreak of war in December. The attack on Pearl Harbor put a stop to all argument over the need for military training. Instructors and trainees were no longer preparing for a war that might or might not come, but were now definitely committed to fight to the finish against powerful enemies.

At the same time, the need for more rapid mobilization of troops made it necessary to shorten the time for replacement training. On 19 December 1941 the War Department ordered all Replacement Training Centers (except those of the In-

[43] Interv, 18 Jul 50, with Col Paul C. Kelly, former director of ORTC training.

[44] Ltr, TAG to CofOrd, 9 Aug 41, sub: Rpt of Training Inspection, ORTC, OO 353/519, DRB AGO.

[45] Memo, Lt Col William C. Bennett, Jr., for Dir of Training, ASF, 3 Jul 42, sub: Training Inspection of ORTC, Aberdeen . . . , OO 353/986, DRB AGO.

[46] MTP 9-1, Ordnance MTP for . . . Replacements . . . , 21 Aug 41, AG 381 (9-12-39), DRB AGO.

The obstacle course was opened in August 1941. It extended over approximately 500 yards of wooded territory and consisted of hurdles, log mazes, rope climbs, a rope traverse across a water-filled ditch, and a gas chamber. Hist of MPTS, XIV, 29–30, OHF.

fantry, Armored Force, and Signal Corps) to reduce the training cycle to eight weeks.[47] The ORTC did not return to the longer training schedule until June 1942, but it adopted a forty-eight hour week as partial compensation for the time lost under the shortened program, and gave more instruction at night. During the early months of 1942 the average trainee was given four weeks of basic military training and four weeks of technical training, but the demand for replacements was so great that many individuals were transferred before completing even this shortened schedule.

ASF Influence on Replacement Training in 1942

When the War Department was reorganized in March 1942, the training division of Army Service Forces replaced the G-3 Division of the General Staff as supervisor of training in the technical services. The new office, headed by Brig. Gen. Clarence R. Huebner, soon began to exercise much closer control over military training within the technical services than G-3 had ever attempted. The need for more intensive and realistic instruction was emphasized, and the chiefs of services were bluntly ordered to "give constant attention to the urgent problem of training" and not to shunt it aside as a matter of secondary importance.[48]

Within the Ordnance Department need for the increased emphasis on training was recognized by General Campbell in June 1942 when he formed a Military Training Division, headed by General Hatcher, and placed it on the same administrative level as the other divisions in the Department.[49] At the same time, a Civilian Advisory Council, composed of noted educators and industrialists, was appointed to advise the Military Training Division.[50] The members of the council conferred at intervals with Ordnance training officers and on several occasions visited Aberdeen and other training centers.

One of the first matters to which the ASF training staff turned its attention was standardization of the basic military training given at the replacement centers operated by the technical services. In August 1942 it issued a detailed four-week training schedule to be followed by all replacement centers and unit training centers under its jurisdiction.[51] The new program required a complete revision of the Ordnance schedule of basic military training. By June 1942 the ORTC had returned to its longer training schedule and was devoting more than five weeks to basic military training under the 254-hour program adopted the year before. The new ASF schedule reduced this to less than 4 weeks, or 163 hours, and sharply reduced the time

[47] Ltr, TAG to CofOrd, 19 Dec 41, sub: Reduction in Length of Training Program at RTC's, AG 320.2 (12-17-41), DRB AGO. Return to the longer cycle was directed by the War Department on 28 February 1942. See AG 320.2 (2-3-42), DRB AGO.

[48] Ltr, CG SOS to Chiefs of Services, 2 May 42, sub: Training of Troops in SOS, OO 353/858, DRB AGO.

[49] In January 1943 General Kutz replaced General Hatcher, who became chief of the Field Service Division.

[50] The members of the Civilian Advisory Council were Dr. Kaufman T. Compton of Massachusetts Institute of Technology, Dr. Robert E. Doherty of Carnegie Institute of Technology, Dr. J. E. Johnson of General Motors, Dr. Harry P. Hammond of Pennsylvania State College, Dr. Alexander R. Stevenson of General Electric, Dr. Ivan C. Crawford of the University of Michigan, and Dr. Arthur C. Willard of the University of Illinois.

[51] Basic Training Program for all RTC's . . . of SOS, Aug 42, incl to ltr, CG SOS to CofOrd, 28 Aug 42, sub: Basic Training Program, OO 353/1060, DRB AGO. See also draft history of ASF training of replacements and units, SPTR 314.7 (1 Jan 45), DRB AGO.

allotted to each of the four main subjects—close-order drill, physical training, marches and bivouacs, and inspections. In two respects the new program was a major forward step: it marked the end of the period when close-order drill was allotted more time than any other training topic, and it more than doubled the number of hours for rifle marksmanship. Events were soon to prove that the decision to limit basic training to 163 hours was unsound and that the virtual elimination of marches and bivouacs from the program was a serious mistake.

Although Ordnance training centers had introduced rifle marksmanship training in the fall of 1941[52] and had given it more and more attention during the first six months of 1942, marksmanship training remained one of the chief weaknesses of Ordnance training until late in 1942. There was no rifle range at the ORTC on which trainees could fire for record, and the supply of both ammunition and rifles for training purposes was strictly rationed. In its survey of replacement training in the spring of 1942 the ASF training division had discovered that the same conditions prevailed at many other replacement training centers, and in July it therefore had directed all of them to intensify their instruction in rifle marksmanship.[53]

In November 1942, when a second Ordnance Training Center was opened at Camp Santa Anita in California, Brig. Gen. Bethel W. Simpson was transferred from Aberdeen, along with a large part of the ORTC staff, and placed in command of the new center.[54] Colonel Outland, commandant of the Ordnance School, was then assigned to head the ORTC, with Col. Paul C. Kelly, a retired infantry officer back on active duty, as his director of training. To these two officers fell the responsibility for administering the new ASF training program after a large proportion of the experienced ORTC officers and enlisted men had been transferred to Santa Anita.

"One of the first things I did after reaching Aberdeen," Colonel Kelly reported, "was to eliminate the parades held every Saturday morning. Parades have their place in military life, we all agree, but it shocked me to see so many thousands of man-hours desperately needed for training being wasted on formal parades—and Colonel Outland agreed with me."[55] The company officers were required to conduct training personally instead of delegating responsibility to NCO's. Company officers were directed to turn over the administrative paper work to their first sergeants and then go out to the training areas and personally take over the task of training their men.

Under the leadership of Colonels Outland and Kelly, close attention was given to what may be called "human relations" in dealing with the new recruits who arrived at Aberdeen. A friendly, understanding attitude was found to be most effective in converting the civilian to a soldier capable of accepting the hardships and responsibilities of modern warfare. Trucks were kept on hand at the railway station to meet every train bringing men to the ORTC, and a mess hall stayed open all night to give new arrivals a hot meal. "We even had their bunks made up for

[52] Memo, G-3 for CofOrd, 9 Oct 41, sub: Rifle Marksmanship, and 8 inds, OO 353.14/8, DRB AGO. Before the summer of 1941, Ordnance troops were given training on the pistol rather than the rifle.

[53] Memo, CG SOS for CofOrd, 8 Jul 42, sub: Small Arms Record Firing, OO 353/4302, DRB AGO.

[54] For further details on the Santa Anita training center, see OTC Hist Santa Anita, OHF.

[55] Interv with Col Kelly, 18 Jul 50.

for them the first night," Colonel Kelly reported. "Not that we coddled anybody or neglected discipline—we just treated them like human beings. And our system paid dividends in the form of better training." [56] The staff psychiatrist at the station hospital supplemented this policy by giving new recruits a series of informal talks on adjustment to Army life. When experiments in the fall of 1942 showed that these "mental hygiene talks" helped trainees to overcome homesickness and resentment toward military regimentation, the talks were made a regular feature of ORTC training.[57] A cleverly illustrated booklet called "The Story of Mack and Mike" was given to all trainees, showing them how Mike adjusted normally to the Army routine while Mack made himself unhappy by resenting every regulation and feeling sorry for himself.

More Combat Realism in Training

In spite of the efforts made during 1942 to improve replacement training in all branches of the Army, results were not entirely satisfactory. The earliest reports received from overseas observers in late 1942 and early 1943 praised the technical skill of Ordnance and other service troops but complained that some were deficient in military training and physical conditioning. One observer, for example, spoke of the "backbreaking work" that had been required to get supplies ashore in North Africa and urged that service troops be physically hardened before being sent overseas. "They cannot be conditioned" he added, "by games, calisthenics, or marching; they must actually manhandle cargo for long hours, during darkness, inclement weather, and rough seas." [58] As a result of such reports, the keynote of Ordnance replacement training during 1943 became combat realism. Although Ordnance troops were not officially classified as fighting soldiers, strenuous efforts were made to toughen them, physically and mentally, to withstand the rigors of field operations and to teach them to work and fight alongside combat troops. Less time was spent in close-order drill and inspections, and more attention was given to living and working under simulated combat conditions.

The most important single step taken during 1943 to improve the training of replacements was the addition of four weeks to the training period.[59] In addition to lengthening the training time, the new program overcame one of the major difficulties of the past by allowing an additional four weeks for processing men in and out of the training centers, travel, and furloughs at completion of training.

While the basic training program was extended and intensified during 1943, improved methods of teaching were also adopted. Instructors became more proficient as they gained experience, and an ever-increasing supply of training aids contributed to the effectiveness of their teaching. Because of the long hours of in-

---

[56] *Ibid.*

[57] (1) Maj. Robert R. Cohen, "Mental Hygiene for the Trainees," *The American Journal of Psychiatry*, Vol. 100, No. 1 (1943). (2) Maj. Robert R. Cohen, "Factors in Adjustment to Army Life," *War Medicine*, V, 2 (1944), 83–91.

[58] Lessons Learned from Recent Amphibious Operations in North Africa, incl to memo, CG SOS for CofOrd, 12 Feb 43, OO 350.05/2444, DRB AGO. See also Training in the Ground Army, AGF Hist Study 11, p. 39, DRB AGO.

[59] Memo, G–3 for CG ASF, 13 Jun 43, sub: Loss Replacements, ASF 320.2 General (12 Jun 43), DRB AGO. The Civilian Advisory Council of the Ordnance Military Training Division recommended in June 1943 that the training period for Ordnance units and replacements be extended to six months. Ltr, Dr. Doherty to Military Training Div, 8 Jul 43 OO 353/4281-4282, DRB AGO.

STREET-FIGHTING TRAINING EXERCISE *under simulated combat conditions at Aberdeen ORTC.*

struction and the vigorous outdoor activity to which most of them were not accustomed, the trainees tended to become drowsy in classes and drop off to sleep when the instruction was dull and uninteresting. Every effort was therefore made to present each subject in an interesting and forceful manner and to use the most effective teaching techniques. In teaching military courtesy, for example, the lecture method was almost entirely discarded in favor of dramatic presentations. With the aid of several assistants, the instructor arranged a series of brief skits, often sparked with humor, to demonstrate the various principles of military courtesy and thus enliven an otherwise dull subject.

Instruction in booby traps, for which eight hours was allotted in the summer of 1943, lent itself admirably to the use of various tricks and surprises to hold the interest of the trainees. The subject was introduced to each class by a training film, followed by a lecture during which large-scale working models were used as training aids. The instructor supplemented his presentation of the theory by actually wiring several booby traps in the classroom. When the men went outside for a ten-minute break they found that the grounds had been wired with countless booby traps containing small firecrackers. The opening of the latrine door, for example, set off a loud blast, and the unsuspecting students who picked up helmets or bottles of Coca-Cola lying on the ground were startled by other explosions. The rest periods were as instructive as the lectures.

Perhaps the best known and most effective training aid developed at the ORTC was a loose-leaf notebook on basic training called "The Ordnance Soldier's Guide." Every trainee was given a copy of this notebook to carry to his classes. First issued as a sheaf of mimeographed sheets clipped to a board, it was later revised and printed. The "Guide" covered all the subjects included in the basic training program, from "ammunition" and "map reading" to "World War II." The brief text was clear and easily understood, and was supplemented by scores of illustrations, most of which were miniature reproductions of large charts used in the classrooms. A distinctive feature of the "Guide" was its provision of blank spaces under many topics for the trainees to write in the data supplied during classroom lectures and demonstrations. When properly filled out, the "Guide" became the soldier's own notebook to take with him when he left the ORTC and keep for future reference.

It was, of course, necessary to adopt teaching methods suitable to the mental ability and previous experience of the trainees. There were wide variations among the men assigned to Ordnance but, generally speaking, they were well above the Army average in mental ability and mechanical aptitude. A comprehensive survey by the ORTC classification section during 1943 showed that the average Army General Classification Test (AGCT) score for the 25,000 white recruits assigned to the training center during the year was 107.8, and the average Mechanical Aptiture Test (MAT) score was 106.5. The corresponding scores for Negro trainees were much lower—79.8 for the AGCT and 77.9 for the MAT—but during 1943 only 8 percent of the arrivals at the ORTC were Negroes. Half the white trainees fell into Classes I and II on the basis of AGCT scores, as compared to 36 percent for the Army as a whole, and only 18 percent were in Classes IV and V as compared to 30 percent for the entire Army. More than half the white trainees and nearly one third of the Negro trainees were high school or college graduates.[60]

The 1944–45 Period

The 1943 pattern of replacement training carried over into 1944 with relatively few changes. The new program (MPT 21-3) issued by ASF in May 1944 reduced the number of hours of close-order drill from twenty to twelve and thus continued the trend started by the first ASF basic training program in 1942. Close-order drill was now allotted less than 5 percent of the total basic training time in contrast to more than 20 percent in the 1940 and 1941 Ordnance programs. Two basic subjects were given increased time—physical training 20 hours instead of 14, and rifle marksmanship 75 hours instead of 68. Marksmanship thus continued to get far more attention than any other subject in the basic training curriculum and was now supplemented by eight hours of familiarization with the carbine and six hours of bayonet drill. Because of the heavy toll taken by malaria among American troops overseas, the new program specifically provided that four hours be devoted to malaria control measures.[61]

[60] Annual Report of Basic Trainees Received at ORTC, 1943, Classification and Assignment Sec, ORTC, OHF. For corresponding figures on other branches of the Army, see Palmer, Wiley, and Keast, *op. cit.*, pp. 17–18.

[61] In September 1943, WD Cir 223 stated that in one active theatre malaria had sent ten times as many soldiers to hospitals as had battle injuries. See also WD Cir 48, 3 Feb 44.

There were occasional minor changes and shifts of emphasis in the program of technical instruction at the ORTC during 1944 and 1945, but the broad outline remained the same as in 1943. The trend toward offering more and more practical work continued in the shop and classroom phases and during the field exercises. All the technical sections changed their training programs at intervals as new equipment came into use by the Army and as reports from overseas recommended revised procedures. But the number of such reports from overseas observers was small. No Ordnance officers visited any of the active theatres to evaluate the training of Ordnance troops until July 1944 when Colonel Slaughter, commandant of the Ordnance School, toured the ETO for several weeks.

During 1944, as during 1943, more men were trained at the ORTC for automotive maintenance work than for any other technical specialty. During 1943, 26 percent of all white trainees had been assigned for training as tank or truck mechanics, and in 1944 the percentage rose for a time to 35. Clerk-typists, supply clerks, and truck drivers formed the next largest groups. Each of the traditional Ordnance specialties—artillery mechanic, small arms mechanic, and instrument repairman—accounted on the average for only about 5 or 10 percent of the total training load.[62]

The number of men in training during 1944 gradually declined from the peak but rose again in the summer of 1945 as the Army-wide redeployment program got well under way. In August 1945, over 5,000 men were received for training at the Aberdeen ORTC—more than twice the average monthly arrival rate of 1943. The number of arrivals quickly declined during the months after the Japanese surrender.[63]

Unit Training

There were three more or less distinct phases of Ordnance unit training during World War II. The first opened in February 1941 and was virtually completed by the time of the attack on Pearl Harbor. The second began in March 1942 when the first "affiliated units" were organized. It overlapped the third phase which began in May 1942 with the opening of a large UTC at Camp Perry near Toledo, Ohio, and ended in the fall of 1943 when most of the UTC's were closed. Some unit training continued during 1944 and 1945, chiefly at Red River in Texas, and Flora in Mississippi, but on a much reduced scale.

The 1941 Program

In the late summer of 1940, in response to a War Department directive, the Ordnance Department drew up three mobilization training programs for Ordnance units. By early October these programs were approved by the G–3 Division and published as MTP 9-2, for maintenance companies; MTP 9-3, for ammunition

[62] Tabulation in ORTC Hist, Vol. VI, Pt. 2, p. 23, OHF. Very few Negro recruits were trained as mechanics because they lacked the education and experience for such training. Most were assigned as munitions workers, carpenter-painters, truck drivers, or clerks.

[63] The number of arrivals, in round figures, at ORTC between 1941 and 1945 were: 15,000 in 1941, 30,000 in 1942, 33,000 in 1943, 24,000 in 1944, and 20,000 through 31 August 1945, a total of 122,000.

These figures are based on charts prepared by the Morning Reports Section, ORTC, included in Hist of MPTC, Vol. XIV, and supplements, OHF. The figures for each year have been rounded off to the nearest thousand. See also Rpts DRB AGO.

companies; and MTP 9-4, for depot companies. All three programs had the same general objectives: (1) "to train a basic ordnance soldier," (2) "to train the individual in the particular duties he will be required to perform in a company," and (3) "to produce a thoroughly trained . . . company which will function as a team."[64] While these MTP's were being prepared, a schedule for training Ordnance units at three Unit Training Centers was drawn up in accordance with the existing War Department troop basis. This schedule called for training 26 maintenance companies at the Aberdeen UTC, 10 ammunition companies at the Savanna UTC, and 6 ammunition companies at the Raritan UTC.

The companies were scheduled to remain in training for thirteen weeks, but War Department mobilization plans provided that units should be ready for field duty, in case of emergency, at any time after one month. Col. Herman U. Wagner, commanding officer of the Aberdeen UTC, therefore decided to devote the first four weeks exclusively to military training in order to prepare the companies to operate under field conditions as soon as possible. Attention was then turned to technical subjects. Here a difficult problem arose because there were only a few members of the UTC staff who were technical experts, and equipment for technical training was scarce. The only tank available to the Aberdeen UTC, for example, was of World War I vintage. As none of the companies had enough competent instructors or enough matériel to provide technical training on all classes of equipment, Colonel Wagner centralized technical instruction along the lines followed at the Ordnance School. All equipment was pooled and placed at the disposal of a staff of instructors who taught regular classes in small arms, artillery, automotive vehicles, and fire control instruments.[65]

When the first thirteen companies departed on 25 June, taking with them most of the experienced cadre, they were replaced by men for thirteen other companies. In most respects, the conditions under which these units started their training were even less satisfactory than those for the first companies. The enlisted men came directly from reception centers, instead of from the ORTC, and arrived with no previous military training. With the exception of one officer and four enlisted men retained from each of the first companies, the cadremen for the second group came directly from the ORTC where they had been given only eight weeks of training. The Aberdeen UTC was thus faced with the task of starting from scratch to give thirteen companies basic military training, technical training, and unit training all within a period of thirteen weeks, and with only a skeleton staff of experienced personnel.[66]

Under the direction of Col. W. I. Wilson, who became chief of the Aberdeen UTC in June, and later under Maj. A. R. Del Campo, the procedures followed in training the first thirteen companies were used to train the second group. Basic military training was given within the companies by company officers and enlisted cadre, and technical training was centralized under the direction of competent instructors. An increased allotment of tools and matériel was available for these units, however, and mobile shops arrived during the summer. One of the highlights of the

[64] MTP 9-2, 1 Oct 40, AG 300.8 MTP (8 Feb 40) (1), DRB AGO.

[65] For a detailed training schedule, see Hist of MPTS, XV, 12-15, OHF.

[66] Interv with Lt Col A. R. Del Campo, Feb 50.

training period was the arrival of thirty new tanks, just off the assembly line at the new Chrysler Tank Arsenal, for emergency modification before shipment to the British forces in North Africa. In September, at the end of their thirteen weeks of training, the companies were sent to their field assignments, and, by order of the War Department, the Aberdeen UTC was inactivated. It had completed the training of twenty-six maintenance companies and had met the requirements for Ordnance maintenance units under the existing troop basis.[67]

In the meantime, the other two Ordnance UTC's, at Raritan Arsenal and Savanna Ordnance Depot, were training ammunition companies. The Raritan UTC, activated in January 1941, trained six ammunition companies during the year and was then placed on stand-by status.[68] The UTC at Savanna Ordnance Depot was activated early in February by a cadre from Raritan Arsenal.[69] Five ammunition companies were trained during the next three months, according to MTP 9-3, and in June the training of five more ammunition companies began. The large percentage of illiterates among the men in this second group posed a serious problem for the UTC staff since the men could not qualify as members of ammunition companies until they had learned to read the labels on boxes. At the conclusion of the training period, there were no assignments for these companies, and they remained at the depot until the end of the year, working part of the time as ammunition handlers during a period of labor shortage. The Savanna UTC was then inactivated in January 1942.[70]

During the winter of 1941–42, while the question of the responsibility for unit training was being threshed out at the General Staff level, the training of units by the Ordnance Department came virtually to a standstill. Three ammunition companies were trained at Raritan early in 1942 but, generally speaking, service units of all kinds were trained during this period by the combat arms rather than by the technical services. Ordnance units that were organic to infantry divisions, for example, were trained by the divisions rather than by the Ordnance Department. This policy continued in effect after the reorganization of the War Department in March 1942, largely because the Army Service Forces had practically no facilities for training units, while the Army Ground and Army Air Forces had extensive unit training programs in operation. The directive establishing the new Army organization provided that the using command would train the units, but the ASF, in addition to the responsibility for training all units required for its own installations, was also directed to train certain units for the AGF and AAF.[71] This directive authorized the ASF to proceed with a large-scale program of unit training during 1942 as soon as training centers could be established.

Recruitment and Training of Affiliated Units, 1942

The resumption of unit training in the Ordnance Department began when the so-called affiliated units were formed in the spring of 1942. At the end of February,

[67] (1) Ltr, TAG to CofOrd, 18 Sep 41, sub: Additional ORTC Capacity, AG 320.2 (9–13–41), DRB AGO. (2) WD GO 9, OTC, 30 Sep 41.

[68] Hist of Raritan Arsenal, Vol. I, Ch. 5, OHF.

[69] Hist of Savanna Ord Depot, Vol. I, Pt. 2, pp. 109–28, OHF.

[70] *Ibid.*

[71] WD Cir 59, 2 Mar 42.

a short time before the reorganization of the War Department was announced, Ordnance was assigned the responsibility for training two base regiments that were urgently required for overseas shipment within three months. Since the time was so short and Ordnance had no unit training center at which to train base regiments, Col. C. Wingate Reed, chief of the Military Personnel and Training Branch, proposed that the Department enlist the aid of commercial organizations in recruiting for these units mechanics who were already skilled in heavy maintenance work. He believed that these mechanics, with a minimum of military training and some familiarization with Ordnance procedures, would be able to function as maintenance troops in a very short time. He based his belief on the proposition that it is easier to train a mechanic to be a soldier than to train a soldier to be a mechanic.[72]

General Wesson approved Colonel Reed's proposal, and on 14 March 1942 the War Department authorized Ordnance to recruit two affiliated base regiments, a maintenance battalion, and a maintenance company, with a combined strength of 300 officers and 5,000 enlisted men.[73] Since no single commercial organization was capable of providing such a large number of skilled mechanics, the Ordnance Department turned for assistance to the NADA. With a total membership of over 40,000 automobile dealers, most of whom employed mechanics in their repair shops, the NADA was admirably suited to serve as a connecting link between the needs of the Ordnance Department and the skilled manpower in commercial garages across the country.[74]

Unlike other technical services, the Ordnance Department had had no previous experience in recruiting and training affiliated units.[75] No plans had been prepared during the prewar years for the organization of such units, nor had commercial organizations been alerted to the possibility that they would be called upon to recruit personnel. As a result, plans had to be formulated and put into effect in great haste.

The two regiments were destined for shipment to North Africa where the German forces were then pushing eastward and threatening Alexandria. Strategic plans required that the regiments be ready for embarkation by the end of June, thus leaving only three months to recruit, equip, and train them. Within the six weeks from 15 March to the end of April, a whirlwind recruiting campaign was conducted and a total of 350 officers and 8,500 men were recruited—a number substantially greater than was required.

Early in May the two regiments reported for training at Camp Sutton on the

[72] Interv, 25 Jan 50, with Capt Champlin F. Buck, Jr., executive officer to Colonel Reed during 1942.

"An affiliated military unit," General Wesson wrote, "is one whose activities so resemble the civilian occupation of its members that it is possible to select personnel from civil life for similar assignments in the Army, enlist or commission this personnel in the Reserve, and call the organization out as an entire unit." Ltr, Gen Wesson to Mr. Harry Sommers, President NADA, 17 Mar 42, OO 322.1/225, DRB AGO.

[73] Ltr, TAG to CofOrd, 14 Mar 42, sub: Constitution and Activation of Certain Ordnance Units, SPAG 320.2 (2-18-42), DRB AGO. These were the 301st and 302d Ord Regts (Base), the 47th Ord Bn, and the 506th Ord Co (HM).

[74] (1) Col. C. W. Reed, "Affiliated Units," *NADA Bulletin*, XV, 4 (1943). (2) Col. C. W. Reed, "The Ordnance Affiliated Units," *Army Ordnance*, XXVIII, 148 (1945), 75-77. (3) Ltr, CofOrd to Sommers, NADA, 17 Mar 42, OO 322.1/225, DRB AGO.

[75] Both the Signal Corps and the Medical Department had made plans during the 1930's for forming affiliated units and had actually activated such units in 1941.

outskirts of the little town of Monroe, North Carolina. Camp Sutton was a new temporary divisional camp at which virtually no facilities or equipment had been provided before the arrival of the troops.[76] The men had to pitch tents for shelter and, as no sewage system had been installed, were forced to spend much of their valuable time digging latrines. The training program consisted of basic military training and familiarization with Ordnance matériel. Because of the lack of adequate facilities for either kind of instruction, improvisation was the order of the day. The local high school, the State Guard armory, and various small shops and warehouses were converted to training purposes, and the officers and men who served as instructors studied the handbooks at night to keep a jump ahead of their students. The arrival of a cadre of veteran instructors from the Ordnance School helped, but the lack of heavy organizational equipment continued to handicap the training.[77]

At the end of the scheduled training period the regiments were not sent overseas as had been planned. Instead, the men were sent individually and in small groups to the Ordnance school at Aberdeen, and to other technical training installations, for intensive training in various specialties such as small arms, artillery, fire control instruments, and tanks. After twelve weeks of individual technical training, the men were then re-formed into units, most of which sailed for North Africa early in 1943.

In recruiting and training three more regiments (the 303d, 304th, and 305th) different methods were used in order to avoid some of the difficulties experienced with the first two affiliated regiments. Officers were selected and trained in advance of the enlisted personnel instead of being placed in command of troops before they had themselves received any military training. Special recruiting teams were organized to choose properly qualified men for specific assignments. To remove all ground for complaint that favoritism entered into the recruiting process, the officers selected to command the units did not participate in the recruitment of enlisted personnel. As a rule, the enlisted men were given ratings somewhat lower than their qualifications warranted, to allow room for promotion later on.

When the resources of the NADA were eventually exhausted, several business concerns volunteered to recruit additional personnel for Ordnance affiliated units. Among these were the International Harvester Company, American Roadbuilders Association, John Deere Company, Associated Equipment Distributors, J. I. Case Company, and the Allis-Chalmers Company. By 15 December 1942, when recruiting for affiliated units was discontinued because of the executive order banning further voluntary enlistments, a total of approximately 1,100 officers and 30,000 enlisted men had been provided for 5 base regiments, 10 separate battalions, and 109 separate companies.[78] Ordnance units were thereafter organized and trained at regularly established Unit Training Centers.

[76] "I regret to advise you," General Campbell wrote, "that unquestionably some mistakes have been made by the Ordnance in raising these units; the camp was not ready for occupation and training facilities could not be procured as fast as the men were raised. Camp Sutton is a new tent camp. . . ." Ltr, CofOrd to Sen D. Worth Clark, 11 Jul 42, OO 320.2/2129, DRB AGO.

[77] Memo, Gen Hatcher for Gen James Kirk, 22 Sep 42, sub: Training of Ordnance Base Regiments, OO 322.1/414, DRB AGO.

[78] For a complete list of all Ordnance affiliated units, see *NADA Bulletin*, Feb 43, p. 24.

291064 O—55——11

Unit Training 1942-45

During the first six months of 1942, the Ordnance Department's responsibility for training—aside from the affiliated units—was not clearly fixed. In addition to the uncertainty as to whether the Ground Forces or the Service Forces should train service-type units, there were also in early 1942 frequent revisions of the War Department troop basis. Ordnance officers responsible for training units were handicapped in making definite plans because they did not know precisely how many units they would be called upon to train during the months ahead. They estimated that a total UTC capacity of from 20,000 to 25,000 would probably be required before the end of the year, but in the spring of 1942 the small UTC at Raritan was the only existing Ordnance facility for conducting unit training, and it was on a stand-by basis. An immediate search was therefore made for suitable sites at which to establish several new and larger UTC's.[79]

The first site to be approved was Camp Perry, adjacent to Erie Proving Ground in northern Ohio. It had a capacity of 4,500 trainees and was converted into an Ordnance UTC on 18 May 1942 to train units for service with the Army Ground Forces. The second new UTC was established at the Mississippi Ordnance Plant, near the town of Flora, Mississippi. This large bag-loading plant was nearing completion in the summer of 1942 under supervision of the Industrial Service, but was not at that time essential to the ammunition production needs of the Department. The Military Training Division therefore arranged in August to convert the plant into a unit training center with a capacity of 7,000. In late October a 3,000-man UTC was established at the Red River Ordnance Depot, and when the Ordnance Training Center at Santa Anita was opened in November, most of its capacity was devoted to the training of units.[80] In addition to these regularly established training centers, Ordnance depots such as Augusta; Mt. Rainier; Fort Crook; Nansemond at Portsmouth, Virginia; Seneca at Romulus, New York; Letterkenny at Chambersburg, Pennsylvania; and Normoyle were used for on-the-job continuation training.

Before the responsibility for motor transport vehicles was transferred from The Quartermaster General to the Chief of Ordnance in August 1942, the training of Quartermaster units for automotive maintenance had been conducted at various AGF installations such as Camp Butner, Camp Sutton, and Pine Camp. Ordnance training officers took immediate steps in September to centralize control of the training of automotive units by establishing three automotive UTC's. The first, and largest, of these centers was opened in October 1942 at the Pomona Ordnance Depot, with a capacity of 3,000. In mid-February 1943 two more were established, one at Holabird Ordnance Depot (capacity 800) and the other at Atlanta Ordnance Depot (capacity 1,800).[81] With eight centers in operation by February 1943, the combined capacity of all Ordnance UTC's rose to more than 24,000. This program of

[79] Interv with Col Wagner, Jan 50.

[80] The OTC at Santa Anita was established on the race track, which had been closed because of the wartime ban on horse racing. It filled the need for an Ordnance training center on the west coast and specialized during 1943 in the training of men before their assignment to units. Hist of OTC, Camp Santa Anita, OHF.

[81] Ltr, TAG to major commands, 5 Feb 43, sub: Establishment of Ord UTC's, AG 353 (2-3-43), DRB AGO.

expansion placed Ordnance far in the lead among the technical services in establishing unit training centers.[82]

All of the Ordnance UTC's established in 1942 encountered difficulties during the early months of their operation because of the limited facilities and lack of experienced personnel. Basic military training was hampered by the lack of rifle ranges, gas chambers, bivouac areas, visual aids such as films and charts, and areas for demonstrating hasty field fortifications, tank obstacles, and field sanitation.[83] Technical training of maintenance companies was handicapped by the lack of shop equipment, sample items of Ordnance matériel, charts, and manuals. Because of the need for speed in activating and training new units, none of the UTC's was fully equipped or manned when it received its first units for training, and, what was even worse, many units were ordered to overseas duty by higher headquarters before they had completed the prescribed thirteen weeks of training. At Camp Perry, for example, of twenty units shipped out during 1942, only three had completed the scheduled thirteen weeks of training. Nine of the units had only seven weeks of training, and others had less than seven weeks.[84] All of these were units that the Ordnance Department was training for the Army Ground Forces, and they were moved at the request of AGF with full knowledge that their training was incomplete.[85]

This divided control over the training of Ordnance units was the source of a great deal of dissatisfaction during 1942. In October, for example, when the Under Secretary of War wrote to General Campbell that he was concerned over the efficiency of Ordnance units in the field, the Chief of Ordnance replied that he was "fully cognizant of the lack of trained personnel in Ordnance field units."[86] General Campbell went on to state that he did not concur in the existing War Department policy of training Ordnance units of the Army Ground Forces. This policy placed primary responsibility for the activation and training of such units with the AGF rather than with Ordnance. "All Ordnance units," General Campbell wrote, "should be activated at least three months prior to the activation of the combat units they are to serve. Until released for assignment to combat units, the training of all Ordnance units should be under the complete control of the Chief of Ordnance." He followed up these recommendations three weeks later with a memorandum for General Somervell requesting that responsibility for the initial three months of training of all Ordnance units be vested in the Chief of Ordnance, that no Ordnance units be released from Ordnance control until the three-month training period was completed, and that the necessary UTC capacity and equipment be made available to the Chief of Ordnance.

This request was not favorably considered, but during 1943 the ASF Training

[82] See chart of UTC strength in Progress of Ordnance Program, 30 Jan 43, p. 25, OHF. In June 1943, 4,000 men completed training at Ordnance UTC's.

[83] For a typical example, see report by the commanding officer of Red River Ordnance Depot quoted in Red River UTC Hist, II, 4, OHF.

[84] Ltr, CG 5th SC to CG SOS, 8 Feb 43, sub: Recommendations Concerning Ordnance UTC, Camp Perry, OO 354.1/70, DRB AGO.

[85] 2d Ind, CofOrd, 19 Feb 43, to ltr cited n. 84, OO 354.1/70 DRB AGO. "Army Ground Forces were completely familiar with the situation," the Chief of Ordnance reported, "and still were desirous of moving these companies from Camp Perry."

[86] (1) Memo, USW for CofOrd, 2 Oct 42, OO 322.1/552. (2) Memo, CofOrd for USW, 2 Oct 42, USW Misc and Subject files—Ordnance. (3) Ltr, CofOrd to CG SOS, 28 Oct 42, sub: Activation of Ordnance Field Units, OO 322.1/552. All in DRB AGO.

Division took several important steps to strengthen the unit training programs of all the technical services. Requirements were prescribed in greater detail, inspections were more rigid and more frequent, and at the end of the summer the time allotted for unit training was lengthened from thirteen to seventeen weeks.[87] In June all UTC's were required to give military training continued emphasis during the technical training phase, to provide more thorough training in first aid, chain of command, and use of weapons for antiaircraft defense. As reports came in from overseas stressing the importance of night operations, the UTC's were directed to give more attention to instructing units to carry out all their operations under blackout conditions. In August ASF headquarters established minimum requirements for the training of all nonmedical ASF units and directed that no unit be reported as ready to perform its mission until the minimum requirements had been met.[88]

The quality of Ordnance unit training steadily improved during 1943 and 1944 as rifle ranges, obstacle courses, infiltration courses, and other facilities for training were constructed at the training centers, and as equipment for shop and field maintenance work became more plentiful.[89] Progress was most clearly reflected in the reports of The Inspector General on Ordnance units before their movement overseas. During 1944, fifty-four Ordnance units were inspected and only two were found to be below the minimum standard. No other technical service with a comparable number of units inspected had such a high rate of acceptance.[90]

After V-E Day there was a brief period of intense activity in the redeployment training of units. In accordance with War Department policy, entire units were transferred from the European theatre to training centers in the United States where they were given special training before moving on to the Pacific. Every effort was made at the Ordnance training centers—chiefly at Aberdeen, Red River, and Atlanta—to adjust the training to the needs of redeployed units, to avoid unnecessary repetition of earlier instructions, and to direct the whole program toward the conditions likely to be encountered in the Pacific area. Most of the technical training consisted of practical on-the-job instruction to bring the men up to date on new procedures. Military training focused special attention on Japanese tactics, identification of Japanese uniforms and weapons, throwing live hand grenades, bayonet practice, camouflage, and malaria control measures.

Because of the nature of unit training it is impossible to compile an accurate and meaningful statistical summary of units trained during World War II. Units varied in size from the bomb disposal squad to the base regiment, and the length of their training period varied from one to six months. Many units were ordered to active field duty before they completed more than half the scheduled program, while others engaged in advanced training for several weeks after completing the basic training requirements. The affiliated units, composed of skilled mechanics, needed

[87] MTP 21-2, 1 Aug 43. This training program applied to RTC's as well as to the UTC's.

[88] ASF Memo S 350-43-43, 28 Aug 43, OO 353/4011½, DRB AGO.

[89] Memo, Maj L. W. Reeves for Dir of Mil Tng ASF, 13 Aug 43, sub: Inspection of the OUTC, Texarkana . . . , OO 353/4081, DRB AGO. "The Ordnance Unit Training Center at Texarkana is considered superior in the conduct of basic field training," the memo stated. "This training is characterized by thoroughness and reality."

[90] ASF Monthly Progress Rpt, 31 Jul 45, Sec. 9, Military Training, p. 11, DRB AGO.

only basic military training and familiarization with Ordnance matériel. Most other Ordnance units were made up of selectees assigned to Ordnance by reception centers, and required the full cycle of basic military, technical, and unit training. But, without taking into consideration all of these variations in the length and scope of the training programs, estimates show that approximately 90,000 men received some degree of training at Ordnance UTC's during the 1941–45 period.[91]

Bomb Disposal Training

Training personnel to dispose of unexploded bombs (UXB's)—whether of the defective-fuze or delayed-action variety—was one of the many new problems the Ordnance Department was called upon to face during World War II. During earlier wars, unexploded bombs or shells had usually been disposed of simply by blowing them up wherever they were found. During World War II, when large-scale bombing raids were launched against centers of population and industry as well as against military installations, use of the crude demolition methods of the past was no longer feasible. A large high-explosive bomb dropped in the middle of an urban business district and buried several feet under the pavement among vital water, gas, and electric lines could not be blown up without incurring tremendous property damage, nor could it be left for hours—or even for days or weeks—to explode at its own appointed time. Means had to be devised for gaining access to the bomb, removing the fuze, stopping the time mechanism, or otherwise rendering the bomb harmless and then digging it out and hauling it away for destruction or salvage. After the destructive bombing raids launched by the Germans in 1940, the need for trained bomb disposal squads became apparent to authorities planning the defense of the United States. No large-scale attacks on American cities were expected, but it was felt that preparations should be made to minimize the destructiveness of any attacks that might occur.[92]

Progress in getting the bomb disposal training program under way during 1941 was hindered by delay on the part of higher authority in deciding who should be responsible for such training. The earliest plans had envisaged an Office of Civilian Defense that would organize and direct civilians in every community to carry out fire-fighting and bomb-disposal operations during bombing raids. But it was not until five days after the attack on Pearl Harbor that the War Department specifically assigned to the Office of Civilian Defense (OCD) the task of disposing of UXB's in the zone of interior, and to the Ordnance Department the same responsibility within all military reservations, overseas departments, and theatres of operations.[93] The Ordnance Department was also assigned responsibility for training bomb disposal personnel, both military and civilian, and was authorized to send an instructor cadre to the bomb disposal school in England to study British methods.

In early December the Chief of Ordnance concurred in this decision to divide responsibility for bomb disposal between the OCD and the Ordnance Department, but further study of the matter convinced

---

[91] Table, prepared by MPTS, in PSP 60, Ordnance Military Training, 1939–44, p. 160, OHF.

[92] For a general view of the bomb disposal problem, see Lt. Col. Thomas J. Kane, "Unexploded Bombs," *Army Ordnance*, XXIII, 134 (1942), 277–82.

[93] Ltr, TAG to CofOrd and others, 12 Dec 41, sub: Disposal of Unexploded Bombs, AG 471.6 (9-9-41) MC-C-M, DRB AGO.

him that the decision had been unsound. "Civilian volunteers cannot be properly trained or disciplined for this hazardous work," he concluded. "Every detail of delayed-action bomb disposal is hazardous in the extreme and requires the utmost in skill, caution, and discipline. Only professionals can develop the skill and experience necessary for such work."[94] Even more important in the eyes of the Ordnance experts who had studied the matter was the need for the strictest secrecy in bomb disposal work so that the enemy would not learn when effective measures for disarming his bombs had been developed. They pointed out that, if the enemy learned what methods were used by bomb disposal squads, he would immediately devise new bombs that would explode when these methods were used. This argument clinched the matter. The December directive was rescinded and the Ordnance Department was given sole responsibility for disposing of all explosive bombs. The OCD was limited to disposing of incendiaries and carrying on "bomb reconnaissance," that is, locating, identifying, and reporting bombs.[95]

Immediately after issuance of the December directive, the Ordnance Department formed a tentative bomb disposal organization at Aberdeen Proving Ground to prepare for the opening of the Bomb Disposal School. Maj. Thomas J. Kane was chosen as commandant of the school and in January 1942 was sent to England, accompanied by eight officers and enlisted men, for instruction in bomb disposal methods. At the same time a small group of British bomb disposal experts—all seasoned veterans of the Battle of Britain—came to the United States with a complete set of British bomb disposal equipment.[96]

The most urgent problem facing the Bomb Disposal School during the spring of 1942 was the need for effective instructional materials. As the school was adjacent to the Proving Ground, it was possible to obtain samples of American fuzes, bombs, and other matériel for study and demonstration, and a bomb disposal museum was started. A large area was set aside as a bomb disposal range where the students could work on actual bombs dropped from airplanes, but there were no films, film strips, charts, and manuals. To meet this need, the official British training film "UXB" was duplicated by the Signal Corps during March, and several film strips, charts, and pamphlets on bomb reconnaissance were prepared by the school staff. By December 1942, well supplied with training aids and qualified instructors, the school was offering eight courses. Three of these were very brief orientation courses including only eight or ten hours of instruction, and one was a correspondence course. The other four, ranging from 45 hours to 180 hours of instruction, formed the backbone of the school curriculum. In addition, instructors from the school gave a sixteen-hour bomb reconnaissance course to top OCD personnel in all states east of the Mississippi and in the states bordering on the Gulf of Mexico and the Pacific Ocean.[97]

The value of this training was twofold.

[94] Disposal of Unexploded and Delayed Action Bombs, incl to ltr, CofOrd to TAG, 7 Jan 41, same sub, AG 471.6 (1-7-42) MSC, DRB AGO.

[95] Ltr, TAG to CofOrd and others, 5 Feb 42, sub: Disposal of . . . Bombs, AG 471.6 (1-7-42) MSC-C-M, DRB AGO.

[96] Hist of Bomb Disposal School, p. 3, OHF. The American mission included Col. Kane, Maj. H. M. Walker, 1st Lt. F. A. Parsons, 1st Lt. W. W. Prichard, 2d Lt. W. R. Nass, M/Sgt. A. E. Keller, T/Sgt. R. E. Metress, T/Sgt. J. E. Pilcher, and S/Sgt. R. S. Felton. The British group was headed by Col. Geoffrey Yates of the Royal Engineers.

[97] (1) The Courses of Instruction Composed by the

On the domestic side, the Bomb Disposal School provided a nucleus of trained personnel for all the Service Commands and civilian defense regions and thus strengthened the nation's civilian defense organization. The significance of this contribution is sometimes overlooked because no enemy bomber formations appeared over American cities during the war to bring the bomb disposal forces into action. In overseas theatres the value of bomb disposal training was clearly demonstrated. In those areas, Ordnance-trained bomb disposal units found plenty of work to do, often working around-the-clock for days at a time. They performed heroic service in neutralizing and removing UXB's, artillery shells, and other explosives from territory occupied by Allied troops. Although their training had not covered all types of explosive items, bomb disposal personnel overseas found that the red bomb on their sleeves made them the target for questions on all kinds of objects suspected of being explosive. The disposal of explosive bombs and shells was not glamorous work, and was not rewarded with additional compensation for all its hazardous nature, but it proved immensely valuable to the fighting troops.

The accomplishment of the Ordnance Department in training more than 300,000 officers and enlisted men during World War II can be seen in proper perspective only when viewed against the background of the prewar years. Before 1940 training was not an important phase of Ordnance operations and accounted for only a small fraction of the annual Ordnance budget. All efforts during the 1930's to prepare for the future were hindered by lack of funds, lack of interest in training activities, and uncertainty as to Congressional action in authorizing a larger Army.

The Selective Service Act of 1940 and the assignment to Ordnance of large numbers of selectees early in 1941 gave the Department an opportunity to strengthen its training organization and try out its plans. Much was accomplished during the year, but Ordnance officers felt that much more could have been accomplished if the War Department had approved their plans for expansion. Because of the uncertainty as to the continuance of selective service beyond one year, no full-scale expansion of permanent Army training facilities was authorized. As a result, the Ordnance Department, along with all other branches of the Army, was forced to train the recruits it received during 1941 under conditions far from ideal.

The effect of this failure to expand training facilities more rapidly during 1940 and 1941 carried over into the first year of the war. The attack on Pearl Harbor injected a new spirit of realism into all Army training, but buildings, equipment, and instructors could not be provided overnight. Moreover, the increased need to train men quickly and in large numbers made it impossible to train them thoroughly. Throughout 1942, Ordnance basic military training was too brief to be very effective and continued to place too much emphasis on traditional garrison subjects such as close-order drill and formal inspections, neglecting rifle marksmanship, field exercises, map reading, and night operations. Lack of essential equipment and facilities such as rifles, ammunition, rifle ranges, and bivouac areas hindered the

Ordnance Department for the Training of Military and Civilian Personnel on Matters Pertaining to Bomb Disposal, Exhibit 1, Hist of Bomb Disposal School, OHF. (2) Ltr, Maj A. E. Keller, Chief of Bomb Disposal Div, OD Bd, to author, 25 Nov 49, OHF.

basic training program all during 1941 and 1942. Technical training, although superior to military training, was also greatly handicapped during the 1941–42 period, and to a lesser extent during the latter half of the war, by the lack of shop buildings and equipment.

No review of Ordnance training during World War II would be complete without reference to its almost infinite variety. The Ordnance School trained enlisted technicians in scores of specialized fields, ranging from cooking and baking to the major overhaul of tanks and heavy guns. It also trained thousands of officer specialists and graduated more than 13,000 officer candidates. Instruction at the Aberdeen Replacement Training Center and the various UTC's covered a wide range of subjects, from elementary military courtesy and close-order drill to the recovery and repair of heavy field equipment at night under simulated combat conditions. The Bomb Disposal School at Aberdeen provided both individual and unit training in the identification and disposal of unexploded bombs. Never before in its history had the Ordnance Department been called upon to train such large numbers of men in so many different specialized fields.

Perhaps the most noteworthy development in Ordnance training during World War II was the streamlining of all school courses and training programs. The broad, general training of the prewar years was discarded in favor of highly specialized and intensive courses of instruction. In all branches of technical instruction, courses were stripped of nonessentials and only the "must-know" information was taught. At the same time, more effective teaching methods were adopted, and great ingenuity was displayed in developing a wide variety of training aids. The success with which this streamlining process was applied to Ordnance training was attested to by a well-known educator, Dr. Robert E. Doherty, president of the Carnegie Institute of Technology, when he said: "The characteristic which distinguishes Ordnance training from all other training with which I am familiar is its intensive nature . . . . In this program I think General Kutz and his associates not only have done a magnificent job for the Army but also have made a significant contribution to education in general."[98]

[98] Dr. Robert E. Doherty, "Combat Knowledge," *Army Ordnance*, XXVI, 144 (1944), 538.

CHAPTER VI

Civilian Personnel and Training

The Ordnance Department during World War II was one of the country's largest employers of civilian workers. No other Army technical service had so large a work force, and the payrolls of few private industries approached in size that of Ordnance. The overseas operations of the Department were carried on by military personnel, but practically all Ordnance installations in the United States—the arsenals, depots, proving grounds, and district offices—were manned by civilians, with only a few officers and enlisted men filling administrative and specialist positions. The only important exceptions to this rule were the military training centers, which were of necessity staffed almost exclusively by officers and enlisted men. All told, the Ordnance Department mobilized more than a quarter of a million workers during World War II, roughly one fourth of all the civilians who worked for the War Department.[1] It trained them in hundreds of different specialties, assigned them to new and unfamiliar tasks, and made steady progress toward developing their skills and promoting efficient teamwork.

In so doing, Ordnance was following its traditional practice. To a large extent an industrial organization, Ordnance had from the earliest days of its history leaned heavily on skilled civilian workmen to staff its manufacturing arsenals and, particularly after the first World War, had come to depend increasingly on civilian employees to operate its storage depots, carry on research projects, and fill thousands of clerical and administrative positions in Washington and the field offices. Throughout the 1920's and 1930's, in fact, civilians on the Ordnance payroll far outnumbered officers and enlisted men, their number rising from a low point of 4,250 in 1924 to 27,000 in June 1940, while the total military strength of the Department remained relatively stable at about 3,000.[2]

In addition to bringing a manyfold increase in the number of Ordnance civilian workers, World War II raised new problems for the Ordnance personnel division.[3] Habits of thought acquired during the years between the wars when economy and careful deliberation were the order of the day had to be discarded, and procedures for hiring, training, transferring, and promoting employees had to be streamlined. Despite having entered the

[1] This figure includes only men and women employed directly by Ordnance; it excludes employees of commercial companies that operated government-owned, contractor-operated plants. The personnel problems encountered at GOCO plants, in so far as they had a bearing on Ordnance history, are considered in Thomson and Mayo, Procurement and Supply of Munitions, MS, OHF.

[2] (1) See Table 3, Ch. II. (2) Hist of Civ Pers Div (hereafter cited as CPD Hist), Vol. I, Ch. A, OHF. (3) Monthly Turnover Rpts, 1920–40, Ord Civ Pers Div files.

[3] The word "division" is used throughout this chapter for the sake of convenience, although the civilian personnel division became a staff branch in June 1942.

war without a well-defined personnel policy and with only a small staff for administering regulations, Ordnance not only developed an effective personnel organization but also contributed in large measure to the formulation of a sound civilian personnel policy for the entire War Department.

Growth of the Working Force, 1938-45

The World War II expansion of the civilian working force began in the summer of 1938. From 12,480 in July 1938, the number of Ordnance employees mounted to over 21,000 in January 1940—an increase of more than 60 percent in eighteen months.[4] Virtually all of this increase was in the field rather than in the so-called departmental service in Washington, and of all field employees, nearly 90 percent worked in the manufacturing arsenals. Most of the remaining 10 percent were employed in the storage depots, including 500 civilian workers in depots in Panama, Hawaii, and the Philippines.

The rise in the number of civilian workers between 1938 and 1940 was only the beginning of the Department's World War II expansion. With over three billion dollars allotted to Ordnance for the fiscal year 1941, the number of civilians on the payroll jumped from 21,051 in January 1940 to 96,263 in December 1941, a 357 percent increase in twenty-four months. After Pearl Harbor the expansion proceeded at an even faster pace and continued throughout 1942. By February 1943 Ordnance employment had reached its World War II peak of 262,772. A single arsenal, Frankford, now employed almost as many civilians as had the entire Department three years earlier.[5] Furthermore, in January 1942 nearly all War Department employees were put on a forty-eight hour schedule, thus increasing substantially the number of man-hours worked each week.

The civilian work force in February 1943 was not only larger than before the war, its distribution was much different. Whereas in January 1940 nine tenths of all Ordnance civilians worked in the manufacturing arsenals, these installations in February 1943 accounted for only about one third of the total work force, or 95,000. The district offices, which had employed only 239 workers in January 1940, had 37,500 employees on their rolls. Thus the arsenals and district offices together accounted for roughly half the total civilian work force in February 1943. The other half worked in the depots and proving grounds, and in the motor bases recently transferred from the Quartermaster Corps.

As the nationwide manpower shortage reached an acute stage early in 1943, the Ordnance Department intensified its manpower conservation efforts, and the number of civilian employees dropped steadily throughout the year. Not all of the reductions stemmed from the manpower conservation program; some came from cutbacks in certain phases of the production schedule and others from increased efficiency as individual workers gained experience on the job. The net result was a reduction in the number of Ordnance civilian employees from 262,772 in February 1943 to 176,384 in December 1943, a drop of 34 percent in less than a year. During the next sixteen months Ordnance civilian employment remained relatively

[4] CPD Hist, I, 9, OHF.

[5] *Ibid.* Figures for field installations are in Monthly Turnover Rpts, 1920-46, Ord Civ Pers Div files. The World War I peak of 88,000 was reached in November 1918.

CEREMONIAL DANCE *at the dedication of the Indian village, Wingate, New Mexico, Ordnance Depot.*

stable at the 176,000 level, except for a temporary increase early in 1945. It declined slowly after V-E Day and then dropped sharply upon the surrender of Japan in August. By the end of 1945 the number of civilians on the Ordnance payroll was 86,667, roughly the same as in November 1941.

Recruiting Ordnance Workers

During the early stages of the emergency, recruitment was carried on primarily by the Civil Service Commission, which was, in theory, prepared to supply properly qualified individuals to fill any government job under its jurisdiction. But as the labor market tightened during 1940 and 1941, the commission was unable to supply the thousands of workers needed by war agencies. Greater authority to hire new workers was granted to local commanders, and after Pearl Harbor more aggressive recruiting methods were adopted, including newspaper and radio publicity and the opening of recruiting offices in centers of labor supply. In the Boston area, for example, a sound truck toured the city during a War Manpower Commission recruiting drive, and a recruiting office was set up on the Boston Common. Ordnance field installations listed their personnel needs with the district offices of the U.S. Employment Service, and recruiting teams composed of Ordnance and Civil Service Commission representatives traveled from town to town enlisting typists and stenographers. In all of their efforts, however, Ordnance installations complained that they were handicapped by Civil Service laws and regulations in competing with private industry for the services of available workers. Private industry could offer inducements such as promises of quick promotions and production bonuses that could not be matched by any government agency.[6]

For the Ordnance Department, recruitment was most difficult at isolated ammunition depots such as Black Hills in South Dakota, Navajo in Arizona, and Wingate in New Mexico. With no large communities nearby, these depots had virtually no local labor supplies to draw upon, nor existing housing and related accommodations for workers brought in from other areas. All of these depots drew a large proportion of their workers from Indian reservations. Recruiting officers, assisted by representatives of the Civil Service Commission, Indian agents, and tribal chiefs, sent trucks to the reservations, gave examinations on the spot, and immediately transported the recruits to the depots. Indian villages built at the depots were dedicated with appropriate ceremonies; weaving racks and looms were provided for Indian women; trading posts and schools were established; and arrangements were made so that the Indians would not have to forfeit their land because they could not farm it.[7]

Other installations resorted to different expedients. At Watervliet Arsenal, for example, groups of so-called commandos were formed by local business and professional men who volunteered to accept employment in the evening or on week ends to help ease the labor shortage. Elsewhere, high school students and teachers were given short-term jobs during the summer months. More than 500 natives of Jamaica and Barbados were employed at Picatinny. Several thousand German and Italian prisoners of war were employed at Ordnance depots and at the Erie Proving Ground, but, by the terms of the Geneva Convention, they could be used only on work not directly connected with the war, such as maintaining roads, loading and unloading nonmilitary supplies, operating heating plants, and making boxes and crates.[8] No such restrictions applied to the Italian Service Units, which were composed of volunteers who supported the reconstructed Italian Government. These units were used on a wide variety of projects and proved their worth.[9]

By far the most important departure from traditional Ordnance practice was the recruiting of large numbers of women for work in shops and depots. Even before the outbreak of war the proportion of women employees in the Ordnance Department had risen from 11.5 percent in the summer of 1940 to 17 percent in July 1941. By the summer of 1942 it had jumped to 30 percent. This rapid increase took place before the manpower shortage reached serious proportions and was accomplished without much formal direction from the Office, Chief of Ordnance. Late in the summer of 1942 the Ordnance civilian personnel division launched an aggressive campaign to induce field installations to employ even more women workers, and as a result, the proportion of

[6] (1) The Story of the Arsenals, p. 97. (2) The Place of the Ordnance Laboratories in Government Research and Development. Both in OHF.

[7] Ordnance Administration, Pt. 3, p. 546, MS hist, OHF.

[8] Ltr, TAG to CG's Service Commands, 14 Aug 43, sub: Labor of POW's, AG 383.6 (12-8-43), DRB AGO.

[9] Ord Admin, Pt. 3, p. 547, OHF.

WOMEN INSPECTORS *working at Picatinny Arsenal.*

women employed rose to a peak of 47.6 percent by the spring of 1945.[10]

There were, of course, many difficulties encountered in recruiting women war workers. Most of the women who applied for work in Army installations lacked previous experience in industrial employment and had, therefore, to be given rather extensive training before being put to work. With some of the more elaborate job processes performed by skilled workmen at the arsenals, "job dilution" was essential before women could be taken on and assigned to the simpler steps in the process, leaving the more difficult tasks for the men. The average woman's lack of physical strength barred her from many jobs, particularly in warehouses where workers were frequently required to lift heavy packages. State laws restricting the weight women workers could lift also had to be considered, as did laws forbidding the employment of women on night shifts. But, in the opinion of most Ordnance administrators, these problems were insignificant in comparison with the contribution to the war production program made by women workers.[11]

[10] (1) Ord Civ Pers Bull 93, 15 Aug 42, sub: Labor Supply. (2) Memo, SW for CofOrd and others, 14 Aug 42, quoted in Ord Procurement Instructions 9,051.1 (3) Ord Civ Pers Bull 115, 9 Oct 42, sub: Employment of Women. All in DRB AGO. (4) Tabulation in PSP 59, taken from monthly reports in Progress of Ordnance Program, Graphic Analysis, OHF. In Washington and in the district offices, women made up as much as 70 percent of the total.

[11] For an account of the difficulties encountered in employing women in the Field Service, see memo, Mr. William M. Hines, Sr., for Gen Hatcher, 14 Jul 43, sub: Reduction of FS Pers, Exhibit 1 in Hist of FS Exec Div, Vol. II, Pt. 2, OHF.

The Struggle for Delegated Authority

In administering its civilian personnel at the start of the war emergency, the Ordnance Department had to comply with the rules and regulations issued by two agencies—the Civil Service Commission and the War Department Civilian Personnel Division. With the former, Ordnance had little complaint and usually managed to adjust promptly the differences of opinion that arose. With the latter there was mounting friction during 1940 and 1941, largely due to the decision of the War Department division to maintain its tight control over personnel activities and not to delegate to the Chief of Ordnance the discretionary authority he desired.[12]

Concentration of authority in the War Department division had gradually developed during the 1920's and 1930's when the number of civilians on the Army payroll had been small enough to permit close supervision of all hiring and firing by a central office in Washington. During the fall and winter of 1940 General Wesson became convinced that the number of civilian employees in the War Department was so large that it was administrative folly to expect that a single office in Washington could, or should, review every personnel action taken by each branch. He urged the War Department division to confine itself to top-level staff planning and policy formulation, and to delegate to subordinate commands full responsibility for putting the plans and policies into effect. The director of the division, Mr. A. Heath Onthank, did not favor such sweeping delegation of responsibility. He recognized the need for gradually assigning authority to lower administrative levels and eliminating some of the congestion in Washington, but felt that hasty delegation of power to untrained personnel in the technical services would lead to endless difficulties. In December 1940, as an intermediate step toward decentralization, he established field personnel offices in each of the corps areas and authorized them to deal directly with local Army installations.[13]

In January 1941 General Wesson wrote a strongly worded memorandum to the Secretary of War requesting that Ordnance be given authority to deal directly with the Civil Service Commission and to hire and fire civilians without referring each case to the War Department for prior approval. He charged that the delays and difficulties encountered under existing procedures had become "a serious impediment to the prosecution of the National Defense Program," and would become even more serious in the future as Ordnance operations assumed larger proportions.[14] The Secretary of War promptly rejected this request on the ground that Ordnance had not made use of the War Department field offices and had not itself fully decentralized personnel functions to its own field establishments.[15] In his reply to this decision, General Wesson defended the Ordnance record on decentralization and called attention to the fact that the arsenals, plants, and depots had not used

[12] This section is based in large measure on: (1) CPD Hist, Vol. I, Ch. F, and appended documents, OHF; (2) intervs, Aug 50, with George W. DeCamp, wartime assistant chief of Ord Civ Pers Div; and (3) intervs, Aug 50, with A. Heath Onthank, Dir WD Civ Pers Div, 1938–42.

[13] (1) Ltr, TAG to Chiefs of Arms and Services . . ., 10 Dec 40, sub: Functions of Civ Pers Field Offices, OSW, AG 230.14 (12–10–40) DRB AGO. (2) Interv with A. Heath Onthank, 28 Aug 50.

[14] Memo, CofOrd for SW, 9 Jan 41, OO 230/929, DRB AGO. See also Key Pers Rpt, Col Reiff H. Hannum, 6 Sep 45, OHF.

[15] Memo, Admin ASW for CofOrd, 11 Jan 41, sub: Civ Pers Procedures, OO 230/1050, DRB AGO.

the War Department field offices because they were all exempt from corps area control. He bluntly declared that he had no intention of granting to these Ordnance installations, many of which had been established only recently and were manned by inexperienced personnel, full authority to deal with the War Department field offices, and thus bypass all control by the Ordnance office in Washington.[16]

On the day that he wrote this reply, General Wesson presented the Ordnance case to the Crowell Committee, which had been appointed to study the problem.[17] He referred to the policy followed during World War I of delegating virtually complete authority in civilian personnel matters to the Ordnance Department, and he contrasted that policy with the cumbersome procedures under which Ordnance was still operating in January 1941. But when the Crowell Committee made its report on 7 February it recommended the policy the War Department Civilian Personnel Division had urged all along—that Ordnance and other War Department agencies delegate to field establishments full authority to handle personnel transactions through the civilian personnel field offices in the corps areas.[18]

All of the War Department agencies concerned concurred in the Crowell Committee recommendations except the Ordnance Department. Several conferences were held during the following weeks to discuss the problem, but little progress was made. Ordnance neither delegated authority to its field establishments, nor used the War Department field offices, and the War Department personnel division continued to hold close control over the appointment, classification, and promotion of Ordnance civilians. The only definite step taken was to assign to Ordnance, as the Crowell Committee had recommended, a "service unit" composed of sixteen personnel experts from the War Department to expedite approval of departmental personnel actions.

On 16 December, less than two weeks after Pearl Harbor, General Wesson repeated the request he had made in January 1941. Before an answer was received, War Department Orders "N" came out, giving all the technical services authority to deal directly with the Civil Service Commission on departmental appointments and ordering them to delegate to their field establishments within six weeks authority to utilize the War Department civilian personnel field offices.[19] Mr. Onthank informed General Wesson that these orders constituted an answer to his memorandum of 16 December and assured him that they provided "all necessary latitude in the procurement and management of civilian personnel." Wesson was unable to share Onthank's optimistic view of the effect of Orders "N." Instead, he saw disastrous implications in the new directive. It put into effect, he wrote, "radical and undesirable changes in personnel procedure" that would "inevitably result in confusion and chaos." He contended that it withdrew control of personnel procedures in the field from the

[16] Memo, CofOrd for Admin ASW, 21 Jan 41, sub: Civ Pers Procedures, OO 230/1014, DRB AGO.

[17] Memo, CofOrd for USW, attn Committee on Civ Pers Procedures, 21 Jan 41, OO 230/991 Misc, DRB AGO. The members of the committee were General Crowell, consultant to the Secretary of War; Arthur S. Flemming of the U.S. Civil Service Commission; and A. Heath Onthank, chief of the War Department Civilian Personnel Division.

[18] Rpt, Crowell Committee, 7 Feb 41, OO 230.2/499 Misc, DRB AGO.

[19] WD Orders "N," 23 Dec 41, sub: Emergency Procedures re Civ Pers, Exhibit 27 in CPD Hist, Vol. I, Ch. F, OHF.

Chief of Ordnance and placed control in the hands of War Department field agencies staffed by inexperienced personnel with little or no knowledge of Ordnance Department problems and policies.[20]

The argument over the application of Orders "N" to Ordnance field personnel came to an end early in February 1942 when the Secretary of War agreed to exempt the Ordnance Department from the order until a classification manual could be prepared to guide Ordnance personnel officers in the field. The manual did not appear until early 1943, and by that time Orders "N" had been rescinded. In the meantime, the March 1942 reorganization of the War Department materially changed the personnel picture. All the technical and administrative services were placed under the jurisdiction of the Army Service Forces, which thereafter assumed the burden of fighting for delegated authority.

The Influence of ASF Personnel Policies

The influence of the Army Service Forces on Ordnance civilian personnel activities was direct and far reaching. The new headquarters not only carried on the fight for delegated authority, but also formulated a broad statement of personnel policy to apply throughout the ASF. It vigorously pushed wage standardization, encouraged the development of improved training programs, and exerted pressure on all the technical services to employ workers more efficiently and reduce the number of employees. In so doing the ASF, as the employer of more than three fourths of all War Department civilian workers, to a great extent set the pattern of civilian personnel management for the Army as a whole.

The development of the ASF personnel program began in April 1942 with the appointment of a staff of experts to survey the status of personnel management in the field installations of the technical services and corps areas.[21] As a sample, the group selected for study the ASF installations in the New York area, including the Ordnance district office, Picatinny Arsenal, and offices and depots of other technical services. After visiting these establishments the investigators reached some rather disturbing conclusions. They reported that the activity carried on under the name of "personnel work" at the ASF installations was of a routine clerical nature and was not regarded as a major management responsibility; that recruitment, induction, and training of workers did not receive the attention they deserved; and that wage administration was not governed by any uniform standard.[22]

When the ASF personnel division tackled the problem of remedying these deficiencies it found itself blocked at the start, as Ordnance had been for the past two years, by the concentration of authority in the War Department Civilian Personnel Division. After several months of discussion, however, the policy that the Ordnance Department had fought for since the beginning of the emergency was adopted. In August 1942 the Secretary of War issued Orders "M" delegating to each of the three major commands—Army

[20] Memo, CofOrd for USW, 2 Jan 42, OO 337/1642, DRB AGO. See also 2d Ind, CofOrd, 15 Jan 42, to memo, Onthank for USW, sub: WD Orders "N," 3 Jan 42, OO 230/3585, DRB AGO.

[21] New York Field Survey, ASF Control Div Rpt 6, May 42, in ASF Control Div files, DRB AGO.

[22] For a detailed description of personnel administration in a district office during the early years, see Hist of Philadelphia Ord Dist, Vol. I, Pt. 4, Ch. 2, OHF. See also Hist of Civ Tng in ASF, Exhibit A, The First Six Months, OCMH.

Air Forces, Army Ground Forces, and Army Service Forces—authority to take final action on nearly all civilian personnel transactions. ASF immediately passed on this authority to Ordnance and the other services and directed them, in turn, to decentralize personnel operations to their field establishments. Since there was now no question of Ordnance field installations having to deal with War Department field offices, and since most of the new depots and plants were now staffed with more experienced personnel officers, the Ordnance Department promptly complied with the ASF directive.[23]

In August ASF published an official statement of policy emphasizing the need for closer attention to such matters as job placement, safety, training, and the establishment of equitable rates of pay.[24] The new Chief of Ordnance, General Campbell, immediately directed his personnel branch to work toward these objectives and also persuaded a prominent industrialist, Mr. Walter C. Pew of the Sun Oil Company, to accept a commission as a lieutenant colonel and come into the Ordnance Department as head of the civilian personnel branch. Mr. Pew accepted the post with the understanding that he was to work closely with the veteran assistant chief of the branch, Maj. George W. DeCamp, who had a thorough knowledge of government procedures. These two men, the one representing private industry and the other government service, were selected by General Campbell to foster in the field of personnel administration the concept of the "Industry-Ordnance team." They served throughout the rest of the war as directors of Ordnance civilian personnel activity.

One of the first problems tackled by the ASF civilian personnel branch in the summer of 1942 was establishment of uniform methods of wage administration in the supply services and corps areas. For employees in the so-called Classification Act positions, rates of pay were fixed by law, but for many in the ungraded positions, such as machinists, munitions handlers, and carpenters, there was no uniformity.[25] No standard wage scale was used throughout the Army, and, as a result, wages paid at Ordnance installations were sometimes out of line with wages paid for similar work elsewhere in government and in private industry. In many labor areas the Army technical services found themselves in competition with each other and with the Navy, Air Forces, and private industry. The situation was obviously one that demanded the immediate attention of the ASF personnel division, for it was a source of endless dissatisfaction among employees and contributed to high turnover rates.[26]

For many years the Ordnance Department had determined the wages of its ungraded employees by surveying the rates of pay for comparable work in local private industries, and had prescribed a set of basic principles to be followed by local commanding officers in making wage surveys.[27] In 1941 Ordnance was the only technical service using wage surveys to de-

[23] CPD Hist, I, 100–105, and appended docs, OHF.

[24] Principles and Policies of Pers Management SOS Hq, Aug 42, Exhibit 4 in CPD Hist, Vol. I, Ch. E, OHF.

[25] These were commonly called "wage board positions" because the wages they paid were determined by wage board surveys rather than by the Classification Act.

[26] The situation in the summer of 1942 is briefly described in The Development of a Pattern of Civilian Personnel Management Throughout Army Service Forces, MS, OCMH.

[27] For the origin of this practice see (1) ODO 369, 24 Jan 22, and (2) Ord Admin, Pt. 3, pp. 603–05, both in OHF.

291064 O—55——12

termine rates of pay. In the spring of 1942 it went a step further by experimenting at two arsenals, Springfield and Picatinny, with the method of job evaluation developed by the National Metal Trades Association.[28] Because this method of classifying jobs according to their level of difficulty represented the practice of the most progressive metal trades industries, its use by Ordnance was carefully studied by the ASF personnel division during the summer of 1942. When the ASF manual on wage administration was issued in October, it embodied the essential principles of the wage survey system and labor classification methods used by the Ordnance Department. The manual was henceforth used as a guide for wage administration in the ASF, and, further to assure uniformity among ASF installations, all wage boards were thereafter headed by a service command officer and included representatives of all the ASF installations in the locality under survey.[29]

Another area of personnel management that received close attention throughout the ASF, particularly during 1943, was conservation of manpower. During the early phase of the emergency, when production had been the paramount need, conservation had been a secondary consideration. In September 1942, as both war production and selective service made heavy demands on the nation's manpower resources, the Ordnance Department took steps to cope with the situation by ordering all its field establishments to reduce their staffs.[30] In November it published a small pamphlet, generally known as the "Blue Book," which outlined a program of conservation, and on the first anniversary of Pearl Harbor, General Campbell, launching a drive to make substantial cuts in the Ordnance payroll, issued a freeze order to the effect that no vacancies were to be filled except with the personal approval of the local commanding officer or district chief.[31] This drive was commended by General Somervell who ordered copies of the Blue Book to be sent, as a model, to all the other technical services.

To conserve manpower, Ordnance made organizational studies to improve operating efficiency, eliminated all but the most essential activities, reduced the number of guards, firefighters, and chauffeurs, and discharged the least efficient employees and chronic absentees.[32] In the Ordnance districts the largest reductions were made in the ranks of inspectors, mainly because of the increased efficiency of individual inspectors, improved inspection by manufacturers, and adoption of sampling techniques. The Pittsburgh Ordnance District, for example, dropped 800 inspectors from its rolls during 1943, and the total employment in that district at the end of 1943 was 50 percent less than in October 1942.[33]

The Field Service was hit hardest by the manpower conservation drive in 1943. By

---

[28] (1) Interv with George DeCamp, Nov 50. (2) CPD Hist, Vol. I, App. to Ch. K, OHF.

[29] (1) Manual, Wage Administration for Ungraded Civilian Jobs in SOS, 26 Oct 42. (2) SOS Civ Pers Memo 19, 23 Sep 42. Both in DRB AGO.

[30] Ltr, CofOrd to Chief of Pittsburgh Ord Dist, 7 Oct 42, quoted in Hist of Pittsburgh Ord Dist, I, 348, OHF.

[31] ODO 366, 7 Dec 42, OHF. A copy of the Blue Book is in CPD Hist, Vol. 100, Ch. E. Col. Gordon C. Baird and Col. Charles D. Wiman headed a manpower conservation group in the OCO to direct the program.

[32] Ltr, Chief of FS to all FS establishments, 12 Jul 32, sub: Authorized Maximum Civ Pers Strength, in Hist of FS Exec Div, Vol. II, OHF. Some of the reduction shown in the reports stemmed from bookkeeping changes, such as the removal from the personnel count of persons on extended leave.

[33] Hist of Pittsburgh Ord Dist, II, 39-40, OHF.

TABLE 9—CIVILIAN ACCIDENT FREQUENCY RATES AT ASF INSTALLATIONS

	Total ASF	Service Commands	Ordnance	Chemical Warfare Service	Corps of Engineers	Transportation Corps
1943	12.3	14.2	7.1	37.7	13.3	20.2
1944	8.7	9.8	5.5	11.8	10.5	14.5
1945	6.3	6.6	4.3	7.9	7.5	11.3

Source: ASF Hq, *Statistical Review World War II*, App. K, p. 165. Data for 1942 are not available. Each figure represents the number of injuries per million man-hours.

the winter of 1942–43 the Industrial Service had passed the peak of its expansion, but the Field Service was just then coming into its own as the storage and distribution agency of the Ordnance Department. During 1943 the Field Service depots not only had to cope with the rapidly increasing inflow of supplies of all kinds from war production plants but also had to handle the steadily mounting outward flow of supplies to troop units overseas. The only reductions in the Field Service work load came in August 1943 when several depots were transferred to private companies for operation under contract. To hold the line, or to reduce its personnel strength, meant for the Field Service the most rigid economy in the use of manpower, adoption of the most efficient operating methods, and the use of labor-saving machinery wherever possible.[34]

One of the major weaknesses in the civilian personnel programs at ASF installations revealed by the 1942 New York survey was the lack of attention to employee safety. Of all the technical services, the investigators found that only the Ordnance Department had an organized accident prevention program. Largely because of the hazardous nature of many Ordnance operations, safety programs were begun in the arsenals and depots many years before the outbreak of World War II and were well established by the spring of 1942. When scores of new loading plants and ammunition depots came into operation in 1942, safety became such an important phase of Ordnance activities that an Explosives Safety Branch was organized in Chicago under the direction of Col. Francis H. Miles, Jr.[35] A statistical summary, compiled by ASF headquarters at the end of the war, shows what a remarkable safety record the Ordnance Department achieved during World War II. *(See Table 9.)*

Training Ordnance Workers

During the twenty years before 1940 the Ordnance Department had not found it necessary to give much attention to training civilian employees. Throughout those years the Department had experienced little difficulty in recruiting skilled craftsmen and professional workers to fill occasional vacancies. Ordnance mobilization planning, however, did not overlook the fact that in time of emergency large

[34] For a detailed statement of FS personnel problems, see rpt, Hines to Chief of FS, 14 Jul 43, Hist of FS Exec Div, Vol. II, Pt. 2, OHF.

[35] (1) ODO 285, 26 Jun 42, OHF. (2) Hist of Safety and Security Div, OCO, I, 12–15, OHF.

numbers of men trained in the production and handling of munitions would be needed. More than six years before war came, Frankford Arsenal revived the four-year course for apprentice machinists that it had discontinued in 1921, and in 1937 Rock Island Arsenal enrolled thirty-six apprentice machinists.[36] The other arsenals soon made similar provisions for training young men in various Ordnance specialties, and by the fall of 1940—more than a year before Pearl Harbor—the training activities of the Ordnance Department had reached such large proportions that a training unit was created within the civilian personnel division.

In the training of many types of Ordnance specialists there was a fruitful exchange between the Ordnance Department and private industry all during the war period. Ordnance employees were trained in the maintenance of specialized types of equipment at factory schools, and employees of industrial firms studied at Ordnance installations. As early as the summer of 1940, for example, six Ordnance employees were trained at the Sperry Gyroscope Company on the maintenance of antiaircraft fire control instruments. A few months later five inspectors and three chemists, who were to be stationed at the Radford Ordnance Works when it was completed, were in training at the Carney's Point plant of the DuPont Company. This process was reversed when Ordnance undertook to train small numbers of operating personnel of the companies that were to operate the new munitions plants under construction in 1940 and 1941. As reservoirs of production know-how, the arsenals and depots trained engineers, chemists, and other technicians selected by the contractors to operate GOCO plants.[37]

One of the most important phases of arsenal training began in the summer of 1940 when courses were instituted for inspectors who were to serve in the districts. Each arsenal instructed the trainees assigned to it on those items it normally produced. Picatinny, for example, trained most of the ammunition inspectors; Frankford offered courses on optical instruments, mechanical time fuzes, and ammunition; Rock Island gave instruction in the inspection of mobile artillery carriages, recoil mechanisms, and machine guns. Later, as the districts made arrangements for training their own inspectors at local trade schools and colleges, the arsenal courses were discontinued.[38]

After creation of ASF in March 1942, the many-sided Ordnance program of civilian training became even more varied and elaborate. At Rock Island Arsenal courses were added for administrative specialists, armament maintenance men, field service supervisors, traffic managers, welders, storekeepers, checkers, and foremen.[39] At Frankford training was given to lens grinders, draftsmen, machine operators, engravers, fuze assemblers, and other specialists in related fields. New employees were trained at many installations to become machine operators, and after they were assigned to production work they

[36] Lt. Col. L. H. Campbell, Jr., "Training Apprentice Machinists," *Army Ordnance*, XIX, 114 (1939), 344–46. See also Brig. Gen. N. F. Ramsey, "Arsenal Craftsmen," *Army Ordnance*, XXI, 129 (1941), 367.

[37] Memo, Lt Col Reiff H. Hannum for CofOrd, 27 Jan 41, sub: Tng Programs, OO 352.11/303, DRB AGO. See also ltr, Col Hannum to Lt Col Frank J. McSherry, 18 Nov 40, OO 352.11/104, DRB AGO.

[38] For further details, see Brig. Gen. C. T. Harris, "Civilian Ordnance Training," *Army Ordnance*, XXI, 126 (1941), 600–602.

[39] Hist of Rock Island Arsenal, Vol. II, Ch. 18, OHF. For a brief description of each course, see Hist of Tng Program of FS Div, in Hist of FS Exec Div, Vol. 108, OHF.

were given additional on-the-job training to improve their efficiency. Thousands of laborers and munitions handlers were trained as explosives operators, and large numbers of women were trained for clerical work.

The most important additions to Ordnance training prescribed by ASF during 1942 and 1943 were the "J" programs, originated for use in war plants by the Training Within Industry Service of the War Manpower Commission.[40] ASF installations were directed in August 1942 to introduce the Job Instructor Training (JIT) course to teach supervisors how to give on-the-job instruction to their subordinates. All supervisors were to be given the JIT course before the end of the year and then, beginning in January 1943, they were to be given the second of the War Manpower Commission courses, Job Relations Training (JRT). JRT dealt with such basic elements of personnel management as stimulating job pride, adjusting grievances, and maintaining discipline. When this program was completed in June, the third phase of supervisor training, Job Methods Training (JMT) was begun. JMT was a program of work simplification designed to show supervisors how to analyze jobs and devise more efficient work patterns.[41]

Of all war production plants, Picatinny Arsenal took the lead in pioneering the JMT course. It conducted the first in-plant JMT Institute in the United States, in October 1942, and thus became the first plant in the country to hold institutes in all three "J" courses. During the following year Picatinny conducted a greater number of ten-hour JMT courses and trained a larger number of supervisors than any other war plant. "From the standpoint of the resulting conservation of manpower, materials, and machine capacity," wrote the author of the JMT course to Col. William E. Larned of Picatinny, "your savings are far ahead of any other private or governmental installation. From every angle your program is far and away the most outstanding in America."[42]

Much of the training given in late 1943 and early 1944 was guided by the replacement schedules drawn up at all Ordnance establishments to provide for the orderly replacement of men inducted into military service. Because the War Department in 1941 adopted the policy of asking local draft boards to grant occupational deferments to its civilian employees only in the most unusual circumstances, Ordnance employees were drafted at a rapid rate after Pearl Harbor. At Rock Island Arsenal, to take one example, 2,500 employees entered military service during 1942 and an equal number during 1943. And, in terms of production line requirements, men were taken into the armed forces in a haphazard fashion, the selection depending more upon their age, physical qualifications, and family status than upon the nature of their employment. To remedy this situation, Frankford Arsenal early in 1943 pioneered the replacement schedule plan for the War Department and demonstrated the practicability of working out long in advance a systematic program to train draft-exempt replacements for men likely to be called for military service. The selective service boards were then requested

[40] SOS Cir 45, 19 Aug 42, sub: Job Instructor Tng Program, DRB AGO.

[41] ASF Civ Pers Memo 77, 3 Aug 43, DRB AGO. For a detailed description of the course as given in one Ordnance district, see Hist of San Francisco Ord Dist, Vol. IV, OHF. The entire volume is devoted to JMT.

[42] Ltr, Clifton Cox, Training Within Industry Regional Dir, to CO Picatinny Arsenal, 21 Oct 43, in Hist of Picatinny Arsenal, Admin Gp, Oct–Dec 43, p. 61, OHF.

to grant temporary occupational deferments, on an individual basis, until replacements for the men could be trained. After replacement schedules were prepared throughout the Department in 1943, each Ordnance installation could plan well in advance for the replacement of men to be taken into the armed forces.[43]

By April 1945, when the European phase of the war was about to end, nearly every activity of the Ordnance Department was covered by a civilian training course of some kind. There were 355 distinct courses being given to employees, most of them of the on-the-job type, and nearly 17,500 persons completed a course during the month. The course producing the most graduates in April 1945 was that on general safety procedures; next in order came orientation and induction training, work simplification, and work measurement.[44]

Statistics on training are apt to be misleading because they were usually kept in terms of the number of persons who completed courses, regardless of the length of the courses or the level of their difficulty. Ordnance courses ranged in length from the ten-hour "J" courses to the four-year programs of apprentice training, and varied in difficulty from typing and truck driving to lens grinding and contract termination. The number of course completions was surprisingly high because many Ordnance employees, probably most of them, completed more than one course of instruction during the war, and some completed a dozen or more. Although Ordnance had only 262,772 employees on its payroll at the peak of its strength, it has been estimated that Ordnance workers chalked up more than 700,000 "completions" between August 1942 (when maintenance of statistics on training began) and August 1945.[45] Although there was occasional criticism during the war that training was overemphasized and "overorganized," and that it interfered with production when workers were taken from their jobs to spend hours in a classroom, the prevailing opinion was that time spent on training was more than reclaimed in increased production, higher morale, and reduced turnover.[46]

Employee Relations

Employee relations were of greater importance to Ordnance during World War II than during the years of peace chiefly because wartime conditions of employment were far different from those before 1941. As the war years brought a "worker's market" in which jobs were plentiful and workers were scarce, the threat of dismissal no longer held any terror for the average employee. He knew that he could find another job in a few days, and he also knew that his employer was eager to avoid the expense resulting from high turnover rates. The problems of management were further complicated as the war years brought into Ordnance employment thousands of men and women with little or no previous work experience, and with little understanding of the need for strict observance of rules and regulations.

When ASF came into the picture in the spring of 1942, there was ample evidence of the need for improved employee rela-

[43] (1) Hist of Frankford Arsenal, IV, 11. (2) Hist of Rock Island Arsenal, p. 289. Both in OHF.

[44] Ord Admin, Pt. 3, pp. 579-80, OHF.

[45] *Ibid.*, p. 569.

[46] (1) Intervs with George DeCamp and others in Civ Pers Div, 1950. (2) Ltr, CO Letterkenny Ord Depot to CofOrd, 30 Mar 44, sub: Evaluation of Tng, OO 353/7109, DRB AGO.

tions at many Army installations. The turnover rate among ASF employees was described as being "nothing less than astronomical. Workers left their jobs wholesale. Out of every 10 people hired, only four or even fewer would remain . . . for as much as one year." [47] Ordnance was no exception to the rule. At Springfield Armory, for example, 4,700 persons were hired between December 1941 and June 1942, but 1,600 resigned during the same period. At Picatinny and Frankford Arsenals the annual turnover rate during 1942 approached 50 percent.[48]

A relatively high turnover rate during the hectic months following the attack on Pearl Harbor was to be expected as workers adjusted themselves to new conditions of employment and shopped around in the worker's market, but in the summer of 1942 the ASF personnel division decided that the rate was excessive and that the time had come to do something about bringing it down to reasonable proportions. One of the first steps taken in this direction was the adoption of a standard procedure for handling employee grievances at all ASF installations. This was the same procedure that had been in force in Ordnance for many years. It provided that an employee, acting by himself or through a representative, should normally take up his complaint first with his immediate supervisor, and that all supervisors should try to straighten out misunderstandings or difficulties presented to them.[49]

In dealing with complaints, personnel administrators in Ordnance and at ASF headquarters recognized that most grievances were of a minor nature but were, like a stone in one's shoe, no less irritating for their small size. They recognized, too, that the great majority of such grievances could be satisfactorily handled at the lowest or next-to-lowest level of supervision if the supervisors had sufficient training and aptitude to do the job. Throughout the ASF during 1942 and 1943, therefore, intensive efforts were made to train supervisors, through the "J" programs, to become more adept in dealing with their subordinates.

The need for care and intelligence in introducing new Ordnance employees to their jobs was best illustrated in the employment of inexperienced women workers. Many women who had never before done any work outside their own homes volunteered for war work and then found themselves unceremoniously assigned to jobs in huge shops or warehouses before they had an opportunity to get their bearings. The most that was done for them was to put in their hands a small pamphlet containing the rules and regulations of the installation. On far too many occasions the women thus hastily put to work found the transition from home to factory too difficult to make and resigned at the end of their first week. The time saved at the expense of proper induction and preassignment training was thus lost as the whole cycle of recruitment and assignment had to be repeated with others.[50]

More attention was also given to the proper placement of new employees. In the early stages of war mobilization, when workers were recruited with all possible

---

[47] ASF Manual M-216, Sec. X.

[48] (1) Hist of Springfield Armory, Vol. II, Book III, p. 153. (2) Hist of Frankford Arsenal, Vol. III, Exhibit M. (3) Hist of Picatinny Arsenal, Admin Gp, Vol. I, Pt. 2, pp. 110–11. All in OHF.

[49] ODO 80–44, 16 Jun 44, sub: Employee Grievance Procedure, OHF. (2) ASF Cir 149, 20 May 44. (3) ASF Cir 171, 6 June 44. Last two in DRB AGO.

[50] Constance McL. Green, *The Role of Women as Production Workers in War Plants in the Connecticut Valley* (Northampton, 1946), p. 28.

speed and when thousands of inexperienced men and women were put on the payroll overnight, careful testing and placement of each individual had been impossible. "The tendency was to take all comers," stated the ASF personnel manual. "The employee was placed on the working force in the hope that in one way or another he would gravitate toward the right job and stay with it."[51] Placement in the Ordnance Department was more highly developed than it was in other branches of the Army because of the technical nature of most Ordnance activities, but it still left much to be desired in the spring of 1942. At Springfield Armory, for example, there was no aptitude testing or preshop training for men during the 1941–42 period.[52] Early in 1943 an Ordnance-wide campaign was launched to give more consideration to the placement of workers. Personnel staffs were directed to draw up a job description for every position, keep a record of each employee's qualifications, and assign each worker to the job for which he was best qualified. This campaign was in line with the provisions of the ASF policy statement of August 1942 and probably contributed as much toward promoting good employee relations and reducing turnover as any other single step taken by the Ordnance Department during the war.

Experience soon demonstrated that in the work history of the average employee, in Ordnance and throughout ASF, two days were of crucial importance—his first day on the job, and the day he quit work. Ordnance personnel administrators concentrated a large share of their efforts on those two days. The first day, or more often the first week, was devoted to the induction and training of the new employee so that he would get started on the right foot. The last day, or the day on which he resigned, the employee was called in for an "exit interview" that had a dual purpose: to persuade him not to leave his job, and to discover what factors were causing him to leave. The employee was encouraged to speak freely and frankly about his reasons for leaving. It was sometimes felt that he chose to conceal his real reasons with a plausible excuse that would forestall further questioning, but the skillful interviewer was often able to discover the underlying causes of dissatisfaction. Among the reasons most frequently given for leaving Ordnance employment—excluding calls to military service—were acceptance of a better job, ill health, and transportation difficulties. Many workers took jobs elsewhere that offered higher pay, entailed less dangerous work, or were more convenient to home. Many Ordnance arsenals, depots, and plants were of necessity situated at remote points, causing workers to make long trips by bus or automobile every day. A large number of women workers reported that they were quitting because of ill health caused by the heavy work to which they were not accustomed, or because they were needed at home to take care of children. When the exit interviews revealed that employees were resigning because of specific conditions within the establishment that could be remedied, steps were taken to eliminate the conditions.

Scientists employed at Ordnance laboratories deserve at least brief mention in this section on employee relations, if only for the fact that a rather comprehensive

[51] ASF Pers Officer's Handbook on Employee Relations, ASF Manual M-216, Sec. X. See also ASF Ann Rpt 1944, p. 312.

[52] Hist of Springfield Armory, Vol. II, Book 3, pp. 170–72, OHF.

survey of their job attitudes was made at the end of the war.[53] To some extent, also, the attitudes of the laboratory scientists were typical of professional workers throughout the Ordnance Department. When the scientists spoke confidentially, and under the cloak of anonymity, they were frequently vitriolic in condemning certain aspects of their employment. A large proportion of them, including more than half the small group of Ph.D's, planned to leave the Ordnance Department after the war ended. Many of these men chose not to remain with Ordnance because they felt there was no assurance that Congress would support an adequate postwar military research program, but all were influenced to some extent by the conditions of employment in Ordnance as they had experienced them during the war. The complaints most frequently voiced were: (1) salaries were too low; (2) there was too much red tape, too many "channels" causing delay and frustration; and (3) professsional men were not treated with sufficient dignity and trust. Among scientists with high professional ratings, one of the grounds for dissatisfaction was the Army-wide practice of placing commissioned officers in top positions—and then transferring them as soon as they became familiar with their jobs.[54] Many scientists resented having to take orders from officers with less experience and less professional education than themselves, and then being denied personal recognition for their own achievements. Complaints of a related nature stemmed from the practice of placing research laboratories at the manufacturing arsenals under control of the arsenal commanders. The arsenals were naturally production minded and did not always evince full sympathy for the research problems of the laboratory. As one scientist described the situation, "It's like living with your mother-in-law. You are welcome, but you're not free." [55]

Many of the complaints made by the scientists were of a petty nature, hardly worthy of professional men holding responsible positions. Many of them centered around being required to observe routine regulations, which the scientists considered as properly applicable only to clerical workers. Research scientists, for example, objected vehemently to punching a time clock and being held to a rigid lunch schedule. Their complaints suggest that some arsenal and laboratory administrators may have shown poor judgment in not allowing more freedom of action to the scientists, many of whom were eager to work overtime on their research projects, and that the scientists themselves might have shown greater willingness to accept the inevitable restrictions imposed by employment in a large organization. Whatever judgment of the situation may be offered, the fact remains that for large numbers of scientific workers Ordnance employment was not sufficiently attractive to hold them after the war.[56]

---

[53] Where Do We Go from Here: A Survey of Organization and Working Conditions at Six Arsenal Laboratories, OHF.

[54] A Survey of Ballistic Research Laboratory, p. 11, OHF. "Military officers with little special knowledge of the work are given responsible positions here," it was reported. "They aren't interested in the projects because they don't expect to stay long. They are like students at school who know they won't have to take the exams."

[55] Where Do We Go From Here, p. 49, OHF.

[56] Nearly a hundred complaints, ranging from the need for more Coca-Cola machines to lack of opportunities for professional advancement, are described in A Survey of Ballistic Research Laboratory, OHF. See also The Place of the Ordnance Arsenal Laboratories in Government Research and Development, OHF.

At the end of World War II the War Department was in a far stronger position, as far as civilian personnel management was concerned, than it had been when the Japanese attacked Pearl Harbor. In few, if any, other areas did the Army make greater progress during World War II. Starting in 1938 and 1939, when it was generally considered to have the least progressive civilian personnel program in the federal government, the War Department made steady progress until it eventually achieved what one Ordnance official labeled "the best personnel program you will find anywhere—bar none." And to the development of this enlightened personnel policy the Ordnance Department made a substantial contribution.

Experience during World War II demonstrated the need for decentralization of War Department personnel administration in time of war, and amply justified the Ordnance Department's unremitting efforts to break down the tight centralized control maintained until August 1942 by the War Department Civilian Personnel Division. Concurrently, World War II experience demonstrated the need for a broad and continuing program to train civilian personnel officers for field installations. At the end of the war the decentralization policy was so firmly established, and was buttressed by such a large force of trained personnel administrators in the field, that it was carried over into the postwar years as a permanent feature of War Department policy.

The months of August and September 1942 formed a great divide in the history of War Department and Ordnance personnel management. These were the months during which the newly formed ASF began to take positive steps to correct the deficiencies in personnel administration revealed by the New York field survey. In August 1942 War Department Orders "M" appeared, delegating to the three major commands—ASF, AAF, and AGF—most of the authority formerly concentrated in the personnel division of the Office of the Secretary of War. Also in August came the publication of a civilian personnel policy for the entire ASF and the launching of an intensive program of supervisory training under the "J" programs. In September 1942 the Ordnance program to conserve manpower was given added impetus, and the commanders of all field installations were directed to employ a larger proportion of women. At the same time, plans were made to standardize wage administration throughout the ASF along the lines dictated by Ordnance experience.

To measure the progress made in civilian personnel management in the War Department during World War II, one need only compare the report of the New York field survey of May 1942 with the conditions of civilian employment that prevailed throughout the Army in the spring of 1945. Although the Ordnance Department at the beginning of the war was more advanced in personnel matters than some other branches of the Army, the New York survey revealed that many of its practices were still in an embryonic state. Its training, safety, and wage administration programs were well established before Pearl Harbor, but the induction and placement procedures at many Ordnance installations left much to be desired. Stimulated and encouraged by enlightened supervision of the ASF personnel division, and given greater freedom of action by the decentralization order of August 1942, Ordnance made steady progress and by 1945 had a well-rounded personnel program administered by a well-trained staff.

CHAPTER VII

Research and Development 1919–40

The Westervelt Board Report

No lesson of World War I was plainer to the United States Army than its need of modern ordnance. Aviation, signal equipment, chemical warfare materials, medical and engineer supplies must also receive study, but the Army's need of more effective artillery was the most obvious want of all. Accordingly, a month after the Armistice General Peyton C. March, Chief of Staff, appointed a board of seven officers to draw up recommendations for field artillery for the U.S. Army of the future. Special orders directed the board to convene in France at the earliest practicable time "to make a study of the armament, calibers and types of matériel, kinds and proportion of ammunition, and methods of transport of the artillery to be assigned to a Field Army." [1] The board was to map out a comprehensive development program. Headed by Brig. Gen. William I. Westervelt from whom it derived its name, the board first met at Chaumont, France, on 12 January 1919. It accumulated its data over a period of months through interviews with French, Italian, and British artillery experts, examination of both Allied and enemy matériel, inspections of plants, and conferences with American generals who had commanded line troops in the AEF. Returning to Washington in April, the "Caliber Board" digested its findings, consulted with the chiefs of Ordnance, Coast Artillery, Field Artillery, and Chemical Warfare, and submitted its report on 5 May 1919. The report was approved by the Chief of Staff on 23 May of that year.[2]

This broad, penetrating survey showed that, as General Westervelt expressed it, "every item of the hardware of war needed improvement"—every type of gun, howitzer, projectile, gun mount, carriage, and vehicle that the U.S. Army used.[3] The report outlined clearly the mission of divisional, corps, and army artillery, pointed out the distinctive problems of each, and

---

[1] WD SO 289-0, 11 Dec 18. The impetus for the study came in part from the Chief of Field Artillery who, making suggestions as to the leading problems and how to approach them, submitted a list of seven qualified officers. (Memo, CofFA for CofS, 5 Dec 18, OO 334.3/W, NA.) The seven were Brig. Gen. William I. Westervelt, Brig. Gen. Robert E. Callan, Brig. Gen. William P. Ennis, Col. James B. Dillard, Col. Ralph McT. Pennell, Lt. Col. Webster A. Capron, and Lt. Col. Walter P. Boatwright. The personnel formed a nice balance between using arms and Ordnance. Field Artillery was represented by General Ennis and Colonels Pennell and Capron; Coast Artillery by General Callan and Colonel Boatwright; and Ordnance by General Westervelt and Colonel Dillard.

[2] William I. Westervelt, "A Challenge to American Engineers," *Army Ordnance,* I, 2 (1920), 59–62, 64.

[3] Westervelt, *loc. cit.*, p. 62.

made definite recommendations.[4] The last three sections analyzed the existing inadequacies of American ordnance. The section that dealt with projectiles emphasized the need for a great variety of developments in fuzes, powders, and shell. The board noted: "There are investigations under way by the Ordnance Department covering this entire subject and the Board recommends that these be continued. It is to be expected that the subject will require extended investigation and is one which can only be adequately handled by a continuing technical body."[5]

The heart of the report was Section IV, "Types of Artillery Recommended: Ideal and Practical." For each class of artillery the board described the characteristics of an "ideal" weapon, and then advised what should be used as a "practical" one. The "ideal" light field artillery piece was of about 3-inch caliber, on carriage, using fixed ammunition and smokeless, flashless propellant—one charge for 11,000 yards, a second for 15,000 yards—time fuzes for shrapnel, and superquick and selective-delay fuzes for shell. It should have maximum ballistic efficiency and maximum bursting charge, the same ballistics for shell and shrapnel and for every type of ammunition used, and a maximum rate of fire of twenty rounds per minute. While work should proceed toward the ideal weapon, the board set as a practical measure the use of 50 percent 75-mm. guns, Model 1916, and 50 percent French 75-mm's. The difference between the "ideal" and the "practical" typified the distance Ordnance designers had to span in nearly all Westervelt projects. A partial summary of recommendations is given in Table 10.

For artillery transport, the board advocated immediate motorization of all weapons larger than 75-mm. guns and 4-inch howitzers. It proposed immediate adoption of the 5-ton and the 10-ton artillery tractors as standard vehicles and the exclusive use of four-wheeled-drive cargo trucks for artillery supply and ammunition trains. In addition to recommending ample reserves of spare parts and adequate repair facilities, the board cited certain particular needs: supply trucks furnished with suitable tool chests and cabinets; immediate manufacture of 150 standard 3-ton, four-wheeled-drive trucks to motorize one regiment of 155-mm. howitzers; caterpillar treads of improved design and construction; artillery tractors with lowered unit ground pressure, improved grousers, and noiseless engine exhausts; waterproofing to allow engines to run submerged for short periods; and a simple form of coupling for towing guns, tractors, or trucks in tandem. Although American mechanical transport appeared to be far ahead of European, the board warned against complacency.[6] Admitting the rapidity of American progress since 1914 when the Ordnance Department began practical experiments with the caterpillar for artillery transport, the report stated:

> Mechanical transport is the prime mover of the future. . . . It is urgent that study

[4] These findings were not approved in entirety by Westervelt, Callan, and Boatwright, who submitted a minority report. The minority view held that organic army artillery was inadvisable and that an artillery reserve was essential not only for the army but also for the corps and division. Rpt, Bd of Officers, 5 May 19, sub: Study of the Armament, Caliber and Types of Materiel . . . to be Assigned to a Field Army (hereafter cited as Caliber Bd Rpt), pp. 61–64, OKD 334.3/1.3, Ord Tech Intel files.

[5] Caliber Bd Rpt, pp. 21–23, OKD 334.3/1.3, Ord Tech Intel files. The Ordnance Committee, set up in July 1919 and working through subcommittees, fulfilled the function of the "continuing technical body."

[6] Caliber Bd Rpt pp. 88–114, OKD 334.3/1.3, Ord Tech Intel files.

TABLE 10—PARTIAL SUMMARY OF CALIBER BOARD REPORT

Class of Artillery	Projectile Weight (Pounds)	Maximum Range (Yards)	Elevation (Degrees)	Traverse (Degrees)	Other Characteristics Desired
Light Field					
3" Gun	20	15, 000	−5 to +80	360	Mechanical transport; 20 rounds per minute.
105-mm. Howitzer	30–35	12, 000	−5 +65	360	Mechanical transport; split-trail carriage.
Medium					
4.7" to 5" Gun	60	18, 000	−5 +80	360	Split-trail carriage; 12,000 lbs. (wheeled), 15,000 (caterpillar); 8 miles per hour; 16 rounds per minute.
155-mm. Howitzer	100	16, 000	−5 +65	360	Split-trail carriage; 8 miles per hour; 5 rounds per minute.
Heavy					
155-mm. Gun	100	25, 000	0 +65	360	Motorized; 6 miles (caterpillar), 12 miles (wheeled).
8" Howitzer	240	18, 000	0 +65	360	Motorized; 4 miles per hour.
Of Greater Power					
194-mm. to 8" Gun	220	35, 000	----------	----------	Same carriage as 155-mm. gun.
9½" Howitzer	400	25, 000	0 +65	360	Caterpillar; 20 tons; 6 miles per hour.
Super Guns (seacoast and field). 8" or 10" Gun	240(8") 510(10")	35, 000	0 +50	360	Universal barbette mount; railway carriages (for all super guns); 50 calibers long; 1 shot per minute.
14" Gun	1, 400	40, 000	0 +50	360	50 calibers long; firing time, 1 hour (prepared position); 8 hours (unprepared).
12" Howitzer	1, 046 700	18, 000 25, 000	+25 +60	360	20 calibers long; 1 hour to occupy field position; railway mount.
16" Howitzer	1, 600	30, 000	+25 +65	360	25 calibers long; railway mount.
AA Guns, Light					
3" Gun	15	----------	0 +80	360	2,600 feet per second initial velocity; caterpillar transport; 12 miles per hour.
4.7" to 5"	45	----------	0 +80	360	2,600 feet per second initial velocity; self-propelled caterpillar; maximum weight 10 tons.
Pack Artillery					
3" Gun	----------	5, 000	0 +45	----------	Use division gun projectiles; telescopic sight.
Infantry Accompanying Gun					
2.5"	10	2, 500	−6 +50	6	2.5 calibers long; maximum weight 300 lbs.; telescopic sight.
Trench Artillery					
6" Mortar	50	4, 000	+40 +65	----------	Great simplicity in design.

In general a smokeless, flashless powder was specified for each weapon.

Source: Caliber Bd Rpt, pars. 29–76, OKD 334.3/1.3, Ord Tech Intel files.

and development be vigorously carried on along these lines, as we are on the verge of changes fully as radical as the introduction of the long recoil field gun carriage, and the country first utilizing the new capabilities opened up by mechanical traction and the caterpillar, will have a great advantage in the next war.[7]

These are only the highlights of the report. The whole was greeted simultaneously with interest, surprise, skepticism, and enthusiasm. General Westervelt in 1920 wrote: "The ideal set by the Board is not an easy one to reach, and I frequently think of the politely amazed look upon the faces of many hardened veterans in high places to whom the Board first revealed its dream of complete motorization."[8] Apart from small arms projects, most of the developments at which the Ordnance Department aimed for the next fifteen years were those outlined in the Westervelt Board report. The postwar innovation whereby not the Ordnance Department but the using arms stated their needs and specified the military characteristics new equipment should have sometimes delayed initiation of new projects, but down into the mid-thirties users and Ordnance Department alike were strongly influenced by Westervelt Board recommendations. Indeed in 1939 and 1940 officers still cited the board as the incontrovertible authority on armament.

Developments in Ammunition

The most complicated task of development confronting the Ordnance Department at the end of World War I lay in the field of ammunition. Combat experience had shown the inadequacies of much of what had been used in 1917–18—inaccuracies, failures, lack of safety features, and a host of needless complexities. But whereas Artillery officers could specify rather exactly what the requirements of guns and vehicles should be, for the development of explosives, propellants, projectiles, and fuzes their recommendations had to be couched in general terms. Here were problems of basic research that ammunition experts themselves had to define, often seeking immediately only interim solutions and waiting till greater knowledge could supply better answers. Hence the ammunition designers had free rein within budgetary limits. Over the twenty years of peace the Ordnance Department dedicated more money to the ammunition program than to any other development work.

Research upon ammunition in the first postwar years was inspired not only by the Caliber Board but also by the necessity of preserving ammunition stored after the Armistice. The latter task involved a series of experiments with methods of determining the stability of smokeless powder, of so storing it as to lengthen the duration of stability, and of drying it more efficiently than by processes formerly used. A good deal of valuable information on these subjects was assembled at Picatinny Arsenal before 1926, notably that on feasibility of the vapor method of drying, which reduced drying time from months or weeks to days.[9] But a more permanent solution of some phases of the powder storage problem would be to develop new nonhygroscopic powders, which because of their chemical composition would not absorb

[7] *Ibid.*, p. 31. Ordnance achievements included development of efficient 5-ton and 10-ton artillery tractors, and heavy mobile repair shops. *Ibid.*, p. 98.

[8] Westervelt, *loc. cit.*, p. 60.

[9] (1) History of Army Ordnance Developmental and Experimental Projects for FY 1920–25 Inclusive (hereafter cited as ODEP), II, 256–91, 479–94, OHF. (2) Interv, 24 Apr 50, with Bruce Anderson, Ammo Sec, R&D Serv.

enough moisture to affect their ballistics or chemical stability even when stored in a damp atmosphere. If at the same time flashless and smokeless qualities could be incorporated, the advantages would be still greater. The search for flashless nonhygroscopic powders, FNH, was accordingly pushed vigorously. The DuPont Company by a special agreement with the Ordnance Department followed one line of investigation, Picatinny Arsenal another, each with considerable success. The peacetime development of a complete line of single-based and double-based nonhygroscopic powders, flashless in many weapons, was one of the most useful accomplishments of the Ordnance Department before 1940.

Meanwhile, other highly important studies went forward on fuzes, on bombs and artillery projectiles, on high explosives and pyrotechnics, on artillery ignition systems, and on improved methods of loading bombs and shells. Special attention was directed toward development of bombs since the relative ineffectiveness of the World War I tear-shaped type and the growing role of air warfare made better bombs imperative. The results of twenty years' work gave the Air Forces of the 1940's a series of cylindrical bombs of greatly increased accuracy and deadliness. Still the number of ammunition projects, all important and frequently interrelated, coupled with the meagreness of funds prevented rapid progress on any one undertaking.[10] In developing artillery ammunition, a particular handicap was the small number of pilot weapons available to test ammunition, for ammunition development could never precede and could only partially parallel development of the weapon for which it was intended. Thus, for example, the abnormal variations in range and velocity that occurred in firing in the low zones with the high-explosive shell M1 designed for the 105-mm. howitzer were not satisfactorily eliminated until rather late in World War II, largely because the 105's were not fired frequently enough during the peace years to provide the data on which to base corrective measures.[11] Nevertheless, while no project could be labeled completed, the work of the ammunition experts between 1919 and 1940 was extremely useful in defining objectives, blocking off blind alleys of research, and carrying forward a number of important investigations.

Perhaps the single most significant achievement was the development of a complete system of artillery fuzes interchangeable in practically all artillery projectiles. The Caliber Board's recommendations emphasized the need of bore-safe fuzes for high-explosive shells and urged reducing the number of types for any particular weapon but did not expressly stipulate combination fuzes or indicate the extent to which the same fuze should be usable in different calibers. The Ordnance Department's work on these problems was along entirely original lines. Design of bore-safe fuzes, so constructed as to prevent detonation of the main charge before the shell had left the gun's muzzle, required a radical departure from World War I safety features and revision of earlier concepts of the quantity of explosive to be used. It was clear that the best way to limit the number of types was to develop combination fuzes, such as combination superquick delayed-action, or

[10] ODEP, II, *passim*, OHF.

[11] (1) Design, Development, and Procurement of Heavy Artillery Ammunition, Nov 44, OHF. (2) Interv, 26 Apr 50, with Robert Marshall, Fuze Sec, Ind Serv.

combination time and superquick, in which a change in setting would make one fuze usable for more than one purpose. One major difficulty was finding designs that would lend themselves to quantity production; during the twenties several types functioned satisfactorily when built in laboratory or experimental shop but proved faulty when produced on a factory basis.[12]

By 1932 several new fuzes had been standardized, but many gaps in any complete system remained. Consequently, that year the Ordnance Department initiated a study of requirements for a series of point-detonating fuzes and arrived at the conclusion that tactical needs demanded four classes of fuzes for high-explosive shell or shrapnel fire, at ground and aerial targets, at both long and short ranges. The study showed the tactical advantages of having all fuzes identical in contour and weight, and designed with setting lugs and threads that would fit all fuze setters and permit both interchangeability in all point-fuzed projectiles and use with all fire control directors and range tables. If time fuzes could be used interchangeably as detonating fuzes in HE shell and as igniting fuzes in shrapnel, and if substantially the same mechanism could be used in all fuzes employing a superquick element, or a delay, powder-train time, mechanical time, or detonator safety element, the simplification for the artilleryman in the field and for the producer alike would be enormous.[13] Upon this difficult task effort was bent from 1934 on. The first satisfactory member of the new "family" of interchangeable artillery fuzes to be completed was a mechanical time fuze (30 seconds), the M43. The second was a combination superquick delayed-action fuze originally issued for use with the 75-mm. pack howitzer, later used with larger calibers. This point-detonating fuze, the M48, adopted in June 1938, was an achievement; unlike the earlier designs of a dual-purpose fuze, it was safe, reliable, easily set, acceptably accurate. In the course of the next two years another superquick delay and a time superquick fuze were adopted as well as a 75-second mechanical time fuze. These five, mechanically and ballistically interchangeable, constituted the series most extensively used during World War II.[14]

Closely allied with fuze development was the redesign of shells. During World War I the U.S. Army had largely depended upon the French for its shells; the only American-designed type was the 3-inch, the shortcomings of which had been apparent. The increased range, greater accuracy, and higher lethality desired in artillery ammunition were to be obtained only by the development of a complete series of shells in which contour, form, and location of the rotating bands, composition of steels calculated to produce the most effective fragmentation, powder charges, and a number of other design features all had to be considered. One early discovery was that elongating and streamlining the shape of the projectile increased the range of a gun without any modification whatsoever in the weapon itself. Yet every change tended to start a chain of new problems. For example, to give projectiles for heavy, mobile artillery the best ballistic shape and maintain stability in flight, designers at first resorted to

[12] ODEP, II, 42–75, OHF.

[13] (1) Ordnance Committee Minutes (OCM) 6808, 18 Feb 28; 90927, 30 Jul 31; 10597, 6 Apr 33. All OCM's are in Ordnance Technical Committee Secretariat files. (2) Ann Rpt CofOrd, 1934, par. 28.

[14] (1) OCM 11364, 29 Mar 34; 11812, 6 Dec 34; 14554, 30 Jun 38; 15133, 29 Jun 39. (2) Interv, 9 May 50, with Robert Cuthill, Ammo Br, Ind Serv.

use of so-called false ogives, that is, light hollow tips. Not only did these thin steel ogives prove hard to manufacture and difficult to secure to the projectile, they also were likely to be dented or injured in shipping. Improved shipping containers met the latter difficulty but the false ogive was nevertheless abandoned for all shells save the 8-inch gun as soon as alternate design progressed further. New testing devices, especially wind tunnels in which the air resistance of variously shaped projectiles could be measured accurately, facilitated all work on shell design. By 1940 standard HE shell had been developed for all weapons from 75-mm. through 240-mm. in a series of projectiles that had the range, accuracy, and killing power sought by the Caliber Board in 1919. Furthermore, small arms ammunition, mortar shells, projectiles for small caliber cannon, and packing of all types had similarly been extensively improved.[15]

Small Arms Projects

Notwithstanding the Ordnance Department's concern to improve artillery and to achieve Westervelt's "complete motorization," development of small arms also absorbed considerable time and money. Perhaps, indeed, before 1936 design of a semiautomatic rifle netted more attention than larger weapons. This concentration of effort upon a small arms project is probably partly attributable to its long prewar history. As early as 1900 the Chief of Ordnance had proposed design of a semiautomatic rifle, and from 1901 to 1916 a great deal of work had been expended on various experimental models, both foreign and American. It was only logical to resume this work which, though interrupted by the war, appeared to be well along in 1919.[16] Doubtless at that time no small arms expert would have believed that acceptance of a suitable model would take another seventeen years. The course of events leading up to adoption of the Garand semiautomatic rifle is worth review because it well illustrates the long-drawn-out process of getting matériel standardized.

In October 1919 John C. Garand went from the Bureau of Standards to the Springfield Armory on express assignment to design a semiautomatic rifle. The problem occupied other designers too, notably Capt. Julian S. Hatcher and John D. Pedersen. With Pedersen, the Department entered into formal contract. The characteristics required for an acceptable design included weight as close to 8 pounds as possible and not in excess of 8.5; caliber as close as possible to .30, with .276 the mimimum; muzzle velocity of at least 2,450 feet per second; and accuracy up to 800 yards. As the result of careful tests on several competing models in 1920–21, the Ordnance Committee in 1923 recommended that twenty-four Garand rifles be made for test by the Infantry and Cavalry. Informed Ordnance technicians were optimistic that acceptance would not be long delayed; in February 1924 General Williams told a House subcommittee that the Ordnance Department had a semiautomatic rifle that promised to be satisfactory.[17] The twenty-four rifles were completed in the spring of 1925, tested at Aberdeen Proving Ground, and then sent to Fort Benning, Georgia, for further

[15] (1) ODEP, II, 3–40, OHF. (2) Interv, 3 May 50, with Granville M. Taliaferro, Ammo Br, R&D Serv. (3) Ann Rpt CofOrd, 1939, pars. 30, 37–39, 46.

[16] (1) Tests and Development of Semi-Automatic Shoulder Arms, 1900 to 1914, OHF. (2) Ann Rpt CofOrd, 1927, pp. 38–39.

[17] WDAB 1925, HR, p. 1004.

JOHN C. GARAND, *designer of the M1 rifle.*

tests. On the basis of these tests Springfield Armory made some modifications and then shipped the rifles to Fort Benning and to Fort Riley, Kansas, for new trials. Meanwhile, models of Pedersen's design were tested and retested.

Expectations for quick completion of the project were not realized. In the summer of 1929 elaborate formal tests of eight types of semiautomatic rifle narrowed the choice to two, the Garand .276-caliber and the Pedersen .276-caliber. After a thorough canvas of the performance and production problems involved in each rifle, the special board of officers charged with making a final decision voted in favor of the Garand. In the interim Garand had begun work on a .30-caliber rifle and soon found that the light weight believed attainable only in the smaller caliber was possible in the larger. The Chief of Staff, General Douglas MacArthur, at this point insisted upon abandoning work upon the .276 and concentrating upon the .30-caliber. By the next year Garand had completed one experimental .30-caliber model, which successfully passed tests at Aberdeen.[18] The Ordnance Department then ordered eighty of this model manufactured for final test by the using arms. Springfield Armory began manufacture in 1932 and finished the job in 1934. Exhaustive tests of the seventy-five rifles sent to the Infan-

[18] (1) Maj. Gen. Julian S. Hatcher, *The Book of the Garand* (Washington, 1948), p. 110. (2) Hist of Springfield Armory, II, 48, 48a, 48b, OHF. Advocates of Pedersen's design long contended that his was superior to the Garand, but careful study of the official comparative tests does not bear them out.

try and Cavalry Boards showed so many stoppages that the rifles were returned for modifications. After some redesign, Ordnance tests indicated a greatly improved rifle, and 1935 tests by the Infantry and Cavalry Boards substantiated this finding.[19] On 9 January 1936 the weapon was standardized as Rifle, Semiautomatic, M1.

Thirty-five years had elapsed since the initiation of the project, nearly seven since the decision to use a .30-caliber gas-operated type. The slowness of progress was partly caused by lack of any sense of great urgency. Let the new rifle be as nearly perfect as possible before standardizing. Full approval of the using arms was clearly desirable before accepting new or radically modified weapons, but the consequent delays were a drawback. Production problems were still to be solved. By 30 June 1936 design of tools, jigs, and fixtures was 95 percent complete, and, as money for tooling became available, production got under way in the latter half of the year. Yet innumerable small alterations were made during the next two years, and changes in details of design, tests, and actual manufacture proceeded simultaneously. By 1938 only some 2,000 rifles had come off the assembly line.[20] The chief consolation over lack of quantity came from testimony on quality; comments of the troops to whom the first production rifles were issued in August 1937 were immediately enthusiastic—and this despite the high popularity of the predecessor, the Springfield rifle M1903. With the new M1 the average rifleman could fire forty shots a minute, and some soldiers as high as a hundred a minute.[21]

Nevertheless, Congressional criticism of the slowness of work on the M1 and of Ordnance development programs as a whole was sharp. One Congressman observed in 1937, "The war has been over nearly 20 years, and we have 80 semiautomatics in the service; and we are still experimenting."[22] As far back as 1926 the Secretary of War had tried to hasten the process of standardization of all matériel, but in 1935 the Chief of Staff was still concerned with the problem. At its root lay a philosophy of perfection held by many members of the General Staff, the using arms, and the Ordnance Department itself. General Malin Craig, Chief of Staff from 1935 to 1939, proposed a system of yearly standardization and annual revision that resulted in a directive ordering use in the 1937 program of only standardized equipment, and freezing the design of standardized items from the moment cost estimates were submitted until manufacture was concluded.[23] But this measure was at best only an alleviation. Difficulties continued. Unequal rates of standardization of closely related items caused great trouble. For example, the 37-mm. infantry gun and carriage was standardized in 1937 but had no ammunition approved for use.[24] Furthermore, unequal rates of standardization of particular components held up acceptance of end items. Of the search for ideal weapons and the delays that

[19] (1) Ann Rpt CofOrd, 1934, par. 37a; 1935, par. 41a. (2) Hatcher, *op. cit.*, p. 113.

[20] Hist of Springfield Armory, II, 74–75, OHF.

[21] Frank J. Jervey, "The New Semiautomatic Rifle," *Army Ordnance*, XIX, 113 (1938), 147.

[22] WDAB 1938, HR, pp. 372–78.

[23] (1) Maj. Gen. Otto L. Nelson, *National Security and the General Staff* (Washington, 1946), p. 302. (2) OCM 7814, 22 Aug 29, p. 27. (3) Memo, CofS for DCofS, 20 Nov 35, sub: Standardization, AG 111 (11–20–35), DRB AGO. (4) Memo, DCofS for TAG, 25 Nov 35, sub: Standardization, AG 111 (11–25–35), DRB AGO.

[24] Memo, CofOrd for Ord Tech Staff, 1 Jul 37, sub: Procurement Planning and Standardization of Materiel, OO 381/8055, NA.

search entailed, one observer later wrote: "The best is the enemy of the good." [25]

Not all development projects, to be sure, ran an unduly long course. Modification and redesign of machine guns, begun immediately after World War I, made comparatively rapid progress. Efforts to improve the ballistic and cooling characteristics of the earlier .30-caliber Browning machine guns produced the M1919A4 in 1925, while later collaboration of Ordnance, Air Corps, and Colt Company representatives developed the .30-caliber M2, which could be either fixed or flexible and permitted either right- or left-hand feed. Similarly useful work on mounts went forward.[26] Still more significant in terms of World War II was the development of the .50-caliber machine gun. In 1930 when the water-cooled .50-caliber Browning machine gun, M1921A, was standardized, the Coast Artillery was satisfied, but Air Corps, Infantry, and Cavalry still lacked what the Chief of Ordnance described as "suitably specialized Brownings." [27] The Air Corps needed lightness, rapid rates of fire, and right- and left-hand belt feeds; tanks required heavy barrel guns with reliable cooling systems. Neither the using arms nor the Ordnance Department believed it possible to have a single machine gun serve several diverse purposes, but in the two years between 1931 and 1933 Dr. Samuel G. Green of the Ordnance Department succeeded in modifying the Browning to make a single basic gun which, varied by special features for special purposes, could meet requirements for all services. The new model, the .50-caliber M2, was so designed that the operating mechanism was the same for each type of gun. The heavy barrel of the tank gun, the water jacket, sleeve, and 45-inch barrel of the antiaircraft gun, and the lighter parts of the aircraft gun, could each be affixed without modification of the receiver. Here was an outstanding achievement, the benefits of which were to be felt all during World War II; manufacturing, maintenance, and troop training were all eased by this simplification of design.

When the Spanish Civil War provided evidence of the operational value of various items of ordnance, American experts began to question whether the .50-caliber machine gun were not really obsolete both for aircraft and antimechanized use. The using arms therefore ran large-scale tests of the .50-caliber in competition with several types of light automatic cannon. The verdict was in favor of the machine gun.[28]

Artillery Projects

While small arms improvements, albeit slow, were thus reasonably satisfactory, artillery development, the primary objective of the Westervelt Board report, made scant headway. The program of research and development had started off energetically in 1919 and 1920, but with the reduction in funds after 1921 it contracted "to cover reasonably well only infantry, pack and divisional matériel, the smallest cali-

[25] Rpt from London, 31 Jul 40, sub: Mobilization of Industry, Rearmament Policies, 2724-A38/12 IG 6620, G-2 file.

[26] (1) Lt Col Emanuel Schugar, Mr. William H. Davis, and Maj Berkeley R. Lewis, sub: United States Machine Guns, Caliber .30 and .50, PSP 36, pp. 21, 48, OHF. (2) Ann Rpt CofOrd, 1925, p. 37; 1927, par. 60.

[27] Ann Rpt CofOrd, 1930, *passim*. For earlier work upon .50-caliber machine guns see: (1) PSP, 36, p. 25, OHF; (2) Ann Rpt CofOrd, 1926, par. 54, and 1927, par. 57; (3) Proceedings Coast Arty Bd, 15 May 23, sub: Project 82, Test of .50-caliber MG, OO 472.54/1143, NA; (4) Proceedings Coast Arty Bd, 17 Jan 25, sub: Project 324, Mount for Cal. .50 MG, OO 473.93/572, NA; and (5) OCM 4425, 29 Jan 25.

[28] (1) PSP 36, pp. 23, 30-32, 58-60, OHF. (2) Interv with Dr. Samuel G. Green, 27 Jun 49.

THE 75-MM. GUN M1923E. *This is the improved model.*

ber of antiaircraft matériel and one type of tank."[29] Corps, army, and seacoast artillery projects, relegated to second place, scarcely moved forward at all. When, for example, tests of 240-mm. howitzer matériel, conducted at Fort Bragg, North Carolina, in 1924 and 1925, showed the need of modifications, the work was indefinitely postponed till money should be available.[30]

The smaller calibers fared somewhat better. Completion of a satisfactory 75-mm. mortar, the 1922E, was a source of special gratification, inasmuch as its predecessor, the Stokes mortar used in World War I, had proved dangerous to the user. The new mortar had a 50 percent greater muzzle velocity, 150 percent greater range, and fired a standard artillery-type shell with fragmentation superior to that of the Stokes mortar.[31] Ordnance engineers also took pride in the design and manufacture of a 75-mm. gun to supersede the French 75, which the AEF used in World War I. Between 1920 and 1925 the Ordnance Department spent over $500,000 on this assignment and turned out eight different models. After thorough testing by the Field Artillery, the 1923E with split-trail carriage was standardized in 1926, and the

[29] Ann Rpt CofOrd, 1924, p. 11.

[30] Ann Rpt CofOrd, 1925, pp. 14–15.

[31] (1) WDAB 1927, HR, pp. 278–79. (2) Ann Rpt CofOrd, 1927, par. 63. (3) ODEP, I, 29–30; II, 20, OHF.

Most of the trouble with the Stokes mortar came from the fuze, which was not bore safe. Caliber Bd Rpt, p. 21, OKD 334.3/1.3, Ord Tech Intel files.

next year the Field Artillery received its first battery of these new 75's.[32] As aircraft assumed a larger role, attention focused on antiaircraft weapons, particularly a 3-inch gun. Joint antiaircraft exercises held yearly after 1925 by the Air Corps, Signal Corps, Corps of Engineers, Coast Artillery Corps, and Ordnance Department gave opportunity to test all features of new matériel. The performance of the 3-inch antiaircraft gun, standardized in 1926, and of new computers, searchlights, and sound-locator systems was considered good, although the percentage of hits on aerial targets remained low. In the manufacture of the 3-inch gun, Watertown Arsenal applied for the first time in production the process of autofrettage or radial expansion. While French producers had long used this process, improvements in the method devised by arsenal engineers produced a superior forging so quickly and economically that the technique was soon applied to manufacture of other guns. Another innovation was the use of removable liners on the 3-inch gun, a scheme that the Chief of Ordnance estimated as saving 50 percent of the cost of retubing by earlier processes.[33] But since the gun had to be returned to the arsenal to have the liner replaced, the advantage of the system during World War II was nil.

These achievements were only a fraction of what Ordnance Department plans encompassed. Modernization of existing guns and carriages about 1930 was given precedence over development of new with the result, deplored by many officers, that design of new matériel was brought practically to a standstill for some years.[34] The scope of research and development work on artillery before 1940 is perhaps best shown by sketching the progress on four items. The choice of the 75-mm. pack howitzer, the 37-mm. antitank gun, and the 105-mm. and 240-mm. howitzers is based upon the contemporary importance attached to the first two and upon the faith combat troops later placed in the last two.

75-mm. Pack Howitzer

The 75-mm. pack howitzer belongs to the specialized group of weapons assigned for use in mountainous country where motorized or horse-drawn artillery cannot go. Easy disassembly for packing on muleback is essential. Before World War I the Ordnance Department had spent a good deal of effort designing a mountain gun better than the English Vickers–Maxim 2.95-inch then in use, but the project was dropped when it was apparent that the AEF would have no use for mountain guns. In 1919 the Westervelt Board, reviving the project, pronounced a pack howitzer to be "one of the items of artillery in most urgent need of development."[35] The ideal weapon should have a caliber of about 3 inches, possible elevation of 45 degrees, a minimum range of at least 5,000 yards, and should be capable of being packed in four separate loads of about 225

[32] (1) ODEP, I, 87, 101, OHF. (2) Ann Rpt CofOrd, 1926, par. 59; 1927, par. 66.

[33] (1) APG, Rpt of AA Exercises by 61st CA (AA) and Ord Pers at APG, 7 Sep–8 Nov 26, pp. 1–4, 58–59. (2) APG, Rpt of AA Exercises . . . 1927, pp. 58–66; 1928, pp. 99–107, 121–38; 1929, pp. 56–57, 63–64; 1930, p. 29, charts facing pp. 30, 51. Both in NA.

For Congressional interest in antiaircraft tests see: WDAB 1929, HR, pp. 519–23; Ann Rpt CofOrd, 1925, pars. 62, 104; 1926, pars. 92, 93; and ODEP, I, 84, 212, OHF.

[34] Memo, Maj J. H. Wallace, FA, for Chairman Ord Tech Committee, 13 Dec 34, sub: Preliminary Estimates for FY 1937, Project 5-R&D, AG 111 (12–13–34), NA.

[35] Caliber Bd Rpt, pars. 70–71, OKD 334.3/1.3, Ord Tech Intel files.

THE 75-MM. PACK HOWITZER M1920. *The tube load is shown here; the recuperator and other four loads are packed similarly.*

pounds each. A first postwar model, the M1920 which incorporated these features, was soon found unsatisfactory, chiefly because recuperator, piston rod, and trail were inadequate.[36] The next six years saw intensive work on models designed to correct these weaknesses and to furnish a mountain gun at least as powerful as new foreign types. Greater range was particularly desired. The weapon standardized in 1927 as the 75-mm. Pack Howitzer M1 had a range of 9,200 yards and weighed 1,269 pounds in firing position. It took rank as one of the most efficient artillery weapons yet devised.[37] The Chief of Field Artillery asserted: "It is a remarkable weapon with a great future . . . . In its adaptability under pack it has exceeded any expectations which could reasonably have been held considering the power of the weapon."[38] Some modifications, chiefly of the recoil mechanism, and a new carriage were completed during the thirties.

[36] (1) *Ibid.* (2) OCM 1621, 16 Aug 21.

[37] E. C. Goebert, "Our New Pack Artillery," *Army Ordnance,* XIII, 75 (1932), 144–50. Maj. Jonathan W. Anderson, FA, had submitted a summary of foreign weapons in May 1922 upon which the Ordnance Committee based its decisions to redesign the American model. See: (1) memo, Maj Anderson, FA representative on Ord Committee, for CofOrd, 4 May 22, sub: Pack Artillery Materiel, with atchd rpt, OO 455.5/133, NA; and (2) OCM 2260, 21 Jul 22; 6407, 12 Aug 27; 6499, 22 Sep 27.

[38] OCM 6407, 11 Aug 27, and incl, ltr, CofFA to CofOrd.

But in spite of faith in the usefulness of this weapon, only thirty-two pack howitzers had been manufactured by 1 July 1940.[39]

37-mm. Antitank Gun

What the ideal future antitank gun should be the Caliber Board made no attempt in its 1919 report to state in detail, for the board assumed that developments of tank armor would necessitate use of a base-fuzed shell, probably of about 75-mm. caliber.[40] It was a singularly prophetic view. While a 37-mm. model for the Infantry was designed and standardized in the late twenties, development of a modern antitank gun was not begun in earnest until 1936. Long before then, European nations had been working on so-called antimechanization weapons. Abroad, stopping the tank was considered the number one military problem. In America as late as the summer of 1931, the Field Artillery Board had announced its continuing confidence in the recommendations of the Caliber Board of twelve years before: .50-caliber machine guns, 37-mm. guns with armor-piercing shot, and 75-mm. guns were suitable means of attacking tanks as built in World War I. "There has been," stated the Field Artillery Board, "no change in armor protection since then to warrant changing the recommendations of the [Caliber] Board."[41]

When the service tests conducted in 1932 convinced both the Field Artillery and the Infantry that the 37-mm. gun, the M2A1, should be marked for obsolescence, the Infantry was left with only an ineffective 1916 37-mm. model. It was another three years before the using arms proposed development of a weapon based upon revised military characteristics. Tests of a Hotchkiss 25-mm. automatic antitank gun during 1935 had produced little useful information. Then in December reports from the military observer in Berlin stirred the Field Artillery and the Infantry to request trial of a German antitank gun that the Rheinmetall Company was offering to foreign governments for test and quantity purchase.[42] This launched the Ordnance Department upon serious study of antimechanization weapons.

After formal request of the Infantry for a new 37-mm. gun and the purchase of a Rheinmetall model for test, Infantry, Field Artillery, and Ordnance spent over a year preparing, revising, and again restating desired military characteristics in keeping with what was feasible.[43] In September 1937 the Chief of Staff injected a note of unexpected urgency in his instructions to the Chief of Ordnance:

> 2. It appears that none of the greater Powers have failed to develop and to have now in use effective anti-tank and intermediate anti-aircraft weapons, while we, on the other hand, have no weapons of this type whatever.
>
> 3. I regard it as of urgent importance that the Ordnance Department concentrate in-

[39] (1) Ltr, CofFA thru CofOrd to TAG, 18 Jan 29, sub: Procurement of 75mm Pack Howitzer Materiel, OO 472.2/626, NA. (2) Ltr, CofOrd to TAG, 10 Apr 30, sub: War Reserve of 75mm Pack Howitzer Ammunition, OO 472.12/1406, NA. (3) OCM 9201, 1 Oct 31 and 11660, 16 Aug 34. (4) Folders in OO 472.2/1801-1950, Oct 39–Apr 40, NA. (5) General Supply Div, FS, Consolidated Supply Rpt, Status of Principal Items of Ord General Supply as of 1 Nov 39 (Form 87), NA.

[40] Caliber Bd Rpt, par. 76, OKD 334.3/1.3, Ord Tech Intel files.

[41] OCM 9145, 27 Aug 31.

[42] (1) OCM 10350, 15 Dec 33; 11397, 5 Apr 34; 11622, 26 Jul 34; 12558, 19 Dec 35. (2) FA Bd Rpt 053-C, 19 Dec 35, NA.

[43] (1) OCM 13348, 14 Jan 37; 13473, 25 Feb 37; 13665, 8 May 37. (2) Ltr, TAG to CofOrd, 30 Aug 37, OO 472.1/3367, NA. (3) Ltr, CofOrd to CofS, 2 Sep 37, sub: Antitank and Antiaircraft Development, OO 472/3371, NA.

THE 37-MM. GUN M1916, *with flash hider attached to barrel.*

tensively on the development of efficient weapons of these two types, putting both of them on an equal first priority, and procuring, or developing something which has already been procured, so that in time of need we may be on a substantially equal footing with a possible enemy.[44]

The program from that moment moved more quickly. The comparison of the German 37-mm. gun with the American experimental model evolved during 1937 appeared to be all in favor of the latter. Where the German gun with a muzzle velocity of 2,650 feet per second would penetrate 1⅝-inch armor plate at 730 yards at normal angle of fire and at 440 yards at a 20 degree angle, the American gun with a muzzle velocity of 2,600 feet per second would penetrate at 1,060 yards and 800 yards respectively. A French 25-mm. and a German 47-mm. gave less satisfactory performance than either 37-mm. The Chief of Infantry therefore recommended that the specifications of the new medium tank then under consideration include armament of the "37-mm. anti-tank gun now being developed by the Ordnance Department."[45] The design that was eventually accepted closely resembled the German Rheinmetall weapon though, by the time the American 37-mm. antitank gun M3 was adopted, the German Army had antitank weapons ranging from 50 to 80-mm., and the Red Army had an excel-

[44] Memo, CofS for CofOrd, 3 Sep 37, sub: Antitank and Intermediate AA Development, OO 472/3373, NA.

[45] Memo, CofInf thru CofOrd for TAG, 16 Nov 37, sub: Characteristics of Medium Tank T5, OI-470.8/550-B, cited in 37-mm Guns M5 and M6, PSP 28, OHF.

lent 45-mm. gun battle-tested in the Spanish Civil War.[46]

The American gun was designed for use not only on tanks but also as a light field gun mounted on its own carriage, adapted to towing either by truck or tractor or by its crew of four men. Hence the Infantry was insistent that the weight of gun and carriage together must not exceed 1,000 pounds. This weight limit precluded a gun of larger caliber. The gun itself was basically one and the same whether mounted on a carriage or in a tank, but because the gun when mounted in a tank had to be shortened six inches, it was redesignated the 37-mm. M5, and later, with a change in the breech mechanism, the M6. The antitank gun M3, for mounting upon the carriage M4, kept a hand-operated breech mechanism. This gun was 6 feet 10.5 inches long, weighed 191 pounds, had a muzzle velocity of 2,600 feet per second, a range of about 12,000 yards, and could fire 25 rounds a minute. Ordnance engineers expended only less effort upon the carriage than upon the gun, inasmuch as the traverse, elevating mechanism, and locking devices were fixed to the carriage.[47] The requirement for ammunition was armor-piercing shot capable of penetrating 1.5 inches of armor on impact 20 degrees from normal at a range of 1,000 yards. By 1938 armor-piercing shot M51 was standardized with tracer, and later also a high-explosive shell with the M38A1 base detonating fuze.[48]

Thus, some four years were devoted to development of the U.S. Army's first antitank gun which, in terms of what the Soviet Union and Germany had ready by 1939, was obsolete before it was standardized. From a military observer in Europe word had come of developments in Germany, and observers in Spain during the Spanish Civil War had opportunity to note the outstanding performance of the Russian 45-mm. antitank gun. Yet the decision to push the 37-mm. was not rescinded. In August 1938, before the Ordnance Department had proceeded far with procurement, the War Department issued explicit instructions to the Chief of Ordnance:

> 1. The Infantry is designated as the most interested using arm for the 37mm antitank gun under AR 850-25.
>
> 2. No development funds will be expended by the Ordnance Department during the Fiscal Years 1939 or 1940 in the development of antimechanized weapons of larger than 37mm caliber. If the necessity for an antitank gun of larger than 37mm caliber develops, the arm responsible for its development will be designated at that time.[49]

This decision of the General Staff, closing the door to alternative design, was deplored by many Ordnance officers. The chief of the Artillery Branch of the Manufacturing Division from 1937 to 1939 later stated:

> The Ordnance Department was well aware that the 37mm gun was totally inadequate as an antitank gun, and many and repeated efforts were made to convince the various interested using services personnel of this fact.
>
> The Infantry personnel were very much impressed with the compact design of the Rheinmetall 37 and at one time in fact demanded a duplicate. The deciding criterion was the overall weight . . . 850 pounds.

[46] (1) Catalogue of Standard Ord Items, Comparison of American, German, and Japanese Ordnance, II, 156–57. (2) Dept of the Army Pamphlet 30–2, "The Soviet Army," Jul 49, p. 22.

[47] OCM 14572, 14 Jul 38; 14762, 27 Oct 38; 14824, 15 Dec 38; 15404, 10 Oct 39; 16197, 22 Oct 40; 16279, 19 Nov 40.

[48] OCM 14801, 25 Nov 38; 15105, 15 Jun 39.

[49] Ltr, TAG to CofOrd, 11 Aug 38, sub: Responsibility for Development of Antitank Guns and of Tactical Doctrine for Their Use, OO 472.1/1736, NA.

This was considered the maximum that four men could comfortably wheel over the ground.

It is my opinion that all of the early artillery of World War II . . . suffered from the continued insistence by the using arms on mobility even at the expense of striking power.[50]

This testimony leads to the conclusion that General Williams' scheme of allowing the using arms to have the final say about types of equipment had been carried to an extreme where Ordnance experts could no longer greatly influence important decisions. Yet a proposal of the Field Artillery in December 1938 indicates that the Ordnance Department missed an opportunity partially to redeem the error imposed by the Infantry demand for a light mobile gun and the consequent directive to design nothing larger. The Chief of Field Artillery, citing observers' information on the antitank guns being built in Europe, requested that the War Department's instructions be rescinded and a more powerful weapon be produced for the Field Artillery. The proposal was for a truck-drawn weapon weighing about 1,500 pounds with a muzzle velocity sufficient to penetrate 2.5-inch armor at impact 20 degrees from normal at a range of 1,000 yards. But the Chief of Ordnance objected that the introduction of an additional weapon with new types of ammunition would complicate production and supply, that the 75-mm. howitzer and 75-mm. field gun effectively supplemented the 37-mm. as antitank weapons, and that the gun requested by the Field Artillery could not weigh less than 2,700 pounds. The Field Artillery withdrew its request.[51] Sixteen months later the Chief of Staff reviewed the question. "It occurs to me," wrote General Marshall in June 1940, "that we should initiate development of a heavier caliber antitank gun than the 37-mm. Reports from abroad indicate that the 37-mm. has been found comparatively ineffective against the heavier type tank armor and that a 47-mm. gun (possibly on a self-propelled mount) may be necessary as an arm for corps and division antiaircraft battalions."[52]

General Wesson's reply evinced no corresponding anxiety. He repeated the substance of his earlier statement that for its weight the 37-mm. antitank gun was very effective; it would penetrate the armor on American light and medium tanks. The 47-mm., a study of which had been conducted in 1939, was not enough more powerful than the 37-mm. to justify development. At least a 57-mm. would be needed, and in view of the existence of the 75-mm. field gun, work on a 57-mm. seemed uncalled for. The 37-mm. supplemented by the 75-mm. with armor-piercing ammunition appeared to be adequate, though perhaps a more powerful gun might be needed to combat heavy tanks.[53] In conclusion he declared that the best way to supply self-propelled antitank artillery was to mount antitank guns on tanks.[54] Six weeks later an observer in

[50] Ltr, Col Steven L. Conner to author, 16 Jan 50, OHF.

[51] (1) Memo, CofFA thru CofOrd for TAG, 6 Dec 38, sub: Antitank Gun of Caliber Larger than 37mm. (2) *Ibid.*, 1st Ind, CofOrd for TAG, 12 Dec 38. (3) *Ibid.*, 3d Ind, CofFA for TAG, 1 Feb 39. All in OO 472.5/9884, NA.

[52] Memo, CofS for ACofS G-4, 3 Jun 40, atchd to memo, ACofS G-4 for CofOrd, 6 Jun 40, sub: Development of Heavier Antitank Gun . . . , OO 472.1/2821, DRB AGO.

[53] Seventeen months later the 3-inch gun M5 was accepted as the antitank weapon for use against the most heavily armored tanks. OCM 17407, 6 Nov 41. See Ch. X, below.

[54] Memo, CofOrd for ACofS G-4, 7 Jun 40, sub: Employment of Antitank Artillery and AA Artillery in Antimechanized Defense, OO 472/3674, DRB AGO.

London was again to protest large-scale production of an "antitank gun whose power does not guarantee success in engaging tanks known to be used by any prospective enemy."[55] But the program for 37-mm. antitank guns continued.[56]

105-mm. Howitzer

In World War I the United States Army had used the 155-mm. howitzer as a divisional artillery piece, but its unsuitabilities for that purpose—its lack of sufficient mobility to be a companion piece to the 75-mm. gun, its wasteful consumption of ammunition, and its lack of volume of fire—combined to convince the Westervelt Board that a howitzer of about 105-mm. caliber should be developed. The reasoning of the board was stated thus:

> The consensus of opinion of artillery officers is that the division artillery missions are best fulfilled by a light field gun and a light field howitzer. . . . There are many instances where the terrain offers such protection to infantry that the field gun cannot bring an effective fire. The howitzer has the great advantage that with a proper set of charges and therefore a choice of trajectories for the same range, protected positions can be chosen for howitzers that guns could not use, and angles of fall on objectives obtained that the normal ammunition of guns would not give. The low muzzle velocity of howitzers admits of their use in harassing fire and allows the use of a projectile double the weight of that of the field gun. Such a howitzer renders excellent service in wire cutting and is a useful projector of gas shells. To insure the mobility required of all divisional artillery, the weight of the howitzer and carriage should not exceed that of the field gun and carriage, or about 4,500 pounds.[57]

The board specified a howitzer mounted on a carriage permitting a vertical arc of fire of from minus 5 degrees to plus 65 degrees and a horizontal arc of fire of 360 degrees. The carriage should be usable interchangeably for either howitzers or divisional light guns. The projectile should weigh about 30 to 35 pounds and should include both shrapnel and shell. A maximum range of 12,000 yards would answer. Semifixed ammunition and zone charges were to be used.

Based upon this recommendation, experienced Field Artillery and Ordnance officers jointly drew up specifications, and in 1920 four carriages and four howitzers were built for test. These models were unsatisfactory. In the course of the next year, at the request of the Field Artillery, a box-trail carriage was designed and tried out with some success, although the Field Artillery Board was unwilling to abandon altogether the split-trail type of carriage because of the wider traverse it permitted. In the meantime, while the Ordnance Department worked upon improved American models of both carriage and howitzer, the Field Artillery tested some of the German 105's, captured in World War I and rechambered to take American ammunition. The using arm's enthusiasm over the German matériel was such that the Field Artillery Board recommended its adoption for service use, but shortage of proper ammunition, the cost of putting the 300 German howitzers into condition, and the lack of uniformity in those on hand from which to prepare drawings for later quantity production led the Chief of Ordnance to protest. The decision of the General Staff was therefore to put the German

[55] Radiogram, London to MID G-2, 21 Jul 40, sub: Selection of Production Types, 2724A38/11, IG 6620, DRB AGO.

[56] See below, Ch. XI.

[57] Caliber Bd Rpt, par. 8, OKD 334.3/1.3, Ord Tech Intel files.

howitzers in storage and have one battery of four new American models manufactured for service test.[58]

For the next three years work upon the 105 was pushed as rapidly as appropriations allowed, for, as the Chief of Ordnance announced in 1926, the development of a satisfactory 105-mm. howitzer was considered the most pressing Ordnance problem. Some $400,000 had been spent upon the project since the end of the war. Cancellation of the requirement of a carriage so constructed as to be interchangeable for gun or howitzer hastened successful design of a carriage, and in January 1928 a split-trail type manufactured at Rock Island Arsenal was standardized as the carriage M1. The howitzer standardized at the same time had a range just under the 12,000 yards desired. A greater deviation from the original specifications was a horizontal traverse of only 45 degrees instead of the 360 degrees stipulated at first. Over-all weight of howitzer and carriage was 3,750 pounds.[59] Before any of this model was produced, modification of the chamber was initiated in order to make possible loading of shrapnel as fixed ammunition. The altered howitzer was called the M2 and officially adopted in 1934. Later, the requirement for shrapnel was canceled.[60]

Fourteen M2 models were manufactured and twelve were issued to the Field Artillery for extended service test between 1928 and 1933. Two were kept at Aberdeen Proving Ground for use in developing ammunition. The howitzer proved satisfactory, but in 1933 the Field Artillery requested redesign of the carriage to provide high-speed characteristics and to eliminate the need of a recoil pit. After thorough study of the problem, design of a new recoil mechanism and of a lighter carriage equipped with pneumatic tires and antifriction bearings began in 1936. Though a satisfactory recoil mechanism was completed in 1939, both experimental carriages had deficiencies. Reduction of weight was particularly important; to effect this, new military characteristics were drawn up. Of the two new models designed according to the revised specifications, the Field Artillery Board in January 1940 pronounced one acceptable if certain minor defects were corrected in production models.[61] The carriage M2 was accordingly standardized on 28 March 1940.

Thirteen of the existing fourteen M1 carriages were modified by adding adapters, drawbars, and brakes to make them suitable for use as truck-drawn artillery, and these modified carriages, designated M1A1, were classified as limited standard. At the same time design of the howitzer was slightly altered by change in the trigger shaft and minor redimensioning of other parts. These changes, applied on a production order for forty-eight M2 howitzers placed in the summer of 1939, occasioned the change in nomenclature to the 105-mm. howitzer M2A1.[62] This was

[58] (1) ODEP, I, 106–11, OHF. (2) Memo, CofFA for CofOrd, 16 May 23, sub: Rpt of Tests of 105 mm Howitzers by FA Bd, OO 472.22/117, NA. (3) Memo, CofFA for CofOrd, 22 Oct 23, sub: Modification of 105 mm Howitzers, OO 472.22/124, NA. (4) 4th Ind to memo in (3), CofOrd for TAG, 31 Jan 25, sub: Approval of Rpt on Test of 105 Howitzers. (5) 5th Ind to memo in (3), TAG thru CofOrd for CofFA, 14 Feb 25. Last two in OO 472.22/141, NA.

[59] (1) ODEP, I, 105–29, OHF. (2) Ann Rpt CofOrd, 1926, pp. 13–14; 1927, par. 68; 1928, par. 58. (3) OCM 6684, 5 Jan 28.

[60] OCM 11395, 5 Apr 34; 11933, 24 Jan 35.

[61] OCM 11020, 5 Oct 33; 12968, 2 Jul 36; 13051, 13 Aug 36; 15639, 23 Feb 40. OCM 15639 gives a complete history of the project from 1933 on.

[62] OCM 15639, 23 Feb 40; 15692, 28 Mar 40.

the divisional artillery piece that reached quantity production early in the war and, used in numbers by troops in every theatre, won the appellation, "work-horse of the Army." Its rate of fire was twenty rounds a minute; it fired thirteen different kinds of shell.

240-mm. Howitzer

The 240-mm. howitzer development project is of peculiar interest, in spite of its short span of life during the peace years, for the plan to design a self-propelled mount for so big a weapon was audacious in 1919. Like the other major artillery items upon which Ordnance designers worked before 1940, the original impetus to develop this huge howitzer came from the Caliber Board. Intent upon rounding out divisional and corps artillery with powerful field army pieces, the Caliber Board recommended an 8-inch gun with a maximum range of 35,000 yards and a 240-mm. howitzer with maximum range of 25,000 yards. The 240-mm. howitzer 1918M1 of World War I with a range of about 16,000 yards would serve as a point of departure in designing the more powerful weapon, but the carriage, to be of a type requiring the least possible preparation for firing, was a knottier problem. "No type of road mount is known which is satisfactory in this respect," stated the report, "but the Board has in mind the development of a caterpillar type. The maximum speed need not exceed six miles per hour."[63] Its difficulties notwithstanding, this project was included in the list of developments upon which the Ordnance Department immediately embarked. But the 240-mm., because of the high cost of developing it, stood low on the list.

In March 1920 the Artillery Division of the Ordnance Department informed the Technical Staff that mounting on a caterpillar-type carriage a howitzer of the power recommended would bring the weight to some 115,000 pounds, far in excess of the 40-ton limit the Corps of Engineers set for its highway bridges. Dividing the load would therefore be necessary.[64] Accordingly, after careful study of alternatives, the decision was reached a year later to design a caterpillar mount driven by an electric motor supplied with power from a gas-electric generator set upon a separate vehicle. The specifications also called for a howitzer with a vertical arc of fire from zero degrees to 65 degrees and for a 345-pound projectile. In order to assemble ballistic data, firing tests of the French Schneider 240-mm. howitzer M1918 and the American model 1918M1 proceeded at both Aberdeen Proving Ground and Fort Bragg during the succeeding two years, but no draftsman was assigned to design of the carriage. While the Ordnance Department realized that the problems involved must make redesign of the howitzer and new design of the carriage a time-consuming undertaking, the priority given the project was too low to permit it to survive the cuts in appropriations of 1924. It was suspended till more money would be available. That time did not come for over fifteen years.[65]

[63] (1) Caliber Bd Rpt, par. 48, OKD 334.3/1.3, Ord Tech Intel files. (2) Crowell, *America's Munitions, 1917-1918*, pp. 83-86.

[64] Memo, Col G. F. Jenks for Technical Staff, 23 Mar 20, sub: 240-mm. Materiel, copy in PSP 26, Design, Development and Production of Heavy Mobile Artillery, OHF.

[65] (1) OCM 1355, 29 Mar 21; 1585, 29 Jun 21; 1594, 9 Aug 21; 2199, 9 Jun 22; 3156, 27 Jun 23; 4110, 8 Sep 24. (2) ODEP, I, 155, 176, OHF. (3) Ann Rpt CofOrd, 1925, pp. 14-15. See above, Ch. II.

Development of Combat Vehicles

Tank Doctrine and Policy Statements

For tanks, problems in research and development were heightened by difficulties that did not obtain in other fields. Experimentation with small arms and small arms ammunition had been a major concern of the Ordnance Department for over a hundred years. For artillery, the Caliber Board's recommendations of 1919 created a consistent pattern of development, whether acceptable to the using arms in all particulars or not. But for tank development, the War Department made no such far-sighted, long-term plans. Suggestions from the Chief of Ordnance in October 1919 that a tank board be appointed to recommend a permanent tank development policy netted no action. In fact, within the next few months the General Staff, without making any study of the future of combat vehicles, arrived at two important decisions that gravely and most adversely affected development for years to come.

The first decision was to abolish the Tank Corps created in 1918. The Tank Corps, the only unit of the U.S. Army that had war experience with tanks, was imbued with enthusiasm and possessed of progressive ideas on tank development. The dispersal of the corps was disheartening to tank advocates and, as one officer later wrote, "was a clear indication that the future use of tanks in war was considered of little importance." [66] The second decision, assignment of tanks exclusively to the Infantry, soon proved to be still more shortsighted. Other nations, to be sure, at the time were similarly making the tank an adjunct of the Infantry, but in the United States the General Staff got this decree incorporated as law in the 1920 National Defense Act. The purpose was to prevent the Tank Corps from ever being reconstituted to plague the Infantry and other arms as a separate mechanized force comparable to the Air arm. The result was twofold: for years it precluded the growth of any interest in cross-country combat vehicles by arms other than the Infantry, and later, when interest widened, it hampered plans to extend the use of tanks in war. As long as tanks were regarded solely as support for the riflemen in attack, Infantry concepts of their use necessarily predominated. When early in the thirties the Chief of Staff recognized the interest of the Cavalry in mechanized equipment, the War Department had to resort to elaborations of nomenclature in order to adhere to the letter of the law: Cavalry tanks were labeled combat cars until in 1940 a separate Armored Force was established.

In the year following the Armistice, while the Ordnance Department waited for the General Staff to announce its policy on postwar tank development, Maj. R. E. Carlson, an American member of the Anglo-American Tank Commission, made a complete survey of the situation and tendered recommendations on types for future development.[67] With these data as a guide and with the approval of the Chief of the Tank Corps and the Chief of Infantry, the Ordnance Department then embarked upon design of a fast medium tank. But tanks are costly. Obviously it was un-

[66] Maj Gen Charles L. Scott, Comments for Hist of Development of Combat Vehicles, 2 Mar 50 (hereafter cited as Scott Comments for Hist of Combat Vehicles), OHF.

[67] Maj R. E. Carlson, Paper on Development of Tanks, 16 Mar 21, OKD 451.25/56, Ord Tech Intel files.

sound to spend large sums of money in producing models that the General Staff would not approve. In a machine so complex as a tank, achieving one desired characteristic often necessitates sacrifice of another. Determination of what is to be a primary consideration in design, what a secondary, must depend on clear understanding of the tactical use intended. Though the Infantry, as the using arm after June 1920, was charged with stipulating the tactical requirements for tanks, these requirements in turn had to fit the general principles of use which only the General Staff was empowered to decide.

Between 1919 and 1922 the General Staff made no move to commit itself. The Ordnance Department had already spent much money on tank development. Some official statement of policy was imperative. In March 1921 the Ordnance Department submitted to the War Department an expanded version of the Carlson report and two and a half months later requested a formal declaration of approved policy and tactical requirements for all tanks. The answer, sent in an indorsement through The Adjutant General's office in April 1922, established the principal basis for tank development for the next decade. It read:

> 1. The primary mission of the tank is to facilitate the uninterrupted advance of the riflemen in the attack. Its size, armament, speed and all the accessories for making it an offensive force must be approached with above mission as the final objective to be obtained in development.
>
> 2. As a matter of economy and simplicity in organization, the number of types of tanks should be kept at a minimum. Reliance cannot safely be placed on a single type of tank, but two types, a light and a medium, should be capable of fulfilling all assigned missions.
>
> 3. These types should be as follows:
>
> (a) The light tank not exceeding 5 tons in weight and capable of being transported on heavy motor trucks.
>
> (b) The medium tank not exceeding 15 tons in weight, thereby bringing it within the limits of average highway bridges, the capacity of railroads and the limit of 15 tons placed by the War Department on the medium pontoon bridge.
>
> 4. Inasmuch as certain progress has already been obtained toward developing tanks of the medium type, first consideration should be given to that type, which is capable of doing all that is required of a light tank, except being transported on trucks. In the development of the medium tank, consideration should be given to the essentials necessary to make it a fighting machine. Its speed should be the greatest possible consistent with the limitation in weight, economy in fuel, and radius of action. The control of speed should permit a reduction to that of the advancing riflemen.
>
> 5. The armament of medium tanks should consist of machine guns and guns of heavier caliber. The guns should be capable of firing upon enemy troops in trenches, and engage hostile tanks on a basis of equality; they should, therefore, be of as large caliber as is consistent with prescribed weight limits and ammunition supply, but no necessity is seen for high angle fire. The radius of the action, vision and maneuverabilities of tanks should permit complete fulfillment of the assigned mission. These essentials should be determined after thorough study and experiment and concurrent with the development of pilot tanks. Auxiliary vehicles, except signal tanks, should not be of a type special to the tank service alone.
>
> 6. The tank is not likely to decrease in importance as a war weapon, but tank construction is expensive and it must be expected that funds will be limited. It is, therefore, directed that developments be conducted along the following lines:
>
> a. The Chief of Ordnance will be allowed great latitude in the development of pilot tank for test purposes, in close cooperation with the Chief of Infantry.
>
> b. The first program will be the development of suitable medium pilot tanks with their equipment, of a weight not exceeding 15 tons, and of a maximum speed

of not less than twelve miles per hour.

c. That for the present funds and effort will be applied principally to development purposes rather than to the construction of complete tank units.

d. The manufacture of complete tank units will not be undertaken until suitable medium pilot tanks have been developed and have been approved by the War Department as the best available type.

e. Tanks will not be designed with a special adaptation to chemical warfare, except that if it be found practicable to do so the tanks should be made gas-proof and supplied with a means of producing non-toxic smoke clouds. In this development, the Chief, Chemical Warfare Service, will be consulted.

f. The development of special auxiliary vehicles for tank service alone will not be undertaken; but there is no objection to the consideration of general purpose vehicles capable of meeting the general needs of the Army, as well as the special requirements for tanks.

g. Expenditure of funds on existing tanks will be limited to the amount necessary to keep those in actual service in repair, and those in storage from deterioration.[68]

The most significant feature of this outline of policy is that it was an outline only. Its two pages are in marked contrast to the fifty-odd closely typed pages of the Caliber Board report. Where the latter gave detailed analysis of artillery items and explored doctrine of use, the General Staff announcement of tank doctrine lay in the single sentence: "The primary mission of the tank is to facilitate the uninterrupted advance of the riflemen in the attack." On this lone commandment hung all the law and the prophets. Apart from specifying weight limit and speed requirements, the General Staff delegated to the Chief of Ordnance and the Chief of Infantry all responsibility for deciding the principal features of tanks. But the 15-ton weight limit in itself made a radical change in the policy Ordnance and Infantry had agreed upon and amounted to scrapping the work already accomplished on 20-ton tanks. The General Staff statement was both belated and restricting. Because of the money involved and because final authority to approve or reject an experimental model could not be delegated along with initial responsibility for design, the lot of the Chief of Ordnance, like the policeman's, was not a happy one. His staff had to use its best judgment in selecting design features; the resulting tanks, built at great cost, must satisfy not only the using arm but the General Staff. The declaration, "The Chief of Ordnance will be allowed great latitude in the development of pilot tanks for test purposes," gave no specific instructions. Later attempts to get the General Staff to amplify this original statement of policy produced various enunciations, but some of these served chiefly to sharpen the controversies that inevitably emerged. A case in point was the switch in emphasis from medium to light tank development. In the considered judgment of the men most familiar with problems of tank design, development before 1931 suffered immeasurably "for lack of a definite and fairly constant policy."[69]

It is true that the General Staff had no more experience than Infantry or Ordnance officers on which to base a sound doctrine of tactical use of tanks. As with any major innovation, such as fighter planes and bombers, doctrine must be

[68] OCM 7814, 22 Aug 29. This item, containing a history of medium tank development up to August 1929, was written by William F. Beasley, Ordnance Department tank expert. The text of the indorsement as quoted above is given on pp. 9093–96. See also Beasley's similar History of Light Tank Development in OCM 7786, 1 Aug 29.

[69] OCM 7814, 22 Aug 29, pp. 9088, 9103–04.

291064 O—55——14

worked out by trial and error, and World War I had ended before sufficient combat data had been accumulated. Furthermore, it is important to note that experiments in employment of tanks were limited by the capabilities of the tanks available at any given time for tests or maneuvers. Doctrine depended upon what tests proved tanks could do, just as development of models possessing certain capabilities depended on designers' understanding of what was needed. Some money and time had to be dedicated to exploring and charting blind alleys. Unlike modifications of a rifle design, changes in tank design cost thousands of dollars. The circle was endless: doctrine depended on tactical use intended; tactical use depended on what tanks were capable of; what tanks were capable of depended on developing models for predetermined use. Had higher authority consistently given the Chief of Ordnance the "great latitude" mentioned in the communication of 1922 and invariably accepted as final the decisions that Ordnance and using arms jointly reached, progress, engineers were convinced, would have been greatly speeded.

While producing no new formal statement of doctrine, in 1927 a terse directive from General Charles P. Summerall, then Chief of Staff: "Organize a Mechanized Force,"[70] was in time to influence strongly the course of development. From the small detachment assembled at Fort Eustis, Virginia—a detachment consisting of a few picked men from the Infantry, from the tank units of the Infantry, from the Cavalry, the Artillery, the Engineers, the Signal Corps, and the Ordnance Department—there emerged a unit whose ideas and experimentation with mechanized equipment laid the groundwork for much of the useful work that followed. The ability and enthusiasm of these men, in the face of the ridicule frequently directed at them by officers of the older arms, was fortified in 1931 by the succeeding Chief of Staff, General MacArthur. "Every part of the army," he directed, "will adopt mechanization and motorization as far as practicable and possible."[71] This revolutionizing order, though really only a repetition of Westervelt Board recommendations, had the effect of arousing all parts of the Army to interest in mechanization. Furthermore, MacArthur's order to the Cavalry to take over the mechanized force project and, with Fort Knox, Kentucky, as headquarters, to expand it, opened the way to a reappraisal of the doctrine enunciated in 1922.

Ten years after the appearance of the first brief policy statement, General MacArthur thus summarized General Staff views in a report to the Secretary of War:

> Upon this arm [Infantry] has always fallen the brunt of the task of dislodging the enemy from defensive positions. The ideal machine for assistance in this mission must of necessity have a high degree of tactical mobility, even at the expense of reducing, if necessary, road or strategic mobility. Remembering that the greatest obstacle to tactical mobility is the band of fire laid down by the defense, an essential requisite in the assaulting tank is sufficient armor to protect against the preponderant mass of this fire, namely, that from all types of small arms. More than this is impractical, at least at present, because every increase in armor means a corresponding loss in speed and cross-country ability. Sufficiently heavy armor to protect from field guns would completely immobilize any machine of usable size. For protection of this kind the tank must rely upon rapid move-

[70] Scott Comments for Hist of Combat Vehicles, OHF.

[71] *Ibid.*

ment, surprise, proper use of ground, and the supporting guns of its own army.[72]

While noting that the airplane had by this time entered into the field of reconnaissance, MacArthur indicated the new role of the Cavalry in mechanized warfare:

. . . the traditional Cavalry missions of covering the advance or retreat of the main army, of conducting terrestrial reconnaissance, and of exploiting victory by pursuing a disorganized army remain unchanged. Cavalry interest in mechanization has therefore been centered principally in armored cars and cross-country vehicles possessing a high degree of strategic mobility, with fighting power and tactical mobility an important though secondary consideration.[73]

Recognition that Cavalry as well as Infantry had an interest in mechanization henceforward gave ordnance designers the advantage of the mechanized Cavalry's active participation in the experimental program but at the same time obliged the Ordnance Department to find compromises to satisfy both using arms. Funds were too small to permit development of a series of tanks for a variety of purposes. Therefore the general solution attempted was to develop tanks for the Infantry, modify these to adapt them to the Cavalry mission, name the Cavalry tanks combat cars, and add a line of fast, armored, wheeled scout cars for Cavalry reconnaissance.

As the 1930's wore on, War Department concepts of what were essential requirements for tanks changed somewhat. Ordnance experts for fifteen years had deplored the imperviousness of the General Staff to the idea that heavier protective armor and, particularly, more powerful guns were of even greater importance than high speed. The Chief of Staff in 1932 had admitted that recent developments in armor-piercing ammunition were complicating tank design and that the new high-velocity bullets promised penetration of any armor then carried on American tanks.[74] But this admission led to no immediate revision of tank requirements or doctrine. In fact in 1933 the Secretary of War announced that it was "absolutely essential . . . to insure, for any vehicle intended for use primarily with the Cavalry or Infantry Division, the production of a vehicle to weigh not more than 7½ tons (preferably less) and to cost substantially less to manufacture than present types." [75] The weight limit was predicated upon the supposition that tanks had to be transported into battle on trucks. Partial conversion to a different view began when observers' reports started to pile up evidence from battlefields of the Spanish Civil War.[76] From this came indisputable proof of the vulnerability of light tanks.[77] Two-man crews, no space for radio, insufficient armor to withstand even .30-caliber armor-piercing shot all added up to inef-

[72] Rpt of CofS in *Ann Rpt SW,* 1932, p. 82.

[73] *Ibid.*, p. 83.

[74] *Ibid.*, pp. 83–85.

[75] 12th Ind to ltr, AGO to CofOrd, 29 Apr 33, OO 451.24/622, cited in OCM 10676, 5 May 33.

[76] OCM 14073, 24 Nov 37.

[77] For example, see Liddell Hart, "Lessons of the Spanish War," *Army Ordnance,* XVIII, 106 (1938), 201–02; and Emilio Canevari, "Forecasts from the War in Spain," *Army Ordnance,* XVIII, 107 (1938), 274–75.

The Italian, Canevari, contended that combat trials showed the need of motorizing artillery rather than infantry, but an American general drew different conclusions: "The Battle of Firente de Ebro convinced both sides that independent tank forces are a delusion and that the role of the tank is the more modest but highly important one of helping the infantry forward." Though, the American declared, the light tank had proved to have a few uses, a more heavily armed and armored slow-moving vehicle was shown to be best for accomplishing the tank's primary mission of serving as accompanying mobile artillery for infantry. Brig. Gen. Henry J. Reilly, "Proving Ground in Spain," *Army Ordnance,* XIX, 114 (1939), 335–36.

fectiveness.[78] The General Staff and Infantry belief that protection from small arms fire was all that was necessary was further shaken by reports that foreign countries were building tanks with much heavier armor and greater fire power than any the U.S. Army had. And finally, tank maneuvers revealed the weaknesses of the American combat vehicle.[79] As a result of these discoveries, speed ceased to be the first requirement.[80] Yet official announcement of revised doctrine failed to appear. Not until the Armored Force was created in July 1940 and the wishes of the Infantry ceased to dominate and those of the Cavalry prevailed did any basic change occur. The thesis proclaimed in a 1939 War Department field manual largely repeated that of the 1923 regulations: tanks were to be employed to assist the advance of Infantry foot troops; mechanized Cavalry would exploit successes. Tanks were to be GHQ reserve.[81]

Progress of the Tank Development Program

Within this framework, built of shifting and often conflicting ideas of what characteristics ideal tanks should have, the Ordnance Department's program of research and development had to proceed. The tank designer of every country is faced with the highly technical problem of finding a balance between the three essential features of tanks: the guns to provide the fire power with which to fight, the armor plate to give crews protection and keep the vehicle in action, and the chassis and power train to give mobility.[82] Powerful guns and turret mountings to insure coverage of the field of fire and armor plate heavy enough to minimize the destructive effects of armor-piercing ammunition immediately build up the weight the chassis must carry. A chassis strong enough to carry a heavy superstructure must have very powerful engines and a sturdy suspension system. Unless the suspension be reasonably shockproof, a tank cannot long withstand the wear and tear of cross-country operations, or travel far by road without extensive overhaul. Unless engines can be designed so extraordinarily compact as to give the needed power without taking up most of the interior of the tank, the frame of the chassis must be wide or high. A high silhouette makes a relatively easy target for enemy fire. A very wide vehicle has less road maneuverability than a narrow one, may be unable to cross bridges, and may seriously impede military highway traffic.

Weight and over-all dimensions thus became vital considerations; but power plants, armor, and armament were equally important for fighting vehicles. The Corps of Engineers stressed the first, for theirs was the responsibility for bridges and roads. The using arms were primarily concerned with getting easy maneuverability, speed and, later, fire power and protective armor. The Ordnance Department, whose mission encompassed maintenance, regarded engines and suspension systems of

[78] Scott Comments for Hist of Combat Vehicles, OHF.

[79] (1) Statement of Gen Craig, CofS, to HR Subcommittee, 21 Jan 38, WDAB 1939, HR, pp. 12–13. (2) Memo, Lt Col John B. Coulter for Exec Off, OCO, 14 Aug 37, OO 321.12/4285 Germany, NA. (3) Ltr, CofInf thru CofOrd to TAG, 16 Nov 37, sub: Characteristics of Medium Tank T5, OO 451.25/7258, NA.

[80] See *Army Ordnance*, XIX, 110 (1938), 103.

[81] Tentative Field Service Regulations, Operations, FM 100-5 (Washington, 1939), Secs. 24–26, 35.

[82] See memo, Lt Col Gladeon M. Barnes for Assistant Commandant Army War College, 15 Apr 38, sub: Tank Development Program for U.S. Army, Barnes file, OHF.

utmost importance. In all the discussion that follows, the reader must bear in mind these desiderata which, by their tendency to mutual irreconcilability, induced prolonged controversy.

Furthermore, the degree to which want of money hamstrung developments can be gauged by a brief comparison of costs and appropriations. In 1931 the cost of a single Christie tank without armor, engines, guns, or radios was $34,500. Seven years later the Chief of Ordnance estimated the cost of a medium tank at about $50,000.[83] While sums allotted to tank development before 1925 were relatively large, from 1925 to 1939 the average was about $60,000 a year. That precluded building more than one experimental model in any one year. But to work out improvements without making test models was to relegate problems to the realm of abstraction. Commercial corporations such as General Motors had annual research budgets in these years running up to $20,000,000. For all development projects, not merely automotive, Ordnance Department funds in the mid-thirties averaged about $1,680,000. At the end of 1939 the Chief of Ordnance begged for $100,000 solely for development of diesel engines for tanks.[84] For nearly fifteen years appropriations permitted steady progress, but at a snail's, not even a caterpillar's pace.

The tank had first been used in combat by the British in the Somme offensive of September 1916. In the next two years the United States, collaborating with the British and French, designed and built several types: a 44-ton heavy tank, the Mark VIII; a 40-ton steam-propelled tank; and a Ford 3-ton and a Renault 6-ton tank. Influenced by its experience with these, the Army after the Armistice inclined to favor development of some heavy and some very light tanks. A small tank force, which could be rapidly expanded if war came, was to be kept as a nucleus for training. Yet the first project launched was the design of a medium tank, which, it was hoped, would constitute an "all-purpose" Infantry tank.[85]

Heavy Tanks

The heavy tank program was short lived. In March 1920 Brig. Gen. Samuel D. Rockenback of the Tank Corps assured a Congressional committee that a few more months would see the development of a much improved heavy tank, "equal to any five of the Mark VIII."[86] His optimism was unfounded. Had the Tank Corps been perpetuated, perhaps objections to heavy tanks would have been withdrawn. But when the National Defense Act named the Infantry as the using arm, work on design of heavy models was canceled and for the next twenty years revival of the project received no encouragement from the General Staff. The reasons were three. First, any tank weighing more than twenty-five tons was too heavy for the emergency bridges already developed by the Corps of Engineers unless the bridges were rein-

---

[83] (1) Robert J. Icks, "Four Decades of Mechanization," *Army Ordnance,* XVII, 102 (1937), 340. (2) Memo, CofOrd for ACofS G–4, 14 Jun 38, sub: Expenditure Program FY 1939, OO 111.3/6826, NA.

[84] (1) ODEP, III, 3–33, OHF. (2) Interv with Harold W. Evans, Chief Automotive Engineer, OCO, 15 Feb 50. (3) Memo, CofOrd for ACofS G–4, 29 Nov 38, sub: Estimates for R&D, FY 1941, OO 111.3/6906, NA. The fiscal records giving the exact breakdown of R&D appropriations before 1940 have been destroyed.

[85] (1) Record of Army Ord R&D, Tanks (hereafter cited as R&D, Tanks), pp. Aoo, 1A1, 1A200, OHF. (2) OCM 7786, 1 Aug 29, p. 9033. (3) Rpt of CofS in *Ann Rpt SW,* 1932, p. 83.

[86] WDAB 1921, HR, p. 519.

forced, and reinforcement was time consuming. The Engineers, themselves short of funds for new development and fearful lest increasing weights make bridge construction a matter of days rather than hours, protested against the adoption of heavy tanks. The second reason for vetoing heavy tanks was the growing conviction that smaller tanks had greater tactical usefulness. British thinking was influential here; the opinion of the British, whose Army first used tanks in battle, was long deferred to as authoritative.[87] And, finally, the cost of building test models of heavy tanks was so much greater than the cost of light and medium tanks that it seemed wiser to spend the limited available funds upon design of types that had prospects of meeting the avowed wishes of the using arms than to invest money in building pilot models with which to demonstrate the capabilities of 40-ton types. So, in the face of occasional protests from the Ordnance Department, heavy tank design was virtually abandoned till combat experience in World War II forced the Army to revise its views.[88]

Light Tanks

Light tanks, though officially approved by the War Department's statement of 1922, received little attention before 1926. The objective set had been a tank of not more than five tons, transportable by truck. Portée, or transport to the line of action, was to avoid needless wear of tracks and chassis. The specifications first laid down by the Infantry Board are of interest because they were so far removed from later concepts. They included a cruising radius of fifty miles, speed of from two to twelve miles an hour across country, armor proof against .30-caliber armor-piercing bullets, armament of one .30-caliber machine gun and one 37-mm. gun so mounted as to be operable by one man, and provision for a crew of two. Work along this line was never pushed far. By 1926, when the Infantry's interest in light tanks began to grow, requirements were altered to attain speed of twelve to twenty miles an hour, weight of not more than six tons, and a gun mount in which a .50-caliber and a .30-caliber machine gun would be interchangeable.[89] The preference for light, fast tanks over heavier ones was nourished, if not induced, by study of British ideas both as expressed in the writings of Liddell Hart and as reported by the Secretary of War after a visit to Aldershot in 1927. A 1928 revision of the Ten-Year-Program called for 72 light tanks, though originally no light tanks had been included, and the reduction of the number of medium tanks from 64 to 16. Up to 1935 emphasis upon speed and maneuverability mounted steadily, culminating in instructions to the Ordnance Department to design a three-ton tank.[90] Impractical though this particular project soon proved, the work expended on 5-, 6-, and 7-ton models between 1926 and 1935 gave engineers much useful data on which to proceed later.

By 1935 the experimental light tanks, T2E1 and T2E2, were given limited pro-

[87] Scott Comments for Hist of Combat Vehicles, OHF.

[88] R&D, Tanks, pp. 1A200–203, OHF. See below, Chs. IX and X.

[89] (1) OCM 7786, 1 Aug 29, pp. 9031–34. (2) ODEP, III, 4, 22, OHF.

[90] (1) Interv with Gen Scott, 21 Feb 50. (2) Ann Rpt CofOrd, 1936, par. 56d(6).

Ordnance attempts to have the entire project vetoed were overruled by the Deputy Chief of Staff. See OO 451.24/2109, 451.24/2119, 451.24/2120, and 451.24/2138 files, DRB AGO, for the correspondence on this subject.

curement status. This designation usually meant that full standardization and large procurement orders would follow unless the items were superseded by something better in the interim. These models later became the M2A1 and M2A2. Manufactured at Rock Island Arsenal in 1935, they differed from each other chiefly in that the M2A1 had a single turret surmounted by a cupola and weighed 18,790 pounds, while the M2A2 had two round turrets and weighed 19,100 pounds. Each was armed with one .50-caliber machine gun and three .30-caliber machine guns. Maximum armor thickness was ⅝ of an inch. The transmission was a sliding gear type. Continental W-670 gasoline engines using 92 octane gasoline gave a maximum speed of 45 miles an hour. In the next two years, in order to meet the demands of the Cavalry for vehicles with 360 degree turret traverse, two models of what were then called "combat cars" were turned out.[91] Most characteristics of these, however, so closely paralleled those of Infantry tanks that the distinction of name was dropped in 1940 and the original combat car M1 was redesignated the light tank M1A2, combat car M2 the light tank M1A1. The most important feature introduced in the original combat car M2 was the Guiberson T1020 Series 4 diesel air-cooled radial engine as an alternate power plant. With the appearance of another light tank model in 1938, the Ordnance Department began to increase the thickness of protective armor and slightly reduce road speed. The pilot tank of the next development, the M2A4, first manufactured at Rock Island in 1939, carried still further the trend toward greater weight and more power. This model, under production as the German panzers swept into Poland, embodied many of the principles continued in later tanks. It marked a turning point in light tank design.[92]

The M2A4 light tank was designed for a crew of four, a driver and assistant driver in the hull, a gunner and a commander-leader in the single turret. Entrance to the vehicle was through armored hatches, which were provided with peep-holes for vision in combat areas. In noncombat zones, the hatches could be opened, permitting direct vision and better ventilation. Armor was of thicknesses up to one inch, with heaviest armor on vertical and near vertical surfaces, which experience had shown were most likely to be hit. The turret could be rotated through 360 degrees by means of a handwheel-controlled mechanism. Power was supplied by either a Continental radial air-cooled aircraft-type engine that operated on 80 octane gasoline or a Guiberson diesel engine. The transmission was of the synchromesh type, with five forward speeds and one reverse. The vehicle was supported by two bogies or suspensions on each side, trunnioned on the front and rear axles. Each bogie consisted of two solid-rubber-tired rollers which, mounted on volute springs, rode the inside of the endless rubber-block track. The action of the volute springs and articulating bogie links kept track tension constant while negotiating obstacles or irregular terrain. The most important change from earlier models was the addition of a 37-mm. gun. Three more .30-caliber machine guns were emplaced, one in the right bow and one on each sponson. Although 27-mm. guns had been used on light tanks in World War I, later military

[91] The Infantry, viewing tanks as a means of covering the foot soldier's advance, considered forward fire sufficient, whereas the Cavalry, envisaging use of a tank emplaced at a crossroad, required all-round fire.

[92] R&D, Tanks, pp. 1A1–1A2, OHF.

thinking had limited armament to .30-caliber and .50-caliber machine guns. This opinion was now discarded. The weight, just over twelve tons, brought this light tank near the weight limit formerly set for medium tanks.[93]

Medium Tanks

Medium tank design had meanwhile pre-empted much concentrated effort, more than was expended on either heavy or light tanks during the 1920's. From 1919 till the early 1930's, Ordnance engineers believed it feasible to achieve a model that would combine the essential characteristics of both the heavy and light tanks used in World War I, provided that weight not be restricted to fifteen tons. The first two postwar models, the medium tanks M1921 and M1922, weighed over twenty tons each. While these designs were not completely scrapped and revisions of the former were carried on for several years, War Department policy as set forth in the 1922 indorsement quoted above made a lighter model necessary. The fifteen-ton tank, Model 1924, was the Ordnance Department's attempt to meet this requirement, but any possibility of success was precluded by specifications of the Infantry and of the Tank Board. The board insisted on armor protection against .50-caliber armor-piercing bullets, a requirement that meant plate an inch thick; provision for a four-man crew; one six-pounder and one machine gun, independently operable; and a speed of twelve miles an hour.[94] The Chief of Infantry and the Chief of Ordnance both concurred in the protest of the president of the Tank Board, Col. Oliver S. Eskridge: ". . . everyone familiar with the tank situation knows that an attempt to build a satisfactory tank within the 15-ton limit is a waste of funds."[95] Reluctantly, the General Staff in 1926 approved shift of emphasis to a 23-ton tank, but ordered continued attention to a 15-ton. Study of both types was therefore carried on for the next nine years. Some of each type were designed, built, and tested, but none was standardized.[96]

In summarizing the accomplishments of tank development work up to 1929, a competent Ordnance engineer stressed the accumulation of data and experience in this field which lacked any technical history to draw upon. But William F. Beasley, in his capacity of automotive man on the Ordnance Technical Staff, observed that progress had been greatly hampered by "making *perfection* in an experimental vehicle the criterion for its standardization" and by "too great a faith on the part of the non-technical people . . . that any difficulty can be overcome by research and development."[97] These comments held true for the next decade. Furthermore, Beasley contended, another source of delay in arriving at a basic design during the twenties had been the dispersion of effort and money upon development of accessories. Compasses, gun mounts, sighting devices, armor plate of increased resistance per unit of thickness, all needed improvement. And a tank commander badly needed some better method of communication with his crew and with other tanks than shin-kicking and waving signal

[93] *Ibid.*

[94] OCM 7814, 22 Aug 29.

[95] Ltr, Col Eskridge to CofInf, 2 Jun 24, sub: Medium Tank, OO 451.25/2098, NA. Subsequent actions may be traced in the twenty-three indorsements.

[96] (1) 23d Ind, ltr, TAG thru CofOrd to CofInf, 11 Mar 26, OO 451.25/2098, NA. (2) Ann Rpts CofOrd, 1929-35.

[97] See Beasley, Hist of Light Tank Development, in OCM 7814, 22 Aug 29.

flags. Hindsight, in the opinion of some Ordnance engineers, suggested that the Department would have been better advised to concentrate exclusively upon development of a successful chassis. Officers of the using arms, on the other hand, firmly believed that more effective tanks depended as much upon having dependable accessories as upon a reliable track and engine.[98]

Perhaps another impediment to the evolution of a satisfactory full-track medium tank was expenditure of time upon so-called Christie or convertible types, designed to operate either on tracks or on solid-rubber-tired bogie wheels. A wheeled vehicle could of course travel over roads at higher speeds without excessive wear on chassis and tires than could a caterpillar-treaded vehicle. The tracks could be put on for cross-country maneuvers. Over the advantages and drawbacks of Christie tanks controversy raged for more than twenty years and, indeed, is occasionally revived today in discussions of Russian tanks that for a time were based on Christie patents.

Engineers agreed that the convertible principle was attractive even though "two-purpose equipment is in general violation of good engineering practice." [99] The Tank Corps, anxious to try out convertible models, in 1919 urged negotiation of a contract with Walter Christie who had already devoted extensive study to the problem. In November 1919 an order for one experimental model was placed and soon afterward the Ordnance Department bought a license to all Christie patents. Christie's first product was tested, returned for modifications, and in 1923 retested exhaustively. But this, like later models Christie built, the Ordnance Department felt displayed major weaknesses, primarily mechanical unreliability. Notwithstanding the defects of the succession of convertible models tested, the using arms persisted in requesting development of this type of tank. Their insistence derived from their conviction that it could keep up with other motor vehicles better than any other kind of tank. Christie's Model 1940, so-called because in 1929 its proponents considered it "easily ten years ahead of its time," in first trials achieved 42.55 miles an hour on tracks and 69.23 miles an hour on wheels. Though these speeds were admittedly possible only under favorable conditions of terrain and highway, the officials of the American Automobile Association who supervised the test were impressed. The Infantry was enthusiastic. Following a test held before a board of high-ranking officers of various arms and services, the Ordnance Department was instructed to procure six of the tanks.[100] Still, most Ordnance officers remained skeptical, believing that the speed of the Christie failed to compensate for its light armor, light fire power, inability to make long runs without overhaul, and lack of room inside for guns, radio, and ammunition. In early 1932 the Chief of Ordnance reiterated a list of practical objections to the convertible type chassis, the tactical and strategic value of which had not, he believed, been fully demonstrated. But, he wrote, in view of opinion prevailing among the users, the Ordnance Department must pursue the development until it arrived at

[98] (1) *Ibid.*, pp. 9098–9101. (2) Interv with Gen Scott, 21 Feb 50.

[99] OCM 7522, 5 Mar 29, p. 8863.

[100] (1) *Ibid.* (2) C. C. Benson, "The New Christie, Model 1940," *Army Ordnance*, X, 56 (1929), 114–16. (3) Memo, TAG for CofOrd, 19 Mar 30, sub: Procurement of Christie Tanks Without Advertising, and 1st Ind, CofOrd for TAG, 29 May 30, both in AG 473.1 (3-1-30), OO 451/4229, NA.

conclusive results, pro or con.[101] So the T3 and T4 experimental medium tanks built in the mid-thirties were both convertible types. Not until 1938, when the T5 appeared, was the convertible principle abandoned.[102]

Christie himself dropped the convertible feature from his models after the mid-thirties, but other elements of his designs continued to attract attention, notably the suspension system he employed. Independently sprung wheels gave the vehicle good riding qualities and increased maneuverability over rough terrain. But Christie always submitted his tanks for trial without guns or gun mountings. The tests therefore could not give final proof of the tanks' durability. Spectacular performance of test models unencumbered with the weight that armor plate, turret, and guns must add was no proof of what the vehicles could withstand when those essentials were added.[103] Examination of Christie's new "High Speed Model T12," demonstrated in 1938, convinced Ordnance automotive experts that this tank, like its predecessors, lacked the features essential in a fighting vehicle. The fighting compartment was much too small, the tank accommodated only a driver and one gunner, the liquid-cooled engine, though powerful, was an aircraft type that would be difficult to procure, and the tracks were of a kind guaranteeing only relatively short life. In short, the disqualifying weaknesses of this light "High-Speed" tank were those of earlier Christies.[104] The suspension system, while having some advantage, was considered not sufficiently sturdy. Instead of adopting the Christie suspension, the Ordnance Department resorted to heavy volute springs as promising far greater strength and hence longer life. Though rubber torsion suspension had been tried out for light vehicles in 1936, either horizontal or vertical volute spring suspension was used in every American tank built after 1938 until in 1942 torsion bar suspension was developed to a point where it could be used for combat vehicles.[105] Unfortunately, the faith in Christie's suspension system, which was cherished by some politicians, newspaper reporters, and officers of the using arms who were not in a position to recognize the defects in the design, gave rise to the notion that the Ordnance Department to save face was stubbornly refusing to accept a superior tank simply because it was the work of an independent designer. Mistaken identification of Christie's independently sprung wheels with torsion bar suspension persisted long after the war and accounts for much of the criticism of the Ordnance Department's rejection of Christie's design.[106]

The year 1938, which saw the appearance of Christie's new "High-Speed" light tank, also brought forth the T5 models of medium tanks. The most prophetic devel-

[101] Ltr, CofOrd to CG Rock Island Arsenal, 8 Jan 32, sub: Studies for Combat Car T3, OO 451.24/514, NA.

[102] (1) Inf Bd Rpt 917, Medium Tank T4, 18 Feb 37, OO 451.25/6622, NA. (2) Ltr, CofOrd to CG Rock Island Arsenal, 20 Sep 37, sub: Medium Tank. T5, OO 451/8724, NA.

[103] Interv with Gen Christmas, 8 Nov 49.

[104] (1) Rpt of Inspection of Christie Tank at Hempstead, L. I., 6 Oct 38, OO 451.25/8209, NA. (2) Memo, Col Barnes for Gen McFarland, 16 Mar 39, sub: Conference on Christie Tank, OO 451.25/8674, NA.

For more detailed description see: ltr, CG APG to CofOrd, 5 May 41, sub: Test of Bigley Tank (Christie Tank Model 1938), OO 451.25/5295, DRB AGO; and OCM 19608, 28 Jan 43.

[105] Ann Rpt CofOrd, 1936, par. 56a. The American patent, No. 2024199, on torsion bar suspension was granted to Gladeon M. Barnes and Warren E. Preston in December 1935. French patents were of earlier date.

[106] For example, in Christie's vehicles the wheels tended to jump the tracks on a turn unless a highly skilled driver were at the controls. With torsion bar suspension this was virtually impossible.

MEDIUM TANK T3, *one of the Christie tanks.*

opment in these was the experimental mounting of a 75-mm. pack howitzer in the turret of one model. A few Cavalry and Ordnance officers had indeed advocated this as early as 1935. Now it was a clear recognition of trends in European design. In 1937 German experts, after visiting Fort Knox, are reported to have stated that the United States led the world both in tank design and in organization of mechanized units. If that was truth, not flattery, the lead was lost in 1938. In spite of a report from Berlin describing the German experimental mounting of an 88-mm. gun in a tank, the Chief of Infantry declared so powerful a weapon as a 75-mm. needless.[107] As a result of this judgment, the pilots of the M2 and M2A1 medium tanks, built the next year, were each armed only with a 37-mm. gun, eight .30-caliber machine guns, and a .45-caliber submachine gun. Meanwhile, the mechanized Cavalry was clamoring for a self-propelled cannon to neutralize enemy antitank guns. Only when the War Department conceded that a 75-mm. howitzer mounted on a combat car chassis was virtually a tank was a new decision reached; approval of designing a tank equipped with a 75-mm. howitzer came at last in July 1940. The Armored Force, headed by a Cavalry officer, Brig. Gen. Adna R. Chaffee, was established that month.[108]

It is worth repeating that between 1919 and 1938 none of the tanks developed was

[107] (1) Scott Comments for Hist of Combat Vehicles, OHF. (2) Interv, 19 Jan 50, with Col René R. Studler.

[108] (1) R&D, Tanks, 1A41–43, OHF. (2) Interv with Gen Christmas, 8 Nov 49. (3) Proceedings of a Board of Officers . . . Hq Seventh Cavalry Brigade, 27 Jul 38, and Inds 1 to 9 to ltr of transmittal, Fort Knox, Ky., to CofCav, 25 Sep 38, OO 472/3496, NA.

standardized.[109] The T5 was the first to be approved. Accepted in June 1939, it was designated the medium tank M2. The medium tanks T4 and T4E1 were shortly thereafter designated Medium Tank M1, Convertible, Limited Standard, though the eighteen manufactured and used at Fort Benning were declared obsolete in March 1940. The caution that characterized the Army expenditure programs during the twenty years between world wars doubtless accounts for the refusal to standardize any tanks, no matter how promising. But Ordnance automotive designers felt that this retarded tank development. They deplored the policy on the grounds that use by troops in training and on maneuvers revealed weaknesses susceptible of improvement in a fashion that proving ground and formal service tests could not do. The perfectionism complained of in 1929 still obtained in 1938. This view the Infantry and Cavalry did not share; they considered it the Ordnance Department's job to get "the bugs out of a design" before shipping a model to troops in the field.[110]

Opportunity to try experimental models on maneuvers did exist, to be sure, after the first units of a mechanized Cavalry brigade were organized in 1931. The mechanized force, assembled at Fort Meade in the summer of 1928 in response to General Summerall's famous four word directive, had paved the way by trying out tactical employment of the tanks then on hand, and in the fall of 1930 that force's successor, a group at Fort Eustis, Virginia, carried on. When some months later the unit was transferred to Fort Knox, Kentucky, to form the nucleus of the first mechanized Cavalry, collaboration of designers and users of combat vehicles was assured. Still, the projected regiment of mechanized Cavalry did not materialize; funds were insufficient to equip it. As late as mid-1939 the tank forces consisted of only one mechanized Cavalry brigade of half strength, the small, partially equipped tank companies with Infantry divisions, and the GHQ units of 1,400 men.[111] The small scale of operations possible with the few tanks available for field trial during the 1930's gave indication rather than conclusive proof of what American experimental models were capable and, still more important, of what they were incapable. Officers of the mechanized Cavalry averred that evolution of tactical doctrine was not affected by delays in delivery of equipment, that fundamentally principles of tactical use of horse Cavalry applied to an armored brigade. But the Ordnance Department continued to believe that the want of enough tanks, armored cars, and auxiliary motor vehicles to conduct extensive maneuvers left automotive engineers with only sketchy evidence on which to base attempts at improved design. Only 19 light tanks were completed in 1936, 154 in 1937, and 74 in 1938. Medium tanks finished were fewer.[112]

One handicap in the development of all types of combat vehicles during the twenty years of peace calls for special mention. This was the lack of suitable engines. The Ordnance Department itself never had money enough to develop an ideal tank engine and, as private industry

[109] In 1928 standardization of the medium tank T1 as the M1 was canceled by the War Department. See: (1) OCM 6723, 24 Jan 28; 6772, 9 Feb 28; 6925, 12 Apr 28; and (2) Hist of Aberdeen Proving Ground, Vol. I, OHF.

[110] Interv with Gen Scott, 21 Feb 50.

[111] (1) *Ann Rpt SW*, 1930, p. 125. (2) Ann Rpt CofOrd, 1932, par. 23s. (3) Watson, *Chief of Staff: Prewar Plans and Preparations*, p. 148. (4) Ltr, CofOrd to CG Rock Island Arsenal, 20 Nov 37, sub: Estimated Deliveries of Tanks and Combat Cars, OO 451/8840, NA.

[112] (1) Interv with Gen Scott, 21 Feb 50. (2) Ann Rpt CofOrd, 1936, pars. 16a, 56a, 56d; 1937, par. 19a; 1938, par. 23a.

had no need for an engine designed to meet the peculiar requirements of tank power plants, there was no commercial development. The lack of power obtainable with the slow-speed marine engines used first and in the later adaptations of aircraft engines affected all other features of design. It lent color to arguments favoring development only of light tanks. Because liquid-cooled engines were thought to be more vulnerable than air-cooled, the automotive engineers centered attention upon air-cooled types. To the success with these before 1938, the Chief of Ordnance, with a touch of complacency, attributed "the superiority of our equipment over that of foreign armies." [113] In 1936 Guiberson air-cooled diesels were first tried. But when the later 1930's brought aircraft needs to the fore, the Air Corps protested Ordnance pre-emption of aircraft engines for tanks just as the Navy later reserved diesels for Navy use. The Ordnance Department was therefore obliged belatedly to find some other solution of its problem. The compromises arrived at, as the development story of World War II will show, gave far from ideal answers.[114]

Auxiliary Vehicles

Apart from the achievements on tanks and combat cars, fulfillment of the Caliber Board's hopes for motorization of the U.S. Army fell far short of the goal. Complete motorization would have meant self-propelled mounts for every weapon the foot soldier could not carry and motor transport for men and supplies as well. About motorization of supply trucks and personnel carriers there was little argument; these vehicles by the terms of the 1920 National Defense Act were a responsibility of the Quartermaster Corps. The motorization of artillery, on the other hand, early came to be a controversial matter. In the years immediately following the appearance of the Caliber Board report, the Ordnance Department undertook a series of development projects on self-propelled gun mounts, but in each case work was halted by lack of money, lack of interest on the part of the Field Artillery, or both. As late as 1938, between 40 and 60 percent of the Army's artillery was still horse drawn. A good many artillerymen contended that horse draft was more satisfactory than machine; horses neither ran out of gasoline nor required repairs and spare parts. If the Field Artillery did not want self-propelled guns, the Ordnance Department could not foist them upon the user, even had the Ordnance Department had funds to develop them. Only the insistence of the mechanized Cavalry enabled the Ordnance Department in 1938 to resume work on gun motor carriages. Yet when, after war broke out in Europe and Army appropriations increased, the Ordnance Department again recommended development of a motor carriage for the 105-mm. howitzer, the Chief of Field Artillery remained adamant in his refusal. Towing, Brig. Gen. Charles H. Danforth decreed, was better. Thus one very important feature of the Westervelt program lapsed.[115]

Towing by tractor was relatively acceptable to the Field Artillery. Horses could always be substituted. So the devel-

[113] Ann Rpt CofOrd, 1938, par. 64a(1).

[114] (1) Samuel H. Woods, Chief Engr Auto Div, Ord Research Center, APG, The Development of Combat Vehicles, Oct 43, p. 4, OHF. (2) Interv with Gen Christmas, 8 Nov 49.

[115] (1) Interv with Col Burnett R. Olmsted, 25 Oct 49. (2) ODEP, I, pp. 68–228, OHF. (3) 2d Ind, ltr, CofFA to CofCav, 17 Dec 38, 3d Ind, CofCav to CofFA, 5 Jan 39, and 7th Ind, TAG to CofOrd, 12 Apr 39, to ltr, Maj Bertrand Morrow to CofCav, 25 Sep 38, sub: Letter of Transmittal, OO 472/3496, NA.

opment of a series of tractors and half-tracks had to be the Ordnance Department's answer to mobility for artillery. Though the Ordnance Department before 1933 had procured and tested trucks for towing artillery, thereafter, by War Department order, procurement of trucks, as part of motor transport, was turned over to the Quartermaster Corps. The Ordnance Department was left in charge of all tracked and half-tracked vehicles, with very few exceptions, for all branches of the Army.[116] This division of responsibility for vehicles was maintained till 1942. Tracked vehicles were preponderantly of commercial design; the Ordnance Department tested various models and devised the modifications that military use required. The Air Corps used some tractors and the Corps of Engineers a number for construction work, but otherwise most tractors were for use as prime movers of artillery. Between 1932 and 1940 the Ordnance Department tested some twenty-three different commercial tractors requested by the Field Artillery.[117]

Half-tracks similarly were developed by the collaborating efforts of Ordnance engineers and automotive engineers in private industry. This type of hybrid vehicle, originating in France, was a small truck or passenger car on which a half-track assembly was substituted for the conventional rear axle and wheel assembly. The design aimed at combining the cross-country mobility of the tracked vehicle with the highway speed of the wheeled. It was considered especially adapted to use as a personnel carrier or as a prime mover for divisional artillery. Some fourteen half-track truck models, a half-track car, and a half-track personnel carrier were tested before 1940, though it was not until 1939 that the armed services took any pronounced interest in half-tracks. In that year their possibilities for various combat operations apparently emerged. Accordingly, the Artillery Division of Industrial Service prepared drawings for a half-track scout car, later labeled the T14, and a pilot model was built in 1941. From engineering studies of this derived the three basic models from which stemmed the whole family of half-tracks used in World War II.[118]

Influence of Budgetary Restrictions

Ordnance research and development problems between world wars may be further clarified by an analysis of what the Department planned and what it accomplished in a given year. The fiscal year 1937 is fairly typical of the period immediately preceding the formal launching of the National Defense program. Appropriations for research and development for 1937 were set at $1,350,000, $90,000 more than for 1936 and $10,000 less than for 1938 and 1939.[119] While the War Department as a whole sought $9,000,000 for 1937, the Bureau of the Budget cut the figure to $7,160,400. Approved Ordnance projects numbered 224 and were classified into 21 groups. Seventeen projects, most of them in the artillery ammunition group, still were based on Westervelt Board rec-

[116] (1) Ann Rpt CofOrd, 1933, par. 18. (2) Interv with Col Van Deusen, 25 Nov 49.

[117] (1) Hist of Tractors, Detroit Arsenal, OHF. (2) Ann Rpt CofOrd, 1934, par. 53; 1935, pars. 56–57; 1936, par. 56; 1937, pars. 60, 61; 1938, pars. 68–69. (3) OCM 13498, 4 Mar 37; 13888, 2 Sep 37.

[118] (1) Hist of U.S. Half Track Vehicles, OHF. (2) Ann Rpts CofOrd, 1934–38, as cited n. 117(2).

[119] In several years larger sums were actually spent for research and development because transfer of money earmarked for other purposes was authorized. For example, see memo, ACofS G–4 for CofS, 6 Apr 39, sub: WD Research and Development Program, FY 1941, G–4/29552, DRB AGO.

ommendations. With cost of material estimated at about $300,000, 70 percent of the money was marked for salaries. Distribution of money among the twenty-one groups was as follows: $249,900 for artillery ammunition, including antimechanization weapons; $111,810 for procurement of artillery ammunition for service test; $101,300 for development of mobile artillery; $76,620 for ballistics research; $67,774 for small arms; $65,000 for railway artillery; $64,000 for artillery fire control; $60,120 for tanks; and smaller amounts for the remaining thirteen groups. Even for individual projects of major importance, the sums allotted had to be small: $2,500 for the light mortar, $800 for the 81-mm. mortar. The $60,000 for tanks was spent largely on the medium tank T5. Most of the 224 projects had been on the books for several years before 1937, some for over a decade. On twenty-one there had been no progress at all; on thirty-four work was only 1 to 10 percent completed.[120]

The question naturally arises as to why the research funds were spread so thin to cover so many items when the urgency of some undertakings would appear wholly to obliterate the importance of others. The answer lies in the fact that the Ordnance Department had to serve all branches of the Army. The Infantry would not acquiesce in devoting all appropriations to artillery development, nor would the Cavalry agree to a program disregarding its needs for armored cars to permit improvement of small arms. Each service had to get a share. The Ordnance Technical Committee mapped out the tentative distribution of research monies, the General Staff decided. In 1937 the apportionment of projects showed Field Artillery holding first place with 68 of the 224. Forty projects were for the Infantry, 35 each for the Coast Artillery and the Air Corps, 21 for the Cavalry, a scattered few for the Engineers and Chemical Warfare, and the rest for "all Arms and Services."[121]

The War Department as a whole appreciated the wisdom of devoting a large slice of its available funds in peace years to research and development. For Ordnance development work alone, the War Department survey of 1929 had recommended an annual budget of not less than $3,000,000. But when total appropriations were small, the operating needs of the standing army and the cost of maintaining equipment already in existence tended year after year to eat up the lion's share of appropriations. Thus for preservation of ammunition larger sums were allotted in the early thirties than for research projects.[122] Tabulation of the relatively stable appropriations for research and development shows how the percentage of the total Ordnance appropriation shrank after 1934, though after 1937, by transfer of funds, more than the original allotment was actually spent.

As 1939 approached, the General Staff deliberately chose to reduce the research budget in the interests of having more money for actual rearmament.[123] But the Chief of Ordnance believed that a large increase for ordnance research and development was of vital importance. His contention was strongly supported by the Chief of Field Artillery, the Chief of Coast Artillery, the Chief of Cavalry, and the Chief of Infantry, who all concurred that

[120] 1st Ind, incl to ltr, CofOrd to TAG, 10 Oct 36, OO 111.3/6186, NA.

[121] *Ibid.*

[122] (1) Survey of WD, 1929, p. 16, NA. (2) Ann Rpt CofOrd, 1934, par. 12b. See above, Ch. III, pp. 64-65.

[123] Watson, *Chief of Staff: Prewar Plans and Preparations*, pp. 42-44.

TABLE 11—ORDNANCE DEPARTMENT TOTAL APPROPRIATIONS AND APPROPRIATIONS FOR RESEARCH AND DEVELOPMENT: FISCAL YEARS 1921–40

Fiscal Year	Appropriations			Actual expenditures Research & Development
	Total	Research & Development	Percent R&D of Total	
1921	$22, 880, 186	$1, 120, 500	4. 9	([a])
1922	13, 425, 960	2, 058, 225	15. 3	([a])
1923	6, 859, 030	1, 400, 197	20. 4	([a])
1924	5, 812, 180	1, 223, 900	21. 1	([a])
1925	7, 751, 272	1, 867, 600	24. 1	([a])
1926	7, 543, 802	1, 013, 500	13. 4	([a])
1927	9, 549, 827	989, 500	10. 4	([a])
1928	12, 179, 856	1, 405, 000	11. 5	([a])
1929	12, 549, 877	1, 369, 500	10. 9	([a])
1930	11, 858, 981	2, 711, 500	22. 9	([a])
1931	12, 422, 466	1, 137, 148	9. 2	([a])
1932	11, 121, 567	1, 311, 352	11. 8	([a])
1933	11, 588, 737	1, 291, 764	11. 1	([a])
1934	7, 048, 455	1, 255, 837	17. 8	([a])
1935	11, 049, 829	1, 266, 500	11. 5	$1, 268, 546
1936	17, 110, 301	1, 260, 000	7. 4	1, 237, 745
1937	18, 376, 606	1, 350, 000	7. 3	1, 350, 018
1938	24, 949, 075	1, 360, 000	5. 5	1, 661, 444
1939	112, 226, 412	1, 360, 000	1. 2	1, 735, 023
1940	176, 546, 788	1, 650, 000	0. 9	1, 941, 338

[a] Data not available.

Source: Stat Br, OUSW, Weekly Stat Rpt Summary 3, 19 Jul 41, p. 9, DRB AGO; and interview with James A. Brown, R&D Serv, 31 Mar 53.

the insufficient funds allotted Ordnance for its development program over the preceding five years had resulted in disastrous delays. For example, the $276,400 marked for all 1940 mobile artillery development, the Chief of Coast Artillery asserted, would not even meet the cost of work on one item, the intermediate-caliber antiaircraft gun.[124]

General Tschappat's summary of the situation in January 1938 was grimly factual: the Ordnance backlog of untouched artillery and automotive development projects totalled $10,000,000, of small arms projects $1,000,000. For ammunition alone, a budget of $1,500,000 a year for several years was imperative inasmuch as new methods and new matériel being developed in a rearming world would add to costs. Research, as distinguished from de-

[124] (1) Memo, CofFA for ACofS G–4, 10 Jan 38, G–4/29552, P&E, R&D Program, 1938. (2) Memo, CofCav for CofOrd, 8 Jan 38, OO 111.3/6589. (3) Memo, CofInf for CofOrd, 7 Jan 38, sub: R&D Program, FY 1940, OO 111.3/6588. (4) Ltr, CofCA thru CofOrd to TAG, 8 Jan 38, sub: R&D Program, FY 1940, OO 111.3/6590. All in NA.

velopment work, had been equally crippled for want of money. The Department had been unable either consistently to apply engineering principles worked out by industry in the decade past or to utilize techniques perfected in Ordnance laboratories. A doubling of research activity was essential for the future. In the absence of qualified ordnance experts in private industry, the Department had to recruit and train its own designers and engineers, a costly business. Purchase of designs from abroad, even if desirable, had been prohibitively expensive: the price recently quoted for rights to a foreign 37-mm. antiaircraft gun had approximately equaled the Ordnance Department's total annual research and development budget. General Tschappat considered $2,500,000 for research and development in 1940 an absolute minimum.[125] Congress appropriated $1,650,000 for this purpose.

Perhaps the refusal of the Bureau of the Budget to allot larger sums to Ordnance research and development and the reluctance of the Congress to vote as much as the budget called for can be partly explained by the tenor of the annual reports of the Ordnance Department in the years preceding 1940. Neither in hearings before Congressional committees nor in annual reports to the Secretary of War did Chiefs of Ordnance betray anxiety. Instead of telling the Congressional committees on military affairs that American ordnance, thanks to lack of money, consisted largely of the obsolete equipment of World War I, Chiefs of Ordnance year after year either avoided making any appraisal or else announced that in quality particular items of American ordnance were as good as or better than those of any army in the world. All officers appearing before Congressional committees were expected to confine themselves to answering specific questions, and not to volunteer information or opinion. The result was that year after year congressmen, trusting to the testimony their questions elicited from the experts, could believe that the United States Army, though small, was equipped with the very best. Similarly, the formal reports from the Chief of Ordnance to the Secretary of War sounded confident; they presented summaries of what had been done but rarely mentioned what was left undone. Because the published annual report of the Secretary of War, which included the summary statements of chiefs of arms and services, circulated widely, discretion apparently seemed the better part of valor. This explanation gains weight from evidence in the correspondence between the Ordnance Department and the General Staff. There, occasionally, the Chief of Ordnance warned of the true situation. It was General Tschappat's letter to The Adjutant General that bluntly described the lag in Ordnance development work up to 1938. Some months later General Wesson reported to the Assistant Chief of Staff, G–4, that the Ordnance Department had not been able to keep abreast of recent developments abroad. Yet in the spring of 1941 General Wesson told a House committee that American weapons were as good as "and in many instances superior to those of any other army in the world."[126] In the face of statements in like vein repeated at intervals during the preceding years, Congress could scarcely be expected to vote large

[125] Ltr, CofOrd to TAG, 8 Jan 38, OO 111.3/6554, NA.

[126] (1) Memo, CofOrd for ACofS G–4, 29 Nov 38, sub: Estimates for R&D for FY 1941, OO 111.3/6906, NA. (2) WDAB 1942, HR, p. 537.

291064 O—55——15

sums of money to meet an exigency that members had little reason to think existed. Here was a situation not limited to the Ordnance Department in dealing with Congress, but representing the twenty-year-long struggle of the whole War Department versus the holders of the purse strings and lagging public opinion.

The Role of Technical Intelligence

As war is competitive and military equipment satisfactory only if it is as good as or better than that of potential enemies, knowledge of what ordnance other nations were developing was at all times of great importance to the United States Army. In appraising the value of technical intelligence reports three questions arise. Was adequate information available? If so, was it studied? How fully and how promptly was it applied? These questions have immediate bearing on the status of Ordnance research and development before 1940.

The formal channel for technical intelligence was through the Military Intelligence Division of the General Staff. Observers abroad dispatched their reports to the Assistant Chief of Staff, G–2, who then relayed the reports to the arm or service concerned. Though occasionally, particularly during the 1920's, the Ordnance Department sent an officer to Europe on a special mission, and during the Spanish Civil War the War Department stationed men on the scene, the usual procedure was to rely upon information forwarded by officers, specifically detailed as observers. Ordnance officers with engineering background were ideally the men to serve in this capacity and to prepare the technical reports on foreign ordnance.[127] But the number of Ordnance officers qualified by experience who also had the necessary command of a foreign language and who had private incomes large enough to meet the expenses of a tour of duty abroad was small;[128] in fact, between 1920 and 1940 there were only nine, and between November 1930 and May 1940 only two—Maj. Philip R. Faymonville in Moscow, and Capt. René R. Studler assigned to London. Thus General Williams' original plan of frequently replacing Ordnance officers abroad fell down and with it the opportunity for them to report upon their findings in person, rather than in writing. In countries to which the Ordnance Department could not supply a liaison officer and during the early thirties when no Ordnance officer was assigned to foreign service anywhere, officers of other branches of the Army transmitted information. Particularly important were Maj. Truman Smith's reports from Berlin.

Over the years a very considerable body of written data on foreign matériel accumulated in Washington. The long tours of duty of both Major Faymonville and Captain Studler, the former from July 1934 to February 1939, the latter from July 1936 to October 1940, gave the Ordnance Department the benefit of uninterrupted series of letters during a specially critical period. The reports from the Soviet Union were general in character, but those from western Europe were of a character to command close attention, for the great munitions makers were located in Germany, France, England, Czechoslovakia, Switzerland, and Sweden. Though Captain Studler was formally assigned to London, his mission was a roving one and

[127] ODO 8, 31 May 17; 104, 4 Jan 18; 222, 25 May 18; 297, 10 Aug 18, OHF.

[128] The annual cost of a tour of duty in London in the 1930's Colonel Studler estimated to have been about $10,000 in excess of Army pay.

included observation of developments in much of western Europe. The number, the details, and the timing of his studies made them peculiarly significant.[129] A list of the subjects he covered in his 300-odd reports reveals the scope of his work.[130]

Sometimes the information in reports was perforce sketchy, consisting of photographs, rather general descriptions, or even merely guesses based on inference. Sometimes, particularly before the war began, the data were detailed, though in the absence of precisely dimensioned drawings Ordnance designers could consider the information suggestive rather than explicit. Technical intelligence reports could supply facts on the observed performance of a piece of equipment and could list general characteristics; more exact details were very difficult to obtain. Ordinarily, the War Department could get engineering details only by purchase from a European munitions maker or by an exchange of information with a foreign government. In any attempted exchange, American officers again and again deplored the weakness of their positions. American military journals, technical magazines, and newspapers so frequently spread across their pages the essential information of a new American development that liaison officers found themselves with nothing to offer and came away empty handed. Yet occasionally they apparently believed it possible to locate supplemental data, for Ordnance officers serving as military observers complained of being kept in ignorance of what further information the Ordnance Department might want. Their reports elicited no response, unless personal correspondents supplied it, and the officers abroad were left unguided. If, as an Ordnance general later averred, the Department followed their work closely and was balked of action only by the indifference of the using arms and by want of money,[131] the observers assembling the information never knew how it was received at home. Real or seeming lack of interest in the Ordnance office in Washington tended to discourage the search for additional data. Reports were primarily valuable for the clues they gave. They indicated the lines of development to pursue rather than how to pursue them.

How carefully men in the War Department studied technical intelligence reports naturally depended in some measure on who saw them. Within the Ordnance Department distribution was orderly. When a report landed in the Office, Chief of Ordnance, from G–2—where it might have been kept for as long as four or five months—it went first to such members of the Technical Staff as were concerned with the subject and then passed on to the Manufacturing Division engineer in charge of the particular item discussed in the report. If the report dealt with tanks, it went to the chief of the Artillery and Automotive Division of the Technical Staff and on to the engineer in charge of automotive design; if with antiaircraft, from the Technical Staff to the engineers responsible for that type of artillery and to the man in

[129] Of Studler's work Col. Raymond E. Lee, in 1940, wrote:

There are few, if any, other ordnance officers alive who have had such opportunities for first hand study and comparison of modern weapon development and use as Major Studler has enjoyed.

For this reason, I recommend that his opinions be given prompt and serious consideration by those authorities who are now making decisions of great magnitude and long range importance to the future of the U.S. Army.

Rpt from London, 31 Jul 40, sub: Mobilization of Industry, IG 6620, 2724-A-38-12, DRB AGO.

[130] See correspondence files of reports from London, Berlin, and Paris, 1936–40, OO 321.12/289, and Incls 1–3 of same file, DRB AGO.

[131] Comments attached to ltr, Gen Barnes to Maj Gen Orlando Ward, 25 Jan 52, OCMH.

charge of artillery ammunition. Thence the original report or a copy would usually go to an arsenal or to Aberdeen Proving Ground, or to both. The routing was designed to give the persons best able to use the information full opportunity to study it. The names of the men who received various reports are often still attached to the original folders. Engineers and designers for each category of ordnance saw the reports that touched their special fields. Presumably each man in turn could truthfully say "Contents noted." Furthermore, from 1920 on an accession list, compiled monthly, was distributed to division heads, so that anyone with a legitimate interest in the information could readily know of any new material that had come in. Many reports were circulated and recirculated several times. They all ended in the files of the Ordnance library.

What use the information derived from military reports was put to is harder to perceive. Reading, even studying, a document is not synonymous with grasping its full import, and understanding its significance is still different from acting upon it. Hints of European experiments or news of achievements abroad may frequently have caused uneasiness or curiosity among Ordnance engineers, but as long as the Department had no money to exploit a discovery, they could reason that further investigation was futile. The optimism, the intellectual vigor, the whole temperament of the individual in charge of developing each field of ordnance might determine whether the Department pursued or ignored a line of research. An underling's ideas could be quashed by the indifference of his superior. How deep an impression particular technical intelligence reports may have made must be largely a matter of speculation. The paternity of ideas is nearly always difficult to fix. Though few ordnance development projects before 1940 can be traced directly to military observers' reports from abroad, some reports may have exerted pronounced influence. A few specific examples may illustrate the workings of the technical intelligence system. In August 1937 Captain Studler reported at some length on the new German 47-mm. and 50-mm. antitank guns he had seen:

The 47mm anti-tank gun is considered of interest as representing a tendency to which reference has been made in earlier reports. . . . The undersigned [has] expressed the opinion that replacement of the German Army 37mm anti-tank gun by one of a larger caliber, probably 47mm or 50mm could be expected.

It will be noted that the initial striking energy of the 47mm is approximately 36% greater than the corresponding energy of the 37mm, with an increase of approximately 15% of total weight of gun and carriage. It is recognized that conclusions of value cannot be drawn without complete data as to comparable external ballistics and actual impact results.

It is of supplemental interest to note that a barrel of a caliber of approximately 50mm and not less than 50 calibers long was seen by the undersigned in a Krupp gun shop at Essen, Germany, on June 23, 1937. Krupp engineers at first denied that such a barrel was in existence and later stated that it was prepared for an experimental model of anti-tank gun. The same engineers indicated that the 37mm gun was considered inadequate by German military personnel.

On the following page of this report there appears a tabulated statement of comparative characteristics of the various anti-tank cannon seen by the undersigned in the course of the past 12 months. Weapons of a caliber less than 25mm have been excluded from the tabulation. The smaller caliber anti-tank guns include Rheinmetall, Solothurn, Oerlikon and Madsen.

The energy and weight figures given in the last two lines of the tabulation are believed to be of interest although they should not be made the basis of evaluation without full consideration of the specific characteristics and of descriptive data contained in manufacturers' catalogues or in individual reports to which reference has been made. For example, the Schneider 47mm, the Bofors 47mm and the Madsen 37mm guns, all with relatively high energy indices, are provided with steel tired carriages and are therefore not suitable for high road speeds.

It will be noted that, of the guns listed, only the British has true all around traverse.[132]

The significance of this information, as Captain Studler stated, lay in its indication of a trend. The exact data were missing. The routing slip attached shows that eventually the report reached the chief Ordnance engineers in charge of artillery design and in due course went on to men at Aberdeen Proving Ground and at Picatinny Arsenal. The men who did the actual work at drafting boards apparently did not see the letter. No one requested more information.

Years later, when U.S. soldiers discovered that German tank and antitank guns outranged theirs, angry American officers charged the Ordnance Department with ineptitude for not knowing what high-powered armament German units possessed.[133] The Ordnance Department had known. G–2 of the General Staff and Ordnance men alike had received warning in 1937. But they had not acted upon the information. Several facts entered in. In the first place, Major Smith, in 1937 the military observer in Berlin through whom the report quoted above was sent, disagreed with Captain Studler's prophecy that German antitank units would in the near future be equipped with guns larger than 37-mm. Major Smith's comment, appended as an indorsement, presumably weakened the impact of Captain Studler's report. In the second place, because the evolution of concepts of defense against tanks had not yet gone far, a light-weight gun to accompany the infantry was still the goal sought. Much later, doctrine would dictate use of tanks versus tanks, and bazookas or recoilless rifles for powerful defense in infantrymen's hands against attacking armored vehicles. Until doctrine changed, the requirement of an antitank gun little or no heavier than the 37-mm. was bound to endure. For what it was, the 37-mm. was a good weapon; it met the requirements as set up. In the third place, be it repeated, in 1937 and 1938 the data available on the German 47-mm. was not enough to permit Ordnance engineers at Rock Island and Picatinny Arsenals to build a 47-mm. gun and make ammunition for it without starting nearly at the beginning of the long development process. A Rheinmetall 37-mm. gun, on the other hand, was at that moment in the possession of the Ordnance Department; it could complete adaptation of that design for the U.S. Army relatively rapidly. And the General Staff wanted something quickly.[134]

On foreign tank developments technical intelligence was copious. Because combat experience with tanks after World War I was limited to the Italian campaign in Ethiopia and the Spanish Civil War, designers of every nation were especially eager to profit from the experiments of others. Though the cost of building a pilot model precluded the possibility of testing every innovation, Ordnance Department automotive engineers scrutinized such data

[132] Rpt from Berlin, 13 Aug 37, sub: Armament and Equipment—Organizational, Standard Rheinmetall 47 mm AT Gun L/34, OKD 472.95/34/2, Ord Tech Intel files.

[133] See below, Ch. XI.

[134] See above, pp. 47–50.

as came into their hands. Some features of foreign design were nearly impossible to learn; in the fall of 1936, in response to an Ordnance Department overture to the British proposing freer exchange of information, the military observer in London replied that the British War Office had never permitted any foreigner to see the inside of a British tank.[135] When in 1933 a young German, ostensibly as a personal hobby, published a book on combat vehicles, *Taschenbuch der Tanks,* a copy sent to Washington soon found its way into the Ordnance technical library and saw constant use. Its photographs, text, and tabular comparisons of the chief characteristics of successive models developed by every nation were so informing that the book was literally thumbed to pieces in the course of the next years.[136] Comments appended to a report of the spring of 1939 covering recent German tank designs indicate that automotive engineers of the Ordnance Department continued to watch the work of other nations. Between 1936 and the end of 1939 more than a score of reports on German, French, and British tanks and tank accessories came in. Apart from the ever-present handicap of too little money to test new devices, American tank design was chiefly obstructed by the failure to modify doctrine of tactical use. Neither designers' ignorance of foreign developments nor bland assumption of the superiority of American automotive engineering was responsible for shortcomings in American tanks of the 1930's.

Many considerations might affect the treatment accorded any piece of technical intelligence and its ultimate value. The reports on the Mohaupt "explosive" may serve as an example. In January 1939 a military liaison officer chanced upon a trail that led him to a young Swiss, Henri Mohaupt, who described in general terms a new type of explosive which he claimed to have developed. A British commission was then secretly investigating Mohaupt's device and upon payment of a fee later witnessed test firings. Correspondence between the American military observer assigned to Bern, Switzerland, and the Mohaupt Company followed, and in July the War Department cabled Captain Studler to pursue inquiries. Captain Studler's report, sent in August, contained a photostat copy of the results of the tests conducted for the British commission and a summary of the most significant features of the explosive as Mohaupt himself set them forth: its effect, "in certain cases" forty times that of TNT for equal weights, its stability, its low cost of manufacture, and the variety of uses to which it could be adapted. Mohaupt claimed also to have developed a fuze that doubled the effect of the explosive. The British officers who had been present at the tests surmised that Mohaupt was using the Neumann principle but, as they assured Captain Studler, although Mohaupt had indeed demonstrated the results he claimed for his explosive, the price he was demanding had led the British to drop negotiations.[137]

While this report aroused some immediate interest in the Ordnance Department, the refusal of Mohaupt and his associates

[135] Ltr, London to ACofS, 8 Oct 36, sub: Exchange of Information between the United States and Foreign Countries Concerning Tank Developments, OO 321.12/4234, Eng, NA.

[136] When a second edition appeared in 1938 engineers in the Ordnance Department were dismayed to find included a detailed description of the new American medium tank with special features, supposedly still a carefully guarded military secret.

[137] (1) Interv with Col Studler, 9 Jan 49. (2) Rpt from London, 12 Aug 39, sub: Ammunition and Pyrotechnics, Mohaupt Explosive, OKD 471.86/280, Ord Tech Intel files.

to divulge any particulars of the construction of his device unless the United States Government paid $25,000 in advance soon halted negotiations: ". . . further interest of the War Department," the Ordnance Department stated, "is contingent upon evidence that either England or some other major European power has acquired rights for use of the device."[138] Thus, caution about spending money delayed matters for a year. Late in 1940 Mohaupt in person came to Washington under the aegis of the American agent of Edgar Brandt, the French munitions maker. Doubtless the fact that Mohaupt had in hand an actual model of a rifle grenade built to his design clinched his argument and won him opportunity to make 200 grenades to test fire at Aberdeen Proving Ground. The demonstration at Aberdeen convinced the Army and Navy men who witnessed it that here indeed was an important "new form of munition." They at once recommended purchasing rights to employ the Mohaupt principle in any form to which it might prove adaptable.[139]

The curious fact then came to light that the essential features of this "new form of munition" had already been offered to the Ordnance Department by Nevil Monroe Hopkins, an American inventor. The Ordnance Technical Staff had rejected Hopkins' design of a bomb built with a shaped charge and rejected it without testing because, the letter to the inventor had stated, his was not a new idea.[140] Several months later the Technical Staff learned from Mohaupt what the British had already guessed, that the Mohaupt projectile achieved its effect not by a new explosive but by similar use of the Munroe principle of the hollow charge. By citing the British patent of 1911 that had caused the United States Patent Office to deny Hopkins a patent, the Ordnance Patent Section thereupon showed Mohaupt's "secret" to be no secret. The upshot was that the Ordnance Department was able to conclude a contract with Mohaupt's company at a much lower price than the Swiss had first demanded.[141] An adaptation of Mohaupt's design later formed the basis of the bazooka rocket.[142]

Estimate of the value of technical intelligence reports on this new type of projectile must be weighed today by recognition of Hopkins' contribution. The reports on the Mohaupt projectile would have served an all-important purpose had they directed the attention of American ammunition experts to the importance of Hopkins' proposal. But the Ordnance technicians who studied the confidential papers from Europe and Hopkins' hollow charge bomb obviously saw no connection between Mohaupt's development and Hopkins', in

[138] Memo, Subcommittee on Explosives for Ord Committee, Tech Staff, 2 Dec 39, sub: Mohaupt Explosive—Submitted by Dr. E. Matthias, Zurich, Item 1291-I, Ord Tech Committee files.

[139] Memo, Subcommittee on Grenades, Artillery Ammunition and Bombs for Ord Committee, Tech Staff, 30 Dec 40, sub: Project for Inaugurating the Procurement of Rifle Grenades following Designs Developed by Mohaupt, Item 16374, Ord Tech Committee files.

[140] "The use of the Munroe effect of explosive," wrote the assistant to the Chief of Ordnance, "has been proposed many times to the Military and Naval services and the phenomenon has been known for years . . . the type of bomb proposed by you would be useful only as a special mission weapon and even then of questionable value." Ltr, Gen McFarland to Nevil Monroe Hopkins, 28 May 40, OO 400.111/11068, DRB AGO. Test of the "Dynamix" explosive Hopkins proposed took place at APG in 1941 but in an ordinary bomb casing minus the hollow charge feature. The "Dynamix" filler alone proved impractical. OCM 20082, 15 Mar 43.

[141] Patent 28030. Photostat copy in OD Patent Sec. Subsequently, Mohaupt's patent applications were held abandoned by the Commissioner of Patents for violation of security.

[142] See Ch. XII, below.

spite of the lead given them by British research chemists' conclusions cited in one report from abroad. The British, in fact, supplied only with the photographic records of the Zurich tests and the British officers' oral descriptions, which the military report made equally available to the United States, proceeded to develop hollow charge projectiles of their own.[143] In the United States the investigation was dropped until the Brandt agent in Washington intervened to get Mohaupt a chance to demonstrate his grenade. Technical intelligence was not involved in that transaction; the 1939 reports from Europe had no influence whatsoever upon the Ordnance Department's decision many months later to test Mohaupt's grenade.

These examples indicate that utilization of technical intelligence was at times both prompt and intelligent, at other times laggardly and unimaginative. For the lapses explanations of a sort can be found: the small staff of officers and trained civilians in the Office, Chief of Ordnance, before 1940, with the consequent multiplicity of assignments for each person which automatically reduced his time for thinking through a problem; the limitations on Ordnance research and development imposed by higher authority both through control of the purse strings and through specifying the characteristics that any new item should embody; and finally the fact that the temper of the American people up to 1939 made American involvement in war so unthinkable that vigorous pursuit of new munitions developments could hardly seem urgent. Ordnance officers and employees carried on their work in a milieu where everyone was more concerned with butter than with guns. Nevertheless, the testimony to a deep-seated complacency, inimical to ideas not originating within the upper echelons of the Ordnance Department, cannot be brushed aside.[144] Nevil Monroe Hopkins, though naturally a somewhat prejudiced judge, voiced the charge: "To the 'expert' smug in his 'superior' convictions, the writer often would like to say—'Better not know so much that much of it is untrue.' "[145]

Still, the Ordnance Department was by no means alone in its too frequent do-nothing attitude. Every branch and service of the U.S. Army, including the Air Corps, displayed it.[146] Indeed many weaknesses of Army Technical Intelligence before 1940 may be fairly attributed less to imperceptiveness or easy goingness of individuals on the General Staff or in the Ordnance Department than to the lack of any systematic routine for following up information. In the first place, military liaison officers had only very general instructions. Neither G-2 nor the Ordnance Department through G-2 had mapped out charts or lists of items upon which data were desired. Military observers were obliged to exercise their own judgment on what would be useful. Correct estimates of what to look for became increasingly difficult as in the course of time the officer serving abroad lost touch with the work of the Ordnance men at home. No regular two-way exchange of information between the Office, Chief of Ordnance, and the observers was provided for. In the second place, when thought-provoking information reached

---

[143] (1) Directorate of Explosives Research, Research Dept. Woolwich, England, "Cavity Effect" of Explosives, A Summary of its History and Service Uses, Sep 41, Incl 1 to OO 350.05/1205, DRB AGO. (2) Group Capt. Claude H. Keith, RAF (Ret.), *I Hold My Aim* (London, 1946), pp. 147-49.

[144] Interv with Col Studler, 19 Jan 40.

[145] Nevil Monroe Hopkins, The Battleship Wrecking Bomb, p. 3, photostat copy in OD Pat Sec.

[146] For example, Air Corps failure to adopt self-sealing gas tanks before 1942.

the Ordnance Department, no recognized procedure existed whereby it could quickly affect policy decisions. An Ordnance draftsman working on the American 37-mm. antitank gun might question whether the 37-mm. would be powerful enough in view of the German development of a 47-mm., but his job was confined to designing a weapon incorporating features determined by higher authority, in this case a 37-mm. He might discuss the question with the engineer in charge of the section, the chief engineer, in turn, with the head of the Technical Staff Artillery Division, the latter with the chief of the Technical Staff and with Ordnance Technical Committee representatives of the using arm and of the General Staff. Not only would this take time, but the chances were at least even that somewhere along the line the discussion would get sidetracked. Both imagination and persistence would be needed to drive home the point that a new European development was rendering obsolete an American design. The users had to be convinced and then the Bureau of the Budget and Congress had to be persuaded to supply the money. It was no one person's job to see that knowledge was translated promptly into appropriate action.

The General Staff looked to the Ordnance Department for expert advice on munitions; the Ordnance Department expected the using arms and G–2 to stipulate their requirements, based on over-all plans of tactical use and evaluation of competitors' equipment. Between these groups important decisions could easily be delayed or altogether lost in the shuffle. The processing of information was at times inordinately slow. If the dates on route slips be a safe index, a military report in the 1930's might take nearly a year to circulate. Some reports remained with G–2 several months and took another six or seven to go the rounds of Ordnance Department offices.[147] Routing technical intelligence within the Ordnance Department was left to a clerk who lacked authority to push matters. By the time decision to act upon a report was reached, the information might well be out of date. Not until the summer of 1940 did the General Staff awaken to the faultiness of its intelligence system and set up the machinery for more effective operations.[148]

[147] The commanding officer at Aberdeen commented at the end of 1937: "Judging from the age of the . . . Reports received at the Aberdeen Proving Ground any method which would tend to speed up the dissemination of information from abroad is desirable." 1st Ind, CO APG for CofOrd, 21 Dec 37, sub: Dissemination of Information, OO 321.12/4301 Eng, NA.

[148] (1) Memo ACofS G–2 for CofS, 16 Aug 40, sub: WD Special Regulation, War Dept, Intelligence, MID 350.051, DRB AGO. (2) Ltr, TAG to Chiefs of All Arms and Services, 6 Sep 40, sub: Intelligence Sections in the Office of Chiefs of Arms and Services, AG 321.19 MID, DRB AGO.

CHAPTER VIII

Wartime Organization and Procedures in Research and Development

It is easy even for participants in the military planning and labors of 1940 to forget the strains, the uncertainties, the hours of frustration, and the moments of despair that marked that summer. Feverish activity within the War Department accompanied anxiety born of the successes of the German armies. As money flowed out for rearming the United States, the Ordnance Department set itself vigorously to its task. Pressure eased slightly after the failure of the German blitz upon England, only to mount to a new height in the fall of 1941 as war in the Pacific loomed ever closer and Hitler's subjugation of all continental Europe seemed imminent. When the disasters of late 1941 and 1942 occurred in the Pacific, grim determination lent new energy to officers responsible for replacing the lost equipment and supplying the Army with weapons more efficient than it had ever had before. The slowness of the build-up in 1943, the hopes for the invasion in mid-1944, the shock of the Ardennes offensive that December, and the ultimate triumph of 1945 formed a backdrop of emotional tension in the arena where the Ordnance Department played its part. The rest of this volume treats of Ordnance research and development work topic by topic, and thus sacrifices much of the drama inherent in the sweep of events. Though clarity has demanded a discussion based on particular aspects of technological problems, the reader must remember that work proceeded in an atmosphere darkening and lightening with the defeats and victories of Allied armies in the field.

Factors Immediately Conditioning Research and Development

Because the time necessary to evolve the complicated mechanisms of modern weapons from initial design to finished product is long, logic suggests that American soldiers must have fought World War II mostly with equipment developed before Pearl Harbor. Down into 1944 this was indeed the case. Yet before V-J Day arrived, American and Allied troops were using a number of weapons that in 1941 were scarcely more than vague ideas. While the truly revolutionizing new items such as the amphibious cargo and personnel carriers, the proximity fuzes, and the homing bombs were not conceived within the Ordnance Department, its staff contributed such innovations as armor-piercing-incendiary ammunition, bazookas, and recoilless rifles. Equally essential to victory were the series of developments pushed to completion upon weapons and vehicles on which Ordnance technicians had worked for years—the 90-mm. antiaircraft and tank guns, the fire control devices, the aircraft cannon, the tanks. Altogether, some 1,200 new or vastly improved items containing thousands of components were designed and produced before midsummer 1945. The difficulties of achieving this feat bear review.

The first handicaps in this race against time were the late start and the necessity for haste. During the peace years money for Ordnance research and development had been little. The backlog of projects in 1940 was large. Yet in the summer of 1940 research and development work upon new Ordnance matériel had to be relegated to a secondary role because the urgency of getting equipment into the hands of troops was so great that quantity production of accepted items had to be the first task. Not until mid-1942 were experts of the Ordnance Department released to work solely upon design and development of new weapons.

Meanwhile, observation of combat in Europe and, later, actual fighting in the Pacific and North Africa revealed weaknesses and gaps in American equipment that added to the list of projects requiring investigation. Thereupon arose the problem of contriving a system of communication whereby Ordnance officers in the theatres could transmit quickly to research and development men in the zone of the interior the exact nature of the changes combat experience dictated. Establishing machinery to effect this took many months and was scarcely in operation until the spring of 1943. Only delegation of many research problems to other agencies enabled the Ordnance Department eventually to supply American and Allied forces with arms and ammunition as good as or superior to the enemy's.

A third problem grew out of the climate and terrain to which fighting equipment was exposed. Corroding dampness, excessive heat, bitter cold, beach landings where stores were drenched in salt water, operations over coral reefs, desert sand, or precipitous mountain trails, through thick jungle or deep snows, all threatened to immobilize or seriously damage munitions. Prolonged, careful, and expensive experimentation was needed to find answers to these problems. Money had not been available in the twenties and thirties. Again the late start added to difficulties, although, in the absence of combat testing, some malfunctions could scarcely have been forestalled.

A final difficulty was the problem of designing matériel that could be mass produced by American industry from available materials. No item, regardless of its perfection of design, could be counted upon unless private companies could turn it out accurately and quickly. In spite of the efforts of the Ordnance districts in the 1930's to prepare manufacturers for munitions production, most firms in 1941 still lacked experience. Hence, simplicity of design was important. Machine-tool shortages also emphasized this need. Furthermore, private industry's inexperience pointed to the wisdom of making as few changes in design as possible once contracts for manufacture had been let and production lines set up. It is true that in some instances success in devising a new piece of equipment depended upon the ability of manufacturers to make intricate parts of extraordinary delicacy. Thus the proximity fuze was made possible by finding producers who could make tiny turbines and generators and miniature radio circuits of utmost exactness and make them by the hundred thousand. But in all cases the less complicated the design, the surer the Ordnance Department was of getting matériel fabricated to specification. Moreover, since adequate stock piles of strategic raw materials had not been accumulated in advance, or because sufficient quantities of the ideal material nowhere existed, development of ordnance was handicapped by the necessity of finding substitute materials—synthetic rubber, plastics, new alloy steels.[1] Shortages of tin and copper launched the attempt to produce steel cartridge cases. Vehicles rode on synthetic tires. Rubber washers gave way to neoprene washers. Tank engines had to be adjusted to burn lower octane gasoline. Use of new materials required extensive preliminary research.[2]

In view of the baffling problems to be solved and the dearth of men qualified by scientific training and experience to deal with them, the success of the wartime research and development program stands as a triumph. It was a job demanding wide collaboration. President Roosevelt's creation of the National Defense Research Committee—NDRC, for short—in June 1940 was an all-important step in aligning civilian scientists to share in the task. The Ordnance Department had opened negotiations some months earlier with the National Academy of Sciences to pursue a number of investigations too remote from the immediate urgent problems at hand to be handled by the overworked staff of the Ordnance Department itself. In October these projects, eighteen of them in the field of ammunition, were turned over to the NDRC. Other assignments followed. By thus enlisting leading civilian scientists to undertake most of the basic long-range research for the military, the United States escaped the consequences that Germany faced after 1942 when lack of co-ordination between projects, subordination of research and development to production, and the resulting recourse to stop-gap measures lost the German nation the fruits of its best scientific knowledge and potential.[3]

For the scientist, a sharp distinction exists between basic research, the seeking of new principles of broad application, and technical research, that is, the application of new knowledge or of previously existing knowledge to a specific new item. The role of research in most government enterprises is logically limited to the latter. Certainly the military departments of the United States Government have rarely been free to pursue basic research save in the realm of ballistics; their responsibility is to apply the broad findings of fundamental research to specific military problems. Even the MANHATTAN Project was, strictly speaking, concerned largely with technical research, for much of the basic research upon the feasibility of splitting the atom had preceded the study of using this force in a bomb. Thus, apart from the work of its Ballistic Research Laboratory, the Ordnance Department never deliberately engaged in basic research, though occasionally men at Watertown, Picatinny,

[1] A Strategic Materials Act permitting stockpiling had been passed by the Congress in June 1939, but the amounts accumulated under this law were limited. See Millett, Mobilization Planning, MS, OCMH, p. 53.

[2] See Ch. XVIII, below.

[3] See Brig. Gen. Leslie E. Simon, *German Research in World War II* (New York and London, 1947), pp. 90–107.

and Frankford Arsenals found themselves constrained to carry on fundamental investigations in such fields as metallurgy and explosives. The Ballistic Research Laboratory at Aberdeen Proving Ground was an exception to the rule because study of the behavior of projectiles inevitably involves exploration of physical and chemical reactions of a basic character, and because no civilian institution in America had ever interested itself in this field.

Even technical research, the next step, came to be too complex and time consuming for the Ordnance Department to handle unaided after 1940. Thereafter until the end of the war, the Army's job on everything but ballistics was primarily one of development rather than of basic or technical research. The delegation of research problems to the National Defense Research Committee, to university scientists, research foundations, and industrial laboratories released the engineering talents of the Ordnance Department for the tasks of transforming laboratory innovations into equipment that could be mass produced. While there were exceptions, most Ordnance Department experimental work from 1940 through 1945 was concentrated upon design and development.

Only after technical research is far advanced can design begin. For design, the formulation of a pattern from which to build working models, is an engineering process entailing the calculation of stresses and tolerances, and the determination of the mechanical and chemical forces required and the strength of materials needed. From the designer's hand come the blueprints and specifications from which test models are built. Development can proceed only when there is a model to work upon, inasmuch as development is concerned with making a design practical by testing, discovering deficiencies, and devising corrections. In producing new military equipment, development is quite as essential as research. It may in fact continue after an item is officially accepted for standardization, although minor improvements are frequently labeled modification rather than development. Changes in techniques of production aimed at increasing output, bettering quality, or cutting costs may result in slight modifications of design, changes usually effected by so-called production engineers. When shortages of strategic raw materials necessitate use of substitutes, other engineering changes are often required.

In all these creative processes many people are involved. Patents are still issued, to be sure, and titles to inventions are still vested in particular individuals who establish their claims to having introduced original features into a device or mechanism. Yet patent offices of every nation ordinarily recognize only a few features of a design as constituting a novel patentable contribution. Modern weapons are nearly universally the product not of one inventor, or even two or three collaborators but of innumerable people. The very source of the initial idea is frequently hard to ascertain and the number of contributors to its development tends to produce anonymity. When the Ordnance Department requested the National Defense Research Committee to undertake research upon any one of a series of problems, the NDRC in turn might delegate investigation of particular phases to scientists or several research groups at universities or foundations. The VT, or radio, fuze, for example, evolved from that kind of collaboration; at the request of the Navy, the NDRC and NDRC contractors worked out the basic electronic features, ballisticians and fuze experts of the Ordnance Department supplied the guiding data to make the fuze workable in ammunition. Though the patent for torsion bar suspension for tanks reads in the name of General Barnes of the Ordnance Department, dozens of automotive engineers aided in the development. Consequently, the discussion of research and development in the pages that follow includes few individual names. Participation was so wide that rarely can individual credit be assigned fairly.

MAJ. GEN. GLADEON M. BARNES, *chief of the Research and Development Service.*

Evolution of Organized Research and Development

Whoever else falls into anonymity, Gladeon M. Barnes cannot. From 1938 to 1946, first as colonel, then as brigadier general, and finally as major general, he was a dominant figure in the Office, Chief of Ordnance, on research and development matters and made his influence strongly felt outside as well. As chief of the Technical Staff before 1940, he scrutinized every project proposed and followed progress on all approved. It was largely his decision that determined what research should be delegated to outside institutions. When in the summer of 1940 General Wesson transferred him to Industrial Service to direct production engineering, Colonel Barnes brought with him his organizing capacity and drive. Though the immediate problem then was to hurry through the blueprints and specifications on accepted matériel in order to get contractors started on production, Barnes' vision of the role research and development should occupy never deserted him. As soon as production was well launched, his opportunity came. By the summer of 1942 ammunition plants were in operation, tanks were beginning to roll out of the Tank Arsenal in Detroit, guns and carriages were emerging from factories in a dozen states, and fire control instruments were in process. Even the newly invented bazooka and bazooka rockets were in production. Convinced, therefore, that the peak of the crisis of initiating manufacture was now passed, General Campbell, the new Chief of Ordnance, placed General Barnes in charge of a separate research and development unit, first called the Technical Division, later the Research and Development Division and still later the Research and Development Service.

Barnes was a skilled engineer, a graduate of the University of Michigan School of Engineering. He was a man of varied ordnance experience, an expert on artillery, sure of his own judgments. An impassioned fighter for his own ideas, he was unwilling to sit by patiently to wait for his superiors to arrive at a vital decision affecting ordnance, and when necessary would take his argument directly to higher authority. When he believed that action was urgently needed, he took upon himself responsibility for starting work not yet officially authorized. His very inability to see any point of view but his own was in many ways an asset to the Ordnance Department at a time when swift action was imperative, though his opponents regarded his refusal to consider contrary opinion a very great weakness. He cut corners, set aside red tape, disregarded orthodox but delaying procedures. His admirers admit that he made mistakes, but they point out that he never pushed upon others blame for his own errors. On the other hand, just as he took all responsibility for mistakes, so, his critics aver, he took to himself credit for the solid work of his predecessors and of his subordinates. He believed an expanded Ordnance Department quite able to carry out a full research program without the intervention of any other agency except in so far as the Ordnance Department itself might contract for particular investigative work with industrial and university laboratories. In 1940 he appeared to question the value of a special committee of civilian scientists committed to the study of possible new weapons, but he was the man first chosen to serve as the War Department liaison officer with the National Defense Research Committee.[4] It was convincing testimony to his competence. While many people found him lacking in warmth and devoid of personal magnetism, throughout the war his opinion carried as great weight with his adversaries as with his supporters on particular issues. His knowledge, his persistence, and his forcefulness combined to fit him for the many-faceted job of directing wartime research and development.

The earlier provisions for Ordnance research and development assigned planning to the Ordnance Committee,[5] design to men in Industrial Service. The system was the outgrowth of General Williams' determination after World War I to have the using arms initiate requests for matériel to meet their needs, specify the military characteristics they desired, and then test the models designers evolved. The onus of responsibility for deciding what was necessary was thus shifted from the Ordnance Department to the combat arms, themselves not always in full accord.[6] Still, the arrangement was workable for many years largely because the Caliber Board had thoroughly mapped out so comprehensive a development program that a long series of projects stretched out before the Ordnance Department to pursue as time and money permitted. The Ordnance Committee with its representatives from the using arms and General Staff discussed, accepted, and rejected specific proposals, listened to reports upon progress, made recommendations to the General Staff for standardization, and finally recorded the formal action whereby a new item was adopted or an old one declared obsolete. The minutes of these meetings, the "OCM's," constituted a valuable source of information on the course of develop-

[4] Hist of Ord R&D Serv, II, NDRC Liaison (hereafter cited as NDRC Liaison) p. 11, OHF.

[5] Early in World War II the name Ordnance Committee was unofficially superseded by the title Ordnance Technical Committee. When the War Department ordered every technical service to establish a technical committee, the Ordnance Committee, though continuing to function just as it had for more than twenty years, came to be called generally the Ordnance Technical Committee.

[6] See Ch. VII, above.

ment of each item. The supervising unit within the Ordnance Department was a group of trained engineers, the Technical Staff, headed by an experienced officer. As Colonel Barnes described it early in 1940: "The Technical Staff is . . . responsible for research and development programs and for the approval of basic drawings of new material. It carries out all functions in regard to research and development, except the execution of the work." [7] The exception was a big one. The work was done by men in Industrial Service in the Office, Chief of Ordnance, in Washington, at the arsenals, or at Aberdeen Proving Ground. Occasionally, as in the case of research on powder, a commercial company undertook some investigation. The Technical Staff was an advising and recording group, not in any real sense an operating unit. The operating group in Industrial Service, on the other hand, had little say about policy and program.

As long as Caliber Board projects were in advance of any nation's accomplishments and as long as the tempo of development work was unhurried, the scheme sufficed. But it was ill-adapted to pushing through the kind of intensive study of alternatives together with the search for totally new scientific devices of war that events in 1939 and 1940 called for. Development work on existing models also suffered for want of a central head to coordinate it. Though in the summer of 1940 General Wesson felt obliged to refuse Colonel Barnes' plea for a separate research and development division dedicated solely to these problems, his assignment of Barnes to an operating position in Industrial Service proved to be a beginning. In spite of the fact that his job was primarily concerned with production, Barnes encouraged orderly progress on development work and himself proposed new lines to follow. The nearly seventy projects that he listed in May 1940 as requiring immediate attention indicate his awareness of what needed to be done.[8] Yet a year after he had taken charge of production engineering he protested the inadequacies of the organizational set-up:

1. The duplication of effort involved in the design and development of Ordnance matériel lies between the Technical Staff and Industrial Service. Take for example, the usual way in which a new project is initiated. A memorandum is prepared in one of the divisions of the Industrial Service and sent through the office of the Assistant Chief of Industrial Service, Engineering to Technical Staff. Technical Staff personnel prepare the O.C.M. It becomes necessary for this second group of officers and civilians to acquaint themselves with this project, either through contact with the office of the Assistant Chief of Industrial Service for Engineering or with the divisions. Often it is necessary to have these O.C.M.'s rewritten as the writer did not quite understand the project. A duplication occurs after the design has been prepared by the initiating division since the drawings must be approved by both the office of Assistant Chief of Industrial Service for Engineering and Technical Staff. After the O.C.M. is approved it is forwarded by letter to The Adjutant General, and after the general design has been approved by Technical Staff its duties cease until the item is ready for test at Aberdeen Proving Ground.

2. Drawings, designs, contacts with industry, follow-up, and all other work connected with development is the responsibility of Industrial Service. Design work is executed in the Industrial Service in Washington, by commercial companies, at the various arsenals, or at the Proving Ground. Difficulties are now encountered due to lack of authority of the Industrial Service at the Proving Ground where the ballistic laboratory and

[7] Memo, Col Barnes, 13 May 40, sub: Expansion of Research and Development Activities, Organization R&D Serv, Barnes file, OHF.

[8] Incl, sub: Estimates, to memo cited n. 7.

automotive design section have been built up. All other design sections and laboratories are under the control of the Industrial Service.[9]

The upshot was the abolition of the Technical Staff and the elimination of the duplicating efforts Barnes deplored but the continuation of research and development activities as an adjunct of production.[10] Only the Ballistic Laboratory at Aberdeen Proving Ground functioned as a true research unit undistracted by the production problems of Industrial Service. Though the new arrangement was an improvement over the old, and though under both systems some very important work was accomplished, far more rapid progress was possible when research and development became an independent division. That had to wait until June 1942.

In keeping with the major branches of Industrial Service, General Barnes divided the duties of his staff along commodity lines, an organizational scheme that he adhered to both while he was within Industrial Service and after he became chief of a separate division. The principal categories of Ordnance matériel were always artillery, small arms, ammunition, and automotive equipment, but these were of course susceptible of combination and subdivision. Just as artillery and automotive design had at one time been combined in one working unit, so in 1940 aircraft armament was specifically included with artillery, while tank and combat vehicle development was put into a separate subdivision. Two years later aircraft armament development became so important that it was separated from artillery. As the Tank-Automotive Center had by that time been set up in Detroit and automotive design assigned there, a Tank and Automotive Development Liaison section was added to the Technical Division in Washington. Similarly, the rocket program, virtually in infancy in 1942, by 1944 had grown to proportions warranting a separate division for rocket development work. To care for the mechanics of administration of all the commodity groups, an executive office was always included in the organization.

A number of special tasks remained that fell clearly neither into any one of the commodity development spheres nor into the domain of administrative work. These were grouped, therefore, into a unit called, for want of a more comprehensively descriptive name, the Service Branch. After the summer of 1942 the Service Branch was responsible for liaison with other agencies dealing with technical developments, such as the NDRC and the National Inventors Council; it co-ordinated the work of the ordnance laboratories at the arsenals and issued the technical reports on their findings; it prepared and disseminated the progress reports consolidated from the monthly reports of each development branch; it formulated and supervised investigations and tests of materials to minimize use of strategic materials and revised specifications accordingly; it supervised the activities of the Ballistic Research Laboratory and acted as a clearing house on ballistic information for the using arms and services as well as for other parts of the Ordnance Department; and finally, through its Ordnance Intelligence unit it was responsible for analyzing features of foreign matériel by study of items sent to this country or described in reports from abroad, and then for preparing the

[9] Memo, Barnes for CofOrd, 14 Jul 41, sub: Suggested Reorganization of Ord Office, Reorganization R&D Serv, Barnes file, OHF.

[10] ODO 183, 29 Jul 41, OHF.

291064 O—55——16

CHART 8—ORGANIZATION OF THE RESEARCH AND DEVELOPMENT SERVICE: 1 JULY 1945

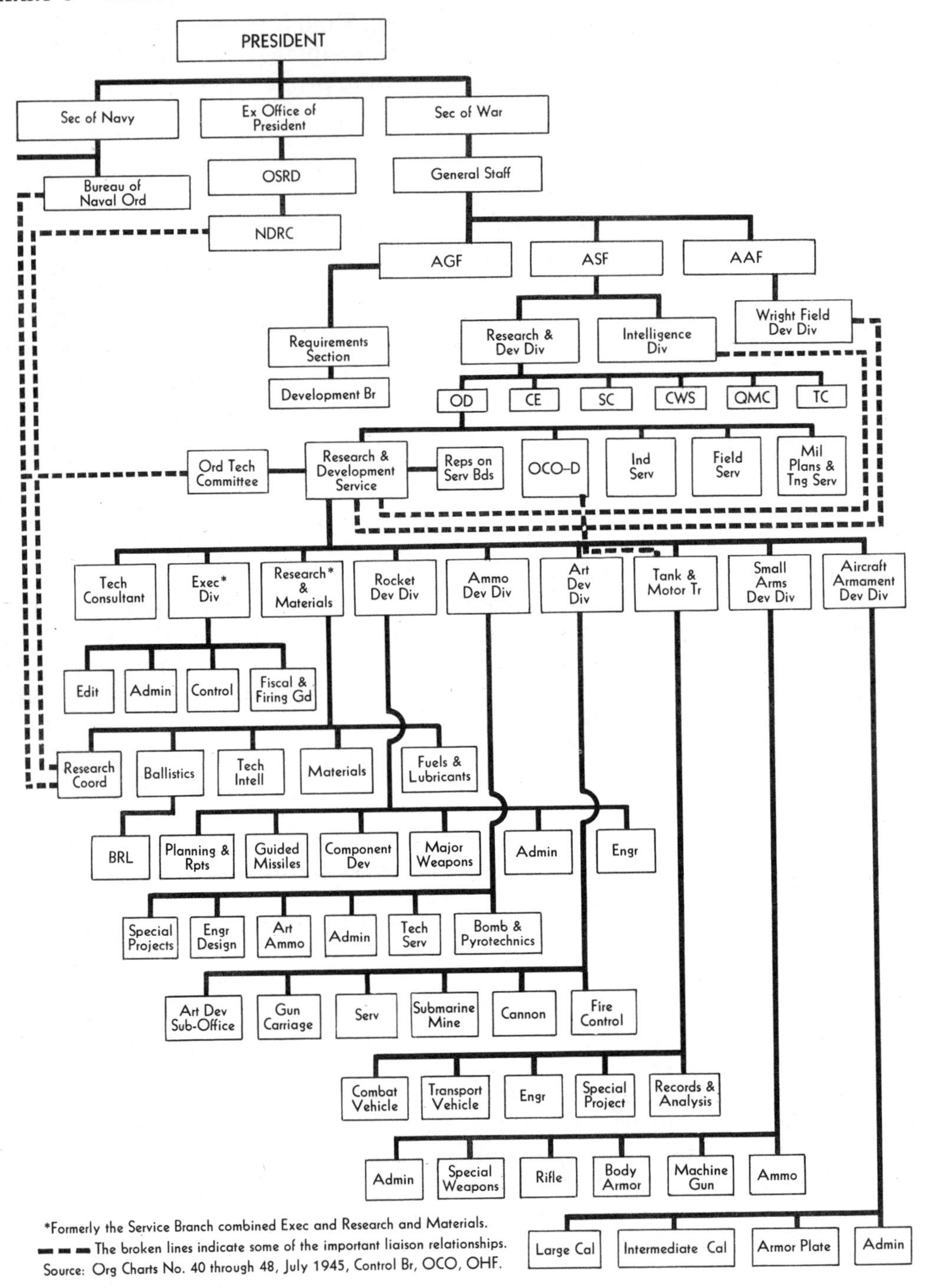

*Formerly the Service Branch combined Exec and Research and Materials.

▬ ▬ ▬ The broken lines indicate some of the important liaison relationships.

Source: Org Charts No. 40 through 48, July 1945, Control Br, OCO, OHF.

RESEARCH AND DEVELOPMENT FUNDS

Fiscal Year	Appropriations		R&D Expenditures		
	Total Ordnance	Research & Development	Total	Within Ordnance	Through Outside Agencies
1941	$3, 023, 913, 998	$6, 173, 000	$6, 162, 000	$2, 494, 785	$3, 667, 215
1942	23, 292, 124, 139	9, 563, 000	36, 789, 999	11, 971, 887	24, 818, 112
1943	9, 948, 319, 237	46, 419, 000	46, 667, 499	9, 021, 732	37, 645, 767
1944	7, 992, 522, 000	80, 345, 840	81, 183, 688	17, 835, 000	63, 348, 688
1945	9, 384, 694, 008	45, 950, 000			

Senate Subcommittee Rpt 5, 23 Jan 45, Pt. I., p. 309, 79th Cong, 1st Sess. The excess of expenditures over appropriations was made possible by authorizing transfers from other funds.

summaries and intelligence bulletins for distribution to other research and development groups to whom the analyses would be useful. The Service Branch thus touched every special field of research and development, sorting, sifting, channeling data, and making available to each group the pertinent information assembled by all the rest. Later some shifting of labels and reshuffling of duties took place, as when the Service Branch became the Research and Materials Division or when the technical reports unit, enlarged to include the technical reference unit, was switched to the Executive Division. But such changes, usually ordered with an eye to saving personnel, did not reduce the scope of the work to be done.[11]

The machinery for handling this heavy load of diverse responsibilities was well laid out on paper. Getting it to work depended on manning it. This was enormously difficult. As long as development work was carried on as part of the production process, General Barnes could use the experienced designers of the Industrial Service for such development work as time allowed. But their number was small, and when research and development were separated, Industrial Service pre-empted a good many. To recruit for the Technical Division men of the desired caliber who had more than general knowledge of ordnance was harder in 1942 than in 1940 and nearly impossible by 1944. For example, two branches of the division in November 1942 had 27 out of 72 authorized military assignments unfilled and 16 out of 45 professional civilian jobs in the Office, Chief of Ordnance, still vacant. Assignment of reserve officers with scientific training was one answer, but the supply of qualified men was limited at all times. In July 1945 the entire research and development staff in Washington numbered only 153 officers, 24 consultants, and 357 civilians of all grades.[12]

Money for salaries was no longer a stumbling block. Though after 1940 a greater proportion of funds than formerly was spent for laboratory facilities, materials, and contracts with outside research groups, appropriations for research and development were generous enough to

[11] (1) Organization Charts, Schedules A and B for Serv Br and Ammo Development Br as of 3 Nov 42, Barnes file, OHF. (2) ODO 5-44, 11 Nov 44 and ODO 58-45, 23 Jul 45, OHF.

[12] (1) Organization Chart, Ammo Div and Serv, 3 Nov 42, Schedule B. (2) Organization Chart 40, Rev. 1 Jul 45. Both in Barnes file, OHF.

provide attractive salaries.[13]

In recruiting research and development personnel, some units fared better than others, the Ballistic Research Laboratory probably best of all. Col. Hermann H. Zornig, whose genius and foresight had largely created the laboratory in the late 1930's, had built well. As its first director he had started a program of vast importance. Consequently, because the laboratory was unique and could transfer no part of its duties to any other agency, Colonel Zornig was allowed to begin enlarging his staff early in 1940. A nonresident Scientific Advisory Council of eminent civilian scientists, appointed in July, interested a number of distinguished physicists and chemists in undertaking assignments at the Aberdeen laboratory. Oswald Veblen of the Institute for Advanced Study at Princeton, Edwin Hubble of the Mount Wilson Observatory, Thomas H. Johnson of the Bartol Foundation, Joseph E. Mayer of Columbia University, Edward J. McShane of the University of Virginia, David L. Webster of Leland Stanford, and others placed the Ballistic Research Laboratory in a position to apply some of the best brains in the United States to basic and technical research problems. Civilian scientists conducted most of the research, though after Pearl Harbor they generally donned uniforms as reserve officers. In June 1941, upon Colonel Zornig's transfer, Maj. Leslie E. Simon became director. Trained at the laboratory under Colonel Zornig, Major Simon carried on the program without any break. In addition to the staff at Aberdeen, a University of Pennsylvania Ballistic Research Laboratory Annex was set up in 1942 to handle some of the ballistic computations, especially those on which the University's differential analyzer could be used. Altogether by mid-1944 the Aberdeen group numbered about 740, including professional people with very special qualifications, officers, Wacs, and enlisted men. All the enlisted men picked for work in the new supersonic wind tunnels laboratory had had earlier academic training in physics, chemistry, mathematics, or engineering.[14]

Relations with Civilian Agencies

The distinction of the staff at the Ballistic Research Laboratory, abbreviated to BRL, was an asset to the Ordnance Department in more ways than one. In addition to the effective work these men accomplished, their stature added prestige to the Ordnance Department in its dealings with civilian groups such as the NDRC. The top-ranking scientists of the academic world, in 1940 newly brought in on defense problems, not unnaturally tended at first to regard the military as men of action unsuited to cope with the intellectual problems of the research laboratory, but respect for the gifts of the officers at the BRL soon obliterated this condescension. In time, civilian employees of the Department's research staff also came to be recognized as possessing the keen intelligence and intensive knowledge of the academic scientist; indeed, many of them had been recruited from universities and important industrial research foundations. Personality clashes, inevitable in any large group, gradually diminished.[15]

Purely professional differences of opinion about how to solve any given problem and

[13] See table, p. 225.

[14] Hist of Ballistic Research Laboratory, Ch. I, pp. 1-15, OHF.

[15] Interv, 12 Nov 49, with Col Claudius H. M. Roberts, Chief of Ammo Development Br, R&D Serv.

friction arising from uncertainties about where whose authority ended—uncertainties inherent in the somewhat vague organizational set-up of the NDRC in relation to the Army technical services—endured longer. Yet from start to finish relations between the Ordnance Department and the chiefs of divisions of the National Defense Research Committee, though not invariably cordial, produced useful collaboration. During the first months of NDRC's life, official machinery for initiating an NDRC research project was slow moving: the technical services submitted projects to The Adjutant General for transmission to the NDRC "from time to time, as conditions warrant." In November 1940 this procedure was simplified by having requests for NDRC help go through The Adjutant General to the War Department liaison officer to NDRC; this officer then arranged a conference between the technical service and the NDRC. But by late 1942 this procedure also proved needlessly roundabout. Thereafter the Ordnance Department, or any other technical service, drew up its request and hand-carried it to the War Department liaison officer, who in turn hand-carried it to the NDRC. In a matter of hours the appropriate subdivision of NDRC might have the research program launched. The Ordnance Department then assigned men from its own research and development staff, usually at least one officer and one civilian expert on each project, to serve as liaison with the NDRC.[16]

The investigations thus delegated almost always involved basic or prolonged technical research that the Ordnance Department was not at the time equipped to handle. A sampling of the more than two hundred projects the Department requested the NDRC to undertake indicates their specialized nature: a basic study of detonations; the kinetics of nitration of toluene, xylene, benzene, and ethylbenzene; jet propulsion; special fuels for jet propulsion; determination of the most suitable normally invisible band of the spectrum for blackout lighting and methods of employing it in combat zones; problems involving deformation of metals in the range of plastic flow; phototheodolites for aerial position findings; the VT fuze; and gun erosion and hypervelocity studies.[17]

Occasionally the NDRC pursued projects along bypaths or into realms that the Ordnance Department felt itself better qualified to handle or considered untimely to have explored at that stage of the war. An attempt of a division of NDRC to participate actively in tank development elicited a sharp protest from a vice president of the Chrysler Corporation after a visit of the NDRC group to a Chrysler plant in Detroit. He declared that the group's lack of familiarity with automotive engineering would involve a costly waste of the time of men who did understand its problems. Though one division of NDRC had pushed through design of the DUKW, the famous amphibian cargo carrier,[18] and

[16] (1) Memos, TAG for Chiefs of all Supply Services, 22 Aug 40, sub: Basic Research for National Defense, AG 381, National Defense (7–29–40) M-WPD-M, and 15 Nov 40 (10–16–40) M-WPD-M, exhibit in NDRC Liaison, pp. 24, 27, OHF. (2) Interv, 12 Jul 50, with Col Ralph M. Osborne, WD Liaison Officer.

[17] NDRC Liaison, Projects OD-02, OD-9, OD-14, OD-16, OD-26, OD-27, OD-34, OD-48, OD-52, OHF.

[18] NDRC enlisted the General Motors Corporation to do the engineering and experimental shop work on this amphibian. The engineers of General Motors gave it its name, D for the year 1942, U for utility, K for front-wheeled drive, and W for two rear driving axles. See J. F. Baxter, *Scientists Against Time* (Boston, 1946), p. 248.

could therefore claim some knowledge of automotive problems, the proposed tank project was canceled. The NDRC report later explained that progress had been blocked by "inability to secure the cooperation of the Chief of the U.S. Ordnance Department and the automotive industry."[19]

Over rocket development also there was some controversy. Though the conflict here was largely between two different schools of thought within the NDRC, and the Ordnance Department was involved chiefly as it had to support one or the other, the question of ultimate control of the rocket research program naturally cropped up. As interest in rocketry mounted, rivalry grew over who was to direct its course. General Barnes contended that all rocket development for the Army should be an Ordnance responsibility; though the Department should seek NDRC help in meeting Army needs, the NDRC, instead of plunging ahead on fruitless projects, should first "determine the military requirements of a device before proceeding with its development."[20] The Chief of Ordnance backed this view by recommending to the Army Service Forces that "all rocket activity" be co-ordinated through the Ordnance Technical Committee. The Ordnance Department won its point, but not until the summer of 1943 was satisfactory co-operation with the NDRC reached.[21] While traces of competitiveness persisted, the general pattern resolved itself into an arrangement whereby the NDRC assumed leadership in one realm, the Ordnance Department in another. The acquisition of basic technical data pertaining to rockets and the making of prototypes of radically different rocket designs fell to the NDRC; the Ordnance department primarily carried out functions of engineering within the scope of at least partly known techniques, and of testing and removing "bugs" from development items, whether originated in the NDRC or in Ordnance.[22]

Suspicious of outsiders and overprotective of its own authority and prestige though the Ordnance Department may have been at times, its attitude toward the NDRC was nevertheless understandable. Ordnance research men were first and foremost engineers rather than pure scientists. Years of study of the practical engineering difficulties of designing military equipment gave them particular respect for the practical as opposed to the theoretical aspects of a problem. Long experience tended to make them impatient with any assumption that the academic scientist could readily master the engineering knowledge necessary to translate a principle into a usable instrument or weapon. Thus the Ordnance Department was reluctant to see the NDRC invade by ever so little the field of design. When the civilian research men were engaged upon highly technical investigations of physical and chemical phenomena applicable to ordnance, the Ordnance Department recognized their findings as invaluable; when they undertook work impinging upon engineering, the Ordnance Department became wary.

---

[19] (1) NDRC Liaison, Project OD-60, OHF. (2) Div 12, NDRC Summary Tech Rpt, 1948, I, 253, OHF. (3) Barnes Diary, 22 Aug 41 and 19 Mar 42, OHF.

[20] Memo, Barnes for CofOrd, 19 Mar 43, sub: Comment on Interim Rpt on Rockets by Joint Staff Planners, OO 471.94/182, DRB AGO.

[21] (1) Memo, CofOrd for ASF, 8 Jun 43, sub: Recommendations of Joint Chiefs of Staff, OO 471.94/660, DRB AGO. (2) Barnes Diary, 30 Jul 43, OHF.

[22] Interv, 12 Jul 50, with Dr. Colin M. Hudson, Guided Missiles Sec, R&D Serv.

Furthermore, the research and development staff, bound by the Army tradition of not defending itself to the public, suffered from some criticisms it considered unjust. Accused by the NDRC of ignoring the potentialities of hypervelocity guns, Ordnance ballisticians explained that research had first to be directed at causes of gun barrel erosion and means of lengthening barrel serviceability, problems more immediately important and more quickly solvable. While NDRC men themselves soon discovered that erosion studies were an essential preliminary and involved exploration of a maze of possible causes, they deplored Ordnance postponement until January 1942 of a formal request for these studies. By then Ordnance technicians had already expended considerable effort on the study of a German tapered bore, high-velocity, light antitank gun and knew at first hand both the difficulties and the costs of barrel erosion.[23] As development of the types of hypervelocity weapons upon which a division of the NDRC wanted to lavish energy must be a time-consuming undertaking, the Ordnance Department deliberately gave priority to the less spectacular allied projects. But when the NDRC successfully developed erosion-resistant stellite liners for .50-caliber machine gun barrels and a nitriding-chrome plating process for small arms bores, the Ordnance Department gratefully acknowledged its debt. It made immediate use of the exhaustive NDRC study of the mechanics of barrel erosion and acclaimed the sabot projectile for the 90-mm. gun and the experimental 57-40-mm. tapered bore gun evolved by the NDRC and its contractors.[24] These achievements secured, Ordnance Research and Development Service was ready to encourage further work on hypervelocity guns. The end of the war halted the plan.[25] Another criticism voiced by civilian scientists charged the Ordnance Department with failure to develop a recoilless gun.[26] The highly successful 57-mm. and 75-mm. recoilless rifles used in the last months of war were in fact conceived, designed, tested, and developed by Ordnance men, virtually unaided. Statements belittling Ordnance research did not grease the wheels of Ordnance-NDRC machinery.

Relations with the NDRC were thus marked by occasional differences of opinion, flickers of mutual distrust and, after the war, some exasperation within the Ordnance Department at what its research staff felt to be NDRC's tendency to claim credit for what the Ordnance Department had itself done. But it is easy to

---

[23] (1) Baxter, *Scientists Against Time*, p. 31. (2) Interv, 6 Jul 50, with Samuel Feltman, Chief of Ballistics Sec, R&D Serv. (3) John E. Burchard, ed., *Rockets, Guns and Targets* (Boston, 1948), pp. 343–74. (4) Hypervelocity Development, Guns and Ammunition, OHF. See also Ch. XI, below.

[24] Burchard, ed., *op. cit.*, pp. 387–414. Upon the sabot, as upon the tapered bore gun, much additional work remained to be done after V-J Day.

[25] NDRC Liaison, Project OD-52, OHF.

[26] Vannevar Bush, *Modern Arms and Free Men* (New York, 1949), p. 25. In discussing pre-World War II military research programs, Dr. Bush states: "But the whole gamut of new ordnance devices—rockets, recoilless guns, guided missiles, proximity fuzes, bazookas, frangible bullets—waited for the pressure of war, appearing then largely outside the organized system of ordnance development, and sometimes in spite of it." This judgment the Ordnance Department repudiates as grossly unfair, inasmuch as the Ordnance Department itself developed two successful recoilless rifles, shared in the work on bazookas and rockets, and eventually, in spite of initial doubts, gave wholehearted encouragement to NDRC work on guided missiles and VT fuzes. In development of the frangible bullet, Ordnance records show that the Ordnance Department was stopped by the Air Forces' unwillingness to develop an armored target plane. During the war NDRC comments in a vein similar to Dr. Bush's fanned the sparks of some resentment within the Ordnance Department. See below, Ch. X.

exaggerate the importance of these difficulties. They rarely interfered with getting on with the job. The undercurrent of slight mutual distrust was never more than an undercurrent.[27] As the war wore on and Army men saw the fruits of NDRC research, their attitudes underwent marked change. This shift was of utmost importance in determining the role of civilian scientists in the postwar organization of the Department of Defense.

The roots of the Ordnance Department's initial distrust of the NDRC lay in the century-old conflict of military versus civilian. The Constitution vested control of the Army in civilian hands, in the President as Commander in Chief and the Secretary of War as his adviser. Beyond that the Army had always believed national defense should be controlled by the military; civilians should be used for particular jobs, but under the aegis of the War Department. To this system the Office of Scientific Research and Development, under which the NDRC operated after June 1941, could well be a threat. Just as Army control over design and manufacture of weapons had been challenged in the 1850's, might not the NDRC in the 1940's take unto itself the Army's direction of military research and development? That many men of the NDRC thought civilian direction desirable there can be no doubt. The official history of the Office of Scientific Research and Development, Dr. Baxter's *Scientists Against Time,* implies this attitude. "The failure to make the most of our possibilities in high-velocity ordnance reveals inadequate civilian influence upon strategic thinking," wrote Dr. Baxter after the war.[28] He repeatedly hints at shortcomings of American ordnance that civilian supervision of research and development would have overcome.[29]

Throughout the war the Ordnance Department was strongly opposed to any such scheme. In explaining why Ordnance officers believed that neither the NDRC nor any other civilian agency should be allowed to govern Army research programs, General Barnes later stated:

> No group of scientists no matter how wise could have undertaken this task with no preparation. It had taken years to train Ordnance officers to understand the meaning of Ordnance equipment in war. NDRC organized a number of very useful committees. However, their usefulness was handicapped by their lack of knowledge of the subject. They needed Ordnance leadership. From time to time we attempted to give them that leadership . . . to tell them what was wanted. . . . In my opinion, if through some political move NDRC had been given the Ordnance job the Allies would have lost the war.[30]

In 1942 General Williams, Chief of Ordnance from 1918 to 1930 and later War Department liaison officer to the NDRC, attempted to allay the anxiety shared by all the supply services:

> The liaison between the Supply Bureaus of the War Department and the NDRC has not been as efficient as it should have been. One of the reasons for this was that there was no clear line of demarcation between the activities of the NDRC and those of the Bureaus. This led to a certain amount of confusion. Also there was a slight feeling of apprehension amongst the Bureaus because they feared they might lose some of their responsibilities and that these would be assumed by the NDRC. It seems to me that

[27] For an illuminating discussion of this thorny question as viewed by men of the NDRC's Division 2, see Burchard, ed., *op. cit.*, pp. 315–27. The point of view there expressed is that military non-co-operation did delay many important projects.

[28] Baxter, *op. cit.*, p. 31.

[29] *Ibid.*, pp. 31, 36, 202, 254–56.

[30] Incl to ltr, Gen Barnes to Gen Ward, 25 Jan 52, OCMH.

these apprehensions are groundless because the NDRC is a temporary organization that in all probability will be dissolved shortly after the termination of the war. The duties and responsibilities of the Bureaus, as stated above, continue in peace as well as in war and are just as important in peace as they are in war.

Closer and more cordial relationship between the Bureaus and NDRC would be greatly to the benefit of the Bureaus.[31]

Gradually, Ordnance fears of the NDRC subsided, though the "clear line of demarcation" of authority was never officially drawn.

Nevertheless, uneasiness long remained lest some scientific super agency be created that would strip the technical services of their research and development functions. A proposal to create an agency coequal with, but independent of, Army, Navy, and Air Forces, to take charge of all national defense research work sounded particularly alarming.[32] By comparison the Research Board for National Security, established in November 1944 as a subsidiary of the National Academy of Sciences, was innocuous since this board received its funds from the military. Not until the Secretaries of the Army and Navy set up the Joint Research and Development Board after the war to co-ordinate Army and Navy research programs, did Ordnance apprehensions disappear.[33] Fifteen months later, in September 1947, the National Security Act of 1947 established within the Department of National Defense the Research and Development Board where civilians and military men shared authority.[34] In 1940 the Ordnance Department would have considered such an arrangement unthinkable, but wartime co-operation with the NDRC left its mark.

With other civilian agencies engaged in munitions development during the war, the Ordnance Department had no altercation. The National Inventors Council frequently submitted new designs of weapons and proposals for innovations, but it served principally as an intermediary between the inventor and the Ordnance Department. Manned by a group of gifted people including a former Chief of Ordnance, Maj. Gen. William H. Tschappat, the council saved endless time for the military by screening the proffered ideas, winnowing the familiar and "crackpot" from those that had some promise. Even then the council in some months passed on to the Ordnance Department as many as a hundred "inventions" to study. Very few could be used, but the Department neither wished nor dared to toss aside any without careful examination.[35] If the Ordnance Committee rejected the idea as impractical or as a duplication of an idea already recognized, there, without argument, the matter usually ended.

The Ordnance Department also dealt with a number of committees organized to advise on particular problems and with special groups within industry. Engineering advisory committees drawn from private industry had been an outgrowth of the early months of the rearmament program. In the fall of 1940, at the Ordnance Department's request, twenty-nine distinct

[31] Memo, Williams, 9 Jun 42, sub: Supply Bureaus and NDRC, in NDRC Liaison, p. 38, OHF.

[32] S 2721, S 2871, and HR 7742, 77th Cong, 2d Sess.

[33] (1) Ltr, Robert Patterson and James Forrestal to Dr. Frank B. Jewett, 18 Oct 45, in Barnes file on Research Board for National Security, OHF. (2) Memo, Gen Barnes for ASF, 2 Feb 45, sub: Projects and Funds for the Research Board for National Security, OO 400.112/18444, DRB AGO. (3) Barnes Diary, 31 Jan 45, OHF.

[34] Research and Development Board, 1 Jun 50, p. 7, OHF.

[35] Interv with Dr. Colin Hudson, 12 Jul 50.

groups had been organized, each of them as an engineering advisory committee on a particular type of ordnance—the tank committee, the gun forging committee, the bomb fuze committee, the pyrotechnics committee, the metallic belt link committee, and the like. The first purpose had been to give manufacturers who had little or no experience in making weapons opportunity to thrash out engineering problems with Ordnance officers and Ordnance engineers. After the first meetings, when by vote of the manufacturers' representatives the committees were given a permanent basis, the discussions produced not only clarifications of existing procedures but also a number of sound ideas for improving designs and simplifying manufacturing methods. These engineering committees at the end of two years became "industry integration" committees, because engineering problems had largely been solved and pressure shifted to increasing production of matériel by the then well-established methods.

Another vital link between the research and development staff of the Ordnance Department and research groups of private industry was the series of research advisory committees. Some of these had existed for years. The Society of Automotive Engineers Ordnance Advisory Committee, for example, had done yeoman service during the 1930's by advising Ordnance engineers on suspension and transmission problems of tank design. The Committee on Petroleum Products and Lubricants gave the Ordnance Department the benefit of wide experience in that specialized field. Perhaps most useful of all, among a host of valuable contributions, was the work of the Ferrous Metallurgical Advisory Committee. Divided into eight subcommittees, its members represented more than two hundred individual companies commanding 85 percent of the steel capacity of the country. At frequent meetings of these men with Ordnance Department experts, research programs were initiated that later resulted in improved processes and conservation of critical alloys. Of the contributions of all these groups General Barnes enthusiastically noted: "Through these committees, the Ordnance Department has maintained close contact with industry and with the best scientific talent in the country and has obtained the cooperation and assistance of these groups in the solution of vital problems pertaining to Ordnance matériel." [36]

Relations with Other Military Agencies

Relations of the Ordnance research and development staff with civilian scientists have been discussed at some length not only because the ultimate outcome was significant but also because it was achieved in the absence of established precedents. The National Research Council of World War I, intended to perform services like those of the NDRC, had been started too late, had had too nebulous authority, and had died too early to provide a pattern for collaboration in World War II.[37] In the 1940's working procedures and mutual

[36] (1) Memo, Gen Barnes for Col Davies, OCO, Control Br, 30 Oct 43, sub: Abolition of Committees, Ord Engr Advisory Committees, Barnes file, OHF. (2) G. M. Barnes (Major General, United States Army (Ret.)), *Weapons of World War II* (D. Van Nostrand Company, Inc., New York, 1947), p. 10.

[37] William F. Willoughby, *Government Organization in War Time and After* (New York and London, 1919), p. 22, citing Exec Order of 11 May 1918. See also, Irving B. Holley, Jr., Ideas and Weapons, Rpt 47 for the Industrial College of the Armed Forces, 1947, pp. 174–79.

responsibilities had to be evolved step by step. Ordnance relations with other segments of the Army, on the other hand, and with the Navy and the Air Forces, followed a relatively familiar pattern. To be sure, the creation of the Army Ground Forces and the Army Service Forces and later the creation of the New Developments Division of the General Staff introduced some new quirks, but controversy, when it occurred, was still a family quarrel to be fought out along well-known lines.

With the Navy, relations were almost invariably harmonious. Co-operation with the Bureau of Ordnance had had a long, untroubled history. Navy and Marine Corps representatives on the Ordnance Technical Committee effected constant liaison on development projects, and a steady exchange of formal and informal reports on work afoot enabled Army Ordnance and Navy to collaborate. Furthermore, after January 1943 high-ranking officers of both Army and Navy held several special conferences to discuss research and development problems common to both services.[38] Division of labor in new fields of research was usually sufficiently defined to prevent duplication of effort. For example, while the Army Submarine Mine Depot was concerned with mines for harbor defense and the Naval Ordnance Laboratory with mines for offense in enemy waters, joint efforts went into developing ship detection devices for use in submarine mines for both purposes, and joint use of mine testing facilities ensued in taking underwater measurements. In the VT fuze program the Navy agreed to sponsor the development of projectile fuzes for both Army and Navy antiaircraft gun shells, the Army the development of fuzes for bombs and rockets for both services. Both services, as well as civilians, worked on adaptations for using the fuzes in other ground weapons.[39]

Collaboration with the Army Air Forces in developing air armament also was eased by years of close association. From 1922 to 1939 an Ordnance liaison officer had always served at Wright Field where Air Corps experimental work was centered. When in the summer of 1939 the aviation expansion program called for an extension of Ordnance work, Maj. Clyde Morgan of the Ordnance Department was assigned as chief of the Ordnance section of the Wright Field Materiel Division. Perpetuation of the division of responsibilities between the Air Corps and Ordnance Department as established in the 1920's made the Air Forces responsible for development of all matériel that was an integral part of the plane—the gun turrets, bomb shackles, and bomb sights—the Ordnance Department for the guns, the gun mounts, the bombs, and fire control mechanisms.[40] Arguments inevitably occurred from time to time over such controversial matters as the advisability of wire-wrapping bombs or the efficiency of the 20-mm. aircraft cannon but, until development of guided missiles began, differences were minor.[41]

---

[38] For example, see: (1) Joint Rpt Army-Navy Conference on Ord R&D, 11 Feb 43, OO 337/5501, and (2) min, Joint A&N mtg on Army Ord R&D, 15 Sep 44, both in A&N Mtgs, Barnes file, OHF. See also interv, 15 Jun 51, with Col Scott B. Ritchie, Deputy Chief R&D Serv.

[39] (1) Col William H. Draper, Jr., and Capt Lewis L. Strauss, USNR, Coordination of Procurement Between the War and Navy Departments, Feb 45, II, 14–15; III, 87, 90. (2) Record of Army Ord R&D, Submarine Mines, Ch. VII. (3) Joint VT Press Conf Release, 27 Sep 45, p. 1. All in OHF. See also Ch. XII, below.

[40] (1) Ordnance in the Air Forces, pp. 13–14, MS in Air University Hist Liaison Office. (2) Hist of Ord Sec, Wright Field, Vol. I, Exhibits A to J, OHF. (3) Interv, 14 Jul 50, with Harry S. Beckman, Bombs and Pyrotechnics Sec, R&D Serv.

[41] Barnes Diary, 21 Nov 42, 21 Aug 44, OHF.

In the summer of 1944 Brig. Gen. Richard C. Coupland, the Ordnance officer assigned as liaison at Army Air Forces headquarters in Washington, urged that the Ordnance Department assume responsibility for development of all guided missiles, commenting that "projects of [this] type are running around loose and being furthered by anyone aggressive enough to take the ball and run."[42] Air Forces and Ordnance Department, as well as the NDRC, had for months been pursuing investigations of this type of weapon. German use of "buzz bombs" and later of the deadly V-2 rockets, about which specialists in the United States already knew a good deal, sharpened awareness of the urgency for work in this field. The field was wide enough to be divided, but obviously the duplication of research or the withholding by one group of data useful to the other must stop.[43] A conference of representatives of the Air Forces and of the New Developments Division of the General Staff in September cleared the air. A General Staff directive followed, charging the AAF with "development responsibility . . . for all guided or homing missiles dropped or launched from aircraft . . . [or those] launched from the ground which depend for sustenance primarily on the lift of aerodynamic forces." Army Service Forces—in effect, the Ordnance Department—was to develop missiles "which depend for sustenance primarily on momentum of the missile."[44] Early in January 1945 the General Staff requested the Ordnance Department to attempt development of a missile suitable for antiaircraft use, though the Air Forces was also working on a ground-to-air missile.[45] No obstructive competition between the services resulted.

With headquarters of the Army Service Forces, the Ordnance research and development staff faced some difficulties, particularly during ASF's first year. The interposition of a new command between the operating divisions of the Ordnance Department and the policymakers of the General Staff and the Secretary of War's office inevitably introduced new channels through which communications must go before decisions were reached and Ordnance requests approved.[46] Since many ASF officers were unfamiliar with the peculiar problems of Ordnance research and development, Ordnance officers were frequently irked at the necessity of making time-consuming explanations to the ASF Development Branch of the whys and wherefores of Ordnance proposals. Nevertheless, as time went on, General Barnes' staff found that watchfulness, plus patience in interpreting a problem to General Somervell's headquarters, generally served to win ASF over. If General Barnes believed a specially important project likely to be side tracked, he bypassed routine channels and went directly to General Somervell, General Marshall, or even to the Secretary of War. Thus, in the face of AGF opposition, he persuaded General Somervell of the wisdom of proceeding with development of a heavy tank and got Mr. Stimson's express approval for making the 155-mm. gun self-propelled by mount-

---

[42] Pers ltr, Gen Coupland to Gen Campbell, 7 Aug 44, Barnes-Campbell Correspondence, DRB AGO.

[43] (1) 2d Ind, CofOrd to ASF, 4 Mar 44, sub: Development of AA Artillery Matériel, OO 471.94/2313, DRB AGO. (2) OCM 23905, 25 May 44. (3) Barnes Diary, 12 Sep 44.

[44] Memo, DCofS for ASF, 2 Oct 44, sub: Guided Missiles, OO 471.6/1290½, DRB AGO.

[45] Ltr, DCofS, to ASF, 18 Jan 45, sub: Guided Missiles Development, OO 471.6/1392, DRB AGO.

[46] For differences of the Ordnance Department as a whole with ASF, see above, pp. 90–95.

ing it on a medium tank chassis.[47] Though the struggle during 1942 to get the highest priority for Ordnance development work was acute, and though later occasional controversies arose, such as those over limited procurement of the T24 light tank and over the heavy tank program, fairly amicable relations came to be the rule. The ASF Development Branch usually accepted the Ordnance Department's judgment about the importance of individual projects and only disapproved a program when it appeared to mean the diversion of industrial facilities from other more pressing jobs. As long as ASF headquarters confined itself to staff jobs of co-ordination and eschewed what Ordnance officers regarded as operational activities, jurisdictional troubles scarcely existed.[48]

In spite of ASF co-ordinating efforts, from time to time friction developed between the Ordnance research staff and the Corps of Engineers and Signal Corps. With the Engineers the differences of opinion over weight and width of equipment in relation to bridge capacity were as old as tanks. The Engineers periodically protested acceptance of vehicles and self-propelled artillery that exceeded authorized limits by even a few inches or a few pounds, for road and bridge maintenance was difficult at best, and unloading tremendously heavy equipment from ships' holds multiplied problems.[49] However justified the Engineers' objections to added weight and bulk, they were usually overridden. Assignment in 1944 to the Engineers of responsibility for all commercial tractors having top speeds of twelve miles or less per hour took out of the hands of the Ordnance Department control of some slow-moving artillery prime movers.[50] With the Signal Corps some conflict was eventually inescapable because of the interrelatedness of electronics, VT fuzes, and fire control instruments using radar. The Ordnance Department disclaimed any wish to "enter the radar business," as the Signal Corps charged, but believed that the Signal Corps should be used only as "an assisting agency" in all development work on fire control and guided missiles. That, in effect, was the ultimate decision reached jointly after V-E Day.[51]

When the Army Ground Forces was created, relations with the using arms were altered somewhat by the interposition of the AGF Requirements Section between the combat arms and the Ordnance Department. The advantages of the new arrangement were twofold: decisions were reached more quickly, and the requirements of one arm were reconciled with those of another. For example, instead of the Chief of Infantry and the Chief of Cav-

[47] (1) Interv with Gen Barnes, 12 Jun 51. (2) Interv, 29 Jun 51, with Brig Gen William A. Borden, Asst to Gen Barnes, 1942 to Aug 43. (3) Interv, 2 Jul 51, with Col John H. Frye, Chief Research and Materials Div, R&D Serv, 1943–45.

[48] (1) Barnes Diary, 23 Apr 42; 13–30 Sep 42; 25 Jul 44; 26 Jul 44: 2 Aug 44; 9 Aug 44: 14 Aug 44; 16 Aug 44; and 21 Aug 44, OHF. (2) OCM 21446, 2 Sep 43. (3) Memo, SOS for CofOrd, 23 Sep 43, sub: Light Tank T24, OO 470.8/415 Tank, DRB AGO.

[49] See Ch. VII, above.

[50] (1) OCM 20342, 6 May 43; 22734, 27 Jan 44; 25117, 14 Sep 44; 26898, 8 Mar 45; 27662, 17 May 45. (2) 1st Ind, CofEngrs to ASF, 16 Sep 43, sub: 120-mm. (4.7") AA Gun Matériel M1 (T1)—Standardization Recommended, OO 472.93/1054, DRB AGO. (3) Barnes Diary, 11 Nov 43, OHF. (4) Memo, CofOrd for ASF, 12 Nov 43, sub: Assignment of Design, Development . . . for Commercial Type Tractors to Corps of Engineers, OO 451.3/702 Tractors, DRB AGO. (5) WD Cir 10, 6 Jan 44.

[51] (1) Barnes Diary, 20 Oct 43, 23 Dec 44, and 30 May 45, OHF. (2) 2d Ind, CSO to ASF, 8 Sep 44, and 4th Ind, CofOrd to ASF, 14 Oct 44, sub: Responsibility for Director T38, OO 413.68/1078, Director, DRB AGO. (3) Min, Conference on Fire Control Equipment, 18 Jan 45, pp. 5, 10, OHF. (4) Memo, Barnes for Campbell, 10 May 45, sub: Ordnance Relationship with Signal Corps, Barnes-Campbell Correspondence, DRB AGO.

alry independently submitting requests for new or improved equipment, to be used for the same general purpose but having slightly different features, the Developments Division of the AGF Requirements Section passed upon the need and prepared a single statement of the military characteristics deemed essential. As in the past, the request with all the pertinent details was then processed through the Ordnance Technical Committee to the appropriate section of the Ordnance research and development staff to act upon itself or to delegate to an outside agency. More often than in peacetime, the Ordnance Department also initiated projects through the Ordnance Technical Committee and submitted to the AGF models for comment and test.[52] Particularly was this the case in developing tanks and self-propelled artillery. It was largely over these that conflicts between the Ordnance Department and AGF arose.

Pronounced differences of opinion about the tactical utility of heavy tanks had first been voiced in 1920 when "heavy" meant any tank weighing more than twenty-five tons.[53] For the next twenty years lack of money as well as War Department disapproval prevented the Ordnance Department from pursuing work upon heavy tanks, but in 1940 and 1941 engineers of the Department's automotive section succeeded in designing and building a sixty-ton model mounting in the turret a 3-inch gun and a 37-mm. gun. The tank was standardized in February 1942 as the M6. Notwithstanding this official approval, the AGF immediately objected. Further tests led the Armored Board to pronounce the M6 unreliable and much too heavy, and consequently procurement was limited to forty tanks. Not one was shipped overseas. Periodic Ordnance proposals to modify the M6 to eliminate its weaknesses never met with approval.[54] But General Barnes was convinced that before the war was over the ground forces would need a heavy tank. He therefore set his arguments and plans in some detail before General Somervell, who concurred in Barnes' proposal to develop a much more powerful tank than any the AGF was willing to adopt at that time.[55]

Fighting in North Africa, in the spring of 1943, was proving that American tanks must have greater fire power than the 37-mm. and 75-mm. guns on the Grants and Shermans could furnish. Though the Shermans, rushed to the British in the autumn of 1942, had helped to turn the tide at El Alamein, in the course of the winter the Germans' increasing employment of long-barreled, high-velocity 75-mm. guns on Panzer IV tanks and the appearance of sixty-ton Tigers mounting 88-mm. guns gave Rommel's troops an advantage. Nevertheless, the AGF was reluctant to accept heavy tanks carrying thicker protective armor plate and mounting bigger guns. The commanding general, Lt. Gen. Lesley J. McNair, doubtless fortified by the advice of officers in North Africa, clung to faith in the superiority of the more mobile, maneuverable medium tank. He demanded more powerful but not heavier guns and tanks; the greater weight of large-caliber guns tended to offset the advantage of the greater mass of the projectiles they fired. As muzzle velocity

[52] Maj D. L. McCaskey, The Role of the Army Ground Forces in the Development of Equipment, AGF Study 34 (hereafter cited as AGF Study 34), pp. 7-13, 21, OHF. The Requirements Section was at first a division at the operating level.

[53] See Ch. VII, above.

[54] (1) AGF Study 34, pp. 37-38, 44-45, OHF. (2) R&D, Tanks, pp. 1A200-204, OHF. (3) Interv with Barnes, 13 Jun 51.

[55] Interv with Barnes, 13 Jun 51.

usually decreases with increased caliber, unless the gun barrel be excessively long, it was axiomatic that the smallest caliber that could deliver a sufficiently effective projectile to destroy the target would be the best. The problem was to design a weapon in which the various factors were most effectively balanced. Use of high-velocity, tungsten-carbide-core, armor-piercing ammunition, known as HVAP, was a partial solution, and subcaliber projectiles with discarding sabot might have been another. The discarding sabot type of projectile was not adopted by AGF because of probable danger to the user.[56] General McNair also disapproved mounting a 90-mm. gun in a medium tank.[57] The M4 series of medium tanks, plus a suitable tank destroyer, would serve, he believed, to defeat German armor.[58] Though advances in metallurgy by 1942 had enabled the Ordnance Department to build light but powerful 76-mm. and 90-mm. guns out of newly developed, thin, higher physical steel, Ordnance men were convinced that medium tanks, whether mounting 76-mm. guns or 105-mm. howitzers, must be supplemented by heavy tanks. The conflict of opinion, which was "fought out bitterly around 1943," was actually three-sided, involving the Armored Force as well as AGF headquarters and the Ordnance Department.[59]

While General Barnes and his staff worked on a series of heavy models embodying the results of Ordnance experience, the Army Ground Forces early in 1944 undertook to draw up a lengthy list of specifications for a "general purpose" tank.[60] These specifications the chief of the tank development unit at the Detroit Tank Arsenal later characterized as "amateurish."[61] The wanted combination of light ground pressure, high speed, great fire power, and heavy protective armor, Ordnance engineers believed, comprised mutually irreconcilable features. When a request was submitted for what the Ordnance Department considered a physical impossibility, the Research and Development Service became indignant at accusations of non-co-operation. Admittedly, pressure to achieve the "impossible" sometimes produced astonishing results, but in prevailing Ordnance opinion shortcomings in American equipment were attributable far less to Ordnance ineptness than to the shortsightedness of the using arms and to the frequent shift of AGF ideas. General Barnes felt that battle trial of some experimental matériel would prove to combat troops that equipment was available that met their needs even though AGF had not thought of it. Between early 1943 and the end of the war he repeatedly urged the battle testing of a series of heavy tanks the tank arsenal had developed. These tanks varied in weight from 45 to 64 tons and carried 90-mm., 105-mm., or 155-mm. guns. The models armed with 105-mm.

---

[56] (1) AGF Study 34, pp. 49–50, OHF. (2) Interv, 25 Jul 50, with Samuel Feltman, Chief Ballistics Sec, R&D Serv.

[57] Ltr, Brig Gen Harold A. Nisley, AGF Ord Officer, to Brig Gen Henry B. Sayler, Chief R&D Serv, 11 Jun 47, Tank and Motor Transport, Barnes file, OHF.

[58] (1) Greenfield, Palmer, and Wiley, *op. cit.*, pp. 423–24. (2) Memo, AGF for CofS, 28 Nov 43, sub: Theater Requirements for New Type Tanks, AGF 480.8/75, DRB AGO. (3) Memo, AGF for CofS, 30 Nov 43, sub: Heavier Armament for Tanks and Self-Propelled Vehicles, AGF 480.8/76, DRB AGO.

[59] See n. 57. The Armored Force frequently supported the Ordnance position.

[60] Hq Armored Center, Mil Characteristics for an Improved Medium Tank, 23 Sep 44, AGF 470.8/106 GNRQT/7078, copy in Tank and Motor Transport, Barnes file, OHF.

[61] Ltr, Col Joseph M. Colby, Chief Dev and Engr Dept, Detroit Arsenal to Mr. F. Gordon Barber, R&D Serv, 14 May 47, Tank and Motor Transport, Barnes file, OHF.

and 155-mm. guns were not tested until after the war. The model mounting a 90-mm. gun fared better. In the face of some opposition from the AGF, permission was at last secured from Secretary of War Stimson and General Marshall to send overseas twenty of the experimental model, the 46-ton T26E3. Nicknamed the General Pershing, this tank with its 90-mm. gun M3 was first used by the 3d and 9th Armored Divisions in the drive from the Roer River to the Rhine. Despite conflicting reports of its performance the tank was standardized in March 1945 as the M26.[62]

Only less prolonged and heated was the disagreement about the value of self-propelled artillery, though the 105-mm. howitzer motor carriage M7 had proved itself in British hands in North Africa. The Tank Destroyer Command took exception to Ordnance proposals to construct a tank destroyer by mounting a 90-mm. gun upon a 3-inch gun motor carriage, and General McNair also objected. Later, the 90-mm. mounted on a tank chassis was enthusiastically received.[63] Over medium self-propelled artillery AGF headquarters again differed sharply with the Ordnance Department. General McNair cited a British report on the battle at El Alamein which stated that the artillery preparation for the advance would have been handicapped if it had been necessary to lift ammunition to the raised platforms of self-propelled guns. When he added that the British had not paid much attention to self-propelled artillery, General Barnes, obviously considering this no valid argument, tartly replied that the British "have not gone very far with anything else either." [64] In each case the Ground Forces was eventually converted, but such items as the 155-mm. howitzer motor carriage M41 were not approved until late in the war.[65]

The technicalities of tank and artillery design will be discussed below.[66] Here it is necessary only to note that the protracted arguments between AGF and the Ordnance Department over these developments were based wholly on professional differences of opinion. In the field of small arms such conflicts did not obtain. But as each side vigorously defended its views on tanks and motorized artillery, each sure of its rightness, relations were often distinctly strained. The controversy assumed such proportions by the summer of 1944 that the General Staff appointed a board to recommend procedures to be followed after the war. The report of the Army Ground Forces Equipment Review Board was submitted in June 1945. It carried further a less drastic plan prepared by the General Staff in 1940, revived in 1941, and then dropped as impractical, to centralize all Army research and development in a War Department Technical Committee, which, it had been hoped, would hasten standardization of new items and at the same time provide sound doctrines of tactical employment.[67] The 1945 report flatly

[62] (1) AGF Study 34, pp. 40, 43, 45–51, OHF. (2) R&D, Tanks, pp. 1A203–76, OHF. (3) Barnes Diary, 25 Feb 44; 2 Mar 44; 2 Aug 44, OHF. (4) See Ch. X, below.

[63] (1) Addendum to OCM 19845, 4 Mar 43. (2) Barnes Diary, 13 Mar 43 and 29 Sep 43, OHF. (3) 3d Ind, ASF for CofOrd, 4 Nov 43, sub: 90-mm. Gun Motor Carriage T71, OO 472.14/74, DRB AGO.

[64] Barnes Diary, 13 Apr 43, OHF.

[65] (1) *Ibid.*, 8 Mar 44, and 6 Apr 44, OHF. (2) OCM 24677, 10 Aug 44; OCM 24857, 24 Aug 44; OCM 28165, 28 Jun 45.

[66] See Ch. X, below.

[67] (1) Memo, Col Barnes for Gen McFarland, Chief of Ord Mil Serv, 9 Feb 40, sub: Research and Development for Ord Dept, R&D Misc, Barnes file, OHF. (2) Ltr, TAG to CofOrd, 2 Jan 41, and 1st Ind, CofOrd to TAG, 9 Jan 41, sub: AR 850-25, OO 300.3/28, DRB AGO. (3) Barnes Diary, 29 Jul 41; 30 Jul 41; 13 Aug 41; 23 Sep 41; OHF.

stated the necessity of vesting control of all development of ground force weapons in the hands of the Ground Forces. "This would necessitate the creation in Army Ground Forces of development groups organized on a functional basis and staffed by users, technicians and civilian specialists." [68] In his reply the Chief of Ordnance repeated his department's conviction that acceptance of this plan would bring disaster.[69] No steps were taken to put the AGF recommendations into effect.

Relations with Theatres of Operations

Theoretically, the Ordnance research and development staff had no direct relations with overseas theatres during the war. The theatre Ordnance officer attached to each theatre headquarters was the liaison between Office, Chief of Ordnance, and combat troops, and his reports were expected to supply comment and criticisms of ordnance in action. Information on enemy equipment might also be transmitted by military intelligence to the G–2 Division of the General Staff and thence to the Ordnance Department. But the system entailed delays, and before mid-1943 reports often lacked the specific data designers needed. Distance was inescapably an obstacle and the chain of command was another. Proposals to dispatch special Ordnance observers to European combat zones early in 1940 had been vetoed by G–2. In 1943 the first Ordnance Technical Intelligence units sent to overseas theatres were not welcome—they added to problems of billeting and feeding without making any immediate contribution to combat.[70] While later they became an accepted part of the intelligence system and assembled invaluable data, throughout the war the Chief of Ordnance—and chiefs of the other technical services as well—felt hampered by faulty communications with the theatres.[71] The surest, quickest way of getting essential information proved to be an unofficial avoidance of "channels" and recourse to personal letters from officers on overseas duty directly to the Chief of Ordnance or the chief of the Research and Development Service. Both officers relied upon this correspondence to supplement official communications.

Problems of Standardization and Limited Procurement

Two problems, be it repeated, were ever present for the Ordnance research and development staff—the problem of devising matériel that would counter any developments of the enemy and then the problem of getting new models approved in time to be of real use in combat. Knowledge of enemy ordnance and of what Allied troops needed to more than match it depended upon the adequacy of military intelligence. The working of the military intelligence system, and particularly of Ordnance Technical Intelligence and the Enemy Equipment Intelligence teams, will be discussed later.[72] There remain to be examined here the consequences of the time lag between the establishment of a requirement and the moment when combat troops

[68] Rpt of AGF Equipment Review Bd, 20 Jun 45, p. 2, OHF.

[69] Ltr, CofOrd to ASF, 20 Sep 45, sub: WD Equipment Review Bd, OO 234/9289, DRB AGO.

[70] Min, Wesson Conferences, 13 Mar 40, 21 Mar 40, and 27 Mar 40, OHF. (2) Hist of Tech Intel Orgn, Unit "A," USAFIME, OHF.

[71] The Chief of Engineers, for example, complained of not getting information from the theatres and late in the war arranged with the chief engineer in the ETO to send reports directly to him. Interv, 25 Jul 50, with Brig Gen Cecil R. Moore, Chief Engr ETO.

[72] See below, Ch. IX.

had in hand the new or improved weapon filling the need. Even when the research and development staff had detailed information from combat zones and, acting upon it, produced a design calculated to meet the want effectively, months or years might elapse before the innovation was accepted by the service boards for standardization. Standardization ceased in the latter part of the war to be a preliminary to use of new items in battle, but before late 1943 it generally was, for the AGF was long opposed on principle to sending matériel into combat that had not received the stamp of approval of the testing boards in the United States. Furthermore, without standardization of a weapon, quantity production was difficult to contrive.

Review of the official peacetime procedures for acceptance of new equipment may clarify the problem. Once standardization was achieved, the responsibility of the Research and Development Service for a particular item ended. It should be noted, however, that even under the pressure of war it took months after an article was standardized to compute quantities required, negotiate production contracts, complete manufacture, and distribute the finished product to the fighting forces. The latter processes could not be greatly hurried.[73] It was in the stages preceding large-scale procurement that the Ordnance Department hoped to expedite matters in World War II by telescoping or skipping altogether some of the ten steps prescribed for standardization.

Of these ten steps the first five were unavoidable and the first four usually taken rapidly. First came the decision, approved by G–4 of the General Staff, that a specific need for a new or improved item existed. Second was the statement of the military characteristics that the article must have in order to accomplish its purpose; physical characteristics such as weight, length, and width, were listed only when they affected the military usefulness of the item. This statement was drawn up by a board of officers of the using arm. An Ordnance officer represented the Department on each board. The third step was the formal initiation of a development program, a procedure handled by the Ordnance Technical Committee. The committee assigned to the project a classification, designating its type, nomenclature, and later a model or T number. Before 1942 the War Department had to approve classification; thereafter Army Service Forces assumed that function. Classification changed during the course of development. Originally labeled "required type," an experimental model was further identified in later stages as "development type."[74] Still later, when variations of a basic model of a development type were called for, the differentiations were marked by E numbers. Thus a series of experimental tanks might be designated T26E2, T26E3, and T26E4. Following the first official classification, the project was turned over to the appropriate unit of the Research and Development Service to work out. Study of the problem might have to be protracted to explore alternative methods of attaining the desired result. In designing and building a first sample or pilot model, scientists, draftsmen, engineers, and technicians might collaborate for years. When a model embodying the stipulated military characteristics was developed and ready for its

[73] The complexities of those procedures, which followed the completion of the research and development task, are analyzed in Thomson and Mayo, Procurement and Supply of Munitions, MS, OHF.

[74] "Required type" was also part of the classification of an item when it was formally accepted. It then became "required type, adopted type."

first tests, its complete classification was "required type, development type, experimental type."

The next five steps in peacetime tended to be long drawn out, as the tests upon the semiautomatic rifle in the 1920's and 1930's show. First the men who had designed and built the pilot model subjected it to a series of engineering tests. Each component had to correspond to the specifications. A model that met these requirements was then labeled "service-test type" and was ready for the next process—service testing. Service tests, conducted by a board under control of the using arm or occasionally by troops in the field, were to determine the suitability of the equipment for combat in the hands of ordinary soldiers. These tests almost always revealed hidden defects, parts too weak for serviceability, instruments inconveniently placed, interference of a control device with operating mechanisms, and the like. Ordnance engineers then undertook modifications of the original design to correct these faults. Even in so relatively simple a weapon as the carbine, service tests produced a list of modifications required for acceptance ranging in importance from knurling of the butt plate to redesign of the rear sight.[75] Modifications might run into the hundreds in complicated pieces such as tanks and artillery. Service tests of the modified models followed until the service boards pronounced them ready for extended service tests. Items such as the carbine might be accepted without extended service tests, but major items were usually tested by tactical units in order to gauge performance under more rigorous trial than the service boards could effect. For these tests production in some quantity was necessary and the equipment procured was classified as "limited procurement type" within the broader classification of "development type." The manufacture of the first "limited procurement type" models gave the producer experience and enabled him to eliminate production bugs.

The final step was largely a formality. If the extended service tests proved the item satisfactory, the Ordnance Committee recommended standardization and the General Staff, or after 1942 the Army Service Forces, approved it. The article then became an "adopted type" and received an M number and name by which it was entered on the standard nomenclature lists. Items less satisfactory than standard items might be classified as "substitute standard" and procured merely to supplement supply. Equipment formerly standard but now superseded by new was often classified as "limited standard" so that it could be used in the field until the supply was exhausted. When equipment was no longer considered suitable for its original purpose, it was classified as either obsolescent or obsolete. The latter was withdrawn from service as rapidly as possible.

Reducing the time consumed from the beginning to the end of the development process had to be done largely in the testing stages. It is true that the AGF proposal to have development carried on under the aegis of the arm laying down the essential military characteristics of a new weapon was clearly aimed at eliminating waste efforts early in the game by preventing the designer from proceeding with a model in which the most important features were sacrificed to less important. The Ordnance Department, on the other hand, believed the solution of that problem lay not in relinquishing development work to the user but in obliging him to stipulate the

[75] OCM 17278, 30 Sep 41.

alternative he considered preferable when it must be *either/or*. If, for example, the Armored Forces wanted tanks with powerful guns and great maneuverability, they must rate heavy armor protection as of secondary importance.[76]

Closer collaboration before drafting-board work was completed and a first pilot model built, more careful consultation between Ordnance policymakers and Ordnance engineers, might sometimes have saved time. Still more important was the role of the Ordnance member of the service board drawing up the statement of desired military characteristics of a new item. Building a sample incorporating unacceptable features could usually be avoided if this Ordnance officer were at once a competent engineer and a salesman skillful enough to persuade the board to request what the Ordnance Department believed feasible and essential features of design. Much depended upon his adroitness and ability. Unhappily, as the war wore on, the ideas of the service boards did not always coincide with those of combat troops overseas, but that was a complication the Ordnance Department could not resolve.[77] Nevertheless, in developing most new items, when time was lost needlessly it was in the course of service testing, modifying, retesting, and extended service testing. If, instead of being submitted to prolonged tests against dummy targets in the United States, new matériel could be shipped to the active theatres for battle trial, then, the Ordnance Department contended, a dual purpose would be served: the research and development staff would have indisputable proof of weaknesses and strong points of the new equipment under real, not simulated, combat conditions, and the armies in the field would have the use of weapons usable even if far from faultless. Later modifications could be made with greater certainty.

Here was a variation of the Ordnance pleas of the 1930's protesting the refusal of the War Department to standardize matériel until it was as nearly perfect as possible. Ordnance engineers concurred in Colonel Studler's statement of 1940: "The best is the enemy of the good." [78] But after Pearl Harbor official standardization was not the point at issue. It was the battle testing of T models. The AGF had some reasons for opposing the shipment to overseas theatres of matériel not yet wholly proved. The scarcity of cargo space early in the war was one; the possible infringement of Ground Forces control over tables of equipment was another; danger to the user, most compelling reason of all, was a third.[79] A failure of a new item to accomplish in battle what it was intended to do might cost far more than loss of time. The Ordnance Department's job, the AGF argued, was to develop, manufacture, and issue battleworthy munitions; it should not expect the using arms to risk the success of their mission—fighting—to prove the adequacy of the Ordnance Department's performance. General McNair repeatedly objected to issuing matériel possessing

[76] See pers ltr, Maj Gen Ernest N. Harmon, CG XXII Army Corps, to Gen Campbell, 10 Feb 45, Campbell file, OHF.

[77] Intervs, 22 Sep 50, with Col Studler, Chief Small Arms Sec, and with Col Richard Z. Crane, Chief Arty Sec, R&D Serv.

[78] See Ch. VII, above.

[79] The Ordnance Department was quite as intent as the using arms upon issuing only safe items. An example is General Barnes' refusal to release the bazooka in June 1942, although War Department officials and British and Soviet witnesses of its first demonstration were eager to get a considerable number immediately. See Ch. XII, below. See also interv, 22 Nov 49, with Gregory T. Kessenich, Chief, Patent Sec OCO.

even minor defects of design.[80] Moreover, battle testing small quantities of a new device introduced the hazard of giving the enemy a chance to develop countermeasures before a successful new weapon could be fully exploited in large-scale attacks.

This line of reasoning was doubtless in keeping with the caution of American field commanders upon which German officers repeatedly commented. German military procedures from the beginning of the war followed the course the Ordnance Department wanted to pursue. Experimental tanks and weapons were committed to front-line action as soon as they could be supplied to a tactical unit. Combat determined the modifications to be made in later German models.[81]

Fortunately, in time, American theatre commanders realized that by requesting experimental items for special tactical operations they could get at least small lots of matériel not yet standardized. Here a major difficulty naturally lay in getting to the theatres knowledge of what new developments in the zone of the interior were available upon request. Late in 1943 the desperate urgency of throwing into battle every kind of equipment designed not for warfare as fought in 1918, but as American soldiers were fighting it in the jungles of the Pacific and against the ingenious and tenacious German armies in Italy, brought about an innovation in procedures. The creation of the New Developments Division of the General Staff in October 1943 was the first step. Its duties included arranging demonstrations of new items to theatre commanders and supervising technical and scientific research and development missions in the theatres. Shipment of "limited procurement" items, largely begun with the Borden mission to investigate theatre needs for jungle warfare weapons, mounted steadily after 1943 though before that October limited procurement had been authorized in a very few instances.[82] Technical bulletins to accompany these experimental weapons were issued by Ordnance Field Service, and teams of instructors to teach troops how to use the new devices were sent abroad in increasing numbers.[83] An extension of the duties of the New Developments Division in August 1944 was significant: "Review [of] requirements for special or exceptional items whose future application can be foreseen, but for which the theatres of operations . . . have not established a requirement." [84]

Meanwhile, General Barnes had found a way to inform both the General Staff and the theatre commanders of ordnance T models obtainable, if asked for. Using the advertising principle that demand can best be created by publicizing the means of satisfying a want, Research and Development Service in the spring of 1944 began to issue a series of descriptive illustrated booklets on development items considered ready for combat trial. These

[80] (1) Interv with Gen Scott, Armored Force, 21 Feb 50. (2) Memo, Gen McNair for Gen Somervell, 12 Apr 43, sub: Heavy Field Artillery, 472/108 GNDCG (3-15-43). (3) Barnes Diary, 28 Jul 43, 29 Jul 43, and 4 Sep 43, OHF.

[81] (1) See Chs. IX and X, below. (2) H. M. Cole, *The Lorraine Campaign* (Washington, 1950), Ch. XIV. (3) Panzer Lehr Brigade 900 at Smolensk, 1941, MS # D-294, OCMH.

[82] (1) WD Cir 267, 25 Oct 43. (2) OD Activities in Limited Procurement 1941-1944, OHF. The list of limited procurement items before October 1943 included a few experimental fuzes and other ammunition development, two fuze setters, two tank telescopes, and a 90-mm. antiaircraft gun mount.

[83] The first technical bulletin to be issued for a nonstandard weapon was for the Grenade Launcher Sight, T59, sent to the Pacific in October 1943. Interv, 20 Sep 50, with Fordyce Edwards, Chief Publications Sec, FS.

[84] WD Cir 333, 15 Aug 44.

"kangaroos" or "matchfolders," so nicknamed because they fitted readily into a pocket, were printed in some quantity and dispatched overseas with demonstration teams or Ordnance officers departing for a theatre.[85] Within the zone of the interior officers of the using arms as well as the General Staff got the matchfolders. How large a part these booklets played in creating theatre demands for experimental items may be problematical. In some cases the matchfolders probably reached division or even company officers who, otherwise unaware of the existence of the new device, could then request a chance to try it in action. Certainly information on T models was disseminated far more widely by these folders than formerly.[86] By the spring of 1945 new weapons under limited procurement numbered 141, and new ammunition items 76.[87] While not all of these were tried in combat, enough were to make battle testing a generally accepted system.

Even standardized equipment was subject to field modifications overseas as experience showed a weakness correctable on the spot. An example was the installation of a turret lock on the light armored car in order to hold the turret in position when traveling. The change was devised in the theatre, and a drawing was prepared at theatre headquarters and circulated to the officers and depot companies concerned and then OCO–Detroit was notified.[88] Later, changes such as this might be incorporated in new production models manufactured in the United States. Improvisations in the field to meet unforeseen combat conditions were numerous and sometimes of considerable permanent value.[89] Here official approval was usually obtained long after the innovation had served its purpose.

Frequently a weapon first sent into combat as a T model was standardized soon afterward, but some matériel remained on limited procurement throughout the war. Thus the multiple rocket launchers for 4.5-inch and 7.2-inch rockets, both used in the European and Pacific theatres in late 1944 and 1945, were not approved for standardization, though the Ordnance Department would have welcomed their official acceptance. In other cases the Research and Development Service preferred to keep as long as possible the closer control of manufacture that limited procurement permitted. The 57-mm. and 75-mm. recoilless rifles consequently kept their T numbers until the summer of 1945, in spite of their satisfactory performance during the spring in Germany and on Luzon and Okinawa. The development of the recoilless rifle was an exception to many rules: no requirement was established and no Ordnance Committee Minutes prepared until after the Small Arms Section of the Research and Development Service had built a workable model and successfully fired it in a demonstration at Aberdeen. The *fait accompli* created the requirement.[90] Only where matériel was excessively bulky, complex, and expensive did AGF reluc-

[85] (1) Kangaroo file, OHF. (2) Interv, 3 Oct 50, with F. Gordon Barber, Developments Vizualization Aid Sec, R&D Serv, 1944–45.

[86] That some of these booklets were prepared primarily to promote "sales" is shown by the folder on the medium T25E1 and heavy T26E1 tanks. In this a sizable part of the brief text is dedicated to urging increased limited procurement orders. Kangaroo file, OHF.

[87] Limited Procurement Supplement to Catalogue of Standard Ord Items, 1 Mar 45, DRB AGO.

[88] ETO Ord Tech Bull 53, 12 Jun 44, DRB AGO.

[89] See Ch. X, below.

[90] (1) Interv with Col Studler, 22 Sep 50. (2) OCM 22989, 24 Feb 44; OCM 28073, 21 Jun 45; OCM 28547, 26 Jul 45.

tance to sanction battle testing endure. Yet even the 46-ton General Pershing tank eventually was sent to the European theatre for battle trial before standardization. Just as the reason for setting up Research and Development as a separate operating division in the Ordnance Department had been the necessity of speeding the development process to get improved equipment to the battle fields as fast as possible, so Research and Development Service learned quickly to cut through red tape. A broad interpretation of what limited procurement meant opened the way for the research and development staff to do its job well.[91]

[91] See AR 850-25.

CHAPTER IX

Competition and Collaboration With Foreign Designers

Most wars are won by outwitting the enemy or by overpowering him with sheer mass of matériel and men. Only rarely in history has an army been so imbued with confidence in itself or with faith in the righteousness of its cause that it triumphed over heavy odds. Germany in 1939 and 1940 had established itself as the greatest military power in the world, a power whose tactics were brilliant and whose weapons appeared to be the most effective men had ever seen. Though the American public even in 1940 was still hoping that the United States might keep out of the European war, the U.S. Army was hurriedly building up its strength in men and equipment to be in a position to defy this power. That challenge meant for the Ordnance Department two primary tasks—putting into the hands of American and Allied troops the greatest possible quantity of matériel, and having available weapons equal to or better than those of the enemy.

The story of quantity production will be told in another volume of this series. Quality was first and foremost a problem of research and development. The succeeding chapters of this volume will discuss the equipment that the Ordnance Department developed for the U.S. Army in comparison with the major items the enemy employed. To explain how differences and similarities came about, it is necessary at this point to look briefly at the circumstances that enabled the Third Reich to equip its army as it did; to review the limitations imposed upon the U.S. Ordnance Department; to trace the steps by which the Ordnance Department after 1940 learned the essential features of enemy designs; and to note how the United States and its allies pooled scientific and technical data in the ceaseless search for weapons superior to any the enemy could command.

Ordnance Research and Development in the German Army

For the Ordnance Department, competition with foreign designers meant primarily competition with Germany. Italy never loomed as a serious contender in the struggle for superiority of weapons, while Japanese equipment, largely imitative of American and European design, was admittedly inferior to both in quality. Not Japanese engineering genius but nature posed the most serious challenge in the Pacific where topography, jungle growth, mildew, and corrosion, rather than enemy fire power or armor, were likely to neutralize the effectiveness of American matériel. A quite different contest unfolded with the senior partner of the Berlin–Rome–Tokyo Axis. Traditionally well versed in the art of ordnance design and able to draw on a vast pool of capable scientists, technicians, and skilled labor, Germany was a competitor who time and again threatened to outstrip the United States in the race for putting deadlier and more efficient weapons in the hands of the fighting forces.

In little over twenty years Germany had risen from crushing defeat to be the mightiest military power in the world. The limitations that the victorious Allies of World War I had imposed in the hope of forever preventing Germany's resurgence as a threat to world peace had had precisely the opposite effect. To quote a statement attributed to Generaloberst Franz Halder, the German Army Chief of Staff from 1938 to 1942, "Germany, as a result of the provisions of the Versailles Treaty, had to disarm and thus denude itself of everything reminiscent of the first World War. Germany consequently started from the most elementary beginnings, unencumbered, and thereby had a distinct advantage over the Allies who clung to many things that no longer were in tune with the changed times."[1] To forestall misunderstandings, it is well to point out that the divorce from the past was in the realm of tactical doctrine rather than of technology. Advanced tactical thinking, not superweapons and mountains of matériel, made the German Army.

To understand how Germany in 1939, a bare four years after formally renouncing its obligations under the Treaty of Versailles, was able to put into the field an army so well trained and equipped that it held virtually the entire world at bay necessitates at least cursory examination of the secret rearmament activities during the interwar period. To begin with, large quantities of weapons that should have been scrapped or delivered up to the Allies were carefully cached by the Army, the Navy, and an armaments industry, all eager to save what they could. In May 1919 the Army issued orders to spirit all fully usable matériel as well as certain semimanufactured parts out of zones likely to come under Allied occupation. At least one of the participants in that operation, the Friedrich Krupp Aktiengesellschaft of cannon fame, reported that by August, little over a month after Versailles, its shipments to the interior ceased because "the demand had been met." Among the more noteworthy items for this particular producer were—shades of things to come—parts for two types of 88-mm. flak guns.[2] As an interesting sidelight, the guiding genius behind the Army's effort to amass a hoard of weapons against the day of Germany's return to power reputedly was Capt. Ernst Roehm, later the notorious chief of Adolf Hitler's storm troopers, who was to meet his end in the blood purge of June 1934. The success of his undertaking can be gauged by the statement that one third of the matériel that the Army needed and procured after the Fuehrer's accession consisted of Roehm's trophies from World War I.[3]

Hand in hand with the salvage of this important, though relatively small, store of

[1] Peter Bor, *Gespraeche mit Halder* (Wiesbaden, 1950), p. 144.

[2] NI–9041, *Die Abteilung Artillerie-Konstruktionen der Fried. Krupp A.G. u. die Entwicklung von Heeresgeschuetzen von November 1918 bis 1933,* a historical MS compiled by the Friedrich Krupp Aktiengesellschaft, Essen, in 1941 (hereafter cited as Krupp MS), Nuernburg Military Tribunals (Subsequent Proceedings), German Military Documents Section (hereafter cited as GMDS), DRB AGO.

[3] (1) Bor, *Gespraeche mit Halder,* p. 103. (2) Ernst Roehm, *Die Geschichte eines Hochverraeters* (Muenchen, 1928), pp. 113–18.

forbidden ordnance went the more vital task of developing new items. If Germany failed to keep step with developments of foreign powers, it could never hope to regain what it considered its rightful place in the sun. Within Germany such work was severely handicapped by the necessity for stringent secrecy. Nevertheless, a great deal was accomplished through dummy business firms that ostensibly engaged in peaceful commercial or technical pursuits while in reality devoting themselves exclusively to weapons research and development. A Krupp branch office in Berlin was only one of several enterprises functioning as a blind of this sort. Disguised as part of a legitimate engineering company, the Krupp branch designed artillery carriages, among them modern mobile carriages for the very guns that another concern was then in the process of modifying for stationary coastal employment as prescribed by treaty terms.[4] While such illicit activities inside Germany were largely restricted to theory, no similar hurdles stood in the way of practical research and development abroad. Krupp's co-operation with Bofors in Sweden was a case in point. In return for license rights to certain steel and artillery patents, employees of the German firm were given unlimited access to plant facilities and technical information on current developments. From 1921 to 1935 a delegation of Krupp experts attached to the Swedish munitions firm kept a steady stream of information flowing back to their employer, who in turn promptly advised the Reichswehr. Under the sponsorship of Krupp German officers went on inspection tours to Bofors to witness test firings of the latest in artillery and ammunition.[5]

Most important of all, and in a sense most extraordinary, were the war preparations of the Reichswehr itself. At the same time that the fatherland publicly bemoaned its reduction to military impotence, the hard core of German soldiery's elite, the officers of the 100,000-man army, ceaselessly worked toward building an even better war machine than the one that had come so close in 1918 to worsting a global host of opponents. These were the men who evolved the special brand of mechanized and mobile warfare that the world, in a later vocabulary, was to know as the blitzkrieg. Economic and industrial mobilization as well as military training for a future war of liberation were studied, planned, and partially put into practice with meticulous detail. As early as 1924 the Army Weapons Office set up an economic mobilization staff for the ambitious, albeit later substantially scaled-down, project of marshaling the resources for an armed force comprising 63 Infantry, 5 Cavalry, and 30 Frontier Guard divisions. Since the need for secrecy prevented direct contact with industry, which would have to produce the arms and equipment for that army, a nationwide underground organization served to procure the required data for integrating essential manu-

[4] Krupp MS, GMDS DRB AGO.

[5] *Ibid.* German Army diehards, to be sure, believed that Krupp and other big industrial leaders were initially not co-operative enough. A historical report entitled *Die Entwicklung der Dienststelle fuer Wehrwirtschaft in Waffenamt 1924–1933* (hereafter referred to as German Secret Rearmement 1924–33) states that one of the difficulties encountered in secret industrial mobilization measures before 1933 was "the indifference of numerous industrialists toward the problems of national defense, their lack of faith in the restoration of Germany's [military] strength, or their fear of economic damage in foreign business connections . . . ." It cited Krupp as belonging to that category. See German Secret Rearmament 1924–33, OCMH. This historical report, comprising documents and excerpts from captured files of the *Feldwirtschaftsamt,* was compiled by the Foreign Office, London, in 1945.

facturing facilities into the over-all plan.[6]

But all the staff planning, research, development, and industrial preparation could be of no avail in the absence of highly trained combat forces capable of translating the newly evolved tactics and techniques into practice. Here the Reichswehr encountered its most serious difficulties. Its forces were severely limited in number, and the primary weapons for the new type of warfare—the tank and the military airplane—were prohibited by treaty. Within Germany, armored training was restricted to tin-and-pasteboard dummy tanks, and flight training to occasional highly secretive excursions with flimsy sport aircraft. If the future army was to be built on more solid foundations than these, the Army had to find more favorable ground than blighted Germany. And so began a long and fruitful period of collaboration with a power similarly intent on rebuilding its military establishment: the Soviet Union.

The exact time of the commencement of Russo-German military collaboration cannot be determined, though subsequent events lend credence to the belief that secret clauses in the Treaty of Rapallo in 1922 represented the cornerstone of the subsequent *rapprochement* between the Red Army and the Reichswehr.[7] Each country had something valuable to offer the other. The Germans had their highly skilled cadre of military leaders, steeped in an intellectual tradition, who could teach the new class of Soviet officers the doctrines of tactical and strategic command. Men like Tukhachevski and Ogorevitch participated in inspection tours and war games and studied German manuals to the point where they finally were more familiar with the contents than their German colleagues. With a view to securing for its armament factories such unimpeded progress as would some day benefit not only the Soviet Union but also the fatherland, the Germans similarly contributed to the rejuvenation of Russian industry.[8] German technicians, engineers, and skilled mechanics went east to teach and supervise. The Reichswehr set up in the Soviet Union entire munitions plants that were managed and largely or wholly staffed with Germans.[9] Lack of money, the stumbling block in American ordnance research and development during the 1920's and 1930's, was hardly a consideration. Only secrecy was of the essence, and, assured of the discreet handling of rearmament matters, the German Government did its best to pad budgets and hide appropriations for military expenditures.[10]

In return for contributions toward strengthening Soviet power, the Russians furnished Germany with the very facilities for practical troop training that could not be maintained within the Reich. Between 1924 and 1930 three German military installations were set up on Soviet territory: a fighter pilot and air observer school at Lipetsk, a gas warfare school at Saratov, and an armored school at Kazan. The secrecy surrounding the entire setup, and the security measures for insuring that

[6] German Secret Rearmament, 1924–33, OCMH.

[7] (1) MS, The Reichswehr and Soviet Russia, General der Flieger Wilhelm Speidel (hereafter cited as MS # P–043 (Speidel)), OCMH. (2) Leonhard Shapiro, ed., *Soviet Treaty Series* (Washington, 1950), I, 381–83.

[8] MS # P–043 (Speidel), OCMH.

[9] MS, *Erinnerungen,* Feldmarschall Walter von Blomberg, GMDS DRB AGO.

[10] (1) MS # P–043 (Speidel), OCMH. (2) MS, Admiralty Translation of the [German] Navy's Battle Against the Treaty of Versailles, OCMH. (3) Wladyslaw Wszebor Kulski (pseud. W. M. Knight-Patterson), *Germany from Defeat to Conquest* (London, 1945), pp. 394–407. (4) Cecil F. Melville, *The Russian Face of Germany* (London, 1932), pp. 124–28.

secrecy, bordered on the fantastic. Men and machines had to be bootlegged across the frontiers. Ammunition and weapons impossible to disguise were carried in small sailboats all the way from German Baltic ports to Leningrad. German soldiers killed in accidents while training on Soviet soil were smuggled back in coffins packed in boxes ostensibly containing machine parts. Particularly knotty problems were solved in even more unusual ways. The fighter planes used at the Lipetsk air base, for example, had been purchased abroad and were powered by British engines that could not be overhauled locally. With their sailboat sea transport organization, the Germans managed to send a certain number of engines each year to English factories where they were overhauled and subsequently returned to Lipetsk.[11]

The number of trainees at the several schools varied, as did local conditions of independence from Soviet interference. At Lipetsk the German fliers had practically unlimited freedom of movement, while the tank students at Kazan apparently were subject to a more rigid regime restricting them to a fenced-in cantonment and even requiring them to wear Red Army uniforms. Nevertheless, professional relations with the Russian hosts were generally satisfactory and the Germans, despite numerous complaints that they gave more than they received, accomplished what they had come for. German officers participated in Red Army maneuvers; German Air observers conducted joint exercises with the Red Air Force; German tankers learned the refinements of armored warfare and tested equipment such as the latest experimental models of Krupp tanks. A small but select body of military leaders, including, among others, Heinz Guderian of later panzer fame, gathered a wealth of practical experience in the warfare of tomorrow.[12] When, upon the accession of Hitler in 1933, German activities in the Soviet Union gradually ceased because of the steadily mounting open remilitarization in Germany itself, a highly trained cadre stood ready to take over the reins of a brand new army.

German rearmament between 1935 and 1939 marked the culmination of the painstaking efforts to preserve the military traditions of bygone years of glory and recreate a war machine that once more would command the respect, if not dread, of the world. After 1933 the production of up-to-date weapons had begun in earnest, with the accent on the mobility and striking power of a well-integrated ground-air team. German tanks underwent a radical transformation. Their formerly wooden cannon suddenly spouted fire and their erstwhile make-believe armor gave way to steel plate.[13] By 1935 even the niceties of a *pro forma* adherence to treaty obligations were ready to be discarded and, along with the reintroduction of compulsory military service, the wraps taken off a well-equipped and even better organized army. It is worth remembering that at a time when America had not a single armored division and still considered the tank a mere adjunct and supporting weapon for the infantry, Germany started with the premise that the tank is a weapon in its own right—the primary offensive ground weapon, in fact, of mobile warfare. Slowing the tank to the rate of advance of foot troops or roadbound artillery would

[11] MS # P-043 (Speidel), OCMH.

[12] (1) *Ibid.* (2) Interrogation of Gen Ernst Koestring, HIC WDGS G-2, OCMH.

[13] Heinz Guderian, *Achtung—Panzer* (Stuttgart, 1937 ?), pp. 157-58.

slow an entire offensive, hostile forces would have time to regroup, and operations might once again degenerate into position warfare in which the objective—forcing a quick decision by destroying the enemy army—could never be achieved. The logical procedure lay not in slowing down the tank but in motorizing supporting infantry and artillery elements and welding all three into one unit capable of delivering a decisive blow in the very opening stage of hostilities. How correct these deliberations and conclusions had been was demonstrated in the well-nigh ridiculous ease with which the panzer divisions, rolling over the level terrain of northern Europe, subjugated Poland and France.

In the United States, Germany's spectacular successes left an impression no less profound than in the rest of the world. For one thing, they provided the impetus toward the creation of the Armored Force for which a number of officers had been clamoring in vain for more than a decade. For another, they set the pace for a revision of combat techniques and corresponding basic reorganization of United States Army forces. But above all, the swiftness and thoroughness of German victories set up a clamor for more and better weapons. The Ordnance Department, only recently come from rags to riches, was expected to stamp new matériel out of the ground. "The enemy was at the gates and was about to land in New York City in the imagination of the hysterical people of that time . . . ," wrote the wartime Chief of Ordnance in speaking of those trying days.[14] A full-fledged myth was in the making about amounts and capabilities of German matériel in general and German tanks in particular. While Germany on the eve of the Battle of France had a grand total of 3,379 tanks, only 2,574 of which actually rolled westward on May 10,[15] French estimates, for example, pegged their number at anywhere from a staggering 8,000 to a conservative 3,700.[16] In reality, French tank strength alone almost certainly equaled, and, combined with British tanks on the Western Front, beyond a doubt surpassed the German total.[17]

Fully as fanciful were reports about the tanks themselves. An article stated:

> One weapon used by the Germans, the heavy break-through tank, came as a surprise to many—military men as well as civilians. . . . Then on May 10, 1940, German break-through tanks, estimated to weigh seventy tons, armed with 77mm or 155mm cannon and flame throwers, opened up a hole in the Little Maginot Line. Through this gap poured . . . massed armored divisions closely backed by infantry in trucks. The age of mechanization had come into its own. . . .[18]

Other accounts perpetuated the legend of "cannon-proof" panzers.[19] But Germany neither had cannon-proof nor superheavy monsters. German machines held little, if any, edge over their adversaries in over-all combat capability. The majority of German tanks were of the Panzer I and Panzer II types that the Wehrmacht itself admitted

[14] Ltr, Gen Campbell to Gen Harmon, 21 Mar 45, OHF.

[15] MS # P-059, German Tank Strength and Loss Statistics, Generalmajor Burkhart Mueller-Hillebrand (hereafter cited as MS # P-059 (Mueller-Hillebrand)), OCMH.

[16] Theodore Draper, *The Six Weeks' War* (New York, 1944), p. 47. The official data of the Vichy-French Ministry of War ran to 7,600. See Daniel Vilfroy, *War in the West* (Harrisburg, 1942), p. 23.

[17] Figures on French tanks in metropolitan France in 1940 vary from a low of 2,965 to a high of 3,615, while British tank strength is uniformly cited at 600. Cf. (1) Draper, *op. cit.*, pp. 47–48; (2) Vilfroy, *op. cit.*, p. 23; and (3) Richard M. Ogorkiewicz, "Armor in Defeat," *Armor*, LIX, 204 (1950), 16–23.

[18] Capt. C. R. Kutz, "Break-Through Tanks," *Army Ordnance*, XXI, 123 (1940), 242.

[19] See Winston S. Churchill, *The Gathering Storm* (Boston, 1949) p. 476.

to be useless against all but a weak and demoralized enemy and unsuited for employment against hostile armor.[20] The six-ton Panzer I, for example, had been proved obsolete during the Civil War in Spain—obsolete not only as much as any production-type weapon is in terms of those in the drafting stage, but obsolete in terms of equipment currently in use by the opposition. With "onionskin" armor and the fire power of only two turret-mounted machine guns, it was easy prey for Soviet 45-mm. tank and antitank guns on the Loyalist side. The contemporary characterization of the light tank as a "mechanical toy, a mere tactical runabout" fitted the Panzer I to the proverbial T.[21] The 10-ton Panzer II, first issued to German armored forces in 1936 but never sent to Spain, fell into the same category.[22] The only material improvements over its predecessor lay in slightly greater fire power, a 20-mm. cannon turret-mounted coaxially with one machine gun.

The first-line tanks of the blitz days in France, the Panzer III and the Panzer IV, similarly were far from being superweapons. Lightly armored, both were highly vulnerable to antitank and direct artillery fire.[23] As to armament, the Panzer III carried a 37-mm. gun, an adaptation of the same antitank gun that as far back as 1937 had proved to be outmatched by foreign matériel.[24] The Panzer IV, armed with the 75-mm. *Kw. K. (L/24),* a gun-howitzer with a maximum muzzle velocity of 1,500 feet per second, was more an armored field piece than a tank designed for toe-to-toe combat with enemy tanks.[25]

All told, German successes in the early stages of World War II resulted from method of employment of weapons—panzer divisions versus single tanks, the heavy mobile punch versus a continuous front—and a highly proficient body of troops. From the days of the Reichswehr, attention had focused on training the individual German soldier; mechanization did not obscure the fact that even the best matériel becomes useless in the hands of men unable to use it properly. Once the peace-trained, battle-hardened core of the Wehrmacht languished in Allied prisoner-of-war enclosures, or lay buried beneath the Russian snows and North African desert sands, no effort of German weapons designers could stave off defeat.

Design and development of Army ordnance were in the hands of the Army Weapons Office. Though roughly analogous to the U.S. Army Ordnance Depart-

[20] MS, The Private War Journal of Generaloberst Franz Halder (hereafter cited as Halder Diary), entry for 18 Feb 40, OCMH.

A breakdown of German tanks by type shows the following (1 April 1940):

Panzer I	1,062
Panzer II	1,079
Panzer III	329
Panzer IV	280
Total	2,750

The remaining 629 vehicles were: flame thrower tanks on Panzer II chassis (7); Czech-origin 35(t) and 38(t) tanks armed with 37-mm. guns (426); and commanders' versions of Panzer I through IV armed only with machine guns (243). Self-propelled artillery and tank destroyers were as good as nonexistent at the time. MS # P–059 (Mueller-Hillebrand), OCMH.

[21] Maj. Gen. J. F. C. Fuller (British Army, Ret.) "The Tank in Spain," *Army Ordnance,* XIX, 109 (1938), 25.

[22] OI Special Interrogation Rpt 34, 4 Mar 47 (hereafter cited as OI-SIR/34), OCMH.

[23] *Ibid.*

[24] (1) Fuller, *loc. cit.,* p. 27. (2) Brig. Gen. Henry J. Reilly, "Proving Ground in Spain," *Army Ordnance,* XIX, 114 (1939), 334.

[25] The abbreviation *Kw. K.* stands for *Kampfwagen-Kanone,* literally battlewagon cannon. The abbreviation *L/24* expresses caliber length. In German practice it denotes length of the gun including breech but excluding muzzle brake. One caliber length equals the diameter of the gun bore. Given that diameter and the number of caliber lengths, the length of the gun can readily be computed.

ment in these functions, its scope of responsibilities extended to somewhat different fields from those of its American counterpart. In addition to small arms, artillery, and ammunition, for example, the Army Weapons Office had charge of all types of engineer and signal equipment. Design and development of antiaircraft artillery, on the other hand, were duties of the Air Force.[26]

Within the over-all organization of the German Army, the Army Weapons Office came under the Chief of Army Equipment and Commander in Chief of the Replacement Army, who had charge of arms development as well as procurement. Control over the commencement of new projects rested with the using arms, and, through them, the General Staff and ultimately Hitler. The impetus for a project might come from a number of quarters: the Army Weapons Office itself, the Fuehrer, private industry, soldiers in the field. Particularly the latter have been credited with submitting many useful ideas and constructive criticisms.[27] Once a requirement was set up, the Army Weapons Office prepared the technical specifications and farmed out the development project to private industrial firms. As a rule, an identical contract was let to two competitors in order to add incentive for the design of the best product possible. Pilot models were returned to the Weapons Office for proof tests, upon completion of which the item was demonstrated to the using arms for their approval or rejection. Then usually followed a limited, or, if necessary, a large-scale battle test. Standardization and further modifications thereafter were up to the using arms, subject, in the case of major questions, to the decision of the Commander in Chief of the Army or the Commander in Chief of the Armed Forces.

During peacetime and the early blitz years that system worked well enough. But once the war spread to new and larger areas and the mounting fury of combat gave rise to an ever-increasing demand for more powerful weapons, the process of development grew more and more haphazard. The Fuehrer's promises of *the* miracle weapon to turn the tide became more eloquent as one abortive offensive followed the other, with the result that wholly unseasoned projects were rushed virtually from the drafting board to the front. Time and again the good features of such weapons were so heavily outweighed by a lack of reliability that repercussions on troop morale overshadowed the short-range propaganda effect. A comment from the Russian front after the first major battle test of the Panther tank illustrates the point:

> In closing, I can't get around adding a few words on a very sad story, despite the fact that it was exactly the way I had thought it would be: Panther. There were a great many who expected the decision to come from the new, untried weapon. The initially complete failure therefore had a somewhat depressing effect, particularly since, on the basis of the Fuehrer Order, special expectations had been aroused. . . . So long as one builds such a valuable weapon, one must not build in an unusable gasoline pump or deficient gaskets. There is no shadow of a doubt that the majority of technical deficiencies resulted from

[26] Unless otherwise cited, material in the rest of this section is based on MS # T-11, Section B-15, OCMH. This manuscript is a 2,200-page co-operative study on the German High Command *(OKH)*, prepared between 1946 and 1948 by General Franz Halder and a group of former German general staff officers under the auspices of the Historical Division, EUCOM. Section B-15 was written by General der Artillerie Emil Leeb, at one time the chief of the Army Weapons Office.

[27] Intel Rpt EF/AM/56, Part I, "General Appreciation of the Rationalization of the German Armaments Industry," Karl Otto Saur, in IN FIAT I 350.09-78, 1 Jun 46, Ord Tech Intel files.

PANZER II, THE "LYNX," *mounting a 2-cm. gun.*

8 RAD PANZERSPAHWAGEN, mounting the 7.5-cm. short-barreled gun.

THE "PANTHER," *mounting a 7.5-cm. gun.*

PANZER VI, THE "TIGER," *mounting an 8.8-cm. gun.*

291064 O—55——18

substitute materials which simply did not measure up to standard. . . . The effectiveness of the Panther weapon is noteworthy. At a range of 7,900 yards a [Soviet] T-34 [tank] was knocked out with the first round.[28]

Even if it wanted to, the Army Weapons Office could do little to remedy the situation. From early prewar days the large majority of ground-force research and development had been conducted by private firms, with the Army's technical agency merely playing a testing and acceptance role. Its own research and development not only was extremely limited in scope but poor to boot.[29] The unbroken string of swift victories between September 1939 and autumn 1941 provided little stimulus for improving on time-honored customs and procedures. Came the denouement of the catastrophic first winter in Russia and a lack of the new and better weapons with which to re-equip almost the entire Army, the Weapons Office was an easy target for those eager to obtain control over ground ordnance design and production. From the time that Hitler finally decreed the conversion of industry to an all-out war effort until the collapse of Germany in May 1945, influence over Army research and development passed more and more into the hands of essentially nonmilitary authorities such as Albert Speer, the Minister for Armaments and War Production, Heinrich Himmler, whose SS was bent on building an industrial empire all its own, and, above all, the Fuehrer himself.

Just as he personally participated in the conduct of operations, to the point where he ultimately made troop dispositions down to battalion level and lower,[30] so Hitler increasingly concerned himself with the details of armament design. Every modification, every new project was brought to the personal attention of the Commander in Chief of the Armed Forces for notice and approval. The soundness of basic principles and the ratio of economic expenditure to probable long-range returns from a new weapon mattered less and less as the military situation continued to deteriorate. So long as an idea held even faint promise of a weapon with which to equalize the growing disproportion between German and Allied resources of manpower and matériel, that idea was tried. Though it stands to reason that not all of the thousand and one projects resulting from this, the Fuehrer's policy, were worthless, the net gains little justified the reckless prodigality that achieved them.

Limitations Upon American Ordnance Research and Development

In contrast to the political control exercised over the German Army, the Chief of Staff of the U.S. Army had the final voice in decreeing American doctrine of tactical use of weapons. Though each of the using arms worked out its concepts of the best means of accomplishing its own mission, the Chief of Staff had to approve them or resolve conflicts of doctrine arising between one arm and another. The Ordnance Department was then responsible for designing the fighting equipment with which to execute the maneuvers planned. If evolution of doctrine were tardy, then design would also be delayed, for design of

[28] Ltr, Oberstleutnant von Grundherr, 14 Jul 43, in experience and inspection report binder, *Panzeroffizier beim Chef Generalstab des Heeres, Akte E, Band 2, Erfahrunger (Reiseberichte)*, GMDS DRB AGO.

[29] For an exhaustive analysis of all aspects of German research and development, see Col. Leslie E. Simon, *German Research in World War II* (New York and London, 1947).

[30] MS # T-113, Unification or Co-ordination: The Armed Forces Problem, General der Artillerie Walter Warlimont, OCMH.

weapons for any army is necessarily shaped by the purpose for which the weapons are to be used. To revert, as an illustration, to the problem of tank employment over which controversy had been vigorous in the 1930's, if the tank were to be regarded as primarily a means of supporting the infantry, tank design would stress cross-country maneuverability and fire power enough to combat infantry heavy weapons but not enough to fight a battle with enemy tanks. If, on the other hand, a tank were to be used as a part of an armored force, design would be focused on fire power sufficient to engage enemy tanks directly and on protection for the tank's crew. Ordnance automotive experts had complained in the 1920's of being handicapped by failure of the General Staff to define tank doctrine, and revision of doctrine of the 1930's, culminating in the creation of the Armored Force in 1940, had required further extensive changes in tank design. A less well-known but perhaps still more serious situation occurred in development of mines. Partly because the War Department only belatedly recognized the tactical importance of powerful antitank mines and mine exploders, and partly because the Corps of Engineers requested only small mines, design of adequate land mines was delayed at least two years. Ordnance ammunition specialists, to be sure, might have argued vigorously the case for mines comparable to the German Teller mines, but combat inexperience together with Engineer insistence would still have militated against early success in persuading the using arm to approve big mines. The mine clearance problem was not satisfactorily solved at all. Whether it could have been met before the end of the war, had the Ordnance Department been requested five years sooner to study it, may be a question, but certainly tardy demand for sound devices made the task of development more difficult.[31]

As the Chief of Staff determined how a weapon was to be used, so after 1919 the combat arms were empowered to list the characteristics it should possess.[32] Thus two limitations were imposed upon ordnance designers: they must devise matériel for predetermined purposes and they must accept the decisions of the combat arms as to what military characteristics would best serve in each weapon to accomplish these purposes. The customer was to be regarded, if not as always right, at least as right until combat proved him wrong. That would be late in the game. In World War II special Ordnance missions, sent to active theatres to observe performance of American weapons or to prepare recommendations for new equipment for, say, jungle warfare, provided Research and Development Service with useful information and some understanding of combat troops' opinion. But redesign or major change had still to be approved by boards of the using arms. The fact that the personnel of those boards changed rather frequently forced Ordnance designers at intervals to refight their case for any given proposal. Moreover, service boards were by no means always well informed on combat problems. While the Ordnance Department could attempt to dissuade the user from establishing requirements that Ordnance experts considered inappropriate or impossible to achieve, neither the Chief of Ordnance nor the chief of Research and Development Service had authority to reject a development project or to modify it materially once it had been ordered.

---

[31] See Ch. XIII, below.

[32] See above, p. 29.

At the risk of belaboring the obvious, the fact must be repeated that the Ordnance Department was a service, quite literally a servant, of the using arms. This fact is frequently misunderstood even within the Ordnance Department itself. Thus one Ordnance writer summarizing the war work of Ordnance Research and Development Service declared:

> It is a common belief that the evolution of new tactics dictates the use of new weapons when, in fact, the reverse is true. For the effective employment of new weapons, new methods of use (tactics) must inevitably be devised. The Research and Development Service, conscious of its responsibility to the using arms and of the necessity for increasingly decisive weapons, took the initiative in the development of much materiel without waiting for the need to be felt on the battlefield.[33]

There is, of course, an element of truth in the statement regarding the relation of weapons to their use. Tactics of modern warfare were revolutionized by the introduction of bombers, fighter planes, and tanks in World War I. At the end of World War II the atomic bomb promised to bring about many changes in strategic and tactical planning. The Ordnance Department, apart from three or four officers advising on fuze problems, had no share in the MANHATTAN Project. Future development of accurate guided missiles might necessitate further revisions of doctrine. But between 1940 and 1945 the Ordnance Department neither devised any weapon that forced fundamental changes in tactical doctrine, nor, save in a few instances, did it anticipate a tactical need by designing an innovation before the fighting forces had requested it. If Ordnance engineers did submit an innovation without having had a specific request, they were obliged to conduct a difficult sales campaign to prevent flat rejection on the grounds that no requirement for it existed.

The Chief of Staff in 1945 emphasized the injustice of criticisms aimed at the Ordnance Department:

> In some of the public discussions of such matters [the quality of American ordnance] criticism was leveled at the Ordnance Department for not producing better weapons. This Department produced with rare efficiency what it was told to produce, and these instructions came from the General Staff of which I am the responsible head, transmitting the resolved views of the officers with the combat troops or air forces, of the commanders in the field.[34]

General Campbell also realized clearly the restrictions upon his Department. In discussing with officers of the line the advisability of developing a trackless tank, Campbell announced:

> As long as I am in the Chair, the Ordnance Department is going to act as a servant of the line of the Army—its public. If the line wants an 18 wheeled car that will run sidewise, we will do our best to give it to the line. If we don't think it can be made, we will advise you to that effect. If you still want it, we will try our best to get it. That is our stand in this car right now. . . . It is up to the line to determine, with our advice, what they would like to have done in this car. As far as the Ordnance Department is concerned, it is your decision.[35]

Experienced Ordnance officers recognized that more persuasiveness on the part of the Ordnance Department might occasionally have saved effort expended on weapons that, when completed, proved

[33] PSP 81, OHF.

[34] *Biennial Report of The Chief of Staff of The United States Army—July 1, 1943 to June 30, 1945 to The Secretary of War*, p. 97.

[35] Conference on the Trackless Tank, Col. William A. Borden, Chairman, 11 Jul 42, Tank and Automotive Br, Combat Vehicle Sec files, Project KG 218, DRB AGO.

unable to accomplish their purpose. The inability of Ordnance officers to induce the Infantry to abandon its demand for a 37-mm. tank gun is one example.[36] Ordnance engineers used engineering language that manifestly often carried little conviction to the combat arms. The layman must nevertheless be astonished at the Ordnance Department's acceptance of responsibility for designing weapons it had deemed unsuitable for the purpose intended and had demurred at developing. Instead of reminding the using arm that any particular development had to follow the specifications laid down by the user and that weaknesses in the resulting weapon were often due to the combination of characteristics demanded, the Ordnance Department was prone to insist that the weapon under criticism was the best of its kind. For the sake of the morale of the general public in wartime, there was reason to announce emphatically and repeatedly that American fighting equipment was the finest in the world. But within the War Department the Ordnance Department exposed itself to unwarranted criticism from other branches of the Army by not explaining the nature of the limitations imposed upon Ordnance Research and Development Service.

Ordnance technicians and engineers, on the other hand, were not invariably in the van. Conservatism marked some phases of their thinking. An example may be found in their unwillingness in 1940 to push development of incendiary bombs, in spite of urgent communications from a military observer in London and later from an officer of the Army Air Forces who had witnessed the blitz. Several incendiary bombs had been under development during the 1930's, but Ordnance ammunition experts by 1940 had come to the conclusion that a demolition bomb could do everything an incendiary could, and more. They turned deaf ears to descriptions of the effectiveness of the magnesium-filled incendiaries that the Germans had rained upon London. The upshot of this indifference was the transfer of the project to the Chemical Warfare Service, which had long had responsibility for chemical fillers. Consequently it was the Chemical Warfare Service, not the Ordnance Department, that developed the so-called napalm bomb that proved peculiarly effective toward the end of the war and later in Korea.[37]

A few blind spots notwithstanding, by and large the Ordnance Department met its assigned responsibilities with distinction. In most cases, as General Marshall stated, shortcomings in American fighting equipment in World War II were attributable not to Ordnance Department slow-wittedness, but to War Department and Ground Forces instructions. That public opinion and Congress all through the 1930's so stressed defense as opposed to aggressive warfare that Army planning was willy-nilly influenced by what amounted to a definite national policy, doubtless largely accounts for delays in evolving tactical doctrine for offense.[38] Those delays in turn retarded Ordnance research and development work. Comprehension of the limits of Ordnance responsibilities is essential to an understanding of the story that follows.

Technical Intelligence

In peacetime, development of American ordnance might be regarded as a search for absolutes rather than relatives. Since

---

[36] See above, pp. 182–86.

[37] (1) Intervs, 4 Apr 51, with Col Studler and with Mr. Frederick V. Ludden, Ammo Br, R&D Div. (2) OCM 15342, 13 Sep 39 and 15427, 25 Oct 39.

[38] See Watson, *op. cit.*, pp. 16–36.

the enemy to be overmatched was unknown, the problem became one of finding the best possible means of defeating any hostile force without considering where a future battle would take place or exactly what equipment the future enemy would employ. Yet there were clear advantages to thinking in terms of besting a particular army and its matériel. The designer inevitably could most readily focus his energies on countermeasures when faced with knowledge of what he must compete with. Americans had long realized that information about the types of equipment in use or under development by foreign armies was an aid, if not actually a starting point, for ordnance research and development work for the U.S. Army. But during the 1930's technical intelligence, that is, data on details of foreign design and manufacturing methods, was so intertwined with military intelligence that what filtered through to the Department was casual and tended to leave research to proceed in a near vacuum. The U.S. Army's disregard of developments in foreign munitions before 1940 is a perpetual source of astonishment to the European.

When the disasters on the Continent occurred in the spring and summer of 1940, American military intelligence still derived only from military observer and liaison reports sent through American embassies. Realization of the need of more and exacter knowledge of foreign weapons had led the Chief of Ordnance in March to request the appointment of two additional Ordnance officers as assistant military observers. Accordingly, in May, Colonel Zornig went to Berlin and Capt. Gervais W. Trichel to Paris. Captain Trichel's mission terminated in June, and Colonel Zornig's in July at his own request, when he discovered that sources of exact information were closed to him.[39] Meanwhile, the extent of what the Ordnance Department did not know about German, French, and British ordnance is plainly revealed in a list of questions prepared by the Office, Chief of Ordnance, in June 1940. A week before the fall of France the Chief of Ordnance asked that military observers in Europe find the answers, and, if possible, send samples of foreign equipment for study in the United States. When the replies came back in the late fall, the papers were circulated narrowly. It is hard to believe that the information had not been long available in Ordnance files. For example, the first question on artillery asked whether the French 75-mm. and 155-mm. gun (GPF) recoil mechanisms were secret; the answer was that neither had been secret since 1918. Moreover, many of the answers to questions on German matériel are known today to have been inaccurate, for captured German documents giving official data on characteristics and performance show how much misinformation the reports contained.[40] But long before the General Staff discovered that, it was obvious that means were inadequate for obtaining knowledge of what ordnance resources the future enemy possessed.

At the end of August 1940 the General Staff inaugurated an Army-wide intelligence system. Every service was to have a unit. The Ordnance Military Intelligence Section was established in September. Its duties were to collate, digest, and disseminate the information that came from G–2 reports and to prepare statements of what

[39] Min, Wesson Conferences, 21 Mar 40, 23 Mar 40, 11 Apr 40, and 4 May 40, OHF.

[40] Special List of Questions on Ord Materiel, 13 Jun 40, and Reply 1st Ind, 27 Nov 40, OKD 470/204.1, Ord Tech Intel files.

further information the Ordnance Department needed in order to solve its current problems. But the section had no immediate part in collecting data abroad and, in the months that followed, much of what the G–2 reports contained dealt with countries that were soon to be allies.[41] Nevertheless, the machinery was now in existence for making use of intelligence reports, and the scope and effectiveness of the intelligence network was to increase greatly as time went on. Circulating Military Intelligence Division special bulletins was the first step in keeping the services informed on foreign developments. By December 1940 G–2 had evolved its procedures about as follows: when an incoming report noted that German tanks were carrying 2-inch armor plate and recommended corresponding increases on American tanks, G–2 sent the information to G–4, the Infantry, the Engineers, the Armored Force, and Ordnance. If the arms and services concurred, G–4 would initiate action to put the change into effect.[42] The chief difference between this system and earlier procedures lay in the speed with which action could be hurried through because every branch of the Army was informed simultaneously. Indeed General Marshall, in discussing Army Intelligence, observed that right up to the time of Pearl Harbor the United States had little more than what its military observers "could learn at a dinner, more or less over the coffee cups."[43]

Within its first year the Ordnance Military Intelligence Section found its task growing in volume and complexity. From the data supplied by the special bulletins of G–2, the small staff of the Ordnance section periodically prepared detailed analyses of information bearing on ordnance. The Ordnance Intelligence Bulletins, averaging monthly nearly fifty pages, circulated among interested agencies outside and units within the Department, so that a considerable body of facts—or guesses—on foreign matériel became available to people needing the data. After May 1941 the reports of the Ordnance section of a new War Department Special Observer Group sent to the United Kingdom that month supplemented routine communiqués.[44] Meanwhile the Ordnance Department was not wholly dependent upon G–2 sources for information. Even before the Lend-Lease Act passed, Ordnance technicians could profit by the exchange of scientific findings among British, Canadian, and American scientists of NDRC.[45] And, as it became clear that the United States was actually, even if not yet formally, committed to supporting Great Britain in the war against Germany, the British put at the disposal of the U.S. Army data both on British weapons and on what British intelligence had uncovered on German weapons. British technical intelligence bridged the gap for the United States until such time as the U.S. Army had trained technical intelligence to act for itself, and, in fact, throughout the war the Ordnance Department used British, Canadian, and Australian reports on enemy equipment.[46]

After Pearl Harbor Ordnance officers

[41] Memo, Actg ACofS G–2 for CofS, 16 Aug 40, sub: WDSR MID WD Intelligence, AG 321.19 MID, DRB AGO.

[42] (1) Special MID Bull 17, 26 Sep 40, G–2/2657-23. (2) Memo, ACofS G–2 for CofS, 2 Dec 40, OO 350.051 MID. Both in DRB AGO.

[43] *Hearings* . . . , Senate, 80th Cong, 1st Sess. on S758, 30 Apr 47, p. 493.

[44] (1) Memo, ACofS G–2 for CofS, 14 Aug 41, 350.051 MID. (2) Ord Tech Services in ETO, AG Adm 604F. Both in DRB AGO.

[45] Baxter, *op. cit.*, pp. 120–23.

[46] See below n. 77.

assigned to theatre headquarters prepared regular monthly reports which sometimes contained explicit information upon enemy ordnance. As early as March 1942 the communications of the Ordnance officer in the Middle East described features of German weapons encountered by the British in the recent battles for North Africa, and a series of photographs of captured equipment arrived at Aberdeen Proving Ground soon after. Some actual specimens of German matériel also were shipped to the States, although in 1942 they formed a thin trickle compared to the flood that was to reach Aberdeen in the summer of 1943.[47] Study of the weapons themselves naturally gave research men in the zone of the interior more useful knowledge than they could derive from reports written overseas, even when they were accompanied by sketches. The chief value of theatre reports to the Research and Development Service lay in the detailed comments on performance of American ordnance. Later in the war special missions sent to active theatres undertook to assemble information upon the functioning of particular types of Allied equipment, to see what other types were needed, or to introduce new experimental models. But on enemy weapons neither these special missions nor the theatre Ordnance officer could ordinarily supply all wanted technical data.

Early in 1942 General Barnes was convinced that research and development would benefit by a more direct flow of technical information than the theatres could readily transmit under the existing system. That summer, as soon as he became head of the separate division for research and development, he launched his proposal. He persuaded G–2 and the rest of the War Department that, because trained Ordnance observers could collect essential detailed data on enemy equipment more competently than could officers trained only in general military intelligence, specially briefed Ordnance teams should be sent to the active theatres. The first Ordnance intelligence mission accordingly went to North Africa soon afterward, in fact some months before American combat troops landed there. A series of units for more permanent overseas assignment could not be provided so quickly. Working out a systematic scheme of indoctrinating Enemy Equipment Intelligence units, as they came to be called, took several months. The first of these new teams left the States in December 1942.[48] Others followed, until by V-E Day units for every theatre had been organized and dispatched. Though originally their mission was to collect samples of enemy equipment and all possible data on it to send to Research and Development Service in the States, in time the units served combat troops more directly by issuing bulletins in the theatres containing information on how to use against the enemy his own weapons captured in an advance. So useful was the work of the Ordnance teams that early in 1944 the commanding general of the Army Service Forces ordered every technical service to organize similar units. Enemy Equipment Intelligence Service teams thus became accepted parts

[47] (1) Progress Rpt Ord Sec, Actg Ord Off Mil North African Mission to CG Mil North African Mission, 31 Mar 42, MNAM Folder, Rpts file, OHF. (2) Memo, Capt Everett S. Davis for Chief of Intel Div ASF, 10 Jul 43, sub: Weekly Activities Rpt of Ord Intel Unit, OO 319.1/3462 Misc, DRB AGO.

[48] (1) Interv with Capt Ernest V. Cameron, Ord Tech Intel, 10 Oct 50. (2) Ord Opns in Middle East Theatre, OHF. (3) WD Tng Cir 81, 6 Nov 42.

of American armies overseas.[49]

These teams were drawn from groups who had trained as tank maintenance men and as small arms, artillery, and ammunition specialists. Familiarity with the features of American equipment qualified them more readily to recognize distinctive and noteworthy characteristics of enemy matériel, a consideration peculiarly important when captured items could not be returned intact to the zone of interior for analysis. In the last year of the war, theatre intelligence staffs recruited additional men for Enemy Equipment Intelligence units by taking volunteers with special experience. At no time did the Ordnance Department make any pretense of giving thorough training in intelligence work. A week of intensive preparation at Aberdeen Proving Ground followed by a week's briefing by the Military Intelligence Division of the General Staff and by the branch chiefs of Ordnance Research and Development was all that was possible. Experience in the field proved to be the best schooling.[50] The officers who had the task of making this new service fulfill its mission in the theatres had a pioneering assignment as difficult as it was important.

In Europe, where Allied invasion of the Continent would give direct access to German factories, laboratories, and experimental stations, the theatre Ordnance officer, Brig. Gen. Henry B. Sayler, realized some months before D Day that an opportunity would exist to go beyond capture and study of particular pieces of enemy equipment; captured German correspondence, laboratory equipment, and records, as well as interviews with prisoners of war who had been engaged in German ordnance research, would enormously enlarge knowledge of enemy development plans and methods. Acting upon General Sayler's suggestion, the Chief of Ordnance arranged to have technical specialists assigned to this task, and in October 1944 the first group, designated the Research and Development Branch of the Technical Division of the Office of the Chief Ordnance Officer, ETOUSA, began its work. The resulting information was assembled and disseminated by a joint British and American agency, the Combined Intelligence Objectives Sub-Committee, usually called CIOS, with headquarters in London. The data thus accumulated in the last six months of the war in Europe, though collected too late to be applied to weapons in World War II, were of utmost long-term value to the Ordnance Department. The work of the CIOS represents an important phase of Allied co-operation on research problems.[51] In the Pacific no comparable investigation was possible until American troops occupied Japan after the war.

The form that technical intelligence activities took in the battle zones and behind the combat lines is part of the story of Ordnance service overseas. Research and Development Service in the zone of interior was affected only by the arrival of captured items at Aberdeen or of photographs sent to the Office, Chief of Ordnance, along with such analyses of enemy

[49] (1) Capt Ernest V. Cameron, Hist of the Ord Technical Intelligence Organization (hereafter cited as Hist Ord Tech Intel), and incl, copy of ltr, CG ASF to CG US Forces in ETO, 14 Mar 44, sub: Enemy Equipment Intelligence Service Teams, OHF. (2) FM 30-15, 7 Dec 43, DRB AGO.

[50] (1) Interv with Capt Cameron, 2 Oct 50. (2) Ltr, Gen Barnes to Col Holger N. Toftoy, 19 Jun 44, sub: Ord Tech Intel Teams in Ord Tech Services in ETO, Annex 5, AG Adm 604F, DRB AGO.

[51] Ord Tech Services in ETO, AG Adm 604F, DRB AGO.

equipment as could be made in the theatres. The Ordnance intelligence unit in Washington was responsible for the ultimate disposition both of actual specimens and of information about them, but a Foreign Materiel Section established at the Aberdeen Proving Ground was the first consignee of enemy weapons and vehicles. From Aberdeen the intelligence unit in the Office, Chief of Ordnance, might shortly decide to send an item to an arsenal or to a commercial laboratory for study—a German machine gun to Springfield Armory, a sample of foreign alloy steel to Watertown, a fire control instrument to Frankford Arsenal. The resulting reports upon the enemy equipment, whether studied by the Aberdeen Foreign Materiel Section and the Ballistic Research Laboratory, by an Ordnance contractor, or by an arsenal, were assembled by the intelligence staff of Research and Development Service who then prepared and distributed summaries of the findings. The summaries might be incorporated in the technical information letters sent to the theatres of operations monthly after April 1943 or might be circulated only among agencies within the United States. Throughout the war the bulk of the significant work on enemy weapons took place at Aberdeen where the firing range, laboratory, and proving facilities made possible comparative tests of American and foreign ordnance.[52]

The Foreign Materiel Section of the proving center at Aberdeen was formally established in September 1942, though it had antecedents in the museum where foreign equipment of World War I and after, all carefully catalogued, had stood on display. Before the end of the year Lt. Col. George B. Jarrett, newly returned from the Middle East, was appointed chief of the section. Jarrett, an arms collector in private life and the curator of the original museum at Aberdeen, was eminently qualified to make the new unit effective. While he was still in the Middle East he had anticipated the need of studying enemy equipment thoroughly and had arranged to ship a few lots back to the Proving Ground. This was the only wholehearted attempt made up to that time to assemble enemy ordnance for technical analysis. The matériel was put to immediate use in schooling the first Enemy Equipment Intelligence units preparing for overseas duty. As the number of items arriving at Aberdeen multiplied, the work of the section increased enormously and the section became a branch with sections under it. One section took charge of the museum exhibits, which were continued for the benefit of a host of visitors—guests at Proving Ground demonstrations, newspaper men, and especially officers detailed to examine the specimens. Another section maintained the Foreign Materiel Branch Library and made analyses of foreign designs and engineering features. A third section acted as liaison with the Office, Chief of Ordnance, and arranged for shipments of items or components to designated laboratories and agencies.[53]

By the fall of 1943 shipments of as much as twenty-six carloads of captured enemy equipment were rolling into Aberdeen at one time. It was not an indiscriminate col-

[52] (1) ODO 327, 19 Aug 42 and 344, 12 Oct 42, OHF. (2) Hist of Aberdeen Proving Ground, Vol. II, Ch. 8, Exhibits H and Q; Vol. III, Ch. 4; and Vol. IV., Ch. 4, OHF.

[53] Hist of Aberdeen Proving Ground, Vol. III, Ch. 4, OHF. In the paragraphs that follow the data derive either from the History of Aberdeen Proving Ground here cited, or from interviews with Colonel Jarrett, Captain Cameron, and Colonel Frye, held respectively on 25 October 1950, 2 November 1950, and 11 September 1951.

lection, as Enemy Equipment Intelligence teams dispatched only new or newly modified matériel. Furthermore, the first sample of each new item captured in the European and Mediterranean theatres went to the United Kingdom, so that only a second specimen could go to the United States. Still the accumulating mass of foreign matériel was tremendous. Deducing from it all possible useful information required careful organization. A description of the successive steps in handling a captured German tank may serve to illustrate the process of studying foreign equipment at the Proving Ground. The Office, Chief of Ordnance, co-ordinated the test program in order to guarantee its proceeding with maximum efficiency and to prevent needless damage to a specimen or unauthorized destruction.

When a tank was captured and shipping space found, the Enemy Equipment Intelligence unit sent word to the intelligence section of Ordnance Research and Development Service in Washington that the tank was en route to the United States. Upon its arrival, port authorities notified the commanding general at Aberdeen, and, after it reached the Proving Ground, the Foreign Materiel Branch photographed it inside and out and reported upon its condition to the intelligence section in the Office, Chief of Ordnance. The intelligence section then communicated with other units of Research and Development Service—the tank division, the artillery division, the ballistics division, the matériel branch—and with agencies outside the Ordnance Department, such as the Signal Corps, if the tank's communication system appeared to have unusual features, or the Chemical Warfare Service, which was interested in the power plant oxygen supply and its susceptibility to gas contamination. Even a branch of the State Department might be concerned, if markings on parts of the tank promised to disclose where parts had been manufactured and thus indicate economic conditions in Germany. On the basis of the requests submitted by all these groups, the Intelligence Section prepared a directive to govern the order and character of the tests to be conducted. Occasionally, some other division of Research and Development Service drew up the test directive, to which the Intelligence Section then gave concurrence. Not until the order from the Office, Chief of Ordnance, appeared could tests begin at Aberdeen.

After the staff at Aberdeen had its instructions in hand, it frequently had to make considerable repairs before the tank could be subjected to road or firing tests. It often demanded sound engineering and great care to ensure accurate reconstruction of the original model. The first trial then might very well be a road and cross-country test to compare the speed and maneuverability of the enemy vehicle with an American counterpart. A check of the time required to traverse the German turret and scrutiny of all electrical controls within turret and body might be the next procedure. Anything novel about the headlights or searchlights had to be noted. Specialists studied the characteristics of the suspension system, the tracks, and the treads, if not already revealed by photographs. The Society of Automotive Engineers War Engineering Board, which gave the Ordnance Department invaluable assistance throughout the war, might undertake careful examination of the design, methods of fabrication, and materials used. Chemical and performance analyses of the oils and lubricants employed might be called for. The fire control and sighting devices might be stripped off and sent to the laboratory at Frankford Arsenal for study, or optical experts brought to Aberdeen might witness performance of the sights in firing tests on the range. If the ammunition for the tank guns had new features of design or used unfamiliar types of fuze or power, the tests might include laboratory examination of a few shells. The projectile might require extensive metallurgical analysis at Watertown Arsenal. In firing the guns, crews and officers had to keep records of their range, accuracy, and penetrating power. Ballisticians of the Research Laboratory might have to prepare comparative tabulations of the German and American ballistic performance.

Upon completion of these tests, American guns would ordinarily fire at the tank in order to find the spots of greatest weakness, test the resistance of the German armor plate, and establish the effective range of American guns and shells designed to combat this type of enemy tank. For example, firing new experimental high-velocity armor-piercing 90-mm. shell at a German Panther tank supplied to Ordnance ammunition experts important information needed to perfect this HVAP ammunition. Metallurgical study of a piece of the tanks' armor might follow if its resistance to penetration or method of fabrication deviated from what past experience had led the Ordnance Department to expect. The final report upon a German tank might thus consist of a good many separate studies. Having assembled these and checked for consistency in the findings and terminology, the foreign matériel staff dispatched copies of the full report to the technical intelligence unit of the Office, Chief of Ordnance, to the chief of Research and Development Service, to G–2 of the General Staff, and to any other units known to have legitimate interest in the data.

Usually men at Aberdeen put the first captured specimen of a new piece of enemy ordnance through careful performance tests, including firing of German ammunition against American tanks. Later samples of enemy equipment were used either for verification of the first set of findings, for target tests of improved American ammunition, or for a check on the quality of materials and minor changes in design employed in later enemy models. Technical intelligence officers overseas endeavored to send a specimen of each weapon to Aberdeen every six months in order to enable the staff to observe any changes in design and materials. Continuous laboratory study of critical parts, components, and fabricating methods was of some strategic value because it provided clues to the current status of enemy manpower, raw material supplies, and production facilities. Sometimes American experts directly copied features of an enemy design and sometimes, by applying an engineering principle used in the captured weapon, were able to improve upon the original.

Technicians and military experts in the zone of interior could thus scrutinize every detail of any piece of captured equipment. In actuality, exhaustive analyses were rare. An NDRC contract with the Battelle Memorial Institute, negotiated in April 1943, aimed specifically at obtaining full information from a series of such studies. But NDRC's summary report at the end of the war declared: "Very little benefit was derived from these studies due largely to the fact that this office [OCO] provided inadequate guidance and direction to the NDRC contractor." [54] The Ordnance Department unfortunately could not spare

[54] NDRC Liaison, Project OP-113, OHF.

men to give Battelle the necessary indoctrination. Because time was short and attempt to ape a foreign competitor might delay vital production, most studies of enemy ordnance concentrated primarily upon comparisons of performance with American.

By the summer of 1944 the Ordnance Department had collected enough data on foreign weapons to issue the Catalogue of Enemy Ordnance Materiel, one volume on German and one volume on Japanese. The form was like that of the Catalogue of Standard Ordnance Items. A considerable list of errata appended to later issues of the Enemy Ordnance Catalogue testified to need for constant revision. Both Ordnance Department and officers of the Ground Forces received copies of these loose-leaf volumes. The catalogues did not, of course, contain estimates of performance of enemy equipment. These appraisals went to the Chief of Staff in a lengthy secret report of May 1945, entitled Comparison of American, German and Japanese Ordnance.[55] Before the war was over, many men of Ordnance Research and Development Service knew a great deal about their competitors' products.

Collaboration with Allied Nations

As soon as Britain's doubts about American co-operation in the fight against the Nazi regime were dispelled, the War Office released a mass of technical and scientific data to be used in developments in the United States. The Tizard Mission of September 1940, a precursor of the series of special missions to America, to London, and to Ottawa, included representatives of the British Army, Navy, and Air Force, the Canadian defense services and the National Research Council of Canada. In the early days the United States got more help on basic research than it gave, though later this condition was reversed, and the American scientific contributions to the joint war effort came to be of vast importance.[56] Following the enactment of the Lend-Lease Act in March 1941, systematic interchange of information and development planning began. NDRC set up a branch in London, and in April the British Central Scientific Office was opened in Washington under the direction of a distinguished British physicist. From the latter office a long list of special technical reports was regularly submitted to the Ordnance Department, with the understanding that copies of any report would be made available upon request.[57] The full collaboration of scientists, accustomed to pooling scientific data through journals and conferences that recognized no international boundaries, was less astonishing than the co-operation quickly established between American, British, and Canadian military representatives.

The first move of the U.S. Army in joining efforts with the British on both procurement and research and development programs was the creation of the Special Observer Group sent to London in May 1941. To the Ordnance section of this group Col. John Coffey was assigned. The mission of the Ordnance section included study of "British establishments" and preparation of reports upon them for the Chief of Ordnance in the States. "British establishments" was in time interpreted to

[55] Comparison of American, German, and Japanese Ord, prepared for CofS, 6 May 45, OHF. See below, pp. 275–87.

[56] See Baxter, *op. cit.*, pp. 119–35.

[57] (1) List of Documents from British Sources received by British Central Scientific Office in June 1943, OO 350.05/4295, DRB AGO. (2) 1st Ind, Col Ritchie, Chief Serv Br, Tech Div, to CO Watertown Arsenal, 21 Jun 43, OO 350.05/2218, DRB AGO.

mean manufacturing plants as well as military installations, so that information upon British manufacturing techniques was available to the Ordnance section. By joint agreement in August, copies of proceedings of the British Ordnance Board were thereafter sent regularly to the Office, Chief of Ordnance, in the States and minutes of the Ordnance Technical Committee to London.[58] Other than the British board proceedings, the information dispatched to Washington during 1941 and early 1942 dealt largely with gaps in equipment or with recommendations for changes in type. For example, a report of late February 1942 urged a number of changes: use of 20-mm. antiaircraft guns in place of 50-caliber machine guns that were ineffective against dive bombers; discard of 37-mm. or 3-pounder tank guns because of their inability "to enter a slugging match with equivalent German guns" and because of the tanks' "insufficient mobility to outrun the [German Panzer IV] tanks"; adoption of 40-mm. Bofors antiaircraft guns as integral parts of equipment for each armored, motorized, or foot division; increase in the range of 105-mm. howitzers and improvement in their antitank fighting characteristics. Furthermore, to speed the receipt of information, this report recommended that technical data go direct to the office that had requested them, instead of through G-2 channels, a recommendation that shortly was put into effect.[59]

After the formation of Headquarters, European Theater of Operations, United States Army, ETOUSA, in the summer of 1942, the Ordnance section of the Special Observer Group became the Ordnance Section of the new headquarters. For Research and Development Service in the zone of the interior the value of this Ordnance unit grew when in April 1943 its function was broadened to include:

a. . . . investigate, follow up, and report to the War Dept, on foreign research and development of all Ordnance and related matters.

. . . .

d. Report on proving ground apparatus and equipment and any manufacturing processes of interest to the Chief of Ordnance.

. . . .

g. Furnish representation for ETO on the British Ordnance Board, various committees, sub-committees, panels, etc., dealing with research and development of Ordnance when such representation is requested by the British.[60]

Thereafter, the volume of explicit information rolling into the Office, Chief of Ordnance, bearing on research and development in the United Kingdom increased rapidly. The stream of reports and memoranda included discussion of tests and experiments under way on American matériel in Britain, descriptions of British experimental work, and sometimes data on German ordnance collected by the British.[61] Only when D Day transferred most activity to the Continent did information from London shrink in importance.

On no other type of matériel was collaboration with the British so extensive and carefully organized as on tanks, tank

---

[58] (1) Ord Tech Services in ETO, AG Adm 604F, DRB AGO. (2) Ltr, CofOrd to MID G-2, 23 Jun 45, sub: Ord Tech Liaison with the British, British Relations, Barnes file, OHF.

[59] Ltr, MID GS to ACofS G-2, 23 Feb 42, sub: Final Rpt on Temporary Duty as Mil Observer in British Isles, OO 350.05/209, DRB AGO.

[60] Hq ETOUSA, Ord Office Order 15, 27 Apr 43, cited in Ord Tech Services in ETO, AG Adm 604F, DRB AGO.

[61] See correspondence in OO 350.05, May 43 to Jun 44, DRB AGO.

guns, and tank accessories. In September 1941 a mission headed by General Wesson, Chief of Ordnance, went to London to confer with the British War Office and Ministry of Supply on production and design problems. British officials at the conferences made some specific requests of the U.S. Army, but offered at the same time a reasoned exposition of what two years of fighting had taught the British about tank and artillery design. British proposals for some heavier tanks with wider tracks and more powerful guns reinforced the views of the automotive experts of the Ordnance Department and doubtless helped eventually to convince the ground forces that bigger tanks were necessary. Description of the guns and armor that the Germans had been using against the British in Africa made a telling argument.[62] In March 1942 a British mission came to Washington to carry the discussions further, though its primary objective was to straighten out questions of procurement. The British Tank Mission and the United States Tank Committee reached agreement on a wide range of questions concerning armored fighting vehicles, but equally important were the proposals for future collaboration. A joint agreement laid down a general policy of maintaining "the fullest of mutual exchange of information and of coordination of plans."[63] Accordingly, members of the British Army staff in Washington, the British Air Commission, and War Supplies Ltd. began to attend meetings of the Ordnance Technical Committee and shortly thereafter Canadian representatives also were admitted.[64]

In August an American Technical Mission went to London. The discussions that occurred that August covered far more than combat vehicles. Indeed, the initial request for the mission listed several items upon which British developments had gone so far that the U.S. Army could only save duplicating effort by examining British findings and techniques in the United Kingdom—notably, a shoulder-type antitank projector with half-round bombs, Probert rifling for guns using forward banded shell, the "Little John two-pounder squeeze attachment," the Burney recoilless gun, and rocket projectiles.[65] Consequently, the mission included experts in seven different fields. General Barnes represented the United States on problems of artillery, self-propelled mounts, and fighting vehicles; Colonel Zornig on metallurgy and gun ammunition; Col. Robert G. Butler on aircraft bombs; Col. Horace A. Quinn on aircraft armament; Col. Gervais W. Trichel on fire control; Mr. Samuel Feltman on ballistics; and 2d Lt. Edward G. Uhl on rockets. Tours of British installations gave the American mission firsthand knowledge of what lines the United Kingdom was following, and conferences held group by group permitted careful exploration of details on each type of matériel. The general conclusions stressed the wisdom of creating routines for fuller, regular exchange of information between Britain and the United States, for officials of both nations recognized that liaison was still far from

[62] General Staff Note for Gen Wesson . . . on specific points concerning tank design and production . . . arising from a meeting . . . at the War Office, 27 Sep 41, and Min of Mtg Held at Claridge Hotel, 30 Sep 41, OO 334.8/4800½, DRB AGO.

[63] Findings and Final Min of Joint British Tank Mission and U.S. Tank Committee, 30 Mar 42, OHF.

[64] Ltr, CofOrd to MID G-2, 23 Jun 45, sub: Ord Tech Liaison with the British, British Relations, Barnes file, OHF.

[65] Msg 2788, Greenwell to CofS, action copy to CofOrd, 9 Jun 42, OO 350.05/810, DRB AGO. For description of the main features of these items, see Ch. XII, below.

complete. They proposed that further exchange of visits be scheduled and that officers assigned to such missions be required to submit written reports on their findings; the reports should be widely and promptly circulated. A final statement read:

> The question of urgency in production [and] conservation of critical materials emphasise the necessity for a true appreciation of simplification in design, with a greater degree of standardisation on common items between the two countries, together with the maintenance of a high quality in manufacture sufficient to perform the duty for which the weapon is required.[66]

In keeping with the spirit of these recommendations, arrangements were made on both sides of the water for close liaison. From London, Col. Frank F. Reed of the Ordnance Section at ETO headquarters regularly sent to Research and Development Service minutes of the North African Armored Fighting Vehicles meetings where every detail was threshed out periodically.[67] Transmitting records of tests and reports on experimentation sometimes ran into a long series of communications covering a period of many months. For example, correspondence and military observer reports describing work on the so-called Sherman DD device began in June 1942 and continued into December 1943.[68] American Ordnance officers assigned to British experimental stations or proving grounds had access to all information, and nothing Research and Development Service in the States wanted to know about British research and development was denied it.[69] Still, it was clear that written reports were no substitute for technical missions. "The best means of close cooperation and exchange of technical information," wrote theatre headquarters in 1943, "is believed to be through the missions sent to this theatre." The report went on to state that the missions should be sent approximately every three months, and from time to time officers assigned to the theatre should be returned for temporary duty in the States.[70] In January 1944 Colonel Reed began regularly to attend meetings of the British Ordnance Board.

Despite a statement of the August mission implying awareness of shortages of materials in both Britain and America, cooperation in conserving raw materials and finding ways of using substitutes was slower than collaboration in other realms. General Barnes upon his return from London had observed that the British up to that time had undertaken no experimentation on use of substitute materials. "Due to the liberal supply of strategic materials from the United States," he wrote, "the British have not felt the same urge to make substitutions as has been the case in the Ordnance Department where pressures exist."[71] Six months later an Anglo-American Conservation Committee with headquarters in London was established with the stated purpose of promoting interchange of information on "all subjects re-

[66] U.S. Technical Mission, Joint Rpt and Findings, Ministry of Supply, London, 26 Aug 42, p. 8, OHF.

[67] Ltr, Col Reed, Ord Sec HQSOS ETOUSA, to Tech Div OCO, 11 Nov 43, sub: Min of Twenty-second North African AFV Meeting, OO 350.05/7469, DRB AGO.

[68] (1) Ltr, Col Reed to Tech Div, 11 Nov 43, sub: Sherman DD (Straussler Flotation Gear), OO 350.05/7389, DRB AGO. (2) Ltr, Col Reed to Tech Div, 1 Dec 43, sub: Sherman DD, OO 350.05/7854, DRB AGO. DD is the abbreviation for "duplex drive," a system adapted for amphibious use of tanks.

[69] Interv with Lt Col William J. Durrenberger, R&D Serv, 22 Nov 50.

[70] Incl to ltr, HQSOS ETO to CofOrd, 6 Jun 43, sub: Agenda . . . for Discussion with Maj Gen John C. H. Lee, OO 350.05/3728, DRB AGO.

[71] Ltr, Barnes to Campbell, 3 Sep 42, sub: Rpt of U.S. Tech Mission to Great Britain OO 350.05/1243, DRB AGO.

lating to economy in use and manufacture, including substitution, simplification, standardization, elimination and salvage, and also . . . [of making] recommendations for the adoption of improved practice . . . in order that the critical materials available to the United Kingdom and the United States shall be used to the greatest advantage." Studies were to cover eighteen raw materials, including aluminum, asbestos, copper, rubber, and zinc, and several processed items such as carbon electrodes and tempered roller bearings.[72] Thus another significant effort was joined on research and development problems.

Although the flow of information to Washington in the first eighteen months of the war was fuller than from Washington to headquarters in the United Kingdom, British officers stationed in the United States were in a position to send directly to British officials data on developments in America. Moreover, after midsummer of 1943 the Ordnance Department sent the British between 3,000 and 5,000 technical and industrial reports every month.[73] In spite of an occasional complaint that some American officers were niggardly in giving out information on manufacturing processes to British representatives in the States, by and large exchange was free enough to benefit both countries.[74]

An example of the kind of data submitted from London to the Ordnance Research and Development staff in the zone of the interior may indicate how much time and money collaboration saved even when British innovations were not adopted by the United States, or when experiments produced negative results. In January 1944 Colonel Reed sent a report on British tests of a two-speed epicyclic tank generator drive. He included the cover sheet of the British Department of Tank Design and the Fighting Vehicle Establishments' report on the generator fitted to the British Humber armored car Mark II. The two-speed epicyclic drive and a magnetic clutch were so set up that the generator would rotate at 3.17 times the engine speed; at 800 revolutions per minute the micro switch would automatically open and the generator would then drive at 1.1 times the engine speed. Tests had revealed weaknesses in the magnetic clutch that were in process of correction. Designs of similar equipment for other armored fighting vehicles, Colonel Reed wrote, were under development. The American automotive experts did not attempt to install this type of generator in American tanks, but having at hand the information on British experiments made it unnecessary for the Detroit Tank-Automotive Center

[72] Memo, Dir Resources and Production Div ASF for CofOrd, 19 Mar 43, sub: Organ of Anglo-American Conservation Committee, OO 334.8/17850, DRB AGO.

[73] Interv, 15 Dec 50, with Col Frye, Chief of Research and Materials Div, R&D Serv, 1943–45.

[74] An extreme example of the inevitable difficulties that sometimes occurred was the situation that arose in the spring of 1945 when a "British Mud Committee" requested permission to visit various American manufacturing plants. The official interchange on matters that affected military design had been completed, but the British committee had then expressed a strong wish to see establishments making automotive transmissions. The Ordnance Department arranged for the visits with a few provisos about not interfering with production. When, according to the indignant report of one Ordnance officer, the British guests arrived at each of the several installations, they discussed very quickly anything relating to military work and proceeded to question company officials closely on American practice and plans for postwar production of automatic transmissions for buses, trucks, and private cars. Upon request for similar information on British plans, the Americans were told that the English group had not been authorized to divulge any detail. To this unusual behavior the American officers objected strenuously. Memo, Maj Parker Berg for Col John Raaen, OD Exec Off, 16 Mar 45, sub: Visits by the British Mud Committee, British Relations, Barnes file, OHF.

291064 O—55——19

to undertake a similar investigation.[75] More positive advantages were in time-saving through adoption of some British developments. An outstanding example was the Canal Defense Light, a powerful searchlight mounted in a specially designed General Grant tank turret, designed to aid in night river crossings. British research developed the CDL unaided. Delivery of complete drawings to the Office, Chief of Ordnance, enabled the Ordnance Department to build 500 of these special turrets in eighteen months, whereas at least two years of preliminary work would have been necessary otherwise.[76] The fact that the CDL device was not widely used did not diminish the value of the collaboration.

Nor was exchange confined to the United States and the United Kingdom. In addition to British intelligence findings sometimes relayed to the Office, Chief of Ordnance, from the British Supply Mission in Washington, the Canadians and Australians supplied considerable useful data. From the latter came information on Japanese weapons that supplemented what American intelligence found. Frequently the Australian reports came by way of London, inasmuch as full liaison dictated having the information available to British as well as to American Ordnance.[77] The United States reciprocated by giving to British Empire representatives complete copies of the monthly and semimonthly reports on all research and development projects and releasing detailed drawings and other specific data when requested.[78] With other allies, exchange was limited by circumstance. The Combined Chiefs of Staff early in 1944 arrived at a statement of policy on release of information to the Chinese by making the criterion the immediate usefulness of data to the Chinese Army in resisting Japan.[79] When political reasons made it desirable to give to Chinese military observers or military missions access to British and American military establishments, special instructions were to be drawn up in advance stipulating expressly what was not to be shown. As the Chinese had little technical data to trade other than information derived from study of captured Japanese weapons, that plan seemed reasonable.[80]

The problem with the USSR was less simple. The Russians were ready to transmit through the American ambassador in Moscow information on captured German ordnance and comments upon the performance of British and American equipment supplied under lend-lease, but showed no willingness to share with their

[75] Ltr, Col Reed to Tech Div OCO, 5 Jan 44, sub: Two-speed Epicyclic Generator Drive, OO 350.05/8760, DRB AGO.

[76] (1) Ltr, TAG to CofOrd, 22 Nov 42, sub: CDL Equipment, OO 350.05/1949, DRB AGO. (2) Ltr, Gen Barnes to CG Hq SOS, 4 Feb 43, sub: CDL Equipment, filed in Final Hist Rpt, AFV and Weapons Sec, Hq ETOUSA, V-E Day, OHF. (3) Interv, 1 Dec 50, with Maj John H. Savage, Tank and Auto Br, R&D Serv.

[77] (1) Ltr, British Supply Mission to Tech Div OCO, 6 Nov 43, sub: Pacific Warfare Tank Types, OO 350.05/7211. (2) Ltr, Special Advisor Small Arms Production, Canadian Dept of Munitions and Supply, to CofOrd 26 Oct 42, OO 350.05/1534. (3) Ltr, Inspection Bd of U.K. and Canada Tech Services to Tech Div OCO, 10 Aug 43, OO 350.05/4754. (4) Ltr, Australian Mil Mission to Ord Tech Intel Div, 1 Sep 43, sub: Japanese Bombs, OO 350.05/5301. (5) Ltr, Hq ETO to CofOrd, 23 Nov 43, sub: Japanese Light Tank M2595, Metallurgical Features, OO 350.05/7786. All in DRB AGO.

[78] See ltr cited n. 64.

[79] The Combined Chiefs of Staff consisted of the U.S. Chiefs of Staff and the British Chiefs of Staff or their designated representatives in Washington.

[80] (1) Ltr, TAG to CG's AAF, AGF, ASF, USAFCBI (Rear Ech), USAFCBI (Forward Ech), 21 Jan 44, sub: Disclosure of Mil Information to the Chinese, OO 350.05/8925. (2) Incl to memo, Chief of Small Arms Br, Tech Div OCO, for Ord Intel Unit, 6 Nov 42, sub: Small Arms (Japanese), OO 350.05/6017. Both in DRB AGO.

allies the fruits of Soviet military scientific research.[81] When, in the spring of 1943, the Ordnance Department was requested by the Joint Intelligence Committee to make recommendations on what disclosures should be made to Russia, the Ordnance Department listed several that should be excluded. The shaped charge was one. "The entire effectiveness of shaped charges," the Ordnance Department indorsement stated, "depends upon the detailed design of the round and this in turn upon the principles of operation. It is believed inexpedient to release this information." Similarly, data on the proximity fuze were not to be released. For .30-caliber and .50-caliber incendiary ammuntion, specifications and round drawings might be sent, but not details of the manufacturing processes. As the effectiveness of this type of incendiary ammunition against aircraft self-sealing tanks depended "entirely upon the dimensions of the bullet tip," the manufacturing processes whereby those dimensions were obtained and the cold-working process that made the bullet nose sufficiently brittle were pronounced to be a military secret. Yet probably because the United States was supplying Russia with a large amount of equipment, the Ordnance Department felt justified in requesting from the USSR answers to a number of specific questions. For example, did Russian experience show single or dual tires to be better for mud operation and what was the type of tread design and construction? Were the Russians using rubber on shear-type bogie wheels and how good was it? Was crude or synthetic rubber used for tire repair? If synthetic, what kind? And if a combination, what composition? Still more searching and less likely to elicit answers were questions about Russian antitank mines, grenades, and self-destroying shell fuzes.[82]

The question of exchange dragged on into the fall, but at the Teheran Conference an agreement was reached calling for reciprocal exchange of data on rockets.[83] Accordingly, when a military mission went to Moscow in April 1944, the Ordnance Technical Intelligence unit attached was instructed to be ready to give out information on American rocket developments and, in return, to learn essentials on Russian. The primary purpose of this Ordnance unit was to study and send back to the States items of German equipment that the Russians had captured but which had not yet appeared on the Western Front. Consequently, when the list of questions prepared by the Ordnance team concerning the detailed characteristics of Russian rockets went to the Soviet Foreign Office, the American officers were reminded that the Ordnance group had been admitted to Moscow to study German weapons, not Russian. There the matter ended.

The collection of German matériel on exhibit in Moscow was, however, so extensive as to be well worth careful examination. Many items were new to the American experts at that time. Most valuable perhaps were a German 88-mm. *Pak 43* and a 75/55-mm. antitank gun, one of each of which the American unit was permitted to ship back to Aberdeen. There was also an array of other vehicles and weapons, a good many of Czechoslovakian,

[81] Paraphrase of telegram, Moscow to Dept of State, 5 Jun 42. OO 350.05/657, DRB AGO.

[82] 1st Ind, 3 May 43, to memo, Secy Joint Intel Committee, Combined Chiefs of Staff, for CofOrd, 9 Apr 43, sub: Disclosure of Tech Information to USSR, OO 350.05/3033, DRB AGO.

[83] Incl to memo, OCO for Joint Intel Committee, 19 Nov 43, sub: Disclosure of Tech Information to USSR, OO 350.05/7457, DRB AGO.

French, Hungarian, Italian, or other national origin. A Russian major general was in charge of the exhibit and had a large, competent staff of specialists ready to discuss with the Americans the noteworthy features of the captured equipment. The Ordnance unit took careful photographs and notes, sent long reports back to the States, and shipped to Aberdeen specimens of a good many items as well. Furthermore, a series of meetings held at the Foreign Office produced some information from tank experts of the Red Army and automotive engineers, though the historian of the American mission observed: "Our operations were . . . limited by the fact that all contacts had to clear through the foreign office resulting in a considerable delay and . . . the additional barrier of the presence of an officer of the foreign office . . . at all conferences." [84]

Some ordnance of Russian design was on hand at Aberdeen Proving Ground after 1942, for leaders of the USSR, concerned with getting a steady flow of matériel to the Russo-German battle front, saw that some give to balance the take was inescapable. Thus a Russian T34 tank mounting a 75.2-mm. cannon was presented to the Proving Ground in 1943. Nevertheless, when the foreign matériel staff there cut out a piece of the T34's frontal armor to analyze metallurgically, the Soviet delegation, on discovering such mayhem, protested vigorously. The tank had been donated to the museum, not to the laboratory. A piece of American armor plate was hastily welded back into the hole; the Russian plate was subjected to thorough study.[85]

Free exchange of technical data between the Western Allies and the USSR was never obtained. Requests of the Ordnance Technical Intelligence unit in Moscow to visit the battle fronts or Soviet proving grounds were refused. By late fall of 1944, as the Allied advance through France and Luxembourg was making available ample information about German equipment of all types, the Ordnance mission to Moscow was dissolved. What the United States learned about Soviet ordnance during World War II largely came from matériel captured from the Germans who had taken it from the Red Army in battle, from interviews with prisoners who had served in campaigns in the USSR, and, toward the end of the war, from captured German documents.[86] After V-E Day Ordnance Technical Intelligence units were able to study more carefully Soviet equipment picked up in Germany. These studies formed the backbone of knowledge the United States Army assembled on Soviet armament.

[84] Hist of Ord Intel Unit—Russian, in Hist of Ord Tech Intel, OHF.

[85] Interv with Col Jarrett, 25 Oct 50.

[86] See above, n. 84.

CHAPTER X

The Search for Greater Mobility in Ground Warfare

Factors Determining Vehicular Development

The keynote of U.S. Army operations in World War II was sounded by the roar of the internal-combustion engine. Two decades of American automotive research and development had relegated animal power, the major tactical prime mover of 1917–18, to the category of military curiosa. Billions of mechanical horsepower in more than two million combat and transport vehicles supplied by the Ordnance Department lent American armies unprecedented mobility and maneuverability, two of the primary requisites for attaining the ultimate objective of military operations—the destruction of hostile military forces in battle.[1]

Destruction itself is the result of fire power, but fire power minus ability to maneuver is ineffective both in offense and in defense.[2] World War I demonstrated that offensive fire power lacking a high degree of battlefield mobility cannot, even though quantitatively vastly superior, force a decision over an equally static, resolute defender suitably armed for his role. A swath of machine gun fire against unprotected assault infantry produced the same result as the murderous hail of artillery fire: it forced the opponent into the bowels of the earth, into safety, instead of annihilating him. Warfare then deteriorated into a meaningless contest of stamina in which ephemeral victor's laurels went to the captor of a few acres of shell-pocked soil. Insatiable, the Moloch of attrition was also impartial, demanding ruinous sacrifices from victor and vanquished alike. With neither side able to break the stalemate with the means at hand, both searched frantically for ways in which to regain freedom of maneuver. The British were the first to come up with a workable solution: mechanical transport with fire power and crew protection in a vehicle capable of traversing almost any kind of terrain over which foot troops would have to advance. The cover name given the contrivance in its development stage hung on; the track-laying armored combat vehicle became known as the tank.

Advantageous as it proved in lending the attacker once more the ability to move on the field of battle, the tank of 1916–18 was far from a panacea for the ills of position warfare. To begin with, the tank itself was a hulking, lumbering affair that traveled more slowly cross country than man could

[1] (1) Civ Production Admin, Official Munitions Production of the United States, July 1, 1940 to August 31, 1945, 1 May 1947 (hereafter cited as OMPUS), pp. 225–55, OHF. (2) FM 100-5, FS Regulations: Operations.

[2] For a discussion of fire power, see Ch. XI, below.

walk. Quite apart from its thin coat of armor—crew protection against only small arms fire—its speed, or lack of speed, spelled extreme vulnerability to hostile defensive weapons. Secondly, friendly artillery, as well as supply, was drawn by horse, or at best, slow-speed tractor, and as such was incapable of rolling fast enough cross country to support a sustained advance in the face of organized resistance. Trucks, though used for transporting infantry, were road bound. Their solid rubber tires, primitive springing, and, above all, lack of adequate motive power, precluded their use save on improved traffic routes. The division, the basic tactical troop unit, could move as a whole only on foot or by rail. True mobility of ground forces in combat was not to be achieved until technology perfected mechanical transport to the point where its inherent characteristics—speed, great tractive power, and economy of operation—could be employed in front and rear echelons alike, and an entire army could fight on the move over most types of terrain. By 1939 that point had been reached.

World War II soon dispelled whatever doubts existed about the merits of mere fire power, however concentrated, versus a lesser degree of fire power coupled with mobility. The fall of France dramatically proved that an army unable or unwilling to maneuver was doomed when confronted by an adversary resorting to highly mobile conduct of operations. Intricate fortifications bristling with heavy artillery—the embodiment of memories of 1914–18—proved worse than useless when the enemy chose to bypass rather than breach them. Tanks employed as pillboxes instead of mobile weapons to carry the fight to the enemy were deathtraps pure and simple. Throughout the war the same lessons were repeated over and over again. Mobile attack invariably carried the day over immobile defense, whether its name was Maginot Line, Atlantic Wall, or Siegfried Line. In 1940 the German tide in little over a month engulfed the same blood-drenched territory between the German frontier and Paris that in World War I had been the scene of four years of struggle. In 1944 the relentless sweep of American mechanized armies covered the same ground in less than twenty days.

Remarkable enough in itself, the complete motorization of U.S. ground forces, the basis for their unrivaled striking power, becomes even more extraordinary in the light of the swiftness with which it was accomplished. Beginning with only a handful of completely developed military motor vehicles at the outbreak of war in Europe, the Ordnance Department eventually furnished to the Allies some forty major types of combat vehicles and sixty-odd major types of transport vehicles.[3] This achievement became possible only through closest co-operation with industry, a long-standing tradition in Ordnance automotive research and development. During the interwar years of lean funds and public apathy toward armaments, only assistance such as that of the Ordnance Advisory Committee, sponsored by the American Society of Automotive Engineers, had enabled the Ordnance Department to keep step with developments abroad.[4] With the advent of war challenging America to outproduce the Axis in equipment capable of superior performance in all four corners of the earth, the Industry-Ordnance team proved one of the most potent weapons in the arsenal of democracy. Automotive, metallurgical, electrical, and

[3] Campbell, *Industry-Ordnance Team*, p. 228.

[4] Barnes, *Weapons of World War II*, p. 199.

rubber engineers from industry, serving on numerous specialized advisory boards and committees, helped solve a million and one perplexing, sometimes seemingly insuperable, problems arising over the design of ordnance vehicles. The military and civilian engineers of the Ordnance Department in turn familiarized their colleagues with the many particular requirements of military motor transport foreign to private industry.

Paramount in the design of any military motor vehicle stood reliability. Since American equipment saw action thousands of ocean miles away from its factories, distance alone ruled out shuttling to the United States for major overhaul. Not even the huge industrial plant of America would have sufficed to equip U.S. and Allied troops if part of industry were devoted to the repair rather than the production of weapons. Finally, shipping space was so limited throughout the war that each cubic foot diverted from the build-up of Allied strength overseas postponed the prospect of victory. Once overseas, motor vehicles had to be capable of traveling under their own power the ofttimes considerable distances from dockside to battlefield before embarking on their intended missions. Mechanical failure in action was intolerable. Each deadlined tank and truck impaired the striking power of Allied ground forces, put even greater strain on already overburdened supply lines, and added to the workload of rear area maintenance and repair facilities. However well suited commercially produced vehicles were for civilian use, they were unable to withstand the rigors of military employment. Though some classes, notably wheeled transport vehicles, were largely adapted from standard commercial design, these too required numerous modifications emphasizing cross-country mobility, ruggedness, dustproofing, waterproofing, corrosion-proofing, minimum bulk, and minimum weight. Appearance of vehicles and components had to yield to the purpose they were meant to serve. Ease of operation, maintenance, repair, and replacement were prerequisite to efficient field service.[5]

Perhaps the broadest and most basic question to be answered was whether large or small-size transport best answered military needs. Honest differences of opinion existed, with each proponent mustering almost equally cogent arguments. Those favoring large vehicles set forth the economies of reduced over-all requirements in material, labor, and fuel, and in operating and maintenance personnel; in rebuttal, the other camp pointed out the greater maneuverability of small vehicles and their greater ease of operation and maintenance, which required less highly skilled manpower. Less bulky to ship, moreover, light trucks could be sent overseas in greater numbers than heavy types, and the more trucks an army had in the field, the less vulnerable it was to immobilization for lack of transportation. The ultimate decision in favor of the small vehicle gave little cause for regret:

> The greatest advantage in equipment the United States has enjoyed on the ground in the fighting so far [wrote General Marshall in the summer of 1945], has been in our multiple-drive motor equipment, principally the jeep and the 2½-ton truck. These are the instruments which have moved the United States troops in battle while the German Army, despite the fearful reputation of its 'panzer armies' early in the war still depended heavily on animal transport for its

[5] Col. Joseph M. Colby, "Tank and Automotive Development," *Journal of Applied Physics*, XVI, 12, (1945), 767.

regular infantry divisions. The United States, profiting from the mass-production achievements of its automotive industry, made all its forces truck-drawn and had enough trucks left over to supply the British armies with large numbers of motor vehicles and send tremendous quantities to the Red Army.[6]

Not so unqualified was the praise accorded Ordnance track-laying equipment, especially when it came to that best known of combat vehicles, the tank. From the landing of U.S. troops in North Africa until V-E Day, tanks drew increasingly severe criticism. In January 1945 Hanson Baldwin wrote in *The New York Times:*

> Why at this late stage in the war are American tanks inferior to the enemy's? That they are inferior the fighting in Normandy showed, and the recent battles in the Ardennes have again emphatically demonstrated. This has been denied, explained away and hushed up, but the men who are fighting our tanks against much heavier, better armored and more powerfully armed German monsters know the truth. It is high time that Congress got to the bottom of a situation that does no credit to the War Department. This does not mean that our tanks are bad. They are not; they are good. They are the best tanks in the world—next to the Germans'.[7]

And on 22 March *The Washington Post* took up the cudgel with the statement:

> A Bronx cheer comes out of Germany to greet the news that the Pershing tank has gone into mass production. It is the opinion of the men at the front, apparently, that they will get the new tank in numbers when it is no longer needed, i. e., when the war is over . . . an investigation is thoroughly in order. It should take up the reasons for the long delay in getting the Pershing into production. It should likewise find out why our tanks are inferior to the enemy's.

No investigation ever materialized. The facts were clear. From the very beginning of the tank program, the Army had staked its fortunes on the medium tank as the fighting tank of its armored divisions and, for better or for worse, remained unshaken in its choice until 24 January 1945 when, after extensive testing, the Armored Board finally recommended that the Pershing or, as it was then known, the heavy tank T26E3, be considered battleworthy after incorporation of minor modifications, and be standardized and shipped to troops.[8] Up to then no recommendations of the Ordnance Department had been able to persuade the using arms to adopt a heavier vehicle than the Sherman. A heavy tank, the M6, had been developed, standardized, and put into production in 1942, but a letter from the commanding general of the Armored Force to the commanding general of the Army Ground Forces on 7 December of that year stated that because of its sixty-ton weight and limited tactical use no requirement for it existed.[9] The same laconic "no requirement" was the standard reply to any proposed vehicle violating the weight limits of Army Regulations 850-15, which prescribed that no tank weigh more than 30 tons or exceed 103 inches in width, though as one Ordnance tank specialist observed, Hitler's tanks violated this American rule.[10]

That, tank for tank, neither the American Grant nor its successor, the Sherman, was a match for the more heavily armored and armed German Tiger, U.S. troops

[6] *Biennial Report of the Chief of Staff of the United States Army, July 1, 1943 to June 30, 1945,* pp. 95–96.

[7] *The New York Times,* January 5, 1945, p. 4.

[8] Ltr, Armored Bd to CG AGF, 20 Jan 45, sub: Heavy Tank T26E3—Recommendation for Approval as Battleworthy, OO 470.8/2192 Tank, DRB AGO.

[9] Ltr, CG Armored Force to CG AGF, 7 Dec 42, 470.8/4 GNOHD, copy in Hist of Heavy Tanks M6, OHF.

[10] Col. Joseph M. Colby, "From Designer to Fighter," *Armored Cavalry Journal,* LIX, 1 (1950), p. 15.

HEAVY TANK M6 AND MEDIUM TANK M3, *above and below, respectively.*

learned in the early days of the fighting in North Africa. Nor were the troops' chances any better when, in Italy and France, they came up against the Panther. The only unquestioned advantages of the American vehicles were their reliability and their somewhat greater radius of action. For the rest, they had to depend on superiority in numbers to surround their adversaries and knock them out in flank attacks. "But," as General of the Army Omar N. Bradley observed, "this willingness to expend Shermans offered little comfort to the crews who were forced to expend themselves as well."[11] Well known though they were to the men at the front, the inadequacies of the Sherman failed to sway the using arms in their determination that this was the very tank with which to defeat Germany. As early as August 1943 the Ordnance Department pointed out that the Sherman was becoming more obsolescent each month and urged the standardization of two types of the newly developed T20-series tanks, the T23E3 and T20E3, in order to set up production facilities for these better gunned and better armored vehicles. "Attention is invited to the fact that unless action along this line is taken at an early date it will not be possible to supply field units with any quantity of the T20 series tanks during the calendar year 1944 . . . ," wrote General Barnes. The request was denied.[12] When Lt. Gen. Jacob L. Devers, Commanding General, ETO, in November 1943 recommended that highest priority be given the development of the T26, armed with a 90-mm. gun, in order to counter the increased armor protection and fire power of German vehicles,[13] the Army Ground Forces voiced its misgivings about the trend toward heavy tanks as inconsistent with American combat doctrine. A memorandum from Brig. Gen. William F. Dean, the chief of the Requirements Division, AGF, to General McNair remarked:

> . . . [the radiogram from General Devers] intensifies the pressure upon Army Ground Forces to immediately commit ourselves to the early production of a thick-skinned tank carrying the 90-mm. Gun. The British and the Ordnance have been convinced for some time that we should initiate such procurement without further delay. . . . Action recommended: a. That the Army Ground Forces go on record as not favorably considering procurement of T26 at this time. b. That any further procurement be deferred pending full service test of pilot models.

General McNair, in reply, approved those recommendations, adding, "I see no reason to alter our previous stand in reply to a communication from the Armored Command—essentially that we should defeat Germany by use of the M-4 series of medium tanks. There has been no factual developments overseas, so far as I know, to challenge the superiority of the M-4."[14] Once again the verdict read that no requirement existed at that time for a medium or heavy tank of the T26 type.[15]

By D Day the status of American armor was as precarious as that of the panzer divisions in 1941–42, at which time Germany had lost qualitative superiority on the battlefield to the Soviet Union. Only

[11] Omar N. Bradley, *A Soldier's Story* (New York, 1951), p. 41.

[12] 5th Ind, Chief of Tech Div OCO for Hq ASF, 12 Aug 43, and 6th Ind, Hq ASF for OCO Tech Div, 23 Aug 43, to basic memo, Asst Chief T-AC for Chief of Ind Div OCO, 20 Jul 43, OO 470.8/103 Tank, DRB AGO.

[13] Radiogram, USFOR London to WAR, signed Devers, 14 Nov 43, CM-IN 8556, 470.8/611 Tanks, DRB AGO.

[14] (1) Memo, Requirements Div AGF for CG AGF, 18 Nov 43, and (2) memo, CG AGF for Requirements Div AGF, 19 Nov 43, Binder 1, AGF McNair file 470.8, DRB AGO.

[15] Memo, CG AGF for CofS, 9 Dec 43, Binder 1, AGF McNair file 470.8, DRB AGO.

the causes underlying these crises differed. The American situation was one of choice, while that of the Germans had been one of necessity. Before beginning its Eastern Campaign Germany, counting on subjugating the Red Army in the customary few months of blitzkrieg, had let armor development lag, while a badly informed intelligence apparatus fed the belief that existing panzer types far outstripped anything the Russians had been able to build. As a result, German tanks that crossed the Soviet frontier during the morning hours of 21 June 1941 were identical with those that the year before had terrorized the world by their exploits in France. They all were there: the machine-gun-toting Panzer I which lasted exactly thirteen days before being recommended for retirement as a burden on the troops; the Panzer II with its 20-mm. cannon, so ineffective that production of the series stopped the month after the invasion; [16] the Panzer III with its face lifted by the addition of armor and a 50-mm. gun replacing the former 37-mm. primary armament; and finally the Panzer IV, unchanged from the 1940 version save for similarly strengthened armor protection. Initial successes of the German armies bade fair to substantiate the estimates of Soviet tanks. Knifing their way through unorganized resistance, the panzers took a murderous toll of antiquated Russian machines. But even within the first two weeks of the campaign, an ominous note was sounded in the East: reports of Soviet vehicles topping anything the Germans had in the way of armament and armor.[17] Though first data turned out as exaggerated as is usual in the case of surprise encounters of new weapons in combat, the truth was formidable enough. The panzer divisions had stumbled on the first-line tanks of the Russians: the 32-ton T34, and the 52-ton KVI which outgunned, outarmored, and outmaneuvered every other tank then on the battlefield.[18] At that time began the race of gun power against armor protection which, for the rest of the war, was to become the biggest problem of both Allied and Axis designers.

A large part of Germany's tremendous losses during the first six months of campaigning in the East were, to be sure, due to factors other than enemy action.[19] The greatest foe of mechanized equipment, for example, turned out to be the muddy seasons and, axiomatically, the Russian winter. In 1941, as in the years following, these natural phenomena wreaked more havoc with German fighting strength than Allied ground and air efforts combined.[20] Lacking the ground clearance and flotation system of their Soviet counterparts, German vehicles helplessly floundered in the bottomless quagmires of autumn and spring mud. Attempts to plow forcefully ahead only compounded disaster. Engines and bearings burned out, gears stripped, and, once winter frost or summer sun made possible the resumption of movement, the countryside was littered with

[16] (1) Halder Diary, 23 Dec 40, and 4 Jul 41, OCMH. (2) MS # P-059 (Mueller-Hillebrand), OCMH.

[17] (1) Halder Diary, 25 Jun 41, OCMH. (2) Heinz Guderian, *Erinnerungen eines Soldaten* (Heidelberg, 1951), p. 148.

[18] KV stood for Klementi Voroshilov, who as Commissar of Defense had been instrumental in the development of the Soviet armored program.

[19] From June to December 1941 total tank losses amounted to 2,757. MS # P-059 (Mueller-Hillebrand), OCMH.

[20] Graphic descriptions of German difficulties in the conduct of mechanized warfare during autumn, winter, and spring in the Soviet Union may be found in Department of the Army pamphlets No. 20-230, "Russian Combat Methods in World War II"; No. 20-290, "Terrain Factors in the Russian Campaign"; and No. 20-291, "Effects of Climate on Combat in European Russia."

unsalvageable wrecks. The trials of winter proved equally severe since neither German soldiers nor their weapons were equipped to fight in the bitter cold. The Russians, adapted to the climate and terrain of their homeland, held the upper hand.[21] Decimated and nearly stripped of arms, the Wehrmacht emerging from its first winter in the East was no longer the fighting machine of the blitz years. Its cadre of battle-tempered veterans had been shockingly thinned and in another year, after Stalingrad, would be only a memory. Replacements, trained in the short period that wartime permits for this purpose to friend and foe alike, were at best only substitutes. No superweapon, however powerful, could ever fill that void.

Chastened by their encounter with Soviet armor and antitank defenses, the Germans proceeded to overmatch them. No other course was open. In 1941 production had fallen to some 500 vehicles short of six months' battle losses,[22] and even with all-out industrial mobilization Germany lacked the plant facilities to compromise quality to get quantity. With new vehicle designs still in the development stage but more powerful guns ready to be installed, the first step was improvisation. Existing tanks were up-gunned and up-armored, albeit with little permanent success since the USSR invariably was prompt in countering with similar measures. Moreover, each modification entailed additional weight and, in the absence of equal increases in power and flotation, contributed nothing toward bridging the gap between Russian and German mobility and maneuverability. On the contrary, the added strain on already overloaded engines and gear trains made German tanks less and less reliable.[23] But in German eyes the mission of the tank—the same, incidentally, as in American combat doctrine, break-through and exploitation—demanded that fire power and armor keep step with the evolution of defensive weapons.

Any conclusion that the German trend toward heavier vehicles denoted a departure from the tried and proven concepts of armored warfare would be erroneous. German service schools in 1943, for example, reiterated the maxims that had been the key to the earlier successes of the panzer divisions. "The mission of the tank unit," students were taught, "consists of opening the way for other elements [of the armored division] into and through the enemy. *All missions (combat missions) are executed by means of the concerted unit attack,* in which antitank weapons and artillery are to be annihilated and hostile armored formations counteracted." [24] In other words, the tank had to be capable of overcoming all types of hostile weapons, which is a long way from saying that these were its primary objectives. American authorities determining the characteristics of U.S. armor held different views. "There can be no basis for the T26 [90-mm. gun] tank," Army Ground Forces officially replied to the suggestion of introducing the better armed and armored, and consequently heavier, vehicle than the Sherman, "other

[21] (1) *Oberkommando des Heeres, Organisations Abteilung (III), Beitrag zum KTB 9.1.1942.* (2) Ltr, *AOK 2* to *Oberkommando Herresgruppe Mitte, Betr: Winter-Erfahrungen,* 28 May 43, *H Gr Mitte Abt Ia, Anlagen zum Kriegstagebuch: Erfahrungsberichte, Heft 3.* (3) Experience Rpt, 24: *Pz Div,* 19 May 44, *Panzer-Offizier beim Chef Generalstab des Heeres, Erfahrungsberichte, Akte E, Band 3.* All in GMDS DRB AGO.

[22] MS # P-059 (Mueller-Hillebrand), OCMH.

[23] *Fuehrervortrag am 28.6.44, General Inspekteur der Panzertruppen, Fuehrer Vortrags Notizen II,* GMDS DRB AGO.

[24] *Panzer-Lehrgaenge "Panther," Kommandeur, Auszug aus dem Vortrag des Major Streit vor den Kommandeuren (Kommandeur Lehrgang Erlangen), September 1943,* in miscellaneous correspondence 1944, *General Inspekteur der Panzertruppen,* GMDS DRB AGO.

than the conception of a tank versus tank duel—which is believed unsound and unnecessary. Both British and American battle experience has demonstrated that the antitank gun in suitable numbers and disposed properly is the master of the tank. Antitank guns either must be put out by armored infantry or equivalent means, or avoided by tanks. The primary mission of tanks is the destruction of those hostile elements which are vulnerable to them—not antitank guns." [25]

Underlying the Ordnance Department's insistence on introducing a basically new tank was its awareness of the inherent limitations of the Sherman, or for that matter, of any tank, for despite its far-from-fragile appearance, a tank represents a mechanism as finely balanced as a watch. Its merits lie in the fact that it combines four essential military characteristics: fire power, maneuverability, speed, and crew protection. Each of these is, in the final analysis, a function of weight. Cross-country mobility, for example, requires low unit ground pressure, which means either a light hull—thin armor, light armament, light power train—or else a wider, and therefore heavier, track with a correspondingly larger and heavier engine and transmission. During World War II no tank of practical size could simultaneously feature maximum armor, fire power, speed, and maneuverability. Every vehicle was a compromise, with qualities deemed more desirable by its users accentuated at the expense of those they considered of lesser importance. But once a satisfactory compromise had been devised, further modifications of major import would inevitably upset that balance and punish the tank by limiting its effectiveness and reliability. It was precisely this danger that loomed in the case of the Sherman.

Its early participation in the fighting in North Africa had shown the Sherman to be in every respect superior to the Axis tanks then on the battlefield. It had contributed a large share to the British victory at El Alamein, its baptism of fire, and had played a prominent role in the westward pursuit of the Italo-German forces. The British forces had the highest praise for the one tank that finally ended a long reign of German qualitative superiority. German reports, in turn, gloomily forecast the doom of Rommel's troops unless equipment capable of dealing with the new American vehicles was sent promptly and in force.[26] But only a few months later, during encounters with a token contingent of German Tiger tanks in Tunisia, the Sherman proved to be outgunned and outarmored—a state of affairs that became even more pronounced with the advent of the Panther tank in Italy.

True, the Sherman had qualities not even remotely duplicated in any German vehicle. Time and again, for example, in both Africa and Italy it took enemy strongholds in mountainous terrain that no German tank could hope to traverse.[27] In point of reliability, it similarly outshone both the notoriously undependable Tiger and the Panther. But it was small com-

[25] Memo, CG AGF for CofS, 30 Nov 43, sub: Heavier Armament for Tanks and Self-Propelled Vehicles, Binder 1, AGF McNair file 470.8, DRB AGO.

[26] (1) Rpt, Gen Barnes to Gen Devers, 18 Jan 43, sub: Ord Annex to Rpt of Visit Abroad, OHF. (2) OKD 385/153.1 quoted in Intel Summary 2, 6–13 Feb 43, OCO–D, OHF. (3) OKD 451.25/417.1 and OKD 451/136.1 quoted in Intel Summary 5, 8–15 Mar 43, OCO–D, OHF. (4) Rpt, *Abendmeldung DAK an Pz AOK vom 3.11.1942*, *AOK Afrika* files, GMDS DRB AGO.

[27] (1) Bradley, *op. cit.*, p. 87. (2) Inspection Rpt, 15 May 44, *Maj Gerlach OKH/Inf Abt Ref IVc (Pz Abw), Bericht ueber die Frontreise zu H Gr C 28.4-6.5.44,* GMDS DRB AGO. (3) War Diary, *XIV, Armee KTB 18 Mai 44,* GMDS DRB AGO. (4) OI-335-44 cited in Intel Summary 53, 9–19 Aug 44, OCO–D, OHF.

fort to the tanker to know that he could count on reaching the scene of action, if at the same time he was equally certain of adverse odds upward of two to one of ever leaving that scene alive.

Placing American armored forces once more on a par with their opponents meant either up-gunning and up-armoring the Sherman or supplanting it with an entirely new vehicle. The first solution, Ordnance designers knew, would prove at best only a stopgap because the balance between fire power, speed, maneuverability, and crew protection that distinguished the tank in the days of El Alamein would be lost. General Barnes opposed such a policy of improvisation on principle, though for a long time without success. The inevitable result was that during the fighting in France, Belgium, and Germany the now badly overloaded Sherman not only was still outgunned and outarmored but on too many occasions, particularly in mud, snow, and ice, outmaneuvered as well by the Panther. The second solution, one that might have been adopted as early as August 1942 when the first of the T20-series tanks was released for production, came to pass only after General Barnes almost singlehandedly overcame the determined opposition that for more than two years had prevented the introduction of a vehicle radically departing from the tried and true pattern of the Sherman. But while accolades for the Pershing tank from the ETO, proved, if nothing else, that the Ordnance Department's labors had not been in vain, one poignant question remained unanswered: Did the intervening advances in development warrant the delay in getting the new weapon onto the battlefield? [28]

From almost the first day of World War II, sharply differing points of view prevailed on the acceptability of new ground weapons. Two issues were involved: the development of items for which no formal requirement had been established, and the battle testing of new equipment. As to the first, Army Ground Forces, for example, vigorously opposed development of weapons that it considered not absolutely essential, regardless of how much they might be desired by men in the field. The Ordnance Department, on the other hand, believed in maintaining a strong lead over the using services in the development of new items. For one thing, Ordnance technicians spent their entire service careers in the study of ordnance, so that their knowledge of the capabilities and inherent limitations of weapons exceeded that of line officers, whose careers were concerned with the tactical use of equipment. As Generalmajor Heinz Guderian, the father of the German panzer forces, once put it when reminded that all technicians were strangers to the truth: "Certainly there is a lot of lying, but one to two years as a rule uncover that fact, when the ideas of the technicians turn out to be unworkable. The tacticians also lie; but in that instance the truth comes out only after the next lost war, and then it is too late." [29]

In the case of tanks, the Ordnance view hardly proved incorrect. The tank capable of holding its own against enemy armor, in other words, the heavy tank advocated by the Department since 1942, proved indispensable in large-scale ground operations. The Ordnance Department, which

---

[28] (1) OCO Tech Div, Hist of Medium Tank T20 Series, OHF. (2) Col. Joseph M. Colby, "From Designer to Fighter," *Armored Cavalry Journal*, LIX, 1 (1950), 14. (3) Ltr, Harmon to Campbell, 10 Feb 45, OHF. (4) Barnes MS, Tank Development, OHF.

[29] (1) Guderian, *op. cit.*, pp. 25–26. (2) AGF Study 34, pp. 14–15, OHF. (3) Barnes MS, Tank Development, OHF.

MEDIUM TANK M4, THE SHERMAN, AND HEAVY TANK M26, THE PERSHING, *above and below, respectively.*

as late as 1943 was criticized for proposing such a vehicle, was barely a year thereafter criticized for its absence from the battlefield. ". . . our tanks when forced to engage in tank vs. tank action," wrote the Army Ground Forces in January 1945, "have had to close to short ranges in order to destroy the opposing tanks. The destruction of the enemy has been accomplished at great cost in tank matériel and personnel and is reflected in the current critical shortage of tanks." [30]

The issue of battle testing was more complex. Army Ground Forces insisted that no new weapons, however promising they looked, be sent overseas until a small number had been tested by the prospective users and all corrections deemed necessary had been incorporated. Ordnance engineers for several reasons deplored the seemingly interminable delay in getting a new tank into action.[31]

Had the Germans been equally insistent on mechanical perfection and as reluctant to battle test new tanks, they would hardly have been able to regain the lead in fire power and armor once they lost it in 1942. As it was, they scored telling successes by rushing virtually the pilot models of their new heavy vehicles to the battlefield. Thus the Tiger, which to the very end of hostilities remained ridden with glaring mechanical weaknesses, was a formidable enough foe in action to become almost synonymous with German prowess in weapons design. Similarly the Panther, with its high-velocity gun and sloping frontal armor, found no match in American tanks until the advent of the General Pershing in 1945. That the Panther in 1942 had been rushed from the drawing board to production line in a scant nine months and consequently was so full of the proverbial bugs that another year and a half passed before it was pronounced really fit for combat, detracted little from its killing power. In the ETO U.S. troops, whose Shermans mechanically outlasted their German adversaries as much as five to one, "were reaching a point where they were becoming afraid to fight in the M4 [Sherman] due to lack of fire power." [32]

Perhaps the most vital clue to the American tank problem during World War II could be found in that indefinable standard of tactical utility, reliability, and durability called "battle worthiness" which, in effect, meant all things to all men. Time and again an alleged lack of that quality resulted in a delay in getting a heavier tank than the Sherman into action. More often than not the sole reason was the limited durability of mechanical components. Yet no measuring stick, statistical or otherwise, was ever devised to ascertain the life expectancy of combat vehicles on the battlefield. The Russian view, though founded on a much less complicated communications problem, offered an interesting parallel in that respect. On the assumption that a tank was almost certain to be knocked out after a brief period of fighting, the Russians considered a lifetime of fourteen hours for its mechanical components to be excellent. American tanks, by comparison, were required to last for a minimum of forty hours. Arbitrary or not, this emphasis on durability rather than re-

[30] Ltr, CG AGF to CG ASF, 30 Jan 45, sub: Heavy Tanks T29 and T30, OHF.

[31] (1) Ltr, Campbell to Harmon, 21 Mar 45, OHF. (2) AGF Study 34, p. 15, OHF. (3) Barnes MS, Tank Development, OHF.

[32] (1) Barnes MS, Tank Development, OHF. (2) Ltr, Harmon to Campbell, 10 Feb 45, OHF. (3) Interrogation of Speer, CIOS Item 28, file XXVI-13, Reich Ministry of Armaments and War Production, DRB AGO. (4) Notes for Rpt to Hitler, 5 Mar 44, *General Inspekteur der Panzertruppen, Fuehrer Vortrags Notizen, Bd. I,* GMDS DRB AGO.

liability for the useful life of a tank deprived American troops of weapons that might, with telling effect, have contributed toward shortening the war.[33]

The mobility of each combat and transport vehicle depended above all on the performance of its components. Power plant, gear trains, and the like had to function reliably and had to be properly attuned. Maximum output at minimum bulk and weight was particularly important because light-weight, heavy-duty vehicles required less power for just their own propulsion and furnished more for the job they were meant to do. Component development therefore comprised one of the principal phases of Ordnance automotive research and development during World War II.

The magnitude of the work accomplished precludes any comprehensive treatment save in scores of volumes. A tank had more than a dozen major components, each consisting of several subassemblies that in turn were made up of perhaps hundreds of parts. Over 25,000 separate parts in all went into a single tank, and each might require complete reworking to permit the construction of an improved vehicle. Space limitations alone dictate an account of only some high lights from the record. Others, intrinsically significant, are of too technical a nature to discuss here. So notable an innovation as the cross-drive transmission, for example, was as complex as it was promising. Hence, discussion in the following pages will deal only with the development of two vital but more readily described features—engines and flotation devices.

Engines

The basic factor determining military mobility was the internal-combustion engine. Two of the obvious advantages of the internal-combustion engine over pack and draft animals were its greater power output per unit of weight and its ability to propel heavy loads at high speeds. From a military point of view, particularly that of an army with supply lines as long as those of U.S. forces in overseas theatres, its other characteristics were even more valuable. Fuels and lubricants took up less cargo space than forage and, unit for unit of delivered energy, were less expensive. Motor vehicles were more easily transported by rail and water than animals and required fewer men with less training for their operation. In service, the gasoline or diesel engine did not eat when it was not working, was not subject to fatigue, and was less vulnerable to injuries than the horse and mule.

To be suitable for military purposes, engines had to pass tests far more stringent than for commercial purposes. They had to function with equal certainty in tropical heat and arctic cold, in desert sandstorms and jungle moisture. They had to be capable of long periods of trouble-free performance with a minimum of care and maintenance. Above all, they had to furnish sufficient power to permit sustained high speeds over all kinds of terrain.

In some types of military motor transport the engine problem could be solved with relative ease. Wheeled cargo and personnel carriers, for example, had much the same power requirements as civilian trucks. Designed and developed by America's automotive industry in co-operation

[33] (1) Ltr, Col Joseph M. Colby to F. Gordon Barber, 14 May 47, OHF. (2) Barnes MS, Tank Development, OHF. (3) Min of Mtg with Lt Gen Lebedev, Deputy Chief of the Supreme Directorate of Armored Corps, Red Army, and Ord Intel Unit at Moscow, 22 Jun 44, OHF. (4) Interv, 16 Nov 51, with Marion W. Cullen, Tank and Auto Br, R&D Div.

291064 O—55——20

with the Quartermaster Corps, these vehicles presented relatively few difficulties in point of motive power when the Ordnance Department assumed responsibility for their design, development, and production in the summer of 1942. But all the more exasperating were the obstacles that had to be surmounted in powering motorized equipment such as tracked vehicles in general and medium tanks in particular. An Ordnance expert intimately acquainted with wartime automotive research and development summed up the situation as follows:

> Our World War II difficulties in obtaining an engine of approximately 500 horsepower for the medium tank is an excellent example of our military engine problem and the awful confusion, loss of time, inefficient utilization of management, manpower, facilities, and material occurring at a critical time. In order to power the medium tank we had to employ six improvised engines, build two new plants, completely tool four plants (one of them twice), and partially tool two plants. These engines came with 5,165 spare parts, 6 sets of tools, 6 sets of maintenance literature, and a constant flow of engineering changes and mass tests to make the improvisations suitable for tank use.
>
> The effect of this situation on training, supply, and maintenance is apparent. The fact that our tanks dominated all battlefields of this war is a tribute to those of the military and of American industry who had the responsibility of getting tanks into the hands of fighting soldiers. The confusion and waste is chargeable directly to the fact that our lack of vision as a nation resulted in insufficient appropriations to have an engine for military use developed, tested, and ready for the emergency.[34]

All told, at least five factors combined to make the medium tank engine one of the thorniest problems of Ordnance research and development during World War II. First and foremost stood the peculiar power requirements of tanks in general.

The tank, unlike trucks or other wheeled vehicles, had to operate primarily away from improved roads and highways and consequently needed a much bigger supply of power to insure maximum speed and maneuverability. (*See Fig. 1.*) In addition, the space limitations of the tank called for a power plant and installation of unusual compactness with no sacrifice of accessibility for quick adjustment, repair, or replacement—the larger the engine, the larger and heavier the hull had to be, and the more time required for routine maintenance and repairs, the longer the tank would be out of action. This need for compactness in turn endangered technical difficulties with cooling systems, air intake and engine exhaust arrangements, air filters, and the like, all of which had a direct bearing on the net horsepower available for the primary job of propelling the tank. Since no analagous power or installation requirements confronted the designers of commercial automotive vehicles, the Ordnance Department during the interwar years had had to begin virtually from scratch in arriving at any semblance of a solution to the tank engine problem. Here entered the shortage of funds, the second factor responsible for the difficulties in procuring a satisfactory engine for the medium tank during World War II.

During the 1930's money for the design and development of a power plant specifically adapted to the unique requirements of full-tracked combat vehicles had simply not been available. Private industry understandably had been little interested in developing a specialized engine in view of the limited orders that the Army was able

[34] Col. Joseph M. Colby, "From Designer to Fighter," *Armored Cavalry Journal*, LIX, 1 (1950), 16.

CHART 9—POWER FOR TANKS

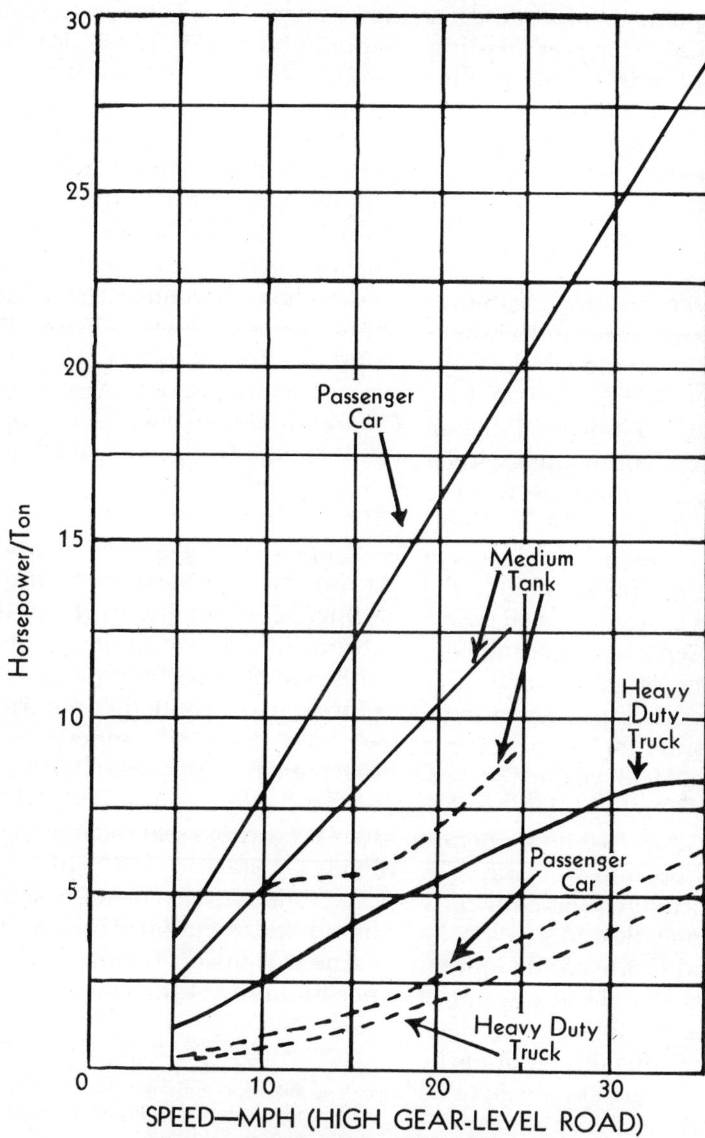

Comparative Power Conditions for Modern Vehicles

Gross weights (full load):	Tons
Passenger car	2
Medium tank	34
Heavy duty truck	13

Source: James R. Custer, "Power for Tanks," Automotive and Aviation Industries, Vol. 89, No. 5 (1 September 1943), p. 17.

to place.[35] Consequently, the Ordnance Department had had to compromise on adapting to tank use whatever existing type of engine would most closely live up to the desired standard, and the modern tank engine had from its very beginning been an improvisation.

The Wright-Continental R-975

The engine chosen by the Ordnance Department for its prewar tanks was a radial, air-cooled aircraft model, the Continental R-670, later redesignated W-670. Practical experience had indicated that an engine of minimum length and with a cross section fitting into a square was the ideal answer to the space problem. Cooling by air similarly made for minimum bulk as well as weight, and eliminated the plumbing intricacies of water-cooled power plants. The 250 horsepower eventually delivered by the Continental W-670 after several years of modification provided a high degree of mobility for the peacetime vehicles, which up to 1938 weighed a maximum of 15 tons. Average engine life mounted to better than 500 hours before a general overhaul became necessary. In short, over-all performance was eminently satisfactory.[36] But, needless to say, for the 30-plus-ton General Grants and General Shermans of World War II an output of 250 horsepower was woefully inadequate. This introduces the third element of the medium tank engine problem—weight.

On the basis of their favorable experiences with air-cooled radials in light vehicles, Ordnance designers in 1938 had looked for a more powerful engine of similar type for the new 20-ton medium tank. They finally chose the 9-cylinder, 400-horsepower Wright Whirlwind, a power plant widely used in training planes and other light aircraft. After several engineering changes, the first installation in the medium tank T5, Phase III, proved a marked success.[37] The R-975, as the Whirlwind was known officially, was adopted for the recently standardized medium tank M2. But by mid-1940, proof tests of America's newest and heaviest tanks had barely begun when events in Europe necessitated the development of an even heavier vehicle, the medium tank M3 or General Grant. With the 30-ton M3 the engine problem became acute as tests of the pilot tank at Aberdeen Proving Ground uncovered serious deficiencies of the R-975. The drawbacks of improvisation became painfully apparent. Available space was insufficient for the engine itself, for proper cooling, and for ready access to accessories. Excessive oil consumption, carburetor air temperatures, and the like, substantially lowered power output and resulted in poor performance. "The engine as presently installed," reported Aberdeen, "is definitely underpowered. Improvements to this installation have increased the horsepower available but the H.P./Wt. ratio is still too low to give completely satisfactory performance." [38] Reports from maneuvers in the southeastern United States similarly indicated that the engine was unsatisfactory as to performance and life.[39] Officers of the Proof De-

[35] Lt. Col. Robert J. Icks, "Engines for Tanks," *Society of Automotive Engineers Journal,* LI (1943), 39.

[36] For a complete development record see Hist of Development of Continental Radial W-670 Engine, OHF.

[37] First Partial Rpt of Pilot Medium Tank T5, Phase III, and Second Partial Rpt on Ord Program 5366, 16 Jan 39, p. 21, Ord Tech files.

[38] APG Rpt 10-57, First Rpt on Design and Test of Medium Tanks, M3 and Thirty-First Rpt on Ord Program 5464, 14 Jan 42, p. 25, Ord Tech files.

[39] Ltr, CG APG to CofOrd, 25 Nov 41, sub: Wright Engine R-975-EC2, OO 412.5/489-46, DRB AGO.

partment at Aberdeen recommended "that additional consideration be given to other power plants with a view to increasing the H.P./Wt. ratio as well as improving the accessibility." [40]

Now, if ever, the moment had come for tackling the tank engine problem at its very roots. Funds for research and development were plentiful. But the hour was late, too late to await the completion of a basically new engine. By 1941 U.S. and Allied troops desperately needed every vehicle that could possibly be produced. As a result, the Ordnance Department had to retain the R-975 despite its shortcomings.

Following the adoption of the General Grant and the subsequent rapid expansion of medium tank production, manufacture of the Wright engine was substantially increased. Continental Motors Corporation, the manufacturer of the W-670 engine for the light tank, began to turn out the R-975 as well. But even the increased production was insufficient to satisfy the huge demand. In fact, the President's directive of 25 September 1941 that a production of 1,000 medium tanks per month be reached by April 1, 1942 and that this figure be subsequently further increased, perhaps even doubled, made it clear that the facilities of no single engine producer would suffice. Moreover, the Ordnance Department soon found itself competing for radial engines with the similarly mushrooming aircraft production program of the Air Forces, a fact that underscored the necessity for not only enlisting additional manufacturing facilities but also for including different types of power plants in the tank program.[41] Thanks to the initiative of Ordnance engineers and the wholehearted co-operation extended them by America's automotive industry, development of alternate engines had meanwhile progressed far enough to forestall a crisis.

The General Motors 6046 (Twin 6-71) Diesel

The first type to be ready was the General Motors 2-cycle diesel engine 6046 Twin 6-71, a modification of a commercial 6-cylinder design with which the Ordnance Department had originally experimented in its light tanks.[42] The medium tank installation consisted of two of these engines joined at their fan ends by a heavy junction plate and at the flywheel ends by a double clutch housing and by a transfer unit that transmitted power to a single propeller shaft. The two clutches were operated by a single pedal, with adjustable linkage providing uniform engagement. Engine synchronization—the two units were geared together and consequently had to operate at uniform speeds—was originally accomplished by two separate hand throttles, an arrangement that later was changed to a linkage system terminating at a single throttle lever. Clutch lockout cables leading to the instrument panel permitted the driver to disengage either

[40] APG Rpt 10-57, *op. cit.*, p. 25, Ord Tech files.

[41] Allocation of R-975 engines to the tank and aircraft production programs was the subject of voluminous correspondence during the months of October, November, and December 1941 between the Under Secretary of War, the Chief of Staff, the Chief of Ordnance, and the Chief of the Air Corps. The Ordnance Department's success in adapting engines of different types to use in the medium tank finally resulted in the allocation of Wright's production to the aircraft program and Continental's production to the tank program. Pertinent letters and memoranda are contained in the following files: USW-Production, RG 104; USW-Tanks, RG 104; and 412.5 Production Div ASF Engines, RG 205. All in DRB AGO.

[42] For a complete development record, see MS, Ord Dev of General Motors 2-cycle diesel engine 6046 (Twin 6-71), OHF.

engine in event of its failure, so that one might operate without the drag of the other. The margin of reserve power was generous. As the result of an innovation in fuel injection, the rated horsepower of each of the two component engines had been raised from 165 to 210. At the governed engine speed of 2,100 revolutions per minute, a medium tank on hard-surfaced roads could travel at 30 miles an hour with both, and at 20 miles an hour with only one engine in operation.

Installation of the engine in the Grant or Sherman, both of which had been designed around the shorter Continental radial, necessitated some slight modifications of the tank interior. The bulkhead of the engine compartment, for example, was cut away to allow the transfer gear case to protrude slightly into the fighting compartment. This solution avoided the weight increase that would have accompanied a lengthening of the hull. Since the heavier engine added about one ton to the weight of the tank, such a saving was highly desirable.

The pilot tank equipped with the 6046 unit arrived at Aberdeen Proving Ground on 30 December 1941, and tests continued until April 1942, when a total of 4,201 miles had been accumulated. A number of difficulties such as the failure of an injector came to light during that period, though none was regarded as serious. A special report on the then existing power plant for the medium tank stated:

> The power plant has very good performance. Mileage and cruising range are better than that of the vehicles with gasoline engines. The cooling and starting characteristics of these engines are equal to or better than those of the standard production M3 tanks. When the engine failures encountered in this new installation have been corrected, the dual 6-71 engines should make a very dependable powerplant. Most of the engine repairs can be done without removing the engines from the vehicle.[43]

But tests on other pilot models as well as experience with production Grants and Shermans powered by the 6046 units revealed a variety of more far-reaching defects. Most of them were attributable to faulty manufacturing, inspection, and assembly caused by the rapid expansion of production. Some, on the other hand, were due to inherent weaknesses of either the unit itself or the installation dictated by the limited space of the tank. The dual clutches, for example, were a prime source of trouble. Unless they were perfectly synchronized, one carried a heavier workload than the other and quickly failed. Since synchronization demanded almost day-to-day adjustments and troops in battle were either too busy fighting or prone to neglect this bothersome maintenance task, clutch failures were common.

Another trouble source was the air cleaners which, because of space limitations, were too small to keep dust and grit from reaching working parts and shortening engine life. There was no similar difficulty in connection with air cleaners on other tank power plants because they did not have two characteristics of the 6046 unit: diesel engines, and 2-cycle engines.

Unlike their gasoline counterparts, diesel engines consume the same volume of air at high or low speeds, and for this reason increase was comparatively simple from 165 to 210 net horsepower in the component engines of the 6046 unit. An increase in the output of the fuel injectors accompanied by a modification of the cylinder liners sufficed to obtain the higher power output. In a gasoline engine no similar

[43] *Ibid.*, citing APG Special Rpt on Existing Engines for Medium Tanks.

increase would have been possible even with supercharging. Though advantageous in this instance, the unvarying air consumption tended to make for a correspondingly large volume of air intake and necessitated larger air cleaners. As a 2-cycle engine, moreover, the 6046 used much more air than the other tank engines, which were of the 4-cycle type. In a 4-cycle engine the burned gases are expelled positively by a separate stroke of the piston, while in a 2-cycle engine they are blown out by a blast of scavenging air nearly 30 percent in excess of the volume displaced by the piston. A 2-cycle engine running at the same speed as a 4-cycle engine takes in air twice as often and therefore needs at least twice as much air.

Considering these circumstances, the air-cleaner problem in diesel tanks becomes readily understandable. Given adequate space, cleaners large enough to prevent engine failures due to dust could readily have been installed. Dust was no problem for the General Motors diesel when buses were driven over hard-surfaced highways, but became a serious one when that same engine powered tanks driving in convoy over dirt roads and cross country, or when tank crews failed to service the air cleaners at the required intervals. Furthermore, the fact that servicing required breaking the air duct between the cleaners and the engine created a hazard that added another, perhaps unnecessary, cause for breakdowns. For since the air cleaners were mounted directly on the engine, this operation opened a large hole into which nuts or even wrenches disappeared all too easily. Starting the engine then wreaked havoc with the blower, and the vehicle was deadlined.[44]

Despite its mechanical imperfections, the 6046 proved its mettle in combat. No doubt much of its popularity originally stemmed from a belief that diesel tanks were less apt to burn than their gasoline cousins upon being hit by enemy projectiles. Ordnance and Armored Force tests conclusively proved this assumption wrong by establishing that the large majority of tank fires were started not by the ignition of fuel but by the explosion of ammunition unprotected in bins. Other reasons for its preference were fully warranted. Like all diesels, the 6046 developed greater torque at low engine speeds than gasoline power plants and therefore required fewer gear changes. For plain lugging power it had no equal. In the summer of 1943, for example, the U.S. military observer in Cairo reported that gasoline-powered tanks frequently were overspeeded and overworked in an effort to keep up with the diesel vehicles.[45] A later report from the same source stated that in the opinion of drivers, repairmen, and officers of the British Eighth Army the diesel-powered Sherman was the best.[46]

The Chrysler A-57 Multi-Bank

Of all the wartime engine developments, the Chrysler multi-bank A-57 was the most striking example of the resourcefulness of America's Industry-Ordnance team. Frankly an expedient for averting the threatened shortage of air-cooled radials in 1941, the A-57 came into existence within the spectacularly short time of four months.[47] A hurry-up call from Ordnance

[44] *Ibid.*, pp. 10–11.

[45] Rpt from Cairo, cited in Intel Summary 21, 15–22 Jul 43, OCO–D, OHF.

[46] Rpt from Cairo, cited in Intel Summary 25, 2–13 Sep 43, OCO–D, OHF.

[47] Unless otherwise cited, material in this section is based on MS, Ord Development of Chrysler A-57 (Multi-Bank) Tank Engine, OHF.

for medium tank engines reached Chrysler in early July 1941, and on 15 November the first of the new engines was completed and installed in a Grant. Test results were impressive enough to warrant its prompt adoption.[48]

The speed with which the A-57 came into being was made possible by the use of standard commercial parts and accessories. Rather than design an entirely new power plant requiring many months to reach the production stage, Chrysler resorted to a multiple installation of its tried and proven "Royal" six-cylinder in-line engine. Original plans called for four of these to be spaced at 90 degrees around a common crankcase, but when Ordnance insisted on more power, a unit of five engines was chosen. The output of each was transmitted to a common bull gear that drove the propeller shaft. Production models of the A-57 delivered 370 horsepower at a governed speed of 2,600 revolutions per minute.

Despite complex appearance, the Chrysler engine was rugged and, if removed from the tank, easy to maintain. No failures of the gear box were reported. The radiator, one of the most vulnerable parts of liquid-cooled tank engines, was well protected by the power unit placed between it and the fan. Accessories such as carburetors and water pumps were the same as those used in automobiles. Nonstandard parts such as ignition wire harnesses and distributors were generally made in accordance with automobile specifications. Because engine, radiator, and fan were mounted together, the power unit could be removed from the tank in one simple operation. Removal involved lifting the engine cover, disconnecting the propeller shaft, two air-cleaner ducts, two exhaust pipes, the gasoline and oil lines, a single plug for all wires, the choke, throttle, and tachometer, and finally unscrewing three mounting bolts. A crew of four required only one hour for the entire process. Placed on a dolly, the unit could be repaired, tuned and tested, and then put back into the tank.

Since the A-57 was longer and heavier than the Continental radial, some structural changes in the tank were necessary. The hull had to be lengthened by some 11 inches; the rear bogie and idler of the track suspension had to be moved toward the rear to correct the imbalance resulting from the addition of roughly three tons of armor plate and excessive engine weight. So modified, however, the Chrysler-powered tank turned out to have slightly lower ground unit pressure than other versions. Many tests proved that the engine provided greater drawbar horsepower than competing gasoline types. The usual experience was that the A-57 could pull its vehicle in one gear higher.

Aberdeen Proving Ground began testing the multi-bank Grant in February 1942. General operation of the engine was satisfactory and the installation furnished ample power for the vehicle. But when the engine was disassembled following the test, inspection revealed that overheating had caused two piston rings to stick and had damaged the connecting rod bearings and inserts. Installed in the tank, moreover, the component engines and accessories were difficult to get at because the compartment, originally intended for the 45-inch-wide Continental radial, was badly crowded by the 55-inch-wide Chrysler unit. That the light automobile accessories

[48] OCM 17578, 26 Dec 41, designated the medium tank M3, with riveted hull and the Chrysler A-57 power plant as medium tank M3A4; OCM 17855, 6 Feb 42, designated the medium tank M4, with welded hull and the Chrysler A-57 power plant as medium tank M4A4.

and materials failed to stand up under the extreme heat and heavy vibration in the tank aggravated the problem considerably.[49] Subsequent tests of a Sherman tank with the Chrysler engine showed similar results, and the conclusions and recommendations of the proof officers read:

Conclusions

1. On the basis of this test it may be concluded that:

a. The engine furnishes adequate power for the Medium Tank M4A4 but continual failures of a minor nature make maintenance of this vehicle extremely difficult.

b. The maintenance of the Multi-Engine power plant is difficult due to the inaccessibility of the parts requiring constant attention. This condition is caused by an extremely crowded engine compartment.

c. The water pump and generator drive belts are subject to overload and resultant failure which may result in serious damage to the engine due to faulty cooling.

d. The ignition system is especially complicated and troublesome.

e. The engine cooling radiator is easily clogged with dirt and foreign particles which seriously interfere with cooling of the engine. . . .

f. The operation of the vehicle in general is satisfactory. Due to the added power of the engine, the driving effort for this vehicle is less than that required for Medium Tanks powered with Wright radial engines.

Recommendations

1. On the basis of the tests conducted on this vehicle it is recommended that:

a. Considerable redesign be initiated in order to make the parts requiring constant attention and minor adjustments more accessible so it will be possible to work on these parts in a minimum of time with the engine installed in the vehicle.

b. The five individual water pumps should be replaced by a single, large, shaft driven pump. This change would eliminate the necessity of having five water pump drive belts as well as clean up the engine in general.

c. The electrical system be made more reliable by installing heavier, dust proof, connections in all wiring. Particular attention should be paid to the distributor caps and similar parts whose successful operation depends on porcelain or plastic dielectrics. These parts should be made heavier so the rough treatment they receive in combat vehicles will not cause them to crack or break.

d. The engine radiator be made more accessible to facilitate easier cleaning of this unit. To accomplish this it is believed that a redesign of the fan shroud could be made whereby the entire radiator could be easily reached by an air or steam hose.

e. The cylinder heads on #3 and #4 engines be held in place by means of cap screws instead of studs in order that the cylinder head gaskets could be replaced without the necessity of removing the whole power plant as is now the case.

f. Extensive redesign should be made in an effort to reduce the weight of the multi-engine power plant. It is believed that the concentration of weight in the rear of the vehicle shortens the life of various suspension parts.[50]

Except for the weight problem, none of the reported difficulties proved insurmountable. And had aluminum been used as extensively on the A-57 as it was on the other tank engines, that objection, too, could have been overcome. The belt-drive troubles were corrected by using a single gear-driven water pump and placing the generator in a cool spot on the floor, where it was driven by a belt from the propeller shaft. Accessibility was improved by raising the five carburetors to a line above the engine and moving the thermostats from the cylinder heads to fittings in the top

[49] First Partial Rpt on Chrysler Multi-Engine Power Plant and First Rpt on Ord Program 5634, 28 May 42, p. 12, Ord Tech files..

[50] First Rpt on Test of Medium Tank M4A4, Pilot, and Twenty-Second Rpt on Ord Program 5568, 18 Mar 43, pp. 4–6, Ord Tech files.

tank of the radiator. All modifications completed, the distributors, thermostats, fuel pump, water pump, and oil filters were readily serviced through the rear doors of the engine compartment. The spark plugs on the bottom banks were accessible through openings in the floor. But before all these improvements had taken place, experiments on other engines had been started.

In October 1942, five Chrysler-powered Grants and an equal number of Shermans underwent tests by the Desert Warfare Board. The board was greatly impressed by the pulling power of the engine, but found that breakdowns of accessories made it unreliable. Neither tank was found suitable for combat. Doubtlessly influenced by this verdict, a conference of representatives of the Allies in early November decided that the M4A4 was not acceptable. Other influences responsible for that decision were probably the facts that the trend of operations in the European and African theatres had allowed a considerable reduction in the medium tank program for 1943 and that the passing of the engine crisis had made it more feasible for the Ordnance Department to limit the number of engines. Nevertheless, 7,500 Chrysler-powered Shermans were built, and after several improvements the engine ultimately gave a remarkable account of itself.

Gasoline versus Diesel

While before 1942 the Armored Force had favored all-out dieselization, it completely reversed its stand during the early months of that year. The turning point came on the occasion of a conference on 26 February for the purpose of reviewing the fuel problem and its impact on the standardization of engines. A thorough discussion brought out a number of maintenance and supply difficulties likely to be encountered on the battlefield if diesel as well as gasoline-powered equipment were used. Adequate quantities of diesel fuel would be available in the United States but not in most theatres of operations. The majority of vehicles were gasoline-powered, and the use of diesels would necessitate a duplicate supply system. General Barnes and Colonel Christmas, the representatives of the Ordnance Department, stated that the time for deciding on any particular type of power plant had not yet arrived, that by the end of another year the Ordnance Department could, if necessary, supply an entire line of either diesel or gasoline engines, but that in the meantime it would have to resort to the maximum number procurable of both in order to assure the success of the tank program. General Devers, representing the Armored Force, declared that the Armored Force would not push the requirement for diesels and would not require diesel engines for various combat vehicles. "This represents," noted General Barnes, "a complete 'about-face' for the Armored Force which up to this time has been demanding that the Ordnance Department use diesel engines 100% for all combat vehicles and tanks." [51]

Following the conference General Somervell, Assistant Chief of Staff, G–4, advocated a stringent curtailment in the use of diesels by U.S. forces. He listed his reasons for such a policy as follows:

1. The Chief of the Armored Force has recommended that diesel engines be used in

[51] (1) Min of mtg held at Room 4302, Munitions Bldg., Thursday, 26 Feb 42, Tab B to memo, Gen Somervell, ACofS, for CofS, 28 Feb 42, sub: Use of Diesel Powered Equipment in the Armored Force, DRB AGO. (2) Barnes Diary, 27 Feb 42, OHF.

all equipment of the Armored Force. This, of course, will greatly complicate the fuel supply problem . . . the maximum production of diesel fuel required will interfere to some extent with production of aviation gasoline, toluene for explosives, and butadiene for synthetic rubber. It will also result in a large surplus of gasoline with no outlet.[52]

A directive from the War Department issued a week after General Somervell's memorandum adopted his recommendations virtually verbatim. All wheeled and half-track vehicles were to be gasoline powered. For tanks, development of gasoline engines should be pushed in order to supplant all diesel-powered tanks as quickly as possible. The latter were not to be shipped overseas but held for service in the United States and for training. Use of the Guiberson diesel engine was to be discontinued as soon as other types were available.[53]

This final decision marked a particularly sharp reversal of previous trends. The Guiberson engine, a radial, air-cooled diesel, had been in use in American light tanks since 1935.[54] A more powerful model developing 370 horsepower had been under development for medium tanks since 1938.[55] After testing this engine, the Armored Force Board in September 1941 had recommended that it be considered more suitable for use in medium tanks than the Continental radial and that as many medium tanks as possible be equipped with it. On the strength of that recommendation an entire new plant had been built at Garland, Texas. But during the conference of February 1942 General Devers announced that he wanted no further orders placed for Guibersons because they had been found unreliable. In April he wrote to General Somervell, now Commanding General, Services of Supply, stating:

In view of our past experience, and the present world situation as to the supply of Diesel fuel, the Armored Force does not desire any type Guiberson Radial Diesel engines for use in Light or Medium Tanks. It is requested that action be taken at once to discontinue the production of Guiberson Radial Diesel engines, and that existing facilities be utilized to increase the production of other standard types of tank engines.[56]

General Barnes vigorously dissented, outlining the position of the Ordnance Department in the gasoline versus diesel controversy:

. . . [General Devers] makes reference to the present world situation as to the supply of diesel fuel as a reason for discontinuing the manufacture of Guiberson diesel engines. Reliable information available to the Ordnance Department does not indicate any difficulty in obtaining diesel fuel in any theaters of operation where gasoline may be obtained, and diesel fuel has a number of obvious advantages over gasoline. In fact, the Ordnance Department considers the diesel engine the proper ultimate engine for tanks and believes that every effort should be made to expedite the development of adequate diesel engines for all tanks. It should be noted in passing that our Army as well as the armies of other United Nations employ large numbers of track laying tractors of commercial origin which tractors are equipped with diesel engines; these tractors are being procured for the Corps of Engineers, the Air Corps, Field Artillery and other branches of the Army. Gasoline propelled commercial tractors are to

[52] Memo, Gen Somervell, ACofS, for CofS, 28 Feb 42, sub: Use of Diesel Powered Equipment in the Armored Force, DRB AGO.

[53] Ltr, TAG to CG's Field Forces, Armies, Corps, Army Air Forces, Chief of Armored Force, and Chiefs of Arms and Services, 7 Mar 42, sub: Use of Diesel Powered Equipment in the Armored Force, copy in Folder 2-2842, AG 412.31, DRB AGO.

[54] OCM 12371, 30 Sep 35, provided for test of Guiberson T-1020 engine for combat cars and tanks.

[55] OCM 14702, 20 Sep 38; 15403, 13 Oct 39.

[56] (1) Hist of Ordnance-Diesel Engine Developments, OHF. (2) Ltr, Gen Devers to CG SOS, 28 Apr 42, ASF Production Div files, DRB AGO.

all practical purposes unobtainable. Further, both the British and the Russians are using and are obtaining from the United States tanks and other vehicles employing diesel engines.

With respect to the Guiberson Model T-1400 Radial Diesel Engine for the medium tank, this is a new development type engine of which 670 only are on order. The cancellation of this project would therefore have but slight effect on the 1942 production of medium tanks, however, since the War Department has already invested a considerable sum of money in this project, it is recommended that this project be allowed to carry on for several months until a reasonable quantity of these engines have been installed in tanks and given an extended test in the hands of troops. This is considered to be in the best interest of the Government and should have no appreciable effect on our tank program. It will be recalled that it was in the summer of 1940 that the Chief of the Armored Force requested that *all* tanks for the Armored Force be equipped with Guiberson diesel engines, at which time the Ordnance Department took the position that this engine was not well enough developed to warrant such a decision and the decision was accepted to continue with the production of the Guiberson diesel engine in a limited way to further its development. This is the policy which has been followed since that time.

In any case, the development of new tank engines such as the Guiberson diesel tank engine is a matter of years and since the Ordnance Department considers that a diesel engine for tanks should be developed, we believe these projects should be allowed to continue in their present status until further data are available.[57]

Nevertheless, in the summer of 1942 production of Guiberson diesels was canceled and the plant at Garland turned over to the Continental Motors Corporation for the manufacture of R-975 gasoline engines. Production of the General Motors diesel continued, in order to fill British and Russian requirements which at the time amounted to two thirds of America's tank output. While development work on diesels for medium tanks proceeded apace, none of the projects—an 18-cylinder Guiberson radial and a 9-cylinder radial—were to be put into production, since in the meantime a satisfactory gasoline engine, the Ford GAA, had made its appearance and development of other gasoline power plants had shown sufficient promise to warrant abandonment of diesels.

The Ford GAA

The Ford GAA tank engine had its origins in a development by the Ford Motor Company for the Air Force. Realizing the need for an aircraft engine with nominal displacement but higher specific output than existing designs, Ford in 1939 initiated development of an upright 60-degree, V-12 liquid-cooled power plant with a displacement of 1650 cubic inches.[58]

Design studies began in the summer of 1940, and by November of that same year a 2-cylinder model was fully assembled and ready for testing. There followed extensive investigations of combustion-chamber design, bearing materials, and engine timing in an effort to obtain peak performance. Within three months the output was raised from 115 to roughly 150 horsepower, much better progress than could have been made with a multi-cylinder model. August of 1941 saw a full-scale 12-cylinder engine mounted on the test stand, ready for a trial run.

Knowing of the good results obtained with the 2-cylinder model, and urgently needing a high-output engine for its 30-ton

[57] 3d Ind, Gen Barnes, Asst Chief of Ind Serv, OCO, to CG SOS, 12 May 42, on basic communication, Gen Devers to CG SOS, 28 Apr 42, ASF Production Div files, DRB AGO.

[58] Unless otherwise cited, material in this section is based on Hist of Development of Ford Tank Engines, OHF.

medium tanks, the Ordnance Department approached Ford with a proposal to develop a power plant to take the place of the underpowered R-975 radial. After a survey of the medium tank's engine compartment, Ford engineers suggested that shortening their engine from twelve to eight cylinders would permit the early production of an adequate power plant necessitating a minimum of alterations to the existing hull. Design and layout of the proposed engine commenced in September 1941, and by January of 1942 the first model was completed.

The new tank engine consisted of five major assemblies: the cylinder block and crankshaft, including pistons and connecting rods; the cylinder heads; the accessory drives; the end cover; and the oil pan assemblies. Each of the assemblies constituted an integral unit and was arranged for easy handling and replacement by soldier mechanics. Extensive use of aluminum accounted for light weight. The cylinder block and crankcase, for example, the bulkiest and therefore heaviest components of every engine, were made of one single aluminum casting. Aside from the weight saved and the ease of handling, this one-unit treatment also resulted in structural rigidity in absorbing the high loads and stresses of the engine without undue distortion. Pistons, cylinder heads, the end cover, the oil pan, and the camshaft cover likewise were aluminum castings. The exhaust manifolds, ordinarily made of cast iron, were made of two stainless steel stampings welded together — another weight-saving feature. Installed, the engine weighed only 1,575 pounds, 2,825 pounds less than the hitherto lightest-weight liquid-cooled power plant for medium tanks—the General Motors diesel—and only slightly over 200 pounds more than the air-cooled Continental radial. The Ford GAA's output of 450 net horsepower was the highest developed by any of the medium tank engines mass produced during World War II. The Continental radial developed 400, the General Motors diesel 375, and the Chrysler multi-bank 370.[59] Because of the high horsepower-to-weight ratio, high output, and compactness of the Ford engine, the Ordnance Technical Committee in January 1942 authorized its use as an alternate power plant for the Sherman tank.[60]

The first three vehicles of the new series were completed in June and immediately underwent tests at the General Motors Proving Ground. Proposing minor modifications and further testing, the Proving Ground recommended that the Ordnance Department accept the vehicle. Equally favorable reports resulted from subsequent trials. Beginning in November 1942 the Armored Force conducted 24-hour-a-day operations of seventeen tanks and upon their conclusion stated that the engine was sufficiently satisfactory to warrant further development. At the same time a series of endurance tests was conducted at Aberdeen Proving Ground and, under the supervision of Ordnance engineers, by Chrysler and General Motors. Nothing more strikingly illustrates the co-operation of the Industry-Ordnance team than the fact that here two competitors were actively engaged in furthering the cause of a third.

Although first results revealed that engine life was unsatisfactory, continuous improvements eventually remedied the most objectionable faults. Structural weak-

[59] Handbook of Ordnance Automotive Engineering (hereafter cited as Handbook of Ord Auto Engr), Vol. I, Sec. II, p. 11.

[60] OCM 17678, 20 Jan 42.

nesses in the crankcase, for example, were overcome by increasing wall thickness and ribbing sections and by changing the design of the main-bearing caps. When the rigid crankcase caused fatiguing and breaking of the crankshaft, a development program was instituted for evolving a sturdier crankshaft by combining various formulas of steel-making and heat treatment. In July 1943 the proving center of Aberdeen Proving Ground, reporting that the Ford GAA engine was very satisfactory for medium tanks and, because more accessible, more easily maintained and serviced than other medium tank power plants, recommended that:

> *a.* The Ford model GAA engine be approved for production as a power plant in the medium tank in such quantities as are deemed necessary to supply demands of the present and immediate future.
>
> *b.* The necessary corrective modifications be placed on the production units as soon as possible.
>
> *c.* Further development work be carried out on this engine with a view to increasing its mechanical reliability.[61]

By the summer of 1943 the Ford engine was well on the way to becoming the standard power plant for medium tanks. Following a comparative endurance test of Sherman tanks powered by the several engines in current use, the Armored Force Board had in May of that year found the Ford to be the best and had recommended its adoption for all medium tanks. Although the outcome of an endurance run at Aberdeen Proving Ground between October 1943 and February 1944 was not wholly so favorable, the Ford engine performed more satisfactorily than the Continental radial, its only serious rival. The General Motors diesel was out of the picture for two reasons: first, because of the ban on the use of diesels overseas, and, second, because its endurance qualities were unpredictable and its reliability the lowest of all engines tested. Employment of the Chrysler multi-bank unit had long since been vetoed, although, interestingly enough, it was found to exceed all others in reliability as well as in economy of oil consumption and in maintenance. Endurance of the Continental was unsatisfactory, particularly under full-load operation over hilly terrain. Overspeeding the engine to brake the vehicle while descending hills was responsible for four out of five major breakdowns.

While the endurance qualities of the Ford GAA were not considered satisfactory because none of the test engines met the 400-hour requirement, its performance before failure was excellent and all failures were similar. Correction of two basic defects—burning out of exhaust valves and breakdown of cylinder-head gaskets—offered prospects of an immediate increase in engine life. Accessibility was equal or superior to other engines tested; fuel consumption was lowest of all gasoline-powered plants; maintenance requirements were lowest and rose only after the valves and head gaskets began to give trouble. All told, the Ford GAA presented better possibilities of immediate improvement than any other engine tested.[62]

The service record of the Ford engine fully justified the expectations of its superior performance. Continuous modifications of design weaknesses ultimately resulted in a power plant that was by far the most popular with the men on the battle fronts. Reports from Europe, for example,

[61] (1) First Rpt on Ford Tank Engine, Endurance Test and First Rpt on Ord Program 5658, 31 Jul 43, pp. 7–8a, Ord Tech files. (2) R&D, Tanks, OHF.

[62] First Partial Rpt on Engines for Combat Vehicles, Endurance Test of, and First Rpt on Ord Program 5739, 15 Mar 44, Ord Tech files.

noted that the engine "served well and reliably during combat operations. Using personnel preferred this engine to the air cooled radial type engine because of its higher horsepower and torque outputs."[63] Had production capacity been great enough, the Ford engine would unquestionably have been adopted as the one and only power plant for American medium tanks.

Flotation for Tracked Vehicles

In the early 1930's when Ordnance engineers faced the problem of increasing the cross-country mobility of combat vehicles, they turned more and more to the use of tracks instead of wheels. Tracks not only enabled tanks and gun motor carriages to cross ditches and pass over other obstacles that stopped wheeled vehicles but also, because of greater ground contact area, provided more support in mud and sand. The support, or flotation, provided by tracks came to be of particular importance as the weight of tank armor and armament increased beyond the capacity of wheels to support it on soft ground.

Design of tracks for the light-weight, slow-moving tanks of World War I had been a comparatively simple matter, but during World War II, as more powerful engines and improved suspensions increased the speed and cruising range of track-laying vehicles, development of suitable tracks became extremely difficult. When designers thought in terms of producing the ideal all-purpose track, they found themselves confronted with a number of irreconcilable requirements. Smooth operation on the highway, for example, could be achieved only at the cost of drastically reduced traction in mud and on rough ground. Wide, cleated tracks, which provided the most flotation and traction for off-highway operations, had many features that made them undesirable for general use: they caused more noise and vibration and added to steering difficulties; they increased the wear on the suspension mechanism; and they offered more resistance to movement, thus adding to the already great burden on the tank engine. Ordnance engineers constantly strove to develop a light-weight track, but they could not save on weight at the cost of durability, for the track had to be strong enough to support the vehicle, take the severe pounding of cross-country travel, and withstand the impact of gun fire and mine explosions. Throughout World War II four aspects of track development were of primary importance—the demand for tracks wide enough to carry heavy loads under all circumstances, the need of better traction, the conflicting requirements for steel and rubber tracks, and the search for adequate, inexpensive track pins.[64]

Wide Tracks and Extension Devices

The theoretical solution to the problem of providing adequate flotation for tanks and other track-laying vehicles operating on soft ground was the essence of simplicity: make the tracks wider. Widened tracks distributed the weight of the vehicle over a larger area and thus lessened the pressure exerted on each square inch of

---

[63] Engine, Ford, Models GAA and GAF, Performance Rpt—U. S. Materiel, ETOUSA, 15 Aug 45, Ord Tech files.

[64] For general comments on the requirements of tank tracks, see: (1) Capt N. G. McLean, Automotive Proof Manual, pp. 45-46, OHF; (2) John M. Nickelsen, Tracks for Ord Vehicles, OHF; and (3) Handbook Ord Auto Engr, Vol. I, Sec. V, OHF. The Nickelsen volume includes descriptions and photographs of all tracks developed between January 1940 and January 1945.

ground. But the use of wider tracks raised a host of thorny problems of design. They made steering more difficult, required the use of dual bogie wheels, and made necessary the adoption of altogether different suspension systems. Further, as the Ordnance Department reported in the fall of 1944, tracks wide enough to bring the ground pressure down to seven pounds per square inch, as requested by the Army Ground Forces, "will result in an overall vehicle width in excess of the 124-inch maximum shipping width now permitted under AR 850-15." [65] Nevertheless, during the winter of 1942–43 when observers in North Africa reported that American tanks had run well in sand but had bogged down in the mud of Tunisia because their tracks were too narrow, Ordnance engineers promptly made the development of wider tracks a high-priority project.[66] At that time the tracks of the Sherman tanks were 16.5 inches wide, with a ground pressure of 14 pounds per square inch. Their immediate replacement by wider tracks was impossible, not primarily because of any difficulty in designing a wider track, although that presented its problems, but because a wider track would not fit existing suspensions. Because of the problems involved in redesigning the whole suspension system and making the production changeover, tanks with wide tracks did not become available until late in 1944.[67]

While tanks with new suspensions were under development, Ordnance engineers produced, as temporary expedients, extension devices known formally as extended end-connectors, informally as duck bills. These were short metal plates that could be bolted to the outside end of each track block to widen the track of the Sherman from 16.5 to approximately 20 inches. They increased flotation by 21 percent and brought the ground pressure for vehicles weighing 35 tons down to less than 12 pounds per square inch.[68] They could be attached to the tracks of any medium tank in the field without undue difficulty and with a total weight increase of only 350 pounds. By the spring of 1944 these extension devices, packed in kits, were available for shipment to overseas theatres to be installed for specific operations at the discretion of the theatre commanders. In October 1944 the Army Service Forces directed that all narrow-track medium tanks shipped overseas be equipped with extended end-connectors, and at the same time theatre commanders were notified that similar extension devices were available for the M5 light tank, increasing its track width from 11.5 to 15 inches.[69]

To develop extended end-connectors for attachment to the outside of tank tracks was not a particularly difficult task, but attaching them to the inside of the track was a different story because there was no room for them between the track and the tank hull. Pending development of tanks with narrower suspensions, Ordnance engineers devised so-called outboard spacers to hold the suspension of the Sherman several inches out from the hull to make

[65] 2d Ind, CofOrd–D to CG ASF, 18 Oct 44, on basic ltr, AGF to ASF, 16 Aug 44, sub: Improved Flotation for Armored Track-Laying Vehicles, AGF 470.8, DRB AGO.

[66] (1) Rpt of Maj J. M. Sills and Mr. Errol J. Gay on trip to NATOUSA, 20 Mar 43, Sec B, p. 5, OHF. (2) Ann Rpt R&D Serv, 30 Jun 43, p. 46, OHF.

[67] For citations of documents pertaining to the development of horizontal volute suspensions, dual bogies, and wide tracks, see OCM 22782, 3 Feb 44.

[68] (1) OCM 22821, 3 Feb 44. (2) Ltr, AGF to ASF, 4 Mar 44, OO 470.8/855 Tanks, DRB AGO. (2) Nickelsen, Tracks for Ordnance Vehicles, pp. 127–30, OHF.

[69] (1) Ltr, ASF to CofOrd, 25 Oct 44, OO 400.37/19133, DRB AGO. (2) OCM 25529, 26 Oct 44; 26645, 8 Feb 45.

TRACK EXTENSIONS *being installed by the crew of a Sherman tank during a lull in combat operations at Baesweiler, Germany.*

room for attachment of extended end-connectors.[70] When the extension devices were attached to both sides of the track they gave it a width of approximately 23.5 inches and a unit ground pressure of only 10 pounds per square inch, as compared with its original 16-inch width and 12-to-14-pound pressure. The speed with which they could be attached and the length of time required to get new tanks with wide tracks into production led the Ordnance Committee to approve installation of extended end-connectors on both sides of tracks in so far as castings and other critical components were available. Although the Ordnance Department considered the installation of the spacers and inside track extensions in the field impractical, it approved, at the request of Army Ground Forces, procurement of kits that would permit field installation.[71]

A further application of the extension principle was approved in January 1945. It was an extended grouser, nicknamed the platypus, that could be bolted to ex-

[70] OCM 24618, 3 Aug 44; 25529, 26 Oct 44; 25753, 16 Nov 44.

[71] (1) OCM 25529, 26 Oct 44. (2) Final Hist Rpt of Armored Fighting Vehicles and Weapons Sec., Hq ETO, 6 Jun 44–24 May 45, p. 17, OHF. For further information on the advantages of extended end-connectors, see also Mediterranean Area Armored Fighting Vehicles, Tech Rpt 26, cited in Intel Summary 66, 30 Apr–15 May 45, and MTOUSA AGF Board Rpt 255, 27 Dec 44, cited in Weekly Battle Performance Rpt 16, 26 Mar 45, OHF.

291064 O—55——21

tended end-connectors to improve both flotation and traction. The term grouser was used to describe either detachable cleats, which could be fastened to the track to provide more traction, or the tread design on the track block. In the latter sense it was termed an integral grouser. The 32.5-inch grousers, which extended from the inside of the track block outward beyond the extended end-connectors, required no modification of the suspension and gave the tank a ground pressure of approximately 8 pounds per square inch. Longer grousers, 37 inches in length, were also developed for attachment to Sherman tanks equipped with spaced-out suspensions and extended end-connectors on both sides of the track. The long grouser brought the ground pressure down to 7 pounds, the figure that the Army Ground Forces had earlier fixed as the maximum for effective operation. Both the long and the short grousers could be installed in the field. Both were approved for production early in 1945.[72]

Late in 1944 tanks with newly designed suspensions and wide tracks came off the production lines. The new Sherman, the M4A3E8, had a 23-inch track and a horizontal volute suspension. The light and heavy tanks both now had torsion bar suspensions, and tracks 16 inches and 24 inches wide, respectively. One of the major design changes necessitated by adoption of the new suspensions and wide tracks was the use of dual bogie wheels. Although this change doubled the number of bogie wheels required for each tank, it distributed the load on each wheel more evenly and resulted in longer wheel life. By the time these tanks saw service in Europe, experience had shown that a track 23 or 24 inches wide was not wide enough to keep a tank from bogging down in deep mud.[73] Extended end-connectors on the old-model medium tanks had widened the track to 23.5 inches, but the use of extended grousers to provide additional width had proved necessary. To make the new wide-track tanks serviceable in deep mud the only answer was repetition of the earlier process of adding extension devices. In March 1945 the Ordnance Committee approved production of kits for field installation of 24-inch grousers on the 16-inch tracks of the light tank M24. These grousers added 3,000 pounds to the weight of the vehicle but lowered the ground pressure to about 8 pounds per square inch. By mid-July even longer grousers, 28 inches in length, had been developed for the M24, and kits to permit their installation were available but did not arrive overseas in time for combat use. V-J Day found the 39-inch extended grouser for the wide-tracked M4A3E8 and M26 tanks still in the development stage.[74]

Track Profiles

While developing wider tracks to increase flotation, Ordnance engineers were also concerned with designing tracks with sufficient traction to keep the vehicles going in deep mud and on icy roads. In 1940 all American tanks rode on smooth rubber-block tracks which, in addition to

[72] (1) OCM 25529, 26 Oct 44; 26607, 8 Feb 45; 26921, 8 Mar 45. (2) Ann Rpt R&D Serv, 20 Jun 45, p. 97, OHF.

[73] "The units are beginning to receive the M4A3E8 with the horizontal volute suspension and wide track," the ETO reported in March 1945. "The mobility in the mud is superior to that of the M4A3. . . . A lower ground pressure than that now provided is still required if the units are to have satisfactory mobility." Second Letter, Rpt of Activities, ETO New Developments Div, to WD New Developments Div, 14 Mar 45, Opns Rpts 97-1117 (15145) Mar 45, DRB AGO.

[74] OCM 26753, 22 Feb 45; 27938, 7 Jun 45; 28848, 23 Aug 45; 31978, 22 Jan 48.

being shock absorbent and long lasting, gave adequate traction on hard-surface roads under normal conditions. When greater traction was needed for muddy roads and cross-country operation, tank crews put on detachable steel grousers, much as a motorist would put chains on his car. These detachable grousers could be bolted to the track blocks and then be removed when the tank returned to the highway. As a rule, they were not put on every track block but only on every second, third, or fourth block, depending on the amount of traction needed and the number of grousers available. The combination of smooth rubber-block tracks and detachable steel grousers was highly satisfactory in most respects, but it had one major disadvantage: the installation and removal of the grousers was difficult and time consuming. In cross-country operations, vehicles frequently encountered so many different types of terrain that it was impractical to install and remove the grousers at every turn.[75]

In 1941 Ordnance engineers attempted to solve this problem by developing the so-called rubber chevron track with a V-shaped tread on each block to give increased traction. To a remarkable degree these tracks combined the good highway performance of the smooth-block rubber track with much of the traction of the detachable steel grouser. Although tanks equipped with this type of track also carried detachable steel grousers for use on extremely soft ground, the grousers were used so little in North Africa by tanks with either smooth or chevron rubber tracks that the Army Ground Forces in 1943 recommended that tanks no longer be required to carry them.[76] The rubber chevron track came closest to meeting the needs of the armored units in North Africa, but just as its development was completed early in 1942 the rubber crisis forced Ordnance to search for a substitute.

Well before Pearl Harbor experiments were under way with steel tracks as possible alternatives to rubber tracks. Most of these early steel tracks had cleats, or integral steel grousers to provide traction in mud. In comparison with the steel tracks developed later, these early types were regarded as flat tracks because their grousers were quite shallow. Deep grousers were not provided in 1941 and 1942 for two reasons: shallow grousers afforded sufficient traction for most purposes, and deep grousers were too hard on the suspensions and caused too much resistance to movement. Toward the middle of the war when Allied armored forces had to contend with deep mud and swamps, steel tracks with deeper grousers to provide more traction were adopted in spite of their disadvantages in other respects. The designs used for the grousers on steel tracks included parallel bars, interrupted parallels, and chevrons, not unlike the tread designs on truck tires. Generally, the armored forces preferred the chevron design, but all types remained in use throughout the war because of the production difficulties in changing over to chevron only.[77]

[75] For a report on combat experience in the Pacific with detachable grousers, see Pacific Warfare Bd Rpt 3, GHQ U. S. Army Forces Pacific, 18 Jun 45, AG Special Files of Observers Rpts 4-7.13/45, DRB AGO.

[76] Ltr, Armored Force Bd to CG AGF, 28 May 43, sub: Elimination of Grousers, and inds, ASF 470.81, Parts and Accessories No. 2, DRB AGO.

[77] (1) Lt Col Jean E. Engler, Rpt on Observations in NATOUSA, 12 Jul–20 Aug 44, Mission files, OHF. (2) NAF RAC Liaison Ltr 5, cited in Intel Summary 35, 14–20 Jan 44, OCO–D, OHF. (3) Col George G. Eddy, Rpt on Special Mission with New Weapons and Demonstration Bd in ETO and NATOUSA, 4 Feb–1 May 44, Mission files, OHF. (4) Interv, 17 Sep 51, with Marion Cullen, Tank and Auto Br, R&D Div. (5) Interv, 25 Oct 51, with Everett W. Holt, Maint Br, FS Div.

When American tanks encountered deep snow and ice, crews found smooth-block rubber tracks and steel tracks of all kinds totally unsatisfactory.[78] As tests by the Ordnance detachment at Camp Shilo in Manitoba, Canada, during the winter of 1942–43 had demonstrated, steel tracks were particularly unsatisfactory on icy roads. Designed for use in mud, not for operation on hard, slippery surfaces, flat steel tracks as a rule failed to cut into the ice. When sharper steel grousers with parallel-bar design were used, they offered no resistance to sideslipping and were sometimes derisively referred to as ice skates. The steel track with chevron design was more effective in preventing sideslipping, but the occasions when it cut into the ice were so infrequent that the track was of little use. The rubber chevron track gave by far the best traction on ice but, because of the loss of natural rubber imports and difficulties in producing chevron tracks of synthetic rubber, most tanks were not equipped with this type of track. In the absence of a suitable track for operation on ice, units in the field resorted to improvisation. Some welded small sections of steel bar to the running surface of the track blocks to form ice cleats; others welded sharp steel spikes to end-connector wedges; still others substituted a rubber track block for every sixth steel block and attached a steel grouser on the block mid way between. The war ended before a satisfactory track or detachable grouser for operation on ice was developed.[79]

Steel Versus Rubber Tracks

Throughout World War II the relative merits of steel and rubber tracks constituted one of the most controversial aspects of the track development program. From 1940 to 1945 the steel track and the rubber track competed for favor; each had its loyal supporters and each could claim superiority under certain conditions. But no track, it should be noted, was made entirely of steel or entirely of rubber. Rubber track blocks were molded on a steel framework consisting of two tubes, or binoculars as they were often called, that extended horizontally through the block to hold the track pins. In both steel and rubber tracks, rubber bushings were used on the track pins to absorb vibration and reduce wear, and were credited with giving American tracks a much longer life than enemy tracks.[80] Early in 1944 steel tracks with rubber backs to cushion the shock on bogie wheels came into use, for experience had shown that all-steel blocks materially shortened the life of the running gear.[81]

Before the United States entered the war, particularly during 1940 and 1941, the smooth rubber track dominated the field. In those years all U.S. Army tracked vehicles rode on rubber because it had smooth riding qualities, did not damage highways, provided adequate traction on hard-surface roads, and, by cushioning shocks, added many miles to the life of bogie wheels, support rollers, and other suspension components. Steel tracks gave

[78] For a compilation of data on this topic see Armor in Winter Warfare, a research report prepared at The Armored School, Fort Knox, Kentucky, June 1950, OHF.

[79] (1) Armor in Winter Warfare, OHF. (2) Final Hist of AFV and Weapons Sec. ETO, p. 19, OHF. (3) ETO Battle Experiences No. 27, 16 Jan 45; No. 42, 21 Jan 45; No. 45, 23 Jan 45; No. 61, 14 Feb 45; Opns Rpt, Battle Experiences ETO, 1-106, 97-11.5, DRB AGO.

[80] (1) Handbook of Ord Auto Engr, Vol. I, Sec. V, OHF. (2) Barnes, *op. cit.*, pp. 208–09, OHF.

[81] OCM 22819, 3 Feb 44, authorized procurement of 200 sets of the rubber-backed T74 track for service tests.

better results in mud than did smooth rubber tracks, but caused more vibration, added to steering difficulties, and increased resistance to movement. Steel tracks were less desirable in terms of weight, always an important consideration in Ordnance design, for they weighed about 25 percent more than rubber tracks. As far as traction in mud was concerned, development of rubber chevron tracks in 1941 partly evened the score; when detachable steel grousers were used, a vehicle equipped with rubber tracks could plow through mud as well as one equipped with steel tracks.[82]

The loss of rubber imports after Pearl Harbor forced a revision of plans for production. As synthetic rubber was not yet available in quantity, nor expected to reach mass production for another year, the only solution was adoption of steel tracks. In January 1942 the Under Secretary of War directed the Ordnance Department to discontinue the use of rubber for tracks at the earliest possible date, and in June the Chief of Ordnance reported that development work on steel tracks had progressed sufficiently to permit changing over from rubber to steel before the end of the year.[83] But by March 1943 the changeover had not yet been made, and General Campbell reported that large quantities of natural rubber would still be required for tank tracks during the last quarter of 1943. He described some of the difficulties of converting to steel tracks as follows:

> The Ordnance Department has been intensively working on the development of steel tracks for light and medium tanks to replace the present rubber block track as a conservation matter. . . . Success has been attained in building steel tracks which will have satisfactory life, but the principal difficulty has been the destructive effect of the steel track upon the running gear of the tank. Our tanks are noted abroad for their sturdiness, reliability and their ability to keep going under adverse conditions. An important factor in this result has been the use of rubber tracks. It is believed that the tank mechanism, especially the suspension system, in time can be changed to withstand the beating which it receives from the steel track. The time required to make the tank equipped with steel tracks the equivalent in reliability to the present tank equipped with rubber tracks, however, cannot be accurately predicted.[84]

In view of the excellent performance of rubber tracks in North Africa and the difficulties encountered in developing satisfactory steel tracks, the Ordnance Department recommended in the early part of 1943 that steel tracks be abandoned altogether and that all tanks be equipped with rubber tracks. After thorough study of the Ordnance proposal, General Minton, director of the ASF Resources and Production Division, agreed that henceforth all tanks destined for shipment overseas should be equipped with rubber tracks. "This opinion is concurred in by everyone with whom I have discussed the question," wrote General Minton. "General Devers will back it 100% . . . ." At the same time, because of the shortage of natural rubber, ASF directed Ordnance to push its synthetic rubber track program to a conclusion as soon as possible and to put steel tracks on tanks to be used in the United States for training.[85]

[82] Rubber for Mechanized Warfare, p. 55, OHF.

[83] (1) Rpt, Elimination of Rubber in Tank Tracks, Tank Automotive Production, ASF Production Div file, DRB AGO. (2) OCM 17918, 12 Mar 42.

[84] Ltr, CofOrd to Mr. William M. Jeffers, WPB, n.d., sub: Rubber Tracks, OO 451.25/4061, DRB AGO.

[85] (1) Memo, Gen Minton for ACofS for Materiel, SOS, 12 Mar 43, sub: Rubber Tracks . . . , ASF 470.8 Tanks, DRB AGO. (2) Memo, CG ASF for CofOrd, 19 Mar 43, sub: Rubber Tracks . . . , Tank and Automotive Products, ASF Production Div file, DRB AGO.

No sooner had these policies been established than demand arose for their reversal. First came a strong appeal from the Armored Force for the elimination of steel tracks on training vehicles because the steel threatened to destroy the paved roads over which they ran. ASF, promptly acceding to this request, directed Ordnance to supply rubber tracks for all tanks, whether for service overseas or in the United States, and to cancel all contracts for steel tracks.[86] This policy had not been in effect more than a few months when strong criticism of rubber tracks, and an appeal for steel tracks, came from troops fighting in Sicily and Italy. Armored forces in Italy reported that, during operations on rocky mountain roads, holes were frequently gouged in rubber tracks, reducing their average life to less than 500 miles.[87] Under these circumstances, field commanders requested that rubber tracks be replaced with the more durable steel tracks in spite of the disadvantages of more difficult steering, greater wear on bogie wheels, and reduction of speed. In view of this situation, ASF authorized Ordnance to ship steel tracks from existing stocks when requested by overseas commanders, and to resume steel-track production.[88] In the meantime, the rubber industry had developed a rubber-backed steel track that overcame many of the drawbacks of the all-steel track. New steel-track production in 1944 consisted largely of this improved type.[89]

During the early part of 1943 the rubber industry had succeeded in producing a satisfactory smooth-block track of synthetic rubber but had not been able to make an acceptable synthetic chevron track. In August ASF directed Ordnance to limit its production of synthetic rubber tracks to the smooth-block type but to continue its efforts, in co-operation with industry, to develop a suitable synthetic chevron track. Although the national stockpile of natural rubber was running low, Ordnance requested permission to continue production of chevron tracks of natural rubber since combat forces had found them superior to all other tracks. It was while this request was under consideration that troops overseas reported difficulties in using rubber tracks on rocky terrain and asked for steel tracks instead. In December 1943 ASF headquarters, recognizing the futility of over-all directives prescribing the type of track to be issued, granted the Chief of Ordnance authority to manufacture both steel and rubber tracks and to issue whatever type he and the using arms jointly determined to be most suitable for specific operations.[90]

Track Pins

Still another important factor in track design was the type of connections used to assemble tracks.[91] In World War II American tanks were the only combat vehicles that rode on tracks assembled with rubber-bushed track pins. These pins had been

[86] Memo, CG ASF for CofOrd, 12 Jun 43, sub: Rubber Tracks . . . , Tank Automotive Products, ASF Production Div file, DRB AGO.

[87] (1) Memo, Dir Production Div, for Dir Reqmts Div, ASF, 2 Nov 43, sub: Rubber and Steel Tank Tracks, ASF Production Div file 423, Rubber. (2) Tech Info Ltr 16, Ord Sec, Hq NATOUSA, 30 Oct 43, AG 470.81 (12 Oct 43), DRB AGO.

[88] (1) Memo, CofOrd for CG ASF, 24 Nov 43, sub: Medium Tank Tracks, and 1st Ind, CG ASF, 12 Dec 43, OO 470.8/610 Tanks, DRB AGO. (2) OCM 22537, 30 Dec 43.

[89] Rubber for Mechanized Warfare, pp. 56–58 OHF.

[90] *Ibid.*

[91] Recommended Program for Postwar Development of Tank-Automotive Materiel, 8 Jun 45, p. 4 Exhibit 5, OCO–D Development Div Hist, Vol. X 1 Apr–30 Jun 45, OHF.

developed during the early 1930's as a replacement for plain steel, or "dry," pins, which performed adequately on low-speed tractors but wore out rapidly on higher-speed combat vehicles. "Doughnut" rubber-bushed pins, rubber rings vulcanized to steel track pins and then inserted into track blocks under pressure, gave rubber-bushed tracks several advantages over those with plain steel pins. Tractive resistance was materially less, especially at speeds over 20 miles an hour, and under heavy loads power loss was proportionally smaller. Track life was longer because the bushing itself absorbed vibration and so prevented wear, and, finally, noise was greatly reduced. The diameter of the track pins and the thickness of the bushing were varied to give the strength required for each vehicle.

The high manufacturing cost of doughnut rubber-bushed pins prompted further research. In the summer of 1941 Ordnance engineers carried on experiments with sleeve or Harris bushings that were nearly as long as the pins.[92] This design was expected to be cheaper to manufacture, provide more uniform stress in the rubber, and have higher strength under load and deflection. But, because the rubber filled the tube completely, there was insufficient room for compression, and continuing deflection caused the bushing to disintegrate. Consequently, American tracks throughout the war used only the doughnut rubber bushing. The Germans and Japanese employed all-metal pins but encountered problems of enormous proportions in keeping their vehicles supplied with tracks. Life of enemy tracks was approximately 600 miles, in contrast to 3,000 miles for many American tracks. At the end of the war Ordnance designers were continuing unabated the search for a dry steel track pin as efficient as the expensive rubber-bushed pin.[93]

The double-pin method of track block construction was used exclusively until late in the war when single-pin steel tracks were introduced on the M18 gun motor carriage, the M24 light tank, and certain wide suspension tanks of the M4 series. While lighter in weight and cheaper to manufacture, single-pin tracks were difficult to disassemble in the field, made more frequent adjustment of track tension necessary, and had shorter life than the double pins since the angular movement that had to be taken up by the track-pin bushing was approximately twice that required if two pins were used. The single-pin tracks, tried on the wide suspension M4A3E8 tank when first used in the ETO early in 1945, gave such inferior service that they were quickly replaced by the double pin.[94] But single-pin tracks for the M18 gun motor carriage and the M24 light tank gave less trouble and remained in use.[95]

By the end of 1943 one fact had become clear: no single track could meet all com-

[92] (1) OCM 16935, 3 Jul 41; 18265, 21 Mar 42. (2) Nickelsen, Tracks for Ord Vehicles, p. 36, OHF. (3) Aberdeen Proving Ground Rpt 21-30, title: First Minor Rpt on Goodyear T-41 Standard Rubber Block Track with Harris Bushing for Medium Tank M3, and Third Minor Rpt on Ord Program 5365, 20 Jul 42.

[93] See OCO-D Development Div Monthly Rpts, 10 Nov 42-10 Jan 45, OHF.

[94] (1) Handbook Ord Auto Engr, Vol. I, Sec. 5, p. 2, OHF. (2) Nickelsen, Tracks for Ord Vehicles, OHF. (3) OCM 19606, 28 Jan 43; 19908 and 19925, 11 Mar 43; 21418, 26 Aug 43; 21500, 9 Sep 43; 22033 and 22034, 4 Nov 43; 22246, 2 Dec 43; 22642, 13 Jan 44; 23583, 20 Apr 44; 23958, 25 May 44; 26573, 1 Feb 45; 26753, 22 Feb 45.

[95] Interv with Marion Cullen, 27 Sep 51. In anticipation of possible difficulty with single-pin M4 tank tracks, dual-pin tracks had also been produced. Thus no delay ensued in changeover.

bat requirements. Best results could be achieved only by employing several types, each designed for a particular purpose. Smooth rubber tracks were best for fast travel over good roads; steel or rubber tracks with detachable steel grousers were best in mud; rubber chevron tracks gave the best traction on ice; on rocky terrain steel tracks lasted longer than rubber. Development could not be limited to pursuit of the ideal all-purpose track but had to be spread out over a wide field, including tracks made of steel, natural rubber, and synthetic rubber, and embodying various designs to improve traction.[96]

Flotation for Wheeled Vehicles

The major problem of World War II in providing flotation for wheeled vehicles lay in developing suitable synthetic rubber tires to replace natural rubber. This task became imperative when crude rubber imports from the Far East were cut off by the Japanese after Pearl Harbor. The ensuing shortage became so critical that only rigid conservation and rapid development of synthetic tires could stave off collapse of both civilian and military wheeled transport.[97] The vast majority of tires for military wheeled vehicles were standard commercial tires of the highest quality obtainable—whether of synthetic or natural rubber, or a mixture—and most had a modified tread to give increased traction for off-road travel. But for two particular purposes tires had to be specially designed. First, to enable combat vehicles to travel some distance after tire deflation by puncture or gun fire, tires had to have extra strong shoulders and sidewalls. And second, low-pressure, high-flotation tires had to be developed for traversing soft ground.

Combat Tires

Long before World War II the Ordnance Department had begun the search for tires proof against gun fire. Experiments in the 1930's with sponge rubber fillers inserted in standard casings and with bullet-sealing (self-sealing) tubes proved the former generally unsatisfactory. The sponge fillers, while puncture proof and impervious to small arms fire, were difficult to mount, apt to develop flat spots when a vehicle remained idle for a few days, added considerable weight, and were subject to blowouts resulting from the heat generated by the semisolid fillers.[98] Bullet-sealing tubes, on the other hand, added negligible weight and rode as well as ordinary pneumatic tires but had unreliable bullet-sealing qualities. This type of tube could seal a hole two inches long without loss of more than 60 percent of initial air pressure in the tube, but could not seal the larger holes caused by projectiles 20-mm. or larger or by small caliber bullets tearing through the tube longitudinally. Furthermore, the plastic coating inside the tube hardened at extremely low temperatures, losing its effectiveness, and under ordinary conditions the heat generated within the tire sometimes caused the plastic to flow to such an extent that the wheels became unbalanced. Despite these limitations, the Ordnance Committee in the spring of 1940 approved bullet-sealing tubes for pneumatic-tired combat vehicles. A year later changes in tube composition gave somewhat improved performance.[99] In addition to work on bullet-sealing tubes and

[96] See Handbook Ord Auto Engr, Vol. I, Sec. V, OHF.

[97] See Ch. XVIII, below.

[98] OCM 10727, 25 May 33; 12596, 16 Jan 36; 14962, 30 Mar 39.

[99] OCM 16917, 26 Jun 41. For additional informa-

modified solid rubber tires,[100] engineers in 1940 began experimenting with standard commercial pneumatic tires equipped with beadlocks, devices designed to prevent deflated tires from creeping on the rim. To use beadlocks, the tires had to be mounted on special divided rims. Since tests showed that standard tires lacked the strength to support the vehicle for more than a short distance after a road hazard or gun fire had deflated the tube, attention centered on developing tires with strengthened sidewalls and shoulders. The stronger tires with beadlock devices, called combat tires, had many more plies than a standard tire of the same size and also interliners of highest quality rubber, which added greatly to the stiffness of the tire casing. Thickness notwithstanding, combat tires when inflated had riding qualities similar to standard tires. By the spring of 1941 combat tires that could run seventy-five miles deflated had been developed. The Ordnance Committee approved limited procurement of these in May 1941 and the following October standardized combat tires with commercial heavy duty innertubes and divided rims for all combat vehicles,[101] and later for scout cars, half-tracks, and a few transport vehicles.

The American combat tire was patterned after a somewhat heavier "run-flat" tire developed by the British for their armored cars.[102] In contrast to the British rubber beadlocks, American metal beadlocks, by permitting the tube to carry more air, resulted in a lower operating temperature within the tire. Trouble with segmented beadlocks at first used on American combat tires led to design of a more rugged hinged type standardized in October 1942.[103] The run-flat advantage of the combat tire was largely offset both by the extra quantity of rubber needed in its construction and by the complexity of manufacture. During 1942 and 1943 the Ordnance Department, besides carrying out a development program for synthetic combat tires, conducted unsuccessful experiments with a tubeless combat tire and with steel restrictor rings for standard tires.[104] As a conservation measure, the Ordnance Committee in March 1943 approved construction of lower quality natural rubber combat tires and a reduction of approximately 50 percent in the original 75 mile run-flat requirement. Approval of a 40-mile run-flat requirement for all combat tires came in November 1943.[105] Tests had shown that the high operating temperature generated by synthetic sidewalls thick enough to support the vehicle over greater distances when no air was in the tube seriously restricted inflated mileage.

In the meantime, as a further rubber

tion on sponge fillers and bullet-sealing tubes see: (1) OO 400.703/11528, OO 451.92/279, OO 451.92/320, OO 451.92/346, OO 451.92/388, OO 451.92/394, and OO 472.12/3953 files, all in DRB AGO; (2) list of R&D Projects in Progress in Ind Serv, OCO, FY 1941, OHF; and (3) rpts prepared in conjunction with Aberdeen Ord Program 5229, OHF.

[100] The "zero pressure" tire tried in 1940 on a 105-mm. howitzer carriage was in effect a hollow shell of a solid rubber tire vulcanized to a steel rim. Since it was hollow, it flexed readily and gave a smoother ride and better traction than a regular solid tire, but at high speeds rapid flexing caused heat failure. (1) OCM 15940, 11 Jul 40. (2) OO 472/986 and OO 472.22/1018 files, DRB AGO.

[101] OCM 16743, 22 May 41; 17341, 16 Oct 41.

[102] During the rubber shortage the British preferred metal to synthetic rubber beadlocks that took a permanent set after they were installed. Rubber for Mechanized Warfare, OHF.

[103] OCM 19066, 22 Oct 42.

[104] (1) See Ch. XVIII, below, for conservation of rubber. (2) OCM 19004, 8 Oct 42; 19490, 23 Dec 42; 21295, 12 Aug 43; 22433, 29 Nov 43. (3) Rubber for Mechanized Warfare, OHF. (4) Lt Col Burton J. Lemon, OCO–D, Rubber, The Ordnance Story of Rubber, Its Problems and Solutions, MS, OHF.

[105] OCM 19922, 11 Mar 43; 22089, 11 Nov 43.

conservation measure, use of combat tires on certain antiaircraft artillery carriages was discontinued because, the Army Service Forces stated, "These guns are generally used outside the actual combat zone, they are usually in a semipermanent emplacement, the prime mover is not equipped with combat tires." [106] Indeed, by late 1943 the shortage of military truck tires had become so acute that sharply curtailed use of combat tires for all vehicles was considered. Two to four truck tires could be produced for every combat tire, and experience had shown that the latter, though highly desirable, was not essential.[107] Fortunately, drastic curtailment proved unnecessary, and throughout World War II large quantities of combat tires continued to roll off production lines.

High Flotation Tires

Operations in North Africa in 1942 and early 1943 proved that regular tires did not provide sufficient flotation in desert sand. Concurrently, need arose for greater flotation in muddy cross-country terrain and on beaches. Tires developed to fill these dual requirements were originally called "desert" tires. But, in as much as desert warfare ended while they were still under development, they came to be used primarily for cross-country operations, and the name gradually became "cross-country" tire.

Initial development work centered on tires for the two most important transport trucks, the 2½-ton 6x6, and the 4-ton 6x6. By January 1943 a satisfactory tire for the 2½-ton transport and amphibian DUKW had been developed, and by May one for the larger truck.[108] The design of both tires was a compromise. The mud and snow tread, which was thinner than the standard because of the larger ground contact area, gave traction in mud. The large cross section and the greater flexibility from thin sidewalls provided flotation and cooler running in hot sand. The extra plies afforded protection against rocks. These tires were operated at low pressure on sand and in mud and were reinflated by air compressors when they ran on hard roads. Because of their greater size, a single high-flotation tire was mounted on each wheel instead of dual tires on rear wheels.

High-flotation tires, like combat tires, had to be mounted on wheels with divided rims and beadlocks. The beadlocks clamped the casings to the rims to prevent creeping at low pressures. These larger tires in some cases also required vehicular modifications such as the alteration of brake drums or limitation of the spring action to prevent tire interference with cargo bodies.[109] For installation on transport ve-

[106] Memo, ASF to OCO, 28 May 43, sub: Elimination of Combat Tires on AA Gun Carriages, OO 451.92/3581, DRB AGO. See also OCM 21063, 15 Jul 43.

[107] (1) Ltr, AGF to ASF, 23 Sep 43, sub: Substitution of Standard Heavy Duty Tires for Combat Tires, Binder 1, ASF 451.92 Tires. (2) Message, WAR to Algiers, 22 Oct 43, CM-OUT 9838, and Algiers to WAR, 12 Nov 43, CM-IN 7371, cited in memo, ASF Rubber Br to ASF Dir of Rqmts, 15 Nov 43, sub: Use of Combat Tires, OO 451.92/496. (3) Ord Tech Committee Subcommittee Item R-222, 17 Nov 43, sub: Non-Combat Type Tires for all Towed, Wheeled Artillery Materiel, Incl Mobile Artillery Carriages, AA Gun Carriages, Caissons, Limbers, and Ammo Trailers Recommended, cited in 1st Ind, ASF to OCO, 18 Nov 43, OO 451.92/496. (4) 2d Ind, OCO to ASF, 28 Nov 43, sub: Use of Combat Tires, OO 451.496. (5) Memo, OCO to ASF, 4 Dec 43, sub: Combat Tires, OO 451.92/498. (6) Memo, OCO to ASF, 6 Dec 43, sub: Use of Combat Tires, OO 451.92/453. All in DRB AGO.

[108] OCM 19547, 21 Jan 43; 19817, 25 Feb 43; 20340, 6 May 43; 20580, 27 May 43.

[109] (1) OCM 21221, 5 Aug 43; 23334, 30 Mar 44. (2) Rubber for Mechanized Warfare, OHF. (3) Interv with Marion Cullen, 19 Sep 51. (4) Interv, 2 Oct 51, with Gerald S. Reinsmith, Tank and Auto Br, R&D Div.

hicles with regular wheel equipment, Ordnance engineers had to devise complicated kits containing the new tires, chains, air compressors, proper tubes, rims, beadlocks, and other equipment. Since the Ordnance Department was concerned with over-all vehicle performance, not tires alone, these so-called desert kits also contained equipment for improving engine-cooling characteristics. Unfortunately, most of the kits were still in the development stage when the Germans were defeated in North Africa, and only a few for the 2½-ton truck were available for service in that campaign.[110] Although the series of desert kits was later standardized, no widespread use was ever made of them.[111]

Interest in the tires themselves remained because, in addition to excellent flotation in sand, they offered some advantage in mud. When the end of the North African campaign shifted emphasis from tires for desert warfare to problems of mud flotation, Ordnance engineers developed a slightly different high-flotation tire for the 2½-ton truck and modified the tire for the larger truck. Both tires had a full depth tread that gave better traction and greater wear. The desert tire for the 2½-ton truck was used mainly on the DUKW.[112] For ordinary highway use the high-flotation tire had certain disadvantages. It made trucks more difficult to drive and maintain and reduced their ability to climb grades. Moreover, it required more crude rubber than a regular tire and, even if pressure were carefully regulated to match changing terrain, was less durable.

Although recognizing the drawbacks of high-flotation tires, the Ordnance Department, in response to requests from the using arms and services,[113] developed another series of kits called cross-country kits, which enabled men in the field to install these tires on transport trucks, trailers, and tractors, and to substitute larger, regular-size tires for smaller tires on certain vehicles in order to improve mud flotation.[114] Development work continued on kits for a limited number of additional vehicles.[115]

Auxiliary Flotation Devices for Artillery Carriages

The flotation difficulties encountered by wheeled artillery in European mud were intensified in jungle terrain. The Borden mission sent to the Pacific in 1943 reported that to increase the maneuverability of artillery pieces, "track-laying vehicles of low unit ground pressure and excellent grouser action must be employed as prime movers, and greater flotation must be given to the towed load by use of skid plates or other suitable means." Of field experiments with B–25 aircraft tires on the 105-mm. howitzer carriage, the mission commented:

> . . . greater ground clearance was provided, the tires did not hang up on stumps but bounced off and the stability of the carriage in firing was not impaired. However, these desirable features were measured against the casualties which would result from the use of

[110] (1) Col Lemon, Rubber, The Ordnance Story of Rubber, OHF. (2) Rubber for Mechanized Warfare, OHF.

[111] OCM 21221, 5 Aug 43.

[112] See n. 109(2), 109(3), and 109(4).

[113] For further information on the development of high-flotation tires and the downward adjustments of requests for these tires see (1) correspondence and min of mtgs filed in OO 451.92/521, OO 451.92/1998, OO 451.92/4338, OO 451.92/4549, OO 451.92/4610 and OO 451.92/4641; (2) Binders 1 and 2, ASF 451.92 Tires; (3) Engr Bd Rpt 796, Low Pressure Tires in Mud, 1 Mar 44, ASF 451.92, 1 Mar 44. All in DRB AGO.

[114] OCM 24265, 29 Jun 44, standardized a series of cross-country kits. The regular tires used were the 7.50-16 and the 14.00-20, 20 ply.

[115] OCM 25229, 28 Sep 44.

these tires which are more susceptible to deflation when hit by fragments than are combat tires, and as a result the theater did not favor introduction of these larger airplane tires.[116]

The first auxiliary flotation devices developed by the Ordnance Department were shoe plates, or skid pans, for the 105-mm. and the 155-mm. howitzer carriages.[117] These steel plates, fitted under the axle and trails of the carriages, supported the load when the wheels sank in the mud. However, the ditch-like ruts that the wheel dug in the mud often hindered prime movers that followed. To overcome this, in 1944 wooden mud sleds that fitted under the wheels were designed for the 105-mm. howitzer, lighter artillery, and certain cargo and ammunition trailers. As wooden sleds could not support the weight of the 155-mm. howitzer,[118] early in 1945 teams were rushed to the theatres to introduce steel sleds, combining less weight and more durability with sufficient strength to support greater loads.[119]

Self-Propelled Artillery

Self-propelled artillery was one of the most controversial weapons of the war. In the 1930's, when the Ordnance Department had urged the advantages of motorizing guns and howitzers, the Field Artillery had contended that towed artillery was more maneuverable, less conspicuous, less likely to be deadlined for repairs, and less expensive. In the case of the self-propelled field gun, these arguments persisted down to the summer of 1944. On the other hand, the self-propelled antitank gun or "tank destroyer" advocated by the Armored Force was accepted early in World War II. It differed from the tank in having thinner armor and an open, rather than enclosed, turret. It was therefore lighter and faster but, while giving the crew greater visibility, also gave them less protection from enemy fire. A more vulnerable vehicle than the tank, the self-propelled antitank gun was designed for hit-and-run tactics rather than for slugging it out with the enemy. Since combat demonstrated that it was valuable not only against tanks but also in support of infantry and armor, the term "tank destroyer" came to be a misnomer. The self-propelled field gun bore little resemblance to either tank or tank destroyer. The big gun dwarfed its carriage, a tank chassis without turret or inner compartment for crew. But the carriage enabled the gun to move out of action before the enemy could get the range and to get closer to the target than had hitherto been possible for heavy artillery. In the end, the using services were converted to gun motor carriages for field guns as well as for antitank guns.[120]

---

[116] Borden Rpt, Jungle Warfare Mission, Missions, Barnes file, OHF.

[117] (1) OCM 23692, 4 May 44; 25523, 30 Oct 44; 25901, 30 Nov 44. (2) WD Tech Bull 9X-44, 24 Jan 44; 9X-45 and 9X-46, 28 Jan 44; 9X-56, 18 Feb 44. (3) Files OO 473.2/237, OO 472/374, OO 428/29, and OO 472.2/229, DRB AGO. (4) Opns Div WDGS Information Bull, Vol. I, No. 7, 10 Apr 44, atchd to memo, ASF for CG ETO, 14 Apr 44, sub: Skid Pans for Field Artillery, ASF 472.2 (14 Apr 44) Opns Rpts, DRB AGO.

[118] ETO Immediate Rpt 20 (Combat Observations), 27 Dec 44, Special Collection Combat Rpts, 97-11.5 (14207), DRB AGO.

[119] (1) ASF R&D file 451.91-1945, DRB AGO. (2) OCM 23876, 18 May 44; 24421, 20 Jul 44; 25823, 23 Nov 44; 26042, 14 Dec 44. (3) Artillery Transportation Accessories: Sleds, Skis and Shoe-Plates, MS, OHF. (4) Daily Log of Activities of Mud Sled Demonstration Teams in Pacific Ocean Area and Western Pacific Area, 7 Jul–17 Aug 45, Special Collection Combat Rpts 8-5.0707/45 (17036), DRB AGO.

[120] (1) OCM 16341, 19 Dec 40. (2) PSP 46, Pt. D, Heavy Self-Propelled Artillery, pp. 5–14, OHF. (3) Cole, *The Lorraine Campaign*, pp. 603, 607. (4) Eddy Rpt, p. 49, OHF. (5) Col. John Lemp, FA, and Maj. Ernest C. Hatfield, Cav, "Tank Destroyers as Assault Guns," *Field Artillery Journal*, XXXV (1945), 244–45. (6) Lt. R. L. McNelly, FA, "Tank Destroyers at

Gun motor carriage development for World War II began in June 1940 when the Secretary of War, on the recommendation of the Board of Officers on the Development of Equipment for Armored Divisions, directed the Ordnance Department to develop a mount for the 75-mm. antitank gun and suggested the chassis of the light tank. The newly established Armored Force appended its own recommendation for the medium tank chassis, because of its capacity to carry more ammunition and a larger crew, and asked that the 105-mm. howitzer be considered as the weapon. Substitution of the howitzer—inherently support rather than antitank artillery—was comparatively easy, but the mount presented problems. The first requisite, high speed, meant light weight, but light weight meant either less carrying capacity or thinner armor. The Ordnance Department was inclined to favor a new commercial high-speed tractor and proposed using the more powerful 3-inch gun as the weapon.[121]

Offsetting the difficulty of adapting the tank chassis to this new purpose was the advantage of expediency. Eventually a faster motor carriage designed especially for self-propelled artillery was developed; in the meantime, after experimentation with wheeled carriages and half-tracks, attention centered on the medium tank chassis. By dispensing with a closed turret and reducing the armor, engineers could give the medium tank M3 or M4 the mobility and speed of a light tank, together with adequate power and room for ammunition and crew.[122] Artillery so mounted soon proved itself on the battlefield. The first to see action was the 105-mm. howitzer mounted on the medium M3 tank, rushed to the British early in 1942. Designated the M7, but called "The Priest" because of its pulpit-like machine gun platform, it helped to defeat Rommel at El Alamein. Observers were impressed by its effectiveness in getting the enemy off balance.[123] Another early weapon developed for antitank use was the 3-inch gun mounted on the medium tank M4, the motor carriage designated the M10. It was popular in North Africa and Italy.[124] To combat the thicker armor encountered in Europe, the new 90-mm. gun was mounted on the same M4 chassis. When a new light tank, the M24, became available, the 105-mm. howitzer was mounted on its chassis. For antiaircraft work, two 40-mm. guns on the M24 chassis served.[125]

The one motor carriage designed especially for self-propelled artillery was an outgrowth of tank destroyer development initiated by the War Department G–3 in

Work—Without the Book," *Field Artillery Journal*, XXXV (1945), 396–98. (7) Barnes, *op. cit.*, pp. 248–57. (8) Lt. [Col.] Lewis R. Soffer, FA, "An M12 Battalion in Combat," *Field Artillery Journal*, XXXV (1945), 29–31.

[121] (1) Ltr, TAG to CofOrd, 19 Jun 40, sub: 75-mm Self-Propelled Gun Mount, and inds, 9 Jul 40, 17 Jul 40, and 24 Aug 40, OO 472.12/6305, DRB AGO. (2) OCM 16341, 19 Dec 40.

[122] (1) Memo, WDGS G–3 for ACofS G–4, 30 Jul 41, sub: Military Characteristics for Development of New Equipment—a Self-Propelled Mount for Anti-Tank Weapons (Light Type), and ind, 17 Dec 41, OO 472.1/2349, DRB AGO. (2) OCM 16867, 19 Jun 41; 16933, 3 Jul 41; 17245, 18 Sep 41; 17294, 2 Oct 41; 17303, 9 Oct 41; 17377 and 17390, 30 Oct 41; 18098, 23 Apr 42. (3) R&D Study, 37-mm. Gun Motor Carriages, OHF.

[123] (1) OCM 18007, 2 Apr 42; 17760, 5 Feb 42. (2) Barnes Diary, 2 Aug 43, OHF. (3) PSP 46, Pt. D, App. D, pp. 47–49, OHF. (4) Barnes Rpt to Gen Devers on Mission to North Africa, p. 2, OHF. (5) *New York World Telegram*, July 21, 1943.

[124] (1) OCM 18006, 2 Apr 42; 18313, 4 Jun 42; 18597, 6 Aug 42. (2) Eddy Rpt, pp. 5, 22, 49, OHF. (3) Barnes Diary, 6 Nov 43, OHF. (4) Lt. Col. J. P. Barney, FA, "TD's Approach Maturity," *Field Artillery Journal*, XXXIV (1944), 775.

[125] (1) OCM 25812, 23 Nov 44; 23978, 1 Jun 44. (2) Barnes Diary, 13 Sep 43; 31 Jan 44; 23 Nov 44. (3) Barnes, *op. cit.*, p. 242. See also Ch. XIV, below.

1941. The objective was a very fast, lightly armored, cross-country tracked vehicle with a low silhouette; it was to be equipped with the Christie suspension. Though G–3 proposed using the 37-mm., in April 1942, following a conference between General Moore of the Army Ground Forces' Requirements Division and General Barnes of Ordnance, a 57-mm. gun was substituted. A few months later when the Tank Destroyer Center asked for the 75-mm. gun, a carriage designated the T67, mounting the larger gun, was built.[126] After tests at Aberdeen comparing this model with other types of tank destroyers, the newly established Special Armored Vehicle Board in the fall of 1942 selected the T67 as the most satisfactory. Further development brought about the substitution of one Wright radial engine for two Buick engines and the more powerful 76-mm. gun for the 75-mm. In its final form the carriage, now the T70, had the new torsion bar suspension. It was faster than any track-laying vehicle ever before produced; on level ground it could do better than 50 miles an hour. So promising was the design and so great was the demand for an effective antitank weapon, that the Army Service Forces in January 1943 ordered 1,000 T70's manufactured without extensive service tests. Testing was carried on throughout 1943 concurrently with procurement.[127]

Improvements provided better slope climbing and better performance in low gear. The T70 was standardized in April 1944 as the M18. Despite early forebodings about the thinness of its armor, it gave excellent service, especially when the 76-mm. gun was fired with tungsten carbide cored ammunition. Like the self-propelled 3-inch and 90-mm. guns, the 76-mm. often functioned as an assault gun in support of infantry and armor. Much of the credit for getting it to the battlefield belonged to Brig. Gen. Andrew D. Bruce, commander of the Tank Destroyer Center, but Ordnance engineers were justifiably proud of the M18 as one of the major artillery developments of the war.[128]

Self-propelled field guns might not have got overseas at all had the Ordnance Department not early developed a motor carriage for the 155-mm. gun and contrived its acceptance by the using services. In the spring of 1941 the Ordnance Technical Staff began development of self-propelled mounts for field guns in calibers up through 155-mm. Experiments showed that tank chassis could be successfully adapted by adding a spade to keep the vehicle steady when the gun recoiled. Ammunition and crew could be carried in an accompanying vehicle.[129] In the face of AGF opposition, it was only by persuading General Somervell to go to the Secretary of War that General Barnes got authority to manufacture a model, the M12, mounting a 1918-type 155-mm. gun. The Army Ground Forces turned down the 4.5-inch self-propelled gun, authorized only a pilot model for the 155-mm. howitzer, and anticipated no requirement during 1943 and 1944 for self-propelled field guns beyond a hundred

[126] Memo cited n. 122(1). (2) Memo, WD G–3 for G–4, 2 Dec 41, sub: Development of Gun Motor Carriage with Christie Suspension for Tank Destroyer Use, OO 472.1/3996, DRB AGO. (3) OCM 18039, 9 Apr 42; 19185, 19 Nov 42.

[127] OCM 19438, 7 Jan 43; 22918, 15 Feb 44.

[128] (1) *Ibid.* (2) Eddy Rpt, pp. 5, 63, OHF. (3) Cole, *op. cit.*, pp. 603, 607. (4) Barnes, *op. cit.*, pp. 246–47. (5) McCaskey, Role of the Army Ground Forces in the Development of Equipment, Study 34, Hist Sec, AGF, 1946, p. 65. (6) Ltr, Col Colby, Chief of Development and Engr Dept, OCO–D, to Mr. F. Gordon Barber, OCO R&D, 14 May 47 [sub: McCaskey Study], OHF.

[129] (1) Memo, Gen Somers, Chief of Tech Staff Ord, for Asst Chief of Ind Serv, Engr, 3 May 41, sub: Self-

M12's. Standardized in 1942, the M12's did not get overseas until 1944.[130] Nevertheless, successful tests of medium self-propelled field guns at Fort Knox and reports from overseas, especially of the Russians' tactics in bringing big guns out of protected positions to fire point-blank on German dugouts, impelled the Armored Board in December 1943 to recommend immediate production of gun motor carriages for medium and heavy artillery. The Army Ground Forces disapproved the recommendation pertaining to the heavy guns, but the Ordnance Department went ahead with pilot models even heavier than the M12. Thus a new 155-mm. gun, the "Long Tom," and the 8-inch howitzer mounted on M4 tank chassis were ready when demands from both European and Pacific theatres brought about authorization for procurement in July 1944.[131]

In the advance across France and through the Siegfried Line, the M12's lived up to General Barnes' expectations. General Hodges considered them invaluable. They could be brought up to within a few hundred yards of strong fortifications and blow them to pieces. Even more effective was the self-propelled Long Tom, the first gun to fire on Cologne. Gun motor carriages, by making possible the employment of heavy cannon for direct fire, introduced a tactical innovation and thus showed how technicians at times could influence tactical doctrine. By V-E Day the foresight that inspired the development of these powerful weapons and the drive that got them into combat was vindicated. By V-J Day the 8-inch gun and the 240-mm. howitzer mounted on heavy tank M26 chassis were ready for shipment to the Pacific.[132]

Propelled Mounts, OO 451/839, DRB AGO. (2) OCM 16859, 19 Jun 41; 17082, 7 Aug 41.

Airborne Equipment

When in April 1940 German paratroopers dropped from the skies into Norway, and in May landed behind Allied lines at Fort Eben Emael in Belgium, military men realized that the Russian parachute demonstrations in prewar maneuvers had inspired a new application of mobility, perhaps even a new form of warfare. Yet since soldiers minus effective weapons could have scant value in the enemy rear save as intelligence agents, in the United States search for matériel suited to parachute and glider delivery necessarily went hand-in-hand with training men and designing aircraft to employ the new technique. Paratroopers could land carrying shoulder and side arms with them, and machine guns and ammunition chests could be separately parachuted without great difficulty. Splitting the load into several parcels might even permit dropping light-weight artillery. Heavier weapons, if made to fit into aircraft, could be flown in later. But if infiltrating units could be supplied with greater mobility than their legs

[130] (1) PSP 46, Pt. D, App. A and App. D, pp. 4–15, OHF. (2) Gen G. M. Barnes, Research and Development in the Ordnance Department During the Second World War, 28 Sep 45, p. 18, OHF. (3) OCM 18584, 6 Aug 42; 18727, 27 Aug 42; 21396, 26 Aug 43. (4) Barnes Diary, 8 Mar 44, OHF. (5) Interv with H. W. Evans, 4 Apr 52. (6) Ltr, Gen Barnes to Gen Ward, 25 Jan 52, OCMH. (7) Ltr, CG AGF to CG ASF, 16 Oct 43, sub: Medium and Heavy Caliber Self-Propelled Guns, OO 472/372, DRB AGO.

[131] (1) PSP 46, Pt. D, App. C, pp. 5–89, OHF. (2) OCM 23098, 9 Mar 44; 23279, 23 Mar 44; 23482, 13 Apr 44; 23653, 27 Apr 44; 24413, 13 Jul 44; 27119, 29 Mar 45. (3) Barnes Diary, 8 Mar 44, OHF. (4) Eddy Rpt, pp. 1, 62, OHF.

[132] (1) Ltr, Gen Barnes to Gen Campbell, 6 Mar 46, sub: Rpt on Heavy Tank Mission, OHF. (2) OCM 27119, 29 Mar 45. (3) Barnes, *op. cit.*, pp. 248–57. (4) Capt. Richard W. Van Horne, FA, "Short Range Firing Against the Siegfried Line," *Field Artillery Journal*, XXXV (1945), 75.

would furnish, their fighting potential would clearly be enormously enhanced.

Airborne Tanks

With this thought in mind, the Ordnance Department in February 1941 held a conference with representatives of G–4 of the General Staff, the Armored Force, and the Air Corps to consider the possibilities of developing a special light-weight tank and an aircraft to transport and land it. Plans for Ordnance to develop the vehicle and for the Air Corps to develop the carrier took shape quickly.[133] As the Pressed Steel Car Company of Pittsburgh had already informed the British Purchasing Commission that an airplane could be obtained without major change in design to transport a 7.5-ton tank, the list of tentative military characteristics for the proposed tank included a weight limitation set at that tonnage.[134] Design studies began at once.

Of the several designs submitted, that of the Marmon-Herrington Company was considered most satisfactory. Manufacture of one pilot model, designated the T9, was approved in the fall of 1941 and followed in January 1942 by a contract for two additional pilot models.[135] In the two later pilot models changes in the original specifications led to assigning a separate designation, T9E1. In as much as experiments with the first pilot had demonstrated that an increase in weight to 7.9 tons was necessary if the tank were to retain many of the important features required, both the Army Air Forces and the British, who were also interested in airborne tanks, agreed that new models might run to that weight.[136] The first T9E1 pilot was completed in November 1942 and was sent to Aberdeen Proving Ground for various road and firing tests. The second pilot, completed shortly thereafter, was shipped to England for test.[137]

Meanwhile, ASF in April 1942 had approved quantity production of T9E1 tanks even before development and standardization were completed. Consequently, the first production models came off the line in December 1942. Extensive tests in 1943 and 1944 by Ordnance and by the Armored Board, together with flight tests in C–54's, initiated several essential changes both in new vehicles and, by field modifications, in those already produced.[138] In August 1944, after production had ceased, the T9E1 airborne tank was adopted as a limited standard vehicle and redesignated the M22. Altogether 830 had been built. Although several hundred were shipped overseas to both U.S. and Allied forces, none was used in combat. In mid-1945, with no future need contemplated, the M22 tanks were declared obsolete.[139]

This checkered career was the consequence of discovery that while the M22 tank could be satisfactorily transported in C–54's, the tank itself possessed many limitations. It had insufficient armor to withstand .50-caliber armor-piercing ammunition; its engines developed very low horsepower; its meagre gas capacity gave

[133] (1) R&D, Tanks, OHF. (2) Barnes Diary, 10 Feb 41, OHF.

[134] (1) R&D, Tanks, OHF. (2) Memo, Lt Col J. E. Upston, WDGS, to Gen Gerow, WPD, 19 Feb 41, sub: Aero Tank, War Plans Div, Folder 4308, WDGS files, DRB AGO. (3) OCM 16747, 22 Mar 41; 17087, 7 Aug 41.

[135] OCM 19545, 21 Jan 43.

[136] OCM 19773, 18 Feb 43.

[137] OCM 19871, 4 Mar 43.

[138] (1) OCM 24935, 31 Aug 44. (2) Files OO 470.8/352 and OO 470.8/782, DRB AGO. (3) AGF file, Opns Rpt.

[139] OCM 28265, 5 Jul 45.

it a limited range of operation; it carried only the light 37-mm. gun; it had too little space for cargo and crew; and it had poor over-all mechanical reliability. AGF exhibited little interest in this airborne tank not only because of these shortcomings but also because of the time consumed in getting it into action. Landing, reassembling, and driving it from the nearest airfield capable of handling C–54's to the scene of combat, perhaps as much as 100 to 200 miles, took so long that the enemy could get to the battlefield tanks with much greater fire power and armor. The airborne tanks would probably then be outnumbered.[140]

The Airborne Center in the summer of 1944 submitted to the ASF plans for an improved airborne tank to be carried inside larger planes then under development and suggested investigation of the possibility of transporting the tank suspended beneath the plane so that launching from a low-flying carrier could be made near the scene of battle. The AAF commented that the C–82 was the only plane under development probably capable of carrying the proposed tank internally. Flight range of the C–82 carrying such a tank would be limited by the reduced fuel load. Moreover, previous research had established the impracticability of launching a tank from a plane in flight, since the average loaded cargo plane had a minimum flying speed of well over 100 miles an hour and the speed the tank could attain was only 40 to 50 miles an hour. Attempts to attach a tank beneath the fuselage of a plane and then lower the tank to the ground after the plane had landed also proved unsuccessful. The Ordnance Department pointed out that a tank with the larger engine, more powerful gun, and heavier armor desired could not be built within the essential weight limitations imposed by aircraft and gliders under development. Improvement of an airborne tank would have to depend upon improving components such as infinitely variable transmission, torsion bar suspension, center guide tracks, and a new turret.[141]

Since rapid development of such an airborne tank would entail establishment of priorities that possibly would interfere with other high-priority projects, the entire matter was restudied. Since it was known that a tank could not be launched from a plane in flight, that the M22 was insufficiently armored to be employed properly in a tank role, that the largest planes under development would be unable to carry a sufficiently heavy model, and, finally, that aircraft could be used more effectively in airborne operations to transport other weapons and additional troops rather than an inadequate combat vehicle, the Airborne Center in December 1944 declared that no need existed for a special airborne tank.[142]

Nevertheless, the decision to forego development of a special airborne tank did not lessen the long-standing AGF desire for air transport of standard tanks. In the latter part of 1944 Ordnance engineers began studying the possibilities of carrying the M24 light tank in the C–82 plane, which,

[140] (1) OCM 24935, 31 Aug 44. (2) 5th Ind, Col Colby to OCO–D, 18 Oct 44, sub: Test of Airborne Tank, OO 470.8/1448 Tanks, DRB AGO. (3) Ltr, Lt Col E. Bibb, 28th Airborne Tank Battalion, to Brig Gen James G. Christiansen, WDGS, 8 Aug 44, Drawer 9980, AGF 470.8, DRB AGO.

[141] (1) Ltr, Airborne Center to ASF, 4 Jul 44, sub: Test of Airborne Tank, with attached blueprints. (2) 2d Ind, AAF to ASF, 14 Aug 44. (3) 5th Ind, OCO–D to ASF, 18 Oct 44. All in OO 470.8/1448 Tanks, DRB AGO.

[142] (1) Ltr, cited n. 141(1). (2) 9th Ind, Hq Airborne Center to Armored Center, 26 Dec 44, DRB AGO.

though still in the development stage, was designed to carry 10 tons of cargo. The solution was to use two planes, disassembling the tank so that its total weight could be distributed into equal loads of less than 10 tons, loads that the dimensions of the C–82 cargo space could accommodate. Preliminary studies showed that this could be achieved by carrying the tank hull in one load and the turret, suspension, tracks and ammunition in a second. In February 1945 the Ordnance Committee approved a complete, detailed study of means of partially disassembling and transporting the M24 and T24E1 light tanks and the self-propelled 76-mm. tank destroyer M18 in both the C–82 and the XCG–10A glider. The glider, recommended by the AGF for standardization and procurement, had cargo capacity comparable to that of the C–82. This study was to include design of equipment for dismantling and reassembling vehicles, for handling the various components, and for fastening them securely in the plane during flight.[143]

Of the two development projects set up at the tank center in Detroit, one concerned with C–82 transport and the other with glider transport of the light tank M24, the latter was the subject of marked differences of opinion within the AAF. The plan worked out by May 1945 during conference between Ordnance and AAF representatives met with AGF disapproval in June. The project for transporting the M24 in the C–82 met with more success. By June 1945 the equipment required to assemble the tank in the field had been designed and trial loadings and unloadings in a C–82 fuselage were under way. Tests showed that a five-man crew using one set of tools could unload and reassemble the tank in four hours and forty minutes or, using two sets of tools, in three and a half hours or less.[144]

Airborne Artillery

The development of light-weight, compact artillery had long been an Ordnance goal. To this aspiration the introduction of airborne operations gave new impetus, and development of artillery designed especially for air transport accordingly began in the fall of 1941. As larger cargo planes and gliders appeared, an ever-increasing variety of weapons could be flown to the battlefields. In 1943 the Ordnance Department began investigating the practicability of transporting by air all items of corps and division artillery. Tests conducted in 1943 and early in 1944 showed that the equipment for the 105-mm. howitzer, 155-mm. howitzer, and 4.5-inch gun battalions could be successfully carried in the largest available planes, the C–47, B–17, and B–24, though disassembly of some items before loading was necessary. The 155-mm. gun, 8-inch howitzer, 8-inch gun, and 240-mm. howitzer all proved too large.[145] Experimental use of aluminum and magnesium in artillery carriage components, such as wheels and trails, began in 1944 and continued after the war. The only artillery items designed specifically for air transport during World War II were the 105-mm. howitzer M3 and its carriage M3A1, the multiple 50-caliber machine gun mount M55, and the 40-mm. antiaircraft gun carriage M5.

[143] OCM 26541, 1 Feb 45; 26715, 15 Feb 45.

[144] (1) OCO–D Development Div Hist, Vol. X, 1 Jan–31 Mar 45, Ch. 6, OHF. (2) OCO–D Development Div Monthly Rpts, Feb, Mar, May, and Jun 45, Projects KG-518 and KG-519, OHF. See also ltr, OCO to ASF, 12 Jul 45, sub: Equipment for Loading Light Tank M24 in a C–82, Cargo Plane—Test by Airborne Board, and inds, OO 470.8/2205 Tanks, DRB AGO.

[145] (1) OCO Tech Div Rpt, FY 1943–44, OHF. (2) First Rpt on APG Project Ord Program, 8–12 Feb 44, OHF.

In the fall of 1941 need was felt for a 105-mm. howitzer transportable by air. Difficulty in getting the standard weapon, without disassembly, through the doorway of the cargo planes necessitated considerable change in both howitzer and carriage, a problem solved by shortening the barrel 27 inches and using the smaller 75-mm. field howitzer carriage. Howitzer and carriage were standardized in March 1943 as the M3 and M3A1, respectively. The M3 fired the same 33-pound shell as the original M2 105-mm. model, but maximum range was reduced from 12,000 yards to slightly over 7,000 yards. Yet its light weight, only 2,500 pounds for both the howitzer and its rubber-tired, high-speed carriage, made the weapon valuable not only in airborne operations but also in amphibious operations, mountain warfare, and for use over soft jungle terrain. Two completely assembled M3 105-mm. howitzers and carriages could be transported in a C-47 in contrast to only one M2 model and carriage disassembled into five major units.[146]

Equally, or perhaps even more successful was the development and production of a multiple .50-caliber gun mount and trailer for airborne operations. When paratroopers captured an enemy airfield it was of the utmost importance to set up an adequate defense immediately in order to hold the field. Against dive bombers and strafing planes, the new trailer mount M55 was invaluable. Its four heavy barreled .50-caliber machine guns in a power-operated turret were mounted on a two-wheeled trailer and could be carried in either a CG-4A glider or in a C-47 plane. The trailer was equipped with removable pneumatic-tired wheels and mechanical jacks for emplacing the mount and leveling it in firing position when the wheels were removed.[147]

To meet the need for a larger caliber automatic gun and mount that could be transported by air for use as either antitank or an antiaircraft weapon, Ordnance engineers redesigned the 40-mm. antiaircraft gun carriage M2A1. The modified carriage, standardized as the M5 in September 1943, weighed considerably less than its ground counterpart; its width was decreased to permit passage through the doorways of the C-46, C-46A, C-47, and C-54 and it rode on two pneumatic tires. The chassis consisted of a center base with one permanently attached outrigger and three removable outriggers which, along with the gun barrel, had to be removed before loading the carriage into the plane. Three men could emplace the carriage in approximately five minutes and raise it from firing to traveling position in about eight.[148]

Paracrates

For equipment to be dropped from airplanes to paratroopers or other ground forces, reducing the weight and bulk of each item solved only part of the problem. There still remained the matter of protecting the items from being damaged when they hit the ground, and to the development of protective containers for this purpose Air Forces and Ordnance engineers devoted considerable attention. They not only developed containers for dropping

[146] (1) OCM 17261, 25 Sep 41; 19910, 3 Mar 43. (2) APG Rpts on Ord Program 5824, 19 Jul 42, and Ord Program 6077, 8-12 Feb 44, OHF. (3) Hist of Rock Island Arsenal, Vol. II, 1939-December 1943. (4) Correspondence filed in AGF 472.2/105-mm. Howitzer-Rg 600, OO 472.22/181, OO 472.22/704, OO 472.22/3002, and OO 472.22/5139, all in DRB AGO.

[147] (1) OCM 22521, 30 Dec 43. (2) OCO Tech Div Rpt, FY 1944, OHF. See also Ch. XIV, below.

[148] OCM 18883, 20 Aug 42; 21099, 20 Jun 43; 21280, 9 Aug 43; 21516, 9 Sep 43.

weapons from planes but also added several new words to the English language, chief among them being "paracrate," the official name for containers that could be floated to earth by parachute, "parachest," a trunk-like container for ammunition, and "paracaisson," a small, collapsible, hand-drawn ammunition cart.[149]

The first and most important paracrates were for the 75-mm. pack howitzer, a weapon developed in the late 1920's for use in mountainous territory and later equipped with pneumatic tires for airborne use. The relatively light units into which this weapon could be broken for transport by mule pack were equally well suited to transport by airplane and drop by parachute. To protect the parts from the shock of landing, during the early months of 1942 engineers designed a series of plywood paracrates to fit each of the seven major parts of the weapon, plus a parachest to hold ten rounds of ammunition and a paracaisson to transport the ammunition after it hit the ground. The nine loads varied somewhat in weight but averaged about 300 pounds; they were floated to the ground by parachutes of different colors to aid in the identification of the loads. When tested in the fall of 1942 in actual air drops at Fort Bragg, these containers gave full protection to the weapon and suffered little damage themselves in the process. Rock Island Arsenal immediately produced fifty sets for further test by the using arms, and in June 1943, with the approval of the Field Artillery Board and the Airborne Command, the entire series was standardized.[150] When combat troops later reported difficulties in finding and reassembling all the parts of the howitzer because of their wide dispersal when dropped, a harness was designed to hold the nine packages together.

While these containers were being tested and approved, Ordnance engineers turned attention to reducing their weight and bulk, making them of some material other than plywood and redesigning them so they could be readily disassembled for shipment overseas. In September 1943 experimental paracrates of corrugated steel went to Camp Mackall in North Carolina for test. When dropped from an altitude of about 1,000 feet upon hard-baked soil they gave good protection to the weapon and withstood the shock of landing better than the plywood crates. Further, as the steel containers were held together by nuts and bolts, they could easily be shipped unassembled at a great saving of shipping space. Because of their many advantages, the steel crates eventually replaced those made of plywood. During 1945 when the scarcity of light-weight metals eased somewhat, consideration was given aluminum and magnesium paracrates, but the war ended before these lighter containers went into production.

The 75-mm. pack howitzer was by far the most important weapon for which paracrates were used, but Ordnance engineers also worked on the development of containers for a variety of other weapons from 37-mm. guns and mounts and flame throwers to 60-mm. and 81-mm. mortars and 57-mm. and 75-mm. recoilless rifles. During 1945 work continued on paracrates for larger experimental matériel and the heavy barreled .50-caliber machine gun.[151]

Trucks

Pressure of time, coupled with acute shortage of light-weight metals, precluded

[149] See Catalogue of Standard Ord Items, p. 161.

[150] (1) *Ibid.* (2) OCM 20854, 24 Jun 43. (3) Ann Rpt R&D Serv, FY 1943, p. 17.

[151] Ann Rpts R&D Serv, FY 1943, 1944, and 1945.

undertaking an elaborate program of designing special airborne trucks and focused attention on means of disassembling standard vehicles to permit their passage through the plane doorways into the narrow cargo space. The ¼-ton jeep could be easily rolled into a plane without disassembly, but the larger trucks required modifications ranging from the relatively simple removal of fenders, bumpers, and other exterior parts of the ¾-ton truck to cutting the frame of the 2½-ton truck back of the cab, splitting the vehicle into two separate units. After this operation, performed at the factory, the two units were bolted together by steel plates and the truck was then classified as an airborne vehicle. When it was to be transported by air, the steel plates were removed and the two parts of the vehicle were loaded on two C–47's. The accompanying airborne preparation kit contained a two-wheel dolly that served to support the front half of the truck while it was being loaded on the plane.[152]

If the vastly greater mobility in ground warfare that airborne operations promised was not fully realized in World War II, the potentialities of the technique for the future were nevertheless well understood. Advances in metallurgy before V-J Day were still too slight to enable engineers to design and build many types of vehicles and weapons at once sufficiently compact, light weight, and sturdy to be suited to air transport. But the research and development program mapped out embodied the hope that in the postwar period developments in airborne ordnance would keep pace with the training of troops in landing and using it.

[152] (1) OCM 20856, 24 Jun 43; 21235, 5 Aug 43; 26686, 15 Feb 45; 26917, 8 Mar 45. (2) OCO–D Development Div Hist, Vols., V, VI, VII, OHF.

CHAPTER XI

The Search for Increased Fire Power in Ground Warfare: Launchers and Fire Control

Fire power on the battlefield had a twofold mission: to destroy hostile troops and matériel, and to facilitate maneuver of friendly forces by compelling the enemy to deploy and seek shelter. To fulfill this mission effectively, fire power had to be capable of responding to the tactical requirements of combat troops from the rifleman to entire corps and armies. Although the theoretical ideal would have been a single weapon answering all those needs, no such solution was feasible up to the end of World War II. Physics, chemistry, and the other sciences involved in the design of weapons had not discovered the principles or materials to equip the individual with the fire power of heavy artillery. The ideal could only be approached through the development of weapons that narrowed the gap between the destructive effect of large-caliber guns and that of small arms. The extent to which that gap was narrowed between 1940 and 1945, and the successes and failures experienced along the way, make up the story of Ordnance research and development in the search for greater fire power in World War II.

The Scope of the Problem

Raising the fire power of American ground forces was a slow and difficult process. During the interwar years the Ordnance Department stood practically alone in exploring the data basic to the construction of improved firearms. Virtually no American in civilian life had concerned himself with investigations to resolve the numerous mysteries of ballistics, with the development of high yield-strength steels for more powerful guns, with the design of more accurate and safer fuzes, or with the composition of better military propellants and high explosives. That progress had been made in these fields, or that American know-how in the art of weapon design had survived the interwar period at all, redounds almost exclusively to the credit of the Ordnance arsenals and their laboratories.[1]

Efforts upon the outbreak of war in Europe to purchase indulgence for past sins of omission came too late. True, the sudden increase in appropriations permit-

[1] See Chapter II, above.

ted the arsenals to reopen shops and augment skeleton staffs, but the years lost could not be brought back. The emergency was too pressing, the time lag between the beginning of research and development on new matériel and its readiness for issue to troops too great to permit the diversion of limited available talent and facilities to fundamental innovations. Aside from one or two exceptions, American combat troops consequently entered the war and won their victories with basically the same types of weapons as those of World War I: the rifle, machine gun, mortar, field gun, and howitzer.

Unlike the designer of military motor vehicles, who could draw on the vast experience and technological progress of private industry in supplanting the horse with the internal combustion engine, the designer of military small arms and artillery was, in a manner of speaking, limited to breeding a better horse. His wartime efforts focused primarily on bettering the performance of existing weapons and adapting them to novel tactical requirements. Amphibious, jungle, and airborne operations, improved protective characteristics of potential targets such as the high speed and thick armor of modern tanks, demanded not only lighter weight and greater mobility, but also greater hitting power, greater accuracy, and higher rates of fire than ever before.

Serious problems arose at every step toward those goals, and the solution of one difficulty immediately begot a host of others. Gun metallurgy, for example, made tremendous strides in developing better steels. Whereas prewar cannon steel had an elastic limit of roughly 60,000 pounds per square inch, some steels developed during the war had a limit of 160,000 pounds.[2] But translating that progress into more powerful guns presupposed the development of more powerful propellants with decreased erosion, flash, and smoke characteristics. And the higher initial velocities of projectiles attainable with these propellants in turn posed complex problems in connection with rotating bands, clearance and crimping of cartridge cases, and twist and form of tube rifling. These were but some of the hurdles in interior ballistics, that part of the science dealing with the motion of projectiles concerned with their behavior while still in the gun. Equally complex problems, discussed later,[3] presented themselves in exterior and terminal ballistics, realms of science dealing with the motion of the projectile after it leaves the muzzle and its behavior upon impact on the target.[4]

World War II marked the first time in history that American troops were equipped with a complete line of all required types of weapons, from side arms to the heaviest artillery piece. Not all these weapons were actually new developments; many of the best known, such as the 75-mm. and the 155-mm. guns, had been adapted from foreign designs. But unlike their fathers in World War I, U.S. troops between 1941 and 1945 were never dependent on foreign matériel. Thanks largely to the farsightedness of the Westervelt Board of 1919, modern versions of all but three large-caliber weapons—the 120-mm. antiaircraft and 8-inch field guns and the 240-mm. howitzer, all completed

[2] Barnes, *Weapons of World War II*, p. 231.

[3] See Ch. XII, below.

[4] For explanation of the theory and application of interior, exterior, and terminal ballistics see, Maj. Gen. Thomas J. Hayes, *Elements of Ordnance* (New York, 1938).

early in the war—stood ready by the time of Pearl Harbor.[5]

Until America's enemies and theatres of operations were actually known, the required characteristics of weapons were of necessity determined largely by guess. Development after 7 December 1941 therefore became a hectic race against the clock to adapt rifles, guns, and howitzers to service in arctic cold, desert heat, and jungle moisture, and at the same time to keep their performance abreast of an enemy as technically competent as the Germans. The task was so great and so intricate that even its most significant aspects can merely be touched upon in these pages.

Increasing Muzzle Velocities

Perhaps the best-known and most urgent phase in the development of greater fire power was the quest for increased muzzle velocities. Muzzle velocity, the speed with which the projectile leaves the bore of a gun, was important primarily in direct-fire weapons such as field guns and tank and antitank guns, because it determined range, flatness of trajectory, and penetrating power of the projectile. In indirect- or plunging-fire weapons such as howitzers and mortars, on the other hand, it controlled largely range alone.

The muzzle velocity of a given gun could be stepped up in several ways. The tube might be lengthened, the projectile made lighter, the propellant charge increased, or more powerful powder employed. Each method had its drawbacks. Lengthening the tube, for example, meant unbalancing the piece and limiting its mobility, as was illustrated by the superlong cannon of the German Tiger II and Panther tanks which, for all their power, seriously handicapped the vehicles in crossing ditches or passing through towns and forests.[6] Again, an increased or more powerful propellant charge built up greater gas pressure that might rupture the tube unless its walls were thickened or made of stronger steel.

While gun designers based many new weapons on existing ones or their components in order to permit quantity production in the shortest time possible, they obtained improved performance, as well as the weight savings required by mobile warfare, by use of new and better materials. The story of the 76-mm. tank gun was a case in point. As soon as events in North Africa indicated the need for a gun of greater power and penetrating ability than the 75-mm. gun M3 of the Sherman tank, Ordnance engineers began work on just such a weapon. If the new cannon were to reach the battlefield quickly and in quantity, it would have to fit into the tank without major modifications to turret or mounts and at the same time obviate need for the lengthy process of developing new ammunition. Taking the existing 3-inch armor-piercing round as their starting point, Ordnance engineers designed around it a new high-velocity weapon made of high-quality steel. The whole development process was incredibly short. The project was initiated on 20 August 1942 and the completed gun, designated the 76-mm. M1, was standardized on 10 September, less than a month later. That same autumn, eighty of the new guns were produced and ready for

[5] (1) Col. William R. Gerhardt, "Artillery Materiel Research and Development," *Journal of Applied Physics,* XVI, 12 (1945), pp. 757–58. (2) Barnes, *Weapons of World War II,* p. 113.

[6] (1) Observations on Armored Tactics, 25 May 45, SAIC/23, OCMH. (2) OI-SIR/34, OCMH.

installation.[7] Compared with the 75-mm. gun M3, the 76-mm. gun M1 weighed roughly 300 pounds more, but attained a muzzle velocity approximately 600 feet per second higher firing armor-piercing ammunition and almost 1,300 feet per second higher firing high-explosive ammunition. Realizing that still heavier guns would be required to insure American superiority on the battlefield, General Barnes in September 1942 ordered the initiation of a project adapting the high-powered 90-mm. antiaircraft gun to use in combat vehicles. Design of the 90-mm. tank gun T7 was completed in December of the same year, but neither the 76-mm. nor the 90-mm. weapons were destined to see action until the autumn of 1944.[8]

Despite the urgent representation of Ordnance officers, all efforts to get the high-powered tank guns to the front failed. In the case of the 76-mm. gun, for example, the first production weapon mounted in a tank was successfully fired from a pilot tank in September 1942, but in November the Armored Force recommended that quantity production be deferred until it had thoroughly tested several pilot models and determined their tactical suitability. The Ordnance Department was specifically instructed to limit procurement to twelve Sherman tanks mounting the 76-mm. gun. Shortly thereafter the entire project was dropped and was not revived until the following spring when the Army Ground Forces approved the diversion of enough tanks mounting the new gun to equip one company. As a result of these and similar delays, the first production tanks equipped with the 76-mm. gun were not completed until January 1944. Almost identical circumstances kept the 90-mm. weapon off the battlefield. Until autumn of 1943 all attempts to interest the Army Ground Forces in the weapon were unsuccessful. As a result, the 90-mm. gun motor carriage M36, the first vehicle to mount the cannon, was not standardized until June 1944, and in July General Dwight D. Eisenhower had to send Brig. Gen. Joseph A. Holly, the chief of his Armored Fighting Vehicles and Weapons Section, to the United States to expedite getting the best American armor-piercing gun to the troops.[9]

The Army Ground Forces objected in particular to what they believed was a trend toward making guns bigger instead of better. In connection with an Ordnance proposal to mount a 105-mm. on a projected tank, for example, the AGF stated:

> . . . in our army we are using an increase in mass of the projectile rather than velocity to secure improved penetrative ability. This condition is intolerable and must be corrected at the earliest possible date through the use of cannon specifically designed for use in tanks and gun motor carriages and by the use of new propellants which will furnish very high velocities with greatly reduced smoke and flash as compared to present propellants. The deficiencies in the penetrative power of our present 75mm, 76mm and 90mm guns as compared to comparable German cannon is a matter of grave concern to our Ground Force commanders and this headquarters . . . .[10]

So far as penetrative power was concerned,

---

[7] (1) Interv, 14 Nov 51, with Paul M. Netzer, Cannon Sec, R&D Div. 14 Nov 51. (2) OCM 18650, 20 Aug 42; 18865, 10 Sep 42. (3) Catalogue of Standard Ord Items (2d ed, 1944), pp. 197–98.

[8] (1) TM 9-2300, pp. 39, 45. (2) Memo, Gen Barnes for Gen Campbell, 11 Oct 44, sub: Hist of Tank Guns, OHF.

[9] (1) Barnes MS, Tank Development, OHF. (2) Memo, Barnes for Campbell, cited above, n. 6(2). (3) Ltr, Gen Campbell to Gen Harmon, 21 Mar 45, OHF. (4) Ltr, Col Colby to Mr. F. Gordon Barber, 14 May 47, OHF. (5) Final Hist Rpt, AFV and Weapons Sec, Hq ETOUSA, MS, n.d., OCMH.

[10] Ltr, CG AGF to CG ASF, 30 Jan 45, sub: Heavy Tanks T29 and T30, photostat in OHF.

the problem was far less one of muzzle velocity than one of production limitations. For when firing the most powerful ammunition, tungsten-carbide core, the most powerful German tank gun—the 8.8 cm. *Kw. K. 43 (L/71)* of the Tiger II or Royal Tiger—and the U.S. 90-mm. gun M3—of the gun motor carriage M36 and the Pershing tank—had almost identical velocities: the German gun attained 3,240 and the American 3,350 feet per second. German no less than American ballisticians and designers were aware that increasing the muzzle velocity and penetrative power of a given weapon beyond a certain point created problems such as excessive erosion, as well as a need for longer tubes, chambers, and cartridge cases, but did not produce a greater effect beyond the projectile's point of impact. The Germans, too, therefore chose the quicker and more reliable course of using a bigger gun when they wanted a greater destructive effect. German vehicle armament such as the 128-mm. cannon of the *Jagdtiger* or tank-destroyer version of the Tiger II, as well as the 150-mm. weapons under development for superheavy tanks such as the 180-ton *Maus,* which was almost completed by the end of the war, gave ample evidence of the definite tendency toward bigness.[11]

Perhaps the best illustration of the limited usefulness of hypervelocities and extraordinary penetrating power were the experiments with tapered bore weapons. In these, the projectile was squeezed to a smaller diameter as it traveled from the breech to the muzzle. Presenting a large cross-sectional area to the powder gases and a small cross-sectional area to the air, the projectile attained high velocity while encountering little air resistance. American experiments in the application of this principle indicated that cylindrical bore artillery employing special projectiles served every purpose of tapered bore guns and at the same time avoided intricate machining problems. The Germans, after diverting plant facilities for the actual production of three sizes of tapered bore anti-tank guns, eventually came to the same conclusion and dropped the project. Although light in weight and capable of good armor penetration, the guns were difficult to manufacture, had a limited effective range because of rapidly decreasing velocity, wore out after about 1,000 rounds, and caused little serious damage after the small projectile cores had penetrated the tank armor.[12]

Rocket Launchers

Another important phase in the Ordnance Department's quest for greater fire power began when tactical developments abroad demonstrated the urgent need for hand and shoulder weapons of so radically improved performance as to exceed the limitations of conventional design. Even before the attack on Pearl Harbor, the fighting in Europe and North Africa showed that currently used small arms were incapable of defeating modern armor. American designers who meanwhile were developing small-size missiles that, by embodying the shaped-charge principle, would penetrate great thicknesses of steel plate, likewise failed when they tried to launch them. The recoil in-

[11] (1) TM 9-2300, p. 45. (2) *Heereswaffenamt Handbuch, Blatt G241,* GMDS DRB AGO. (3) Illustrated Record of German Army Equipment 1939–1945, Vol. III, compiled by The War Office, London (1947), pp. 7–9, 36–40, OCMH. (4) Interrogation of Col Friedrich Geist, former Chief of Development Br, Tech Dept, Speer Ministry, 4 Aug 45, OHF.

[12] (1) Simon, *German Research in World War II,* p. 189. (2) G. B. Jarrett, Achtung Panzer: The Story of German Tanks, 1948, MS, photostat, OHF.

duced in weapons based on the conventional principle of internal combustion severely damaged the launching device even when it rested on the ground; firing it from the shoulder was obviously out of the question. The search for a practicable means of getting a shaped-charge missile on its way to the target finally ended when recourse to rocket propulsion eliminated recoil altogether. The launching device, the bazooka, was merely a tube, open at both ends, that fired an electrically triggered rocket. While the new weapon had less accuracy and range than a rifle or machine gun, it lent the individual soldier hitting power heretofore possible only with artillery guns.

Although the most difficult problem in the development of the bazooka centered on its propulsion, several significant modifications to the launcher itself proved necessary during the course of the war. Thus, when reports from the field began pouring in late in 1942, a number of changes were introduced—a web sling to facilitate carrying, a shield to protect the face of the soldier firing the launcher, and a correction to ensure contact between the launcher and the band on the rocket. A trigger-operated magnet replaced the batteries powering the firing mechanism of the first models. The new device, relatively impervious to extremes of temperature and dampness, facilitated field maintenance and supply, particularly in the tropics where fungus tended to corrode and affect electrical connections. Wire-wrapping the launcher tube to give greater strength and eliminating the contactor box constituted modifications marked enough to require by July 1943 a new model designation, the M1A1.[13] More drastic changes followed almost at once when the Commanding General, Airborne Command, requested a model that could be taken apart and carried in two approximately equal loads for paratroop use. The using arms also asked for a better sight, addition of a safety switch, improved shape of a two-position stock, and other lesser modifications. These were incorporated in the rocket launcher standardized in October 1943 as the M9. In the last model standardized before the war ended, weight was reduced more than five pounds by making the tube of aluminum instead of steel. This, the M18, never got to the front.[14]

Despite the simplicity of the rocket launcher as compared to a rifle, machine gun, or conventional artillery piece, the bazooka's development again illustrates the fact, familiar to every designer, that one desired change usually entails a host of other changes. The two-piece bazooka soon showed weakness in the coupling ring by which the two lengths of the launcher tube were screwed together; much sturdier forged coupling components then had to replace the original ring. Substitution of the mechanical electric firing mechanism for the batteries solved some problems only to create others when pronounced deviations in performance appeared in the field. To cope with this situation the Department had to procure testers enabling Ordnance units in the theatres quickly to determine whether or not the electric firing mechanisms were functioning. The testers in turn required modifications as faults showed up.[15] The noteworthy feature of this story of constant redesign is that production of the bazooka continued uninterrupted,

---

[13] (1) OCM 19696, 11 Feb 43; 19800, 25 Feb 43; 21203, 5 Aug 43.

[14] OCM 21882, 21 Oct 43; 25894, 30 Nov 44; 26985, 15 Mar 45; 27497, 3 May 45; 27761, 24 May 45.

[15] OCM 23408, 6 Apr 44; 24922, 31 Aug 44.

MULTIPLE ROCKET LAUNCHER T34 *mounted on a Sherman tank.*

and, imperfections notwithstanding, Allied troops in all parts of the world used it with great effectiveness.

Despite the wartime progress in rocket development, many unsolved problems remained. Neither shoulder weapons such as the bazooka nor multiple launchers such as the 4.5-inch T34, a sixty-tube cluster fired from the Sherman tank, were very accurate. Their primary value lay, in the first instance, in giving the foot soldier for the first time in history the equivalent of hand-carried artillery powerful enough to stop tanks, and in the second instance, in providing a ground weapon that could quickly cover an area with a hail of fire. Compared with conventional artillery, their only unquestioned advantage was the low cost of the simply made launching device. Otherwise, their inaccuracy made rocket weapons a poor substitute for artillery.[16] That the enemy experienced similar difficulties is evidenced by the comment of a German general who, when asked his views on the *Panzerschreck,* the counterpart of the bazooka, replied: *"Faute de mieux, on se couche avec sa femme."*[17]

Recoilless Rifles

The last year of World War II saw the introduction of two new weapons with many of the advantages but substantially fewer disadvantages than those of rockets: the 57-mm. and 75-mm. recoilless rifles. Both fired regular artillery-type shells at velocities and with an accuracy comparable with those of standard guns, but entirely without recoil. Both were light

[16] Barnes, *Weapons of World War II,* pp. 48–49, 177.

[17] Observations of Armor Employment, SAIC/17, 24 May 45, OCMH.

enough to be hand-carried into action. The 75-mm. model could be fired from the standard tripod of the .30-caliber machine gun; the 57-mm. rifle weighed a mere 44 pounds and was readily fired from the shoulder or from a combination bipod-monopod.[18]

Development of the recoilless rifles took an amazingly short time. Early in 1943 the Small Arms Division of the Research and Development Service commenced a study of the principles involved, and shortly thereafter directed Frankford Arsenal Laboratory to make a detailed analysis. With help from data on foreign nonrecoil guns, derived primarily from German specimens captured in North Africa, and a complete computation of interior ballistics, the whole basic theory of the projected weapons was worked out and the first pilot model completed on 27 July. Test results from the pilot formed the basis for designing the weapon proper, and in October the first gun was completed. Designated Rifle, Recoilless, 57-mm., T15E1, the weapon was successfully proof-fired at Aberdeen Proving Ground between 8 and 10 November. Design of the 75-mm. version began in March 1944 and the first pilot was completed and fired that September.[19]

The principle of the recoilless feature was relatively simple. A perforated cartridge case allowed a portion of the propellent gases to escape to the rear through vents in the breech. Pre-engraved rather than solid driving bands on the projectile obviated problems of engraving pressures and contributed to the smooth functioning of the rifle. Anyone doubting its performance could put a glassful of water on the tube and fire without spilling a drop.

Reports from users overseas were enthusiastic. Both in the Pacific and in the European theatres the 57-mm. and 75-mm. recoilless rifles proved highly effective against point targets such as tanks and pillboxes. Airborne troops, who at last had a really light-weight, high-powered weapon for their specialized missions, testified, "The effective range of the [75-mm. recoilless] gun for direct fire is the range of visibility. It is as accurate as an M1 rifle and you can hit a tank any place you desire. . . ."[20]

Very Heavy Artillery: "Little David"

But while the mobility of modern armies gave rise to the development of powerful, close-support weapons such as the bazooka and the recoilless rifle, it well-nigh doomed to extinction those types of artillery that by their very size and weight were ill-adapted to overseas shipment as well as to high-speed, cross-country warfare. In the age of attack and heavy bombing aviation, airborne operations, and, finally, supersonic rockets and guided missiles, the siege howitzer and superrange gun were both too vulnerable and too limited in usefulness to warrant the man-hours and materials that went into making and operating them. Although the Germans devoted untold efforts to the design and construction of large-caliber railway mounts and oversized mortars, these monsters made little else than good news copy. The 80-cm. "Gustav," for example, a railway gun firing a 16,540-pound projectile over a range of over 29 miles (51,400 yards), required a complement of some 40 separate cars,

[18] TM 9-2300, pp. 84–87.

[19] Design, Development and Production of 57-mm. Rifle, T15E3, 75-mm. Rifle, T25, PSP 78, May 1945, OHF.

[20] (1) Excerpt from Observer's Rpt 71 [ETO], n.d., in Press Release folder, OHF. (2) Barnes, *Weapons of World War II,* p. 52.

75-MM. RECOILLESS RIFLE M20, AND THE "LITTLE DAVID" 914-MM. MORTAR T1, *above and below, respectively.*

could move only on double-track lines, and took 45 minutes just for the loading of a single round. Its performance at Sevastopol and Leningrad was disappointing.[21]

The Ordnance Department developed only one superheavy weapon, the 914-mm. mortar T1, "Little David." For sheer size, it topped anything even the Germans had ever attempted. Comprising two major assemblies, the tube and base, it weighed 172,900 pounds. Despite the necessity of using two powerful tractors to tow tube and base, officers of Research and Development Service quaintly pronounced this giant "highly mobile." Its projectile weighed 3,650 pounds, including 1,589 pounds of high explosive, and was fired by a maximum propelling charge of 218 pounds of powder. Its range was roughly 9,000 yards. Five men were needed to load the propelling charge, two to ram the projectile into the muzzle, and two equipped with hand brushes had to crawl into the bore to clean it.

Development on Little David began in March 1944 as the result of a requirement for a new weapon to destroy partially buried, reinforced-concrete works that the Army expected to meet in the ETO. By 31 October the tube and base section of the first pilot had arrived at Aberdeen. Subsequent test firings revealed the need for several modifications in the base components and the method of emplacement because of the severe shock of firing and the heavy recoil. Following numerous test firings and further changes of tube, base, and ammunition, the weapon was demonstrated to General Marshall, General Somervell, and other high-ranking officers on 16 July 1945. The end of hostilities soon after canceled plans for shipping the weapon to the Pacific and prevented the use of Little David in combat.[22]

Fire Control

Since the most efficient performance of a weapon in firing its projectiles is useless if fire is so faultily directed as to miss the target, one of the most important Ordnance efforts to provide Allied forces with greater fire power was to obtain more accurate fire control. Devices for observing targets and aiming weapons had been under study and development by Ordnance engineers for many decades before 1941, but World War II brought a need for a wide variety of new and improved fire control instruments both for antiaircraft batteries and for firing at fast-moving ground targets such as tanks and trucks.[23] The basic principles of fire control instruments used in World War II were the same as those of World War I, but after 1940 Ordnance engineers worked steadily toward increasing the accuracy and range of fire control matériel, reducing the work required of gun crews, providing illumination for night firing, and designing instruments that would be light enough for easy transport and yet strong enough to withstand rough handling. In addition, Ordnance engineers were constantly faced with the necessity of designing instruments that, although built with the precision of a fine watch, could be speedily mass produced with minimum use of skilled manpower and strategic materials.[24]

The term "fire control instruments"

---

[21] (1) Simon, *op. cit.*, pp. 190-91. (2) Guderian, *Erinnerungen eines Soldaten*, pp. 271-72. (3) MS # T-111, Sec. B15 (Leeb). (4) TM-E 30-451, Handbook on German Military Forces, VII-53, OCMH.

[22] Record of Army Ord R&D, 914-mm. Mortar M1, n.d., OHF.

[23] See: (1) Ch. XIV, below; (2) Crowell, *America's Munitions, 1917-1918,* Book I, Ch. 6; and (3) *The Ordnance Sergeant*, IV, 2 (1942).

[24] The Research and Development Service in 1944 prepared a four-volume detailed and comprehensive

covers a large number of items, ranging from the simple iron sights on a .30-caliber rifle to the complicated instruments employed in directing a large artillery piece at an unseen target many miles away. It includes both "on-carriage" and "off-carriage" equipment, the former consisting chiefly of such instruments as sighting telescopes and elevation quadrants, and the latter including range finders, binoculars, observation telescopes, compasses, and plotting boards. A mere listing of all the fire control instruments used in World War II, with model numbers and modifications, would fill a small book. Discussion here can cover only the general principles guiding the research and development work on a few representative classes.[25]

Telescopes and Binoculars

At the start of World War II Ordnance designers of telescopes and binoculars were seriously handicapped by a lack of domestic production of many types of optical glass. Before 1941 the United States had imported from Germany types not made in America, but the outbreak of war abruptly cut off this source of supply. As a result, Ordnance designers did not have a free hand in developing instruments embodying the most advanced scientific principles since they could use only the types of optical glass that the United States glass industry could produce in quantity. In 1940 only five standard types could be used, and not until 1944 was a wide range of glasses available.[26] Not only the Ordnance Department but also the Navy, the Army Air Forces, and other branches of the service were keenly interested in sighting, aiming, and photographic equipment. In many instances the development and production problems of all services were closely related. As none of the military agencies had adequate facilities and sufficient trained personnel to carry on singlehanded the research required for an aggressive development program, they all turned for assistance to leading manufacturers of optical instruments and to university laboratories. In this process the National Defense Research Committee and other government agencies performed invaluable service in co-ordinating and directing a large share of the essential research.[27]

The fact that each caliber of gun posed special problems for the designers of fire control matériel was another major influence on Ordnance research and development in this field. No matter what efforts were made at standardization, sighting and aiming equipment, particularly telescope reticles, had to be tailored to fit the individual weapon and its ammunition. Not only did each caliber require a special telescope, but each telescope required a special mount, and in many cases Ordnance engineers devoted as much effort to the design of the mount as to the design of the telescope itself. The mount had to hold the telescope in exactly the right position in relation to the gun tube and the control gears, and had to provide for carefully

history of the development of fire control instruments. (Development of Fire Control for Antiaircraft Artillery, 4 vols., OHF.) These volumes contain countless references to pertinent documents and are illustrated with hundreds of photographs of all types of fire control instruments. There are also a brief history of the Frankford Arsenal Fire Control Design Division and a comprehensive study of the production and procurement of fire control matériel in the Ordnance Historical files.

[25] See *Ordnance Sergeant, op. cit.*

[26] Interv, Oct 51, with John E. Darr, Jr., Chief of FA Fire Control Br, R&D Serv.

[27] Div 16, NDRC, *Optical Instruments,* Vol. I (Washington, 1946).

regulated movement of the telescope over a wide range of vision. Since nearly every new design or major modification in weapons and ammunition demanded some change in the sighting and aiming apparatus, the development of fire control instruments and mounts was a never-ending process.

In designing telescopes to meet the requirements of the using arms, Ordnance engineers frequently found themselves faced with the task of reconciling the irreconcilable. Three of the fundamental characteristics of a telescope—degree of magnification, extent of the field of view, and size or complexity of the instrument—were so interrelated that a gain in one characteristic usually meant a loss in one or both of the others. Greater magnification could be achieved only at the cost of decreasing the field of view unless additional elements were used and the telescope was made bulkier and heavier. Similarly, the field of view could not be widened without sacrificing magnification or enlarging the instrument. Because it was impossible to design a telescope that was at one and the same time small in size, powerful in magnification, and broad in its field of view, Ordnance designers had to evaluate the importance of each of these characteristics in terms of the purpose for which each telescope was intended and then adopt the most acceptable compromise.

As weapons with greater recoil, such as the 3-inch gun, came into more general use, need arose for telescopes with a longer "eye distance," the distance between the observer's eye and the eyepiece of the telescope. This introduced another set of irreconcilable factors. When, for example, the Tank Destroyer Board requested a 3-power direct-sighting telescope with an eye distance of eight inches for use with the 3-inch gun motor carriage, the Ordnance Department had to report that telescopes built to these specifications would result in such a restricted field of view, such a small exit pupil, or such a large instrument that none would be acceptable. A close approximation to the desires of the Tank Destroyer Board was achieved in the spring of 1943 with the T108, a 3-power telescope with an eye distance of 6.5 inches. A novel feature of this instrument was its use of plastic rather than glass optics. Although the Tank Destroyer Board received the T108 enthusiastically, the Ordnance Department recommended that it be given only limited procurement status until further experience with plastic optics under field conditions had been gained. When produced with glass optics, this telescope was standardized in the spring of 1944 as the M79C.[28]

The straight tube telescope was one of the most extensively used instruments for the control of direct fire, but it had certain disadvantages, chief of which was that the gunner in sighting had to stand behind the gun where he might be in the way of other members of the gun crew. This drawback was eliminated by the use of a more complicated instrument, the elbow telescope, which permitted the gunner to stand to one side of the gun. With the exception of its roof prism, which bent the light rays at a right angle, the optical characteristics of the elbow telescope resembled those of the straight telescope and followed the same course of development. Roof prisms, however, were difficult to manufacture in

[28] (1) Fire Control for FA and Inf Weapons, pp. 111–18, OHF. (2) OCM 23542, 20 Apr 44; 23923, 25 May 44. For a discussion of the use of plastic optics in telescopes during the war see *Optical Instruments*, Vol. I, Ch. 8.

quantity, and during 1942 production lagged behind military requirements. To meet this exigency Frankford Arsenal in the fall of 1942 constructed an experimental telescope with an inverting prism but, by the time it had been tested and found satisfactory by the using arms, production on the roof prism instruments had caught up with demand. The remarkable increase in the roof prism production rate resulted from the co-operative efforts of the NDRC, the Bureau of Standards, and the Ordnance Department in developing a method for using grinding machines to perform a large part of the work formerly done by hand by skilled craftsmen.[29]

The panoramic telescope was far more complicated than either the straight tube or elbow telescope, and to improvement of its design Ordnance engineers devoted a large share of their efforts. The panoramic telescope combined a telescope and periscope so that the observer, without exposing himself or changing his position, could see in any direction. It could be used to lay the weapon in direction for indirect fire or to sight for direct fire. At the start of World War II the standard panoramic telescope was the M12, adopted in August 1940 to replace the M1917, which had been in general use since World War I.[30] It incorporated improvements in optical design and manufacturing methods that had been made during the interwar years. The M12 originally had a reticle similar to that of the M1917, with horizontal and vertical crosslines and a mil scale on the horizontal line but, as this was not suitable for direct fire against moving targets, it was replaced on medium artillery weapons by a grid-type reticle with vertical lines to measure lead and horizontal lines to measure range. This reticle enabled one man to aim the gun quickly at a moving target, but as a rule the panoramic telescope was used only for laying the gun in direction while a quadrant was used for laying it in elevation for indirect fire against a distant, stationary target.[31]

In 1940, when the task of supplying the expanding Army with thousands of binoculars suddenly loomed large, the standard military binocular was the Type EE, a World War I instrument. The inadequacies of the "Double E" binocular had been recognized as early as 1921 when responsibility for development of binoculars had been transferred from the Signal Corps to Ordnance, but no substantial progress had been made during the peace years toward designing a new binocular or modifying Double E to make it waterproof and shock resistant.[32] To meet the urgent supply requirements established in 1940, the Ordnance Department was forced to supplement existing stocks of Type EE by purchasing binoculars of commercial design that could be speedily produced by the optical industry. To avoid the delay involved in developing, testing, and setting up production facilities for a new design, a Bausch and Lomb binocular with approximately the same military characteristics as the Type EE was standardized in November 1940 as the M3, and others of the same type manufactured by other companies were later standardized under different model numbers.[33] After

[29] (1) Fire Control for FA and Inf Weapons, pp. 91–105, OHF. (2) *Optical Instruments*, Vol. I, pp. 394–406.

[30] OCM 16005, 8 Aug 40, approved in OCM 16045, 29 Aug 40, standardized the M12 and reclassified the M5, a modified version of the M1917, as substitute standard.

[31] Fire Control for FA and Inf Weapons, pp. 16–67, OHF.

[32] OCM 1376, 8 Apr 21.

[33] (1) OCM 16247, 17 Nov 40; 16278, 22 Nov 40. (2) Fire Control Materiel, Procurement and Produc-

thousands of M3-type binoculars had been issued, reports came in from overseas observers describing the disastrous effect on these instruments of unavoidable rough handling, submersion in water during landing operations, and exposure to extremes of temperature. The M3 was then redesigned to make it stronger and more nearly waterproof, and, at the same time, the laboratory at Frankford Arsenal developed a new compound, capable of withstanding extremely high and low temperatures, for sealing the optical lenses to the metal cells. To prevent the condensation of moisture on the optical elements within the binoculars, a small amount of silica gel was placed in each to absorb whatever moisture penetrated the casing. The new model was standardized early in 1943 as the M13 and continued, with only minor modifications, as the standard military binocular for the rest of the war.[34]

Another widely used instrument for spotting targets and observing the effects of artillery fire was the battery commander's telescope, commonly called the BC scope. During World War I, and for many years thereafter, the standard BC scope was the M1915, a 10-power binocular with a very narrow field of view. Various attempts were made to widen the field, provide illumination for the reticle, and make other modifications in this instrument during the 1920's and 1930's, but it was not until 1935 that the Field Artillery Board, after summarizing the deficiencies of the M1915, called for the development of an entirely new instrument. The field of view of the M1915, the board pointed out, was so small that, when observation of fire was made, many rounds fell outside its field. In addition, its light-transmitting power was low and its angle-measuring system inaccurate and hard to keep in adjustment.[35]

Nearly seven years elapsed before a newly designed BC scope was ready for test early in 1942. The new instrument had a larger field of view, better light-transmitting qualities, an improved reticle, and other advantages. Although the Field Artillery Board found it superior in many respects to the M1915, it also found the new instrument inaccurate in the measurement of angles, largely because, by specification, it was designed for use by an observer wearing a gas mask. When the Field Artillery Board dropped this requirement, the telescope was modified to correct its inaccuracies and was standardized as the M65 early in 1943. While this work was in progress, the M1917, a telescope of French manufacture similar to the M1915 but of higher power, was provided with an instrument light and adopted as substitute standard.[36]

Range Finders

In the development of range finders for use with field artillery and heavy infantry weapons, Ordnance engineers faced many of the same problems encountered with telescopes and binoculars. Since range finders operate on the principle of measuring the acute angle of a right-angled trian-

tion of Binoculars, Foreword, PSP 33, OHF. The M3, M8, and M9 were essentially the same, but their parts were not interchangeable because they were made by different companies.

[34] (1) OCM 20063, 1 Mar 43; 20307, 29 Apr 43. (2) TM 9-1580, Mar 45.

[35] Fire Control for FA and Inf Weapons, pp. 286–98, OHF.

[36] OCM 19755 standardized the M65, and OCM 18934 made the M1917 substitute standard. When it was found that the M1917's in stock had been made by four different manufacturers and were not identical they were redesignated M1917B1, M1917B2, M1917B3, and B1917B4. OCM 19219, 19 Nov 42.

gle that has the range finder as its base and the target as its apex, the accuracy and effective range of the instrument depend in large measure on the length of the range finder and its degree of magnification. A range finder with a tube 30 inches long obviously has more limited potentialities than does one 30 feet long. Large range finders could be installed at fixed installations such as seacoast artillery batteries, but, for an army on the move, the range finder had to be small, usually not more than one meter in length, and easily transported. The smaller range finders, moreover, had to be rugged enough to maintain their precise optical arrangements intact under rough handling.[37]

The standard Field Artillery range finder of World War I was the one-meter M1916, an inverted-image, coincidence-type instrument that measured ranges from 400 yards to 20,000 yards. With slight modifications this instrument remained standard for the next twenty years, although Ordnance and the Field Artillery both saw the need for a range finder that would be lighter, more rugged, less visible, and better adapted for quantity production. Late in 1939 work on three improved experimental models was begun, but none proved markedly superior to the M1916. Finally, in the summer of 1942 samples of one-meter range finders being produced in Canada for the British Army were procured for test by the fire control laboratory at Frankford Arsenal and by the Field Artillery Board and the Infantry Board. One of these British instruments, designated T16, was lighter, less bulky, and more accurate than any other range finder yet tested. Furthermore, it was more easily manufactured, cost less, and used less strategic material. It was therefore standardized in December 1942 as the M7 for field artillery use and, with modifications, as the M9 for infantry. At the same time the M1916 was classified as limited standard and development of all other experimental one-meter range finders was canceled.[38]

Sights for New Types of Weapons

The introduction during World War II of the recoilless rifle and the bazooka brought the need for new sights but posed no serious fire control problems. The absence of recoil with the 57-mm. and 75-mm. recoilless rifles actually simplified sighting, as it permitted the use of telescopes with short eye distances.[39] When the earliest bazookas appeared in 1942 they were equipped with simple ring sights, which did not prove accurate enough to satisfy the using arms. An optical sighting device was then developed but had to be abandoned because the calcite crystals required for its manufacture were not available. The hinged-bar sight, adopted instead, showed appreciable inaccuracy in alignment when in combat and was soon replaced by a reflecting sight that could be mounted without modification of either launcher or sight bracket. It consisted of a plane disc-shaped ocular having a small reticle at its center opposed to a concave transparent mirror that partially reflected the reticle pattern and partially transmitted light. All bazookas produced in late 1944 and in 1945 were equipped with these reflecting sights.[40]

[37] *Ordnance Sergeant*, IV, 2 (1942), 132–33.

[38] (1) Fire Control for FA and Inf Weapons, Ch. 1, OHF. (2) OCM 19194, 19 Nov 42; 19310, 10 Dec 42.

[39] See OCM 26926, 15 Mar 45, for a detailed discussion of telescopic sights for the 75-mm. rifle. OCM 25247, 28 Sep 44, and 25346, 5 Oct 44, recorded adoption of the rifle and stipulated that telescopic sights calibrated in yards for direct fire and panoramic sights for indirect fire be provided.

[40] (1) Rocket Launchers, PSP 20, pp. 21–22, OHF. (2) OCM 21964, 28 Oct 43; 22673, 20 Jan 44; 25177, 21 Sep 44; 25414, 12 Oct 44.

Night Lighting Devices, Filters, and Lens Coatings

The development of special night lighting devices for fire control instruments was a minor but significant field of research during World War II. During World War I ordinary commercial flashlights shielded with a helmet or other object had been used for illuminating the scales and levels of aiming devices, but during the 1930's Ordnance engineers turned their attention to the development of lights specially designed for fire control instruments. The battery commander's telescope M1915 was the first for which a lighting unit was standardized.[41] Designated Instrument Light M1, it consisted of a battery case with one dry cell clamped to the telescope and a flexible cord leading to a lamp that could be directed on the scale and level. For large-caliber weapons elaborate lighting systems powered by storage batteries were developed only to be rejected by the using arms on the ground that they were too difficult to install and service, used an excessive amount of exposed cable, and were too expensive. As a result, the flashlight type using standard dry cells was adopted for all fire control instruments.

A different approach to the night light problem was through the use of materials that glowed in the dark. As early as 1939 the Field Artillery Board had tested reticles with luminous lines and dots but had rejected them because they glowed only after it was too dark to see the target.[42] Luminous materials were successfully used on the level vials of the gunner's quadrant, an instrument that had long been an especially difficult problem because it was normally used in an exposed position and could not be illuminated by a conventional light without danger of being seen by the enemy. Early in 1944 luminous vials were tested by the using arms and approved for issue, with first priority going to units equipped with the 155-mm. gun and the 8-inch howitzer. Meanwhile, immediately after Pearl Harbor, General Barnes had hopes that infra-red illumination could be used for directing night fire, and a request went to NDRC to work out an electron telescope capable of penetrating darkness as well as fog and smoke. Even for small arms some efforts went into devising sights for night firing. While investigations of various methods proceeded in the United States, the problem was also explored in the United Kingdom. The Weapons Branch of the Ordnance Maintenance Division in the ETO reported late in 1943 that an illuminated collimator, attachable to rifle or carbine but easily removable for day service, had given satisfactory performance in tests at ranges up to fifty yards. But decision of the using arms that these devices were not needed canceled further work.[43]

Another minor but important phase of fire control research was concerned with antiglare filters and protective lens coatings. In October 1942 the Desert Warfare Board conducted tests on red, amber, and neutral filters submitted by the Ordnance Department, but reported that, although each had advantages under certain conditions, none was sufficiently helpful to warrant adoption. More successful were experiments with nonreflecting coatings on glass surfaces and the use of solid glass prisms in periscopes in place of mirrors. All

[41] OCM 15609, 8 Feb 40.

[42] OCM 15094, 15 Jun 39.

[43] (1) Memo, Gen Barnes for Mr. H. W. Dix, 12 Dec 41, sub: Infra-red Illumination, OO 334.9/1281, DRB AGO. (2) Memo, Col Joel G. Holmes, Deputy Chief Ord Off, Hq ETO, for Small Arms Div, R&D Serv, 25 Dec 43, sub: Night Sighting Device for Small Arms, OO 350.05/8546, DRB AGO. (3) Interv, 5 Nov 51, with Amos C. Bonkemeyer, Light Weapons Sec, Small Arms Div, R&D Serv.

during the war years Ordnance engineers carried on numerous experiments to develop antirain and antifog coatings, hoods for protection against sun and rain, and mechanical modifications to increase ease of operation. An Ordnance detachment tested the performance of all types of fire control equipment under conditions of extreme cold at Fort Churchill in Canada during the winter of 1943–44 and brought back much valuable information on both design and maintenance. In June 1944 Frankford Arsenal formed a committee to study the protection of fire control instruments and their carrying cases from the ravages of fungus growth and other types of deterioration experienced in tropical climates. The committee directed its efforts chiefly toward the use of protective coatings, the development of moistureproof sealing, the incorporation of silica gel desiccants, and the employment of a volatile fungicide within the instruments.[44]

Sighting Equipment for Armored Vehicles

The important role assumed by tanks and other armored vehicles in the late 1930's created new problems for the designers of fire control matériel, for it meant that guns used against tanks had to be aimed far more rapidly than in the days when they were employed only against stationary targets, and the tanks themselves had to be equipped with ingenious devices for observing and sighting. Broadly speaking, Ordnance designers met the first of these problems by developing telescopes with so-called antitank reticles, which enabled the gunner to take the proper lead on the target and adjust for range at the same time. A telescopic sight with an antitank reticle was standardized in 1938, as the M6, for the 37-mm. gun, then considered an antitank weapon, and other sights of similar design were developed later for other guns. To enable antiaircraft weapons to perform their secondary mission of firing at ground targets, they also were equipped with sighting telescopes having antitank reticles.[45]

Before 1940 the only way tank crews could make observations without opening the turrets and exposing themselves to enemy fire was through direct vision slots in the turret. These narrow openings were not satisfactory because they weakened the armor and exposed the crew to danger from shell fragments. In search of a better means of observation, the Ordnance Department in 1937 tested various devices operating on the periscopic principle, including the Gundlach periscope developed by an officer of the Polish Army.[46] Foreign observers considered the Gundlach periscope superior to anything else available at that time, but it proved unsuitable for American tanks, which did not have enough space in the turret to permit the observer to move his head from side to side as the periscope required. In the fall of 1940, therefore, Ordnance engineers began work on the design and manufacture of two experimental tank periscopes, the T1 and T2, each containing a straight telescope for gun sighting. As these periscopes were linked with the gun so that their line

[44] (1) Various exhibits in the History of Frankford Arsenal, Fire Control Design Division, Vols. VI–X, OHF, provide detailed information on the Fort Churchill tests and the tropicalization mission sent to the Canal Zone in early 1945. (2) On the use of silica gel and volatile fungicides, see OCM 25525, 26 Oct 44, approved by OCM 25774, 16 Nov 44.

[45] (1) Fire Control for FA and Inf Weapons, p. 106, OHF. (2) Fire Control for Armored Vehicles, Sec. II, OHF.

[46] OCM 13485, 25 Jan 37.

of sight moved with it, the gunner, without moving his head, could aim the weapon for direct fire simply by centering the proper telescope reticle markings on the target. The linkage mechanism was hard to keep in adjustment, but after completion of tests at Aberdeen Proving Ground early in 1941 the two periscopes were standardized as the M1 for the 75-mm. gun and the M2 for the 37-mm. gun. When the heavy tank M6 was standardized later, the M1 periscope, with a different telescope, was used with the heavy tank's 3-inch gun.[47] In spite of these developments, reports from overseas observers stated that, because of poor periscopic vision, tank crews generally preferred to fight with turrets open.[48]

Following standardization of the M1 and M2, several other periscopes were tested and adopted but it was not until 1943 that a major new development appeared. This was a periscope with one high-powered telescope on the right side for sighting distant targets and a periscope with a reflex reticle on the left side for sighting near-by targets. Frankford Arsenal in February 1942 submitted sketches of such a periscope with the designation T8, and completed two pilots by July. The T8 offered much greater accuracy and stability of bore sighting than did existing periscopes, but its manufacture required the use of highly skilled optical and mechanical workers for long periods of time, and the cost of each periscope amounted to approximately $1,000. After extensive tests the Armored Force Board and the Army Ground Forces concluded that one T8 was so much superior to existing periscopes that its standardization was warranted in spite of the high cost. After modifications to facilitate quantity production, the instrument was standardized as the M10 and was put into production in the summer of 1944.[49]

In addition to the periscopic telescope, tank gunners used a straight telescope mounted inside the tank for direct sighting through an aperture in the turret. To minimize danger to the crew, this aperture was kept as small as possible—no larger, in the early part of the war, than a .30-caliber bullet. The problem was to provide a telescope small enough to fit this keyhole-sized aperture, powerful enough to give adequate magnification and a wide field of view, and yet short enough to be used in the space available inside the turret. Progress toward meeting these specifications was steady, beginning in the fall of 1942 with standardization of the M51, a 3-power telescope with a field of view of more than 12 degrees. During the winter of 1942–43 several new telescopes with better optical characteristics were developed, and in July 1943 one was standardized as the M70. It was later replaced by a 5-power telescope, the M71, which had a wider field of view and increased light-gathering power. The M71 was standard equipment on nearly all tanks early in 1945. A major innovation in tank telescopes appeared near the end of the war when the M83, a variable-power instrument, was standardized. This telescope could be readily adjusted to provide 4-power magnification with a relatively wide field of view or 8-power magnification with a much narrower field. The former adjustment was used for aiming at

[47] (1) OCM 16654, 24 Apr 41; 16753, 22 May 41; 18059, 13 Apr 42; 18283, 28 May 42.

[48] (1) Intel Summary 12, 3–11 May 43, OCO–D, OHF. (2) Interv with Gordon A. Harrison, 21 Mar 51.

[49] OCM 22064, 11 Nov 43; 22390, 16 Dec 43. At the same time the M3 and M5 became obsolete and the M4 and M8 limited standard.

near-by targets or for locating distant targets and the latter for sighting on distant targets.[50]

Gyrostabilizers

In contrast to their success in improving telescopes and periscopes, Ordnance engineers made little progress in other areas. In spite of persistent efforts to adapt infantry and field artillery range finders to tank use, no satisfactory range finder for tanks was developed. In 1944 and 1945 attempts were made to evolve an integrated tank fire control system that would properly relate the ranging, computing, and aiming functions, but at the end of the war this project was still in the development stage.[51]

More difficult than the design of sighting devices themselves were some of the problems of utilizing them to best advantage. To realize fully the benefits from a high-power tank telescope, for example, it had to be able to function while the vehicle was moving. If the gunner could accurately lay his weapon only at a dead stop, his tank might present, at least momentarily, a choice target for hostile artillery. Some means had therefore to be devised for stabilizing vehicle armament during travel over rough terrain. Borrowing a page from the Navy, which had long employed such a mechanism on its waterborne artillery, the Ordnance Department adopted the gyrostabilizer.[52]

The working principle of the gyrostabilizer rested on the well-known behavior of the gyroscope—a rapidly spinning wheel or disc that tends to resist movement away from the axis about which it is spinning. The gyro control, the heart of the gyrostabilizer, consisted basically of a gyroscope mounted on the gun cradle with its axis parallel to that of the gun. Any slight displacement of the gyro control from its vertical position set forces in motion that returned it, and with it the gun tube, to its point of origin. The gun thus maintained its aimed position while the tank moved over the rises and depressions of average rough terrain. But it is well to remember that the gyrostabilizer neither aimed the gun to begin with, nor kept it on target when the tank went up or down hill or when the target moved. Its sole function was to keep the manually aimed gun on a line of sight selected by the gunner.

The problems attendant upon the development of a gyrostabilizer for vehicle armament were numerous. Unlike the gyrostabilizer of the naval vessels, the entire mechanism had to fit virtually into a nutshell and had to withstand shocks far more severe than those occasioned by the buffeting of wind and waves. Despite the fact that at the outbreak of war development had barely passed the laboratory stage and the few stabilizers that did reach the front quickly went out of adjustment, subsequent improvements were marked enough to merit careful attention. When a newly designed mono-gyro control was found to increase the percentage of hits by a factor of two or three to one as compared

[50] (1) OCM 19044, 22 Oct 42; 20837, 24 Jun 43; 21070, 15 Jul 43; 20892, 1 Jul 43; 21134, 22 Jul 43; 24247, 29 Jun 44; 27509, 3 May 45; 27936, 7 Jun 45. (2) Hist of Frankford Arsenal, Fire Control Design Div, VII, 19–20, OHF. (3) *Optical Instruments*, pp. 444–51.

[51] Memo, Lt Col Louis Rossetto, Chief of Fire Control Design Div, Frankford Arsenal, for CofOrd, 8 Sep 45, sub: Review of Mission of Fire Control Design Div, and incl, cited in Hist of Fire Control Design Div, Vol XII, OHF.

[52] Unless otherwise cited, material concerning gyrostabilizers is based on the following: (1) Handbook Ord Auto Engr, IX, 8–12, OHF; (2) R&D, Tanks, 1A9–10, 1A53–54, OHF; (3) Development Record of Traversing Mechanisms and Stabilizers, n. d., OHF.

with unstabilized guns, the device was immediately placed in production. With further improvements, it was used thereafter on numerous light tanks, many of the medium General Grants, and the entire series of General Shermans.

Although their stabilized guns gave American tankers a clear-cut advantage over their opponents—most notably the Germans, who by the end of the war had not succeeded in building a workable stabilizer [53]—reports from overseas indicated limited use of the gyrostabilizer in combat. In 1943 an officer returned from the fighting in Sicily stated that despite very careful maintenance no one used the gyrostabilizer to good advantage. He believed that it had possibilities only if it were simplified and if extensive training were given the troops on its operation. All told, he thought gyrostabilizers not worth the effort to put them in tanks; accuracy of fire was so important that tank crews preferred to halt before firing.[54] Again, a report on the ETO in late 1944 stated, "experience has proven that tank crews have no faith in gyrostabilizers and will not use them. No amount of training seems to convince the tank crews of the value of firing while moving. The gyrostabilizer is an expensive piece of tank equipment never used, and it could be left out of tanks scheduled for theaters of operations." [55] Consistent evidence in the same tenor finally moved Ordnance to recommend the abandonment of stabilizers, a step that would have permitted a reduction of both maintenance time and expense. But that recommendation was disapproved, and the stabilizer remained. Intensive training of troops in its use made its mark at the very end of the war. In mid-August 1945 AGF reported, "many tank battalions are using gyrostabilizers extensively." [56]

Fire Control for Seacoast Defense Batteries

Although none of the seacoast gun batteries guarding the coasts of the United States went into action against an invading enemy fleet during the war, for years before Pearl Harbor, and months after, the Coast Artillery Corps and the Ordnance Department devoted much attention to the development of fire control systems for these weapons. Since coastal guns, along with antiaircraft guns, were designed for defense of United States territory, they had high priority during the period when national military policy emphasized defense against invasion, and remarkable improvements were made in the speed, range, and accuracy of the guns to keep them abreast of developments in the design of naval vessels. The problems of designing fire control apparatus for seacoast artillery, though simpler in most respects than for antiaircraft, were nonetheless challenging. Seacoast guns had to be aimed rapidly and at long range against fast-moving, heavily armored targets in a field of fire that usually offered no landmarks or reference points. Because large seacoast guns wore out after firing only a few hundred rounds and could not be used again until they

[53] CIOS Preliminary Target Investigation Rpt by 12th Army Group, cited in Intel Summary 72, 31 Jul–8 Aug 45, OCO–D, OHF.

[54] Interv, Col P. W. Gillon and Maj D. W. Hoppock with Capt Norris H. Perkins, formerly of 66th Armored Regt, at Walter Reed Hospital, 1 Oct 43, copy in Overseas Ltrs, Misc, OHF.

[55] Office memo, Maj W. F. Jordan, Tank and Motor Transport Div, R&D Serv, for Col W. A. Weaver, Exec Asst, R&D Serv, 20 Nov 44, sub: Notes on Equipment for Armored Division Based on Battle Experience, Misc Missions folder, Barnes file, OHF.

[56] Memo, Lt Col Severin R. Beyma for CG AGF, 28 Jul 45, sub: Use of Stabilizers on Tanks, and 1st Ind, Hq AGF for CG ASF, 15 Aug 45, OO 470.8/2236 Tanks, DRB AGO.

were relined at an arsenal, it was highly desirable that the number of misses be kept to a minimum. Most of the instruments used for aiming seacoast guns were basically the same as those used with field artillery weapons, but others, such as gun data computers and transmission systems, were developed to meet problems peculiar to seacoast artillery.

During World War I many different instruments were needed to provide seacoast guns with accurate firing data. A typical position-finding problem required the use of a plotting board, set-forward rule, prediction scale, deflection board, range correction board, percentage corrector, and spotting board. As each of these instruments was operated by from one to four men, the number of "read and set" operations required, the time consumed, and the possibilities for error were all great. The Coast Artillery Corps as early as 1919 drew up specifications for a computing device that would perform many of these calculations automatically, thus saving time and manpower and eliminating some chances for error. Two decades of research and development finally led to the standardization in September 1940 of the gun data computer M1 for use with long-range batteries. It was a 5,000-pound instrument, approximately seven feet long, three feet wide, and three feet high, costing about $100,000. It consisted of nine interconnected units, a target position generator, wind component indicator, ballistic correction unit, predictor, range elevation converter, parallax unit, and three triangle-solvers. For use with small coastal guns, the Coast Artillery Board in the spring of 1941 recommended that a seacoast computer be constructed along the same lines as the electrical antiaircraft directors then under development. This recommendation led to the standardization in May 1943 of gun data computer M8.[57]

While work on gun data computers was under way, fire control engineers also investigated possible ways of transmitting data from observation posts to plotting rooms, and from plotting rooms to gun positions. At the start of the war data of this type were transmitted orally by telephone. The observers at each post took readings simultaneously at the sound of a bell that rang at stated intervals, and then telephoned the data to the plotters. This method of transmission was slow and offered many opportunities for error on the part of the operators; when gun data computers were adopted the oral transmission of data by telephone became definitely outmoded. To enable the computing devices to operate with full effectiveness, it was necessary to provide them with a constant flow of data transmitted instantaneously and accurately from the observing stations and a corresponding outflow of computed data to the gun positions. The latter type of transmission covered relatively short distances and posed less difficult problems than did the longer-range transmission of data from so-called base-end stations, which might be as far as thirty miles from the plotting room. Under the aegis of NDRC the various components of a long-range data transmission system were developed during 1942, including azimuth transmitters, elevation

[57] (1) OCM 20330, 6 May 43; 20564, 24 May 43; (2) Ltr, CA Bd to CG AGF, 8 Apr 43, sub: Computer T12, OO 413.68/466, DRB AGO. When this computer was adapted for use with different guns, mounts, and ammunition, a capital letter was added to the designation, as M8C, M8D, and so on. For detailed description of the M8, see Hist of Frankford Arsenal, Fire Control Design Div, III, 5–6, OHF.

transmitters, and corresponding receiving devices. Early in 1943 these items were standardized as parts of the computers with which they were used.[58]

The seacoast fire control apparatus used during World War II depended upon so many observation posts and such an elaborate system of communication, and operation presented so many technical difficulties, that competent authorities feared the system would collapse in an actual attack. Little use had been made of radar for directing fire of seacoast artillery, but its successful employment by the Army Air Forces and the Navy led, at the end of the war, to a study of its potentialities for seacoast defense. Yet two years after a decision of 1946 to install radar at all modern batteries, the plan was abandoned because of the increasing effectiveness of other means of defense.[59] In 1948 all large-caliber seacoast guns and their fire control instruments were declared obsolete. Thus ended the long and important history of Ordnance efforts to develop instruments for aiming the large guns guarding the nation's coastal frontiers.

[58] (1) Fire Control for Seacoast Arty, pp. 68-76, OHF. (2) OCM 17044, 31 Jul 41; 18037, 9 Apr 42; 18621, 13 Aug 42; 18999, 8 Oct 42; 19603, 28 Jan 43.

[59] Rpt of WD Seacoast Defense Armaments Bd, 1 Nov 46, OHF. In 1946 a board of officers appointed to survey the nation's seacoast defenses recommended that radar be installed immediately at modern batteries and that only those elements of the old fire control system be retained as were necessary for the operation of batteries not equipped with radar devices. Signal Corps radar then began to replace the more conventional instruments until the obsoletion of all seacoast guns canceled the work.

CHAPTER XII

The Search for Increased Fire Power: Ammunition

Neither smoothly functioning guns nor perfection of aim can make fire accurate if the projectile is unstable in flight, since the flight characteristics of a projectile fired from any kind of weapon, whether from rifled gun bore or smooth mortar or rocket-launcher tube, affect the projectile's ability to reach its target. Hence, exterior ballistics are as important as interior ballistics, fire control, or the terminal ballistic elements that determine the effect upon the target when reached. Study of the motion of projectiles through the air and their behavior during flight constitutes a special, highly complicated branch of science, the problems of which are frequently baffling even to experts. Various design features of the projecting weapon, such, for example, as the dimensioning of the chamber of a gun or the twist of the barrel rifling, may have as much bearing upon accuracy of fire as does the character of the propellant or the shape of the projectile. The desired result depends upon a complex of factors. Gravity, air drag, wind forces, the weight and distribution of the weight of the projectile, the velocity at which it is launched, and the angle of projection must all be reckoned with.[1] Careful observation of these phenomena and computation of exact data require elaborate measuring instruments and computers. Germany was far ahead of the United States and Britain in this field of work. As early as 1940 German scientists were using an intermittently operating supersonic wind tunnel in developing radio-controlled bombs, rockets, and flak shell, while the U.S. Army was still trying to obtain data for bombs and rockets at subsonic velocities. After the completion of the Wright Field wind tunnel, the Air Forces and Ordnance Department were in a better situation than formerly, but not until the fall of 1944 was a supersonic tunnel ready for use at Aberdeen Proving Ground.[2] Nevertheless, throughout the war the work of Ordnance ballisticians, particularly at the Ballistic Research Laboratory, was vitally useful. Though their services in providing the armed forces with the means of obtaining accurate fire were essential, the discussion here must be limited to some of the simpler phases of the intricate problems involved.

Barrel Rifling and Design of Projectiles for Conventional Weapons

In conventional artillery and small arms, the rifling of the barrel gives the pro-

[1] For explanation of theory and application of exterior ballistics see Hayes, *Elements of Ordnance*, Ch. X.

[2] Record of Army Ord R&D, Ballistic Research Laboratory, APG, Pt. I, pp. 222–24, OHF.

jectile a spin calculated to ensure sufficient stability in flight to carry it to its target. Stability is important solely because it is a big factor in achieving accuracy. Projectiles fired from smooth bore launchers usually had to rely upon fins for stability, though German technicians in World War II produced a curiously shaped finless mortar projectile which, shot from an unrifled bore at a low velocity, obtained stability from the air flow about it.[3] American Ordnance engineers before the war was over evolved rifled tubes for a 4.2-inch chemical mortar and for the enormous 914-mm. Little David. But most American mortars, like most American rockets used in World War II, were fin stabilized, not spin stabilized.

Except for hand grenades and mortars, which fired only at relatively short ranges, the U.S. Army had used rifled weapons almost exclusively since the 1870's. Consequently, despite incomplete knowledge of why projectiles shot from rifled bores behaved as they did, Ordnance ballisticians by trial and error over the years and by study of the findings of French scientists had arrived at sound general principles of gun bore and projectile design. They early learned that a long twist in the rifling might produce so little spin on the projectile that its stability in flight would be adversely affected, whereas a needlessly short twist not only put excessive pressure on the barrel but might actually lessen the projectile's range. During World War II designers studied or restudied virtually every rifled weapon then in use or under development to determine the most satisfactory rifling twist. Though production problems forbade making desirable changes in many guns, in some the advantage offset the cost. For example, the 76-mm. tank gun, originally rifled with a twist of one turn in 40 calibers, was later made with one turn in 32 in order to get a faster spin on the projectile. Conversely, when experiments at Springfield Armory indicated that the twist in Garand rifle barrels was shorter than necessary and that two grooves would serve as well as four, because of the effect upon production no revision of design was authorized. Two-groove barrels were, however, made for the 1903 and 1917 rifles, arms for which demand was less.[4]

Shapes of standard projectiles, on the other hand, were not much changed from the elongated boat-tailed contour established as standard before World War II began. Thus, correcting inaccuracies in the 105-mm. high-explosive shell proved to be not a question of redesign of the projectile, but of improved banding, closer dimensions, smoother finish of the shell, and use of two granulation powders, that is, powders of two different cross-sectional thicknesses. When a new weapon was under development, refinements were sometimes effected in the projectile, such as the thin-ogived, long boat-tailed shape given the 120-mm. projectile to reduce air drag. But over-all restudy of this feature of ballistical elements in conventional ammunition had to await the postwar era.[5] Mortars, also, though newer to the U.S. Army than artillery and shoulder arms, underwent rather few important changes in projectile design. Fixed tail fins and the cylindrical or tear-shaped contours standard before

[3] Interv, 9 Oct 51, with George Stetson, Ballistics Sec, R&D Div.

[4] (1) Interv, 10 Oct 51, with Herman A. Matson, Chief of Cannon Sec, R&D Div. (2) Interv, 2 Feb 44, with Col George A. Woody, CO Springfield Armory. (3) Springfield Armory Experimental Div Monthly Progress Rpt, Apr 43, OHF. (4) Hist of Springfield Armory Vol. II, Book II, pp. 249b–249c, OHF. (5) OCM 19053, 22 Oct 42.

[5] See n. 3, above.

1940 remained the accepted design for all but the giant Little David. The Bureau of Standards, at Ordnance Department request, worked out a redesign of the 60-mm. shell in order to improve stability by shifting the center of gravity further from the center of pressure and by some reshaping of the fins, but this model was not ready in time for use in World War II. The shell for Little David was nearly cone-shaped and was pre-engraved.[6]

Special Projectiles To Give Hypervelocity

Some exploration of new types of ammunition for both artillery and small arms did take place, in hopes of attaining hypervelocities without excessive barrel erosion or radical changes in design of the projecting weapon. Hypervelocity, producing a flattened trajectory in the projectile's flight, would of course not only improve the chances of a hit by shortening the time of travel toward a moving target, but, by conserving the kinetic energy of the projectile, would heighten the destructive effect of a strike. Thus, the search for hypervelocity involved, simultaneously, considerations of interior, exterior, and terminal ballistics. Its advantages in increasing accuracy of fire were clear. Against a tank 1,500 yards distant moving at 30 miles per hour, NDRC later figured that a shot fired at a velocity of 3,550 feet per second reduced the lead needed with 2,030 feet-per-second velocity from 105 feet to 60 feet and quadrupled the allowable error in estimating range.[7] But apart from lengthening the gun barrel and thereby adding undesirable weight, the means of getting velocities of more than 3,000 feet per second reduced themselves to two: an increase of the powder charge in relation to the weight of the projectile or use of higher potential propellent powders.

In the first category one possible solution lay in applying the "squeeze principle" to fire a specially designed projectile from a gun barrel narrowed by tapering the bore or by addition of a conical adapter. As early as 1932 the Ordnance Department had tested a tapered bore sporting rifle with a skirted bullet designed by an American-born German engineer, Hermann Gerlich. From a barrel of which the grooves in the middle section were diminished in depth from .75-mm. to .13-mm., a 125-grain monel metal bullet fired at a muzzle velocity of 4,406 feet per second. But as accuracy was unsatisfactory and the bullet tended to fall apart on impact, the rifle was clearly unsuitable as a military weapon.[8] Not until 1942, following discovery of the German Army's apparent success with artillery tapered bores and British interest in an application to small arms, did the Ordnance Department renew investigation of possibilities in a small-caliber weapon. Patterning its work in general on the British Littlejohn gun designed by a Czech named Janecek, Frankford Arsenal in July 1942 began development of a projectile to fire from a .45-inch .50-caliber machine gun barrel with a muzzle adapter that reduced the exit diameter to .35 inch. A projectile with a

[6] (1) R&D Serv, Development of 60-mm. and 81-mm. Mortar Ammunition, pp. 12–15, 17–18, 21–22, 25, 27–28, 31, OHF. (2) Barnes, *Weapons of World War II*, pp. 168–74.

[7] Div 1, NDRC, Summary Tech Rpt, Hypervelocity Guns, 1946, p. 10, Arty Br, R&D Div files. This study analyzes every aspect of hypervelocity known in World War II and describes fully the NDRC research program in this field.

[8] (1) Extract, NDRC Rpt A43, Brief Hist of Tapered Bore Guns, copy in Hypervelocity Development, Guns and Ammo, OHF. (2) Interv, 2 Nov 51, with Dr. Frederick H. Carten, Ammo Br, R&D Div.

GERMAN 28/20-MM. ANTITANK GUN

.35-inch hard core was surrounded by a soft envelope that bulged in the center so as to leave at that point a void between the core and the envelope. The projectile was rotated by the rifling in the cylindrical section of the barrel bore, but on reaching the tapered portion, the projectile's deformable envelope was swaged into firm contact with the core so that the bullet left the gun with a reduced diameter and with the shape of a conventional armor-piercing projectile. Despite extended research on a large number of types of bullets, the laboratory technicians found no design with suitable exterior ballistics. Bullets tended to disintegrate upon emerging from the barrel and had such ballistic instability that muzzle velocities proved greater in fire from a barrel without the conical adapter than from a barrel with it. Incendiary ammunition, moreover, could not be fired from this type of weapon. The whole project of producing caliber .50/.35 ammunition was therefore dropped in the fall of 1943.[9]

Meanwhile, the Ordnance Department had been trying various applications of the squeeze principle to artillery projectiles. In 1941, when the British captured from Rommel's army, near Halfaya Pass, a light antitank gun with bore tapered from 28-mm. to 20-mm. and a few rounds of its "arrowhead" ammunition, American interest in Gerlich-type weapons revived. A report describing the distinctive features of both gun and ammunition, and British reports of tests, inspired the Ordnance Committee to request immediate design of weapons and projectiles as nearly identical to the German as possible. At the same time, because a report from the Ballistic Research Laboratory indicated that equally high velocity could be obtained without tapered bores, the decision was reached to make several cylindrical bore guns employing ammunition similar to the

[9] Record of Army Ord R&D, Vol. II, Small Arms and Small Arms Ammunition (hereafter cited as SA and SA Ammo), Book 2, Small Arms Ammunition, p. 171, OHF.

hard-cored soft-sleeved German type, in order to compare performance with that of American copies of the German and with that of a captured model to be sent to Aberdeen.[10]

While awaiting completion of the American 28/20 matériel, Ordnance engineers experimented with affixing tapered adapters to the muzzles of standard 37-mm. and, later, 57-mm. guns, so that from the former the projectiles would emerge with a 28-mm. diameter, from the latter with 40-mm. Though capture of a German arrowhead projectile for a 41/29-mm. gun in mid-1942 showed that the Germans were then placing a good deal of faith in tapered bore weapons, careful tests convinced the Ordnance Department by late 1943 that in all artillery a cylindrical bore without an adapter but using a light hard-cored projectile served every purpose of the tapered bore. The former suffered far less wear, gave greater accuracy of fire, and over long ranges maintained higher velocities.[11] Thereafter the Ordnance Department bent its efforts to developing tungsten carbide-cored rounds for conventional weapons and delegated to NDRC the pursuit of discarding sabot projectiles and other ways of attaining hypervelocity.[12]

Propellants for Conventional Weapons

Because getting a shot to the target depended on other factors than design of the launcher and the shape of the projectile, propellent powders and primers also had to be considered. Indeed, to get sufficient velocity to ensure accurate fire from conventional weapons, use of a more powerful propellant was the only alternative to increasing the ratio of propellant to weight of the projectile. Ordnance specialists had long known that in other weapons besides the 105-mm. howitzer the nature of the propellent powders influenced accuracy of fire. Unfortunately, during the 1920's and 1930's money for research in this realm had been so meagre that, apart from developing relatively smokeless nonhygroscopic powders, the Ordnance Department had accomplished little.[13]

The qualities of the ideal propellant were easy to name: a chemical composition producing neither flash nor smoke and causing little barrel erosion, having low flame temperature and low chamber pressure, yet giving very high velocity,[14] a powder largely impervious to moisture and made of readily available materials easily manufactured in quantity. Achieving any one of these features was no poser. The trouble came in trying to combine all wanted qualities in one package. Low flame temperature threatened to cause loss of velocity; reduction of flash increased smoke. While improved ignition systems in artillery ammunition contributed to lessening both obscuration and muzzle flash, the chemical composition of the

[10] (1) OCM 17188, 25 Aug 41. (2) Hypervelocity Development, Guns and Ammo, OHF.

[11] (1) See n. 10(2), above. (2) Memo, Military Mission North Africa for CofOrd, 1 Jul 42, sub: German Arrowhead 41/29-mm. (Gerlich AT), OO 350.05/1046, DRB AGO. (3) Ltr, Gen Barnes to Dr. Vannevar Bush, 20 Jan 42, OO 334.9/1523, DRB AGO.

[12] (1) Memo, Maj Charles D. Bordman, Hq AGF for CG ASF, attention Dir Requirements Div, Development Br, 13 Mar 44, sub: Sabot Ammunition, and inds 3 thru 10, OO 385.2/125, DRB AGO. (2) NDRC Liaison, OD 52, OHF. (3) Memo, Gen Barnes for CG ASF, 22 Mar 44, OO 385.2/1495, DRB AGO. (4) Rpt Artillery Ammo Br, R&D Serv, 30 Nov 45, OO 471.14/830, DRB AGO. (5) Div 1, NDRC, Summary Tech Rpt, Hypervelocity Guns, pp. 557–58, Artillery Br, R&D Div files.

[13] See above, Ch. VII.

[14] Occasionally reduced rather than heightened velocity was desirable, as in the case of short-range high-angle firing. See discussion in Barnes, *Weapons of World War II*, p. 78.

powder remained the chief factor to consider. Adding potassium sulphate to propellant for antiaircraft fire, where flashlessness was all important, helped to solve one problem. But it was no answer to the demand for a wholly smokeless and flashless propellant for field artillery where smoke would obscure gunners' vision and muzzle flash reveal the tank or battery position.

The search for a compound at once smokeless and flashless had its beginning in the requirement established by the Westervelt Board in 1919. Ordnance chemists, following British experiments, in the early 1920's offered the using arms samples of nitroguanidine which, to a degree unobtainable in any other known propellant, had both properties. But nitroguanidine in combustion gave off such noxious ammonial fumes that the Field Artillery vetoed its use. The Ordnance Department, with no customers in prospect, then abandoned all thought of building plants to make it. But ammunition specialists found no satisfactory substitute. Twenty years later the Navy seized upon nitroguanidine as the one feasible answer to novel conditions of combat. For the first time American ships in the Pacific were having to fight in small harbors where maneuvering was all but impossible. Flash by night betrayed the vessel's position and smoke by day made second rounds inaccurate. Negotiations with Canada in 1943 for purchase of nitroguanidine from the one plant upon which British and Canadian forces were also depending succeeded in meeting Navy needs but left no surplus for the U.S. Army. Until shortly before V-E Day the Army Ground Forces were unconvinced of the value of this propellant. By then, urgent demand could not create facilities to produce it in quantity, and the Ordnance Department could procure only small lots for test and experimental firing.

Whatever the advantages of nitroguanidine, neither that nor any other known composition was ideal for all purposes. Even in conventional artillery and small arms ammunition, where ballisticians understood propellant behavior better than in rockets and recoilless rifle ammunition, compromises were inescapable. The primary requisite for one weapon or one particular use tended to be different from that for every other. Propellants suitable for a 90-mm. shaped charge, where low velocity was acceptable, would not answer for a 76-mm. tungsten carbide-cored projectile, the design of which was directed at achieving very high velocity. In addition to these problems, World War II introduced the new element of extremes of temperature at which ground firing must take place when Allied troops were fighting in dry desert, damp jungle heat, and in the subzero winter weather of northern Europe. Series of propellants, therefore, were needed to cover widely varying contingencies.[15] Since basic research as well as prolonged applied research was necessary, many problems remained unsolved at the end of the war. But the field was explored more thoroughly than ever before in the United States, and lines of investigation were clarified for postwar development.

In processing propellants, industry and Ordnance made considerable advances during the course of the war. One new method, developed by the Hercules Powder Company, for washing nitrocellulose

[15] (1) Min, Joint A&N mtg on Army Ord R&D, 15 Sep 44, p. 17, A&N Mtgs, Barnes file, OHF. (2) Interv, 15 Oct 51, with Lt Col Roy E. Rayle, Projectile Sec, R&D Div. (3) Interv with Bruce Anderson, 7 Mar 52.

in a continuous filter instead of in large tubs by the old "settle and decant" system, washed more thoroughly and thus improved the stability of the nitrocellulose. The DuPont Company found that, in winter, use of preheated alcohol to dehydrate nitrocellulose reduced the dehydration time cycle, bettered the yield, and made a more uniform product, which in turn made better powder. The Radford Ordnance Works carried on extensive experiments to improve manufacturing and testing techniques as well as to find better chemical compositions. Yet in the spring and summer of 1945 reports of the Combined Intelligence Objectives Subcommittee, established to locate data in Europe on Axis research and manufacturing procedures, indicated that Germany had developed several processes more effective than those of the United States. The most novel German method was one of casting propellent grains by adding a paste of moist nitrocellulose and diethyleneglycoldinitrate, DEGN, to molten TNT and pouring the mixture into steel molds to cool. Grains as large as 1,000-mm. were cast this way. After the war complete sets of the German equipment deemed most useful and novel went to Picatinny Arsenal for study.[16]

Design of Projectiles for New Weapons

Meanwhile, rockets and, later, recoilless rifles, were introducing unfamiliar ballistic problems. Both types of weapon were so designed as to fire at low velocities, the bazooka as low as 260 feet per second, the 57-mm. recoilless rifle at just over 1,200, and the 75-mm. at only 1,000 feet per second. While those velocities would make no difference in the ultimate striking power of hollow-charge projectiles, the slowness of flight gave a curved trajectory that made judging range and lead more uncertain and thus lessened the chances of a hit. As rockets, carrying their propellent charges within their casings, were initially heavy but lost weight as the propellant burned during flight, maintaining stability was peculiarly difficult. In recoilless rifle ammunition the propellant, though firing the projectile minus the shell, necessarily lost some of the energy needed to impart high muzzle velocity because of the partial dissipation of the gases rearward. Yet tests proved the accuracy of the recoilless guns comparable to that of small-caliber artillery.[17]

For ground-launched rockets, as for mortar shell, fins affixed to the round appeared at first to be the most practical way to provide stability, though in retrospect the question arises why no one in 1940 recalled that the famous Hale rocket of 1855 was spin stabilized. Doubtless the example of the British, who at the time of the Battle of Britain had to produce rockets quickly, if at all, influenced American designers. And finned rockets promised to be simplest to design and make. But the optimum shape of the fins and the method of fastening them to a rocket, which must be shot out of a tube launcher, remained to be determined. The 3.25-inch target rocket, designed not for combat but for training antiaircraft gunners, was launched from long rails since accuracy of fire was unimportant. Consequently, in that model large flat-ended fins that gave adequate stability of flight could readily be hooked onto the rocket case and cause no interference

[16] Smokeless Powder Program of Ord Dept in World War II, PSP 17, pp. 14–16, 50–52, 57–70, OHF.

[17] Design, Development and Production of the 57-mm. Rifle T15E3 and 75-mm. Rifle T25, PSP 78, Pt. 1, p. 4, and Pt. 2, p. 13, OHF.

when the rocket was fired. Fins on tube-launched rockets had to be designed to fit the launcher. The principal features of the first American combat model, the 4.5-inch rocket, were folding fins and electrical firing. The rocket itself was long and slim. Fins, folded back into the neck of the case, opened up by inertia and were kept open by air flow after the rocket emerged from the tube. The smaller 2.36-inch bazooka rocket, on the other hand, was built with a series of fixed fins somewhat resembling the feathers of an arrow but fitted into the narrowed case neck so as to have the same diameter as the rocket motor. Fixed fins shrouded by an outer ring were also used on the 7.2-inch series developed in 1943.[18]

When Allied troops encountered German rockets and discovered that they were spin stabilized, the Ordnance Department, convinced that the Germans must have good reasons, undertook to develop a series of similar design. Only as the multiple-nozzled experimental types were tested did the virtues of spin stabilization become clear. Accuracy was greatly improved because the flow of gases through the eight canted vents rotated the rocket at about 10,000 revolutions per minute, thus keeping it on its course, whereas in firing finned models frequent slight misalignments of the thrust with the axis of the rockets caused veering. When the latter type was launched at low velocity across the wind, the fins tended to act like a weather cock and swing the projectile into the wind. Furthermore, a folding-fin rocket equipped with a proximity fuze might develop enough flutter in the fins as they unfolded to activate the fuze prematurely. Elimination of fins and fin rings reduced parasitic drag on the rocket and thus lengthened range even with a heavier explosive charge in the warhead. And, finally, finless rockets were easier to load quickly into multiple and automatic launchers. The first 4.5-inch spin-stabilized model, the T38, in fact proved to be as accurate when fired from a short launcher as from a long one, though postwar tests showed long launchers necessary for other rockets. Two variations of the T38 were standardized in the spring of 1945, while work on spin-stabilized 7.2-inch rockets was pushed vigorously.[19] But as shaped-charge rockets would lose much of their effect if rotated in flight, all high explosive antitank (HEAT) rounds were fin stabilized.

Rocket Propellants

Difficult though the program was for improving propellants for conventional weapons, the question of developing suitable rocket propulsion was still harder to answer. From the very beginning everyone concerned with rocket research agreed that single-base powders would lack the necessary energy and that double-base, that is, nitrocellulose and nitroglycerine combined, must be used. Double-base powder made by the solvent process had been manufactured in the United States for a number of years for use in intermediate and heavy artillery. This method employed a solvent of acetone and alcohol to make a glue-like substance, or colloid, from which grains or flakes could then be formed. About 1939 the Hercules Powder Company found a way of producing a solventless double-base powder plasticized

[18] (1) Rockets, Development, Production and Performance PSP 20, pp. 2, 4, 9–10, 14, OHF. (2) Interv, 18 Oct 51, with Lt Col Berkeley R. Lewis, Rocket Sec, R&D Div. (3) OCM 17047, 31 Jul 41.

[19] (1) Interv with Col Lewis, 18 Oct 51. (2) PSP 20, pp. 19–22, 41–42, 46–47, OHF. (3) OCM 26967, 15 Mar 45; 27298, 12 Apr 45.

by heat and pressure and then rolled out into sheets for mortar increments. But neither was readily adaptable to rockets, where a solid stick or grain, not sheet powder, was needed, and where the essential quality of even burning precluded using a grain with so much as a minute crack or fissure. For even a tiny crack in a burning grain of powder would create peaks of pressure at particular spots of the encasing rocket motor tube and thus either burst the tube or cause erratic flight.[20] Consequently, to get safely usable rocket propellant made by the solvent process meant using grains of small cross section—in technical phraseology, thin-webbed powder—in which malformations occurring in drying would be few and inspection could be exacting. A method of manufacturing solventless double-base powder by a dry-extrusion process had been developed in the late 1930's by the British. This produced much thicker-webbed, and therefore longer-burning, grains but required enormously heavy presses to extrude or compact and force out the powder into the desired shape.[21]

In 1941 American scientists split into two schools of thought on the relative merits of solvent and solventless double-base powders for rockets. Dr. Charles C. Lauritsen of the California Institute of Technology, and in 1941 vice chairman of one of the NDRC divisions, had been much impressed by British rocket work and strongly recommended dry-extruded powders. Though at that time no facilities existed in the United States for producing it, the Navy, with contracts let through NDRC to the California Institute of Technology, chose to focus efforts on obtaining thick-webbed solventless types. The Ordnance Department, on the other hand, agreed with the views of Dr. Clarence N. Hickman of the Bell Telephone Laboratories, then chief of an NDRC group working on rocket developments at Indian Head, Maryland. Hickman advocated use of wet-extruded powder because of the shorter burning time and greater strength of the thin-webbed grains produced by this process. Quite apart from theoretical advantages, the urgency of quickly getting some usable type led Ordnance to center its program about solvent powder. When toward the end of the war the Army's rocket specialists concluded that the long-burning, thick-webbed solventless powder was after all generally better for rocket propellant, Navy preemption of facilities for dry-extrusion obliged the Army to continue to rely largely upon the wet-extruded.[22]

Wet-extruded propellant was made by suspending the powder in a solvent that swelled the nitrocellulose to make a dough. The dough was forced through dies to form sticks, or grains, of powder from which evaporation then dried the solvent. As satisfactory drying to produce flawless grains could be obtained only with thin-webbed powder, it was clearly necessary to use a number of small grains in each rocket in order to get a sufficiently heavy

[20] (1) For a fuller account of developments in both solvent and solventless powders, see PSP 17, and Dr. E. H. Hemmingway, Historical Rpt on Solventless Rocket Program, both in OHF. (2) A series of abstracts of the detailed reports of the work done by Radford Ordnance Depot is contained in K. E. Balliet, Summary Rpt, 1 Oct 45, in a collection of the Johns Hopkins University Applied Physics Laboratory.

[21] (1) Interv with Col Lewis, 23 Oct 51. (2) Interv, 25 Oct 51, with Harry La Tourette, Chief of Raw Materials Sec, Ammo Div, Ind Serv, 1945.

[22] (1) PSP 20, pp. 14–16, OHF. (2) Interv, 11 Sep 51, with Dr. Colin Hudson, Guided Missiles Sec, R&D Div. (3) For an account of the work done at the California Institute of Technology for the Ordnance Department, see Hist of ORDCIT Project to 30 Jun 46, MS, OHF.

charge. That, in turn, complicated the problem of designing a trap to hold the series of powder sticks in the rocket motor, so that unburned portions of the grains would not be ejected by the high-pressure gases in front of the motor ends. Col. Leslie A. Skinner of the Ordnance Department and Dr. Hickman eventually found the answer in a stamped metal ring with scallops through which passed "cage" wires. The centrally perforated powder sticks were then hung on these wires. The wires had rivet heads to hold them in the scalloped ring.[23] When experiments began on spin-stabilized rockets, the problem arose of how to keep the rotation from rattling the powder sticks around in the spinning tube, thus causing uneven burning. Development of a new powder composition made into a single thick-webbed grain with a redesigned trap to hold it in place promised to be satisfactory.[24]

Early in 1944, indeed, powder chemists found several new chemical compositions that offered advantages over the types originally employed. The new were slower burning, operated at lower pressures, and were therefore usable at a wider range of temperatures. Moreover, they could be produced by either the solvent or the solventless process. Before the new compositions were available, the fast-burning propellants tended to develop such high pressures within the motor tubes as to make them unsafe to use at very high temperatures. Premature explosions close to the launcher endangered life and limb of the user and friendly troops in the vicinity. At low temperatures the rocket might fail to ignite or might burn only intermittently. In fact, frequent motor failures in the 4.5-inch rocket, standardized in September 1942 as the M8, obliged the Ordnance Department to discontinue mass production in June 1943 and restudy the design. As reducing the amount of propellant presented the alternative of lowering the pay load proportionately or else of lessening the range, designers undertook to strengthen the motors without increasing their weight. Motors made of heat-treated, seamless, alloy-steel tubing proved able to withstand an internal pressure of 10,000 pounds per square inch and, coupled with a stronger head, extended service temperature limits to cover a range of 20° to 120° F.[25]

The Bazooka Rocket

Though the bazooka and the bazooka rocket had a preternaturally short history from the inception of the idea to the moment when combat troops first fired rockets from the new shoulder launcher, the story of the weapon's development may serve to illustrate the uncertainties attending the evolution of rockets as modern military weapons. The birth of the bazooka merits attention for several reasons. The weapon was an innovation. It combined great fire power with great simplicity. It met quite admirably a particular need. It was designed, produced, and placed in the hands of troops in record time. And, perhaps because of its spectacular features, the tale of how it took shape has been confused by rival claimants for credit. As one of the participants in the project later wrote, "the number of 'inventors' of the bazooka has fallen and risen as troubles developed and

[23] Burchard, ed., *Rockets, Guns and Targets,* pp. 20–21.

[24] PSP 20, pp. 27–28, OHF.

[25] (1) PSP 20, pp. 17–19, 27, OHF. (2) OCM 22778, 17 Sep 43. (3) For discussion of the difficulties of rocket design, particularly before thick-webbed powders were available, see Burchard, ed., *op. cit.,* pp. 11–13.

were cured, the stage having been reached in one part of its career where only those who worked on it could be found to claim any connection with it."[26]

The bazooka and the bazooka rocket came about in a rather devious fashion. The shaped charge, fired by rocket propulsion, and the launcher were the result of several men's pooled efforts. Rockets were used long before Francis Scott Key wrote of "the rockets' red glare."[27] The principle of the shaped charge was promulgated by the physicist C. E. Munroe as early as 1880, when he discovered that shaping high explosive with a hollow cone at its forward end focused the explosive waves on one point and thus gave greater penetration per unit weight of the explosive. The innovation embodied in the bazooka lay in the combination and adaptation of these well-known principles and basic inventions, which imagination and skill converted into a practical new weapon. The design was steadily improved upon as production of the first models went forward.

Rockets, today part and parcel of the accepted equipment of national defense, were little considered in America between 1860 and 1940; they were superseded when rifled artillery offered greater accuracy of fire. Though signal rockets were widely used during World War I, only one man endeavored to revive interest in rockets as a supplement to conventional artillery fire. That man, Dr. Robert H. Goddard, Professor of Physics at Clark University, was the true father of modern rocketry. In the fall of 1918 this gifted physicist offered the Ordnance Department the fruits of his investigations: a 1-inch, a 2-inch, and a 3-inch tube launcher, each 5.5 feet long, and designed to fire, by an electric mechanism, rocket projectiles of 1.4 pounds, 8.5 pounds and 16.5 pounds, respectively. Just before the Armistice he demonstrated his "recoilless gun" or "rocket gun" at Aberdeen Proving Ground with results that Ordnance Department witnesses summarized as proving the validity of the principle he employed. Goddard had to use a wick fuze in place of the electric firing mechanism, which he had not had time to perfect, and solid sticks of powder instead of nitroglycerine sticks with a single perforation. Yet even with these crude substitutes marring the performance, the report of the proof officer admitted the possibility that these guns "could be developed to operate successfully against tanks." But the lack of suitable powder and need of further work upon the electrical firing mechanism coupled with the Armistice led the Ordnance Department to shelve the project. Goddard died without receiving any acclaim for this pioneering work, though comparison of his rocket gun with the bazooka adopted twenty-four years later shows how closely the 1918 model approximated the later weapon. Only the circumstance that Dr. Hickman, then a young Ph. D. from Clark University, worked with Goddard in 1918 gave some continuity to the studies that produced the antitank rocket weapon of World War II.[28]

In 1933 the U.S. Army created a one-man rocket unit by assigning Capt. Leslie A. Skinner to study the possible use of rockets. Skinner was handicapped by limited funds to expend on research and

[26] Col. Leslie A. Skinner, "Birth of the Bazooka," *Army Ordnance*, XXVII, 146 (1944), 261.

[27] For discussion of earlier rocket developments, see James Cutbush, *System of Pyrotechny* (Philadelphia, 1825), and Henry B. Faber, *The History and Development of Military Pyrotechnics*, 3 vols. (Washington, 1919).

[28] Memo rpt . . . Test of 1″ 2″ and 3″ Recoilless Guns, Ord Program 2594, APG, 20 Nov 18, photostat in OCO Patent Sec files.

by the indifference of his fellow officers. Hence, before 1940 the project made little headway. The British, on the other hand, in the mid-thirties perceived the potential usefulness of rocket barrages against aircraft, where volume and power of fire might compensate for lack of accuracy. By the time of the London blitz the British had developed rockets that took some toll of the Nazi bombers and fighters. The Navy in September 1940 requested NDRC to undertake a jet-propulsion research program, and in December the Army, urged on by the British experience, made a similar request. At the same time the Ordnance Department purchased British rockets and a projector for study. Thus, the American rocket program was born.[29]

The 2.36-inch bazooka rocket was not initially part of the Army rocket program at all. It grew out of the search for a way to use a shaped-charge projectile that an individual soldier could fire from the shoulder. The first shaped-charge projectile to get serious consideration from the Army was the rifle grenade designed by Henri Mohaupt.[30] A grenade fitted with a special Mohaupt head and designed for fire from a spigot launcher was produced and standardized as the high-explosive antitank grenade M10. The spigot launcher resting on the ground much like a mortar had the serious drawback of dispersing the fire widely. Firing the grenade with blank cartridges from a rifle or from a .50-caliber machine gun necessitated resting the butt on the ground in order to get an elevation high enough to get sufficient range. The heavy recoil severely damaged the guns.[31] Without a suitable projector, the powerful new projectile promised to be relatively useless.

At this point the chief of the Ordnance Department Patent Section, Gregory J. Kessenich, already familiar with the details of the Mohaupt shaped charge, conceived the idea that the basic faults of the antitank grenade could be remedied by converting the grenade into a rocket. Using a rocket made with a hollow charge and launched from a shoulder projector that an individual soldier could carry and fire would give the destructive effect of the grenade but would eliminate both the high-angle trajectory and the breakage of the rifle stock that made the M10 antitank grenade unsatisfactory. Early in August 1941 Kessenich, armed with sketches embodying his idea, presented his proposal to Col. Wiley T. Moore, chief of the engineering group of the Small Arms Division. Colonel Moore, who had just designed an attachment for the rifle to fire the rifle grenade, immediately saw the possibilities of Kessenich's sketches and approved his enlisting the interest of Major Skinner of the Ordnance rocket unit. The sketches and a copy of the Westfaelisch Patent of 1911, which covered the hollow charge phases of the plan, Kessenich accordingly turned over to Major Skinner.

Experimentation with rockets had meanwhile been progressing at the Navy Firing Ground at Indian Head, Maryland, where Major Skinner and his assistant, 2d Lt. Edward G. Uhl, were collaborating with Navy experts and a group of civilian scientists under Dr. Hickman of NDRC. Some months later Major Skinner completed a first conversion of the M10 grenade by adding a rocket element to the base of the grenade. About the same time Lieutenant Uhl completed a tube launcher

[29] Ammo Div, Ind Serv, Rockets, Notes on Design Development and Production (hereafter cited as Rocket Notes), pp. 1–2, PSP 20, p. 3, OHF.

[30] See Ch. VII, above.

[31] (1) See above, n. 26. (2) Small Arms Div, Ind Serv, Rocket Launchers, PSP 20, pp. 5–8, OHF.

THE BAZOOKA. *The original 2.36-inch model M1 is shown at left, the improved model M9 at right.*

that looked like a piece of stovepipe equipped with a trigger and handle. The handle contained dry batteries to supply energy electrically to ignite the rocket motor. In April 1942 Colonel Moore, then at Frankford Arsenal, produced a factory-made 54-inch launcher and factory-made parts for the converted grenade.[32] With the further help of Dr. Hickman and the NDRC group, the Ordnance rocket unit had a few "respectable" antitank rockets ready for trial by May 1942. Captain Uhl, dressed like "the man from Mars," fired the first rocket from his shoulder at the test ground of NDRC, and the next day demonstrated launcher and rockets at Aberdeen Proving Ground. He improvised a sight by using a piece of nail found on the ground. The new weapon was christened that day: its resemblance to the comedian Bob Burns' bazooka led the colonel who fired some of the rockets to dub the device the "bazooka." The name stuck.

The effectiveness of the rocket with dummy heads fired at a moving tank impressed the onlookers. A few days later a formal demonstration was held at Camp Sims, D. C., when high-ranking officials of the War and Navy Departments, Allied governments, and NDRC witnessed the real thing in action against a medium tank. British observers now opened negotiation for samples and Russian military staff members present at this trial immediately requested that they be supplied with some

[32] (1) Interv, 6 Feb 50, with Gregory Kessenich, Chief of Ord Patent Sec. (2) Memo, Lt Col Charles E. Herrstrom, Chief of Ord Patent Br, for Maj H. H. Ferguson, Legal Div, 18 Nov 44, sub: AT Rockets and Launchers, copy in Ord Patent Sec files. (3) Blueprint, 13 Mar 42, Ord Patent Sec files.

of the new launchers even though development was still in progress. General Marshall at once issued verbal orders that 5,000 launchers and 25,000 antitank and 5,000 practice rockets be procured. The E. G. Budd Company made the rockets. On 30 June 1942 the Ordnance Committee formally standardized the 2.36-inch antitank rocket as the M6, and the launcher as the M1.[33]

The bazooka is thus an example of a co-operatively developed weapon in which the Army, Navy, and civilian agencies all played a part. It provided a powerful addition to infantry armament. The projected rockets could penetrate three inches of homogeneous steel armor plate at an angle of impact up to 30 degrees from normal, and retain full penetrative power up to their maximum range of 650 yards. Fired against masonry, girders, railroad tracks, or heavy timber, as well as against armor plate, they were highly destructive. While improvements upon both rocket and launcher were admittedly necessary, the first models were satisfactory enough to warrant obsoletion of the original antitank grenade from which the rocket had derived. Orders for 120,000 rockets were placed in June and in July for 75,000 launchers to be completed by the end of the year. Modifications of design of rocket fins and launcher sights were incorporated into the production units as these orders were filled.[34]

More drastic changes soon became necessary. Misfires obtained with the original type of ignition squib led first to substitution of a new type, but by May 1943 reports of serious malfunctions had become so frequent that the services were instructed to suspend use of the rocket pending investigation. The Ordnance Technical Committee recommended a new design of rocket motor body, using a different steel in the stabilizer tube and employing a new type of powder trap and fuze-base cover. Still more important as a safety measure was reduction of the propellant. Extensive tests showed that powder sticks cut from 23 inches to 20.75-21 inches in length gave sufficient propulsion but greatly lessened the danger of prematures even at extreme temperatures. With these changes approved, the standard bazooka rocket was designated the M6A1, the practice rocket the M7A1. Teams equipped with the new parts, materials, tools, and repair kits to make the modifications of both rockets and launchers were sent to the active theatres in July 1943.[35] Some months later the M6A3 and M7A3 rockets were standardized with ogives reshaped to lower the angle of effective impact and with cylindrical fixed fins to increase stability in flight. Substitution of copper cones for steel resulted from discovery that copper cones obtained about 30 percent greater armor penetration than the steel cones of identical design.[36] Moreover, in response to theatre requests the Ammunition Division of Industrial Service developed waterproof wire clamps to seal the fuze assembly against entry of water around the safety pin and thereby reduce malfunctions due to moisture:

Because rockets were relatively little known weapons, improvements often hinged upon fresh basic research. Hence, at the request of the Ordnance Depart-

[33] (1) OCM 18246, 20 May 42; 18421, 30 Jun 42. (2) Skinner, *loc. cit.*, pp. 262-63. (3) PSP 20, pp. 8-10, OHF. (4) Rocket Notes, pp. 4-11, OHF.

[34] (1) PSP 20, pp. 10-12, OHF. (2) Rocket Notes, pp. 10-16, OHF.

[35] OCM 20534, 27 May 43; 20684, 10 Jun 43; 21080, 15 Jul 43; 21203, 5 Aug 43.

[36] OCM 21679, 8 Sep 43; 22933, 17 Feb 44; 28141, 28 Jun 45.

ment, the Bureau of Standards in the summer and fall of 1944 conducted a number of wind-tunnel tests of fin assemblies, and Picatinny Arsenal investigated ignition characteristics calculated to give the most dependable functioning of the 2.36-inch rocket at all temperatures. Fuzes also required careful study. Experiments to develop a whole series of special bazooka rockets—smoke, incendiary, chemical, and others—brought about standardization of the M10, a smoke rocket, but no others.[37] In every case the commercial companies having production contracts collaborated both in the designing work and in finding shortcuts in methods of manufacture. Joint efforts of the Atlas Powder, DuPont, Hercules, and American Cyanamid Companies improved rocket powders, while concerns assigned contracts to develop experimental components or assemblies, particularly fuzes, added to the knowledge of what new features were desirable or attainable by mass-production methods. Throughout the war the scientists of NDRC and the universities with which they contracted were amassing data on explosives that were invaluable in all phases of the rocket program.

The success of the 2.36-inch bazooka rocket inspired NDRC to propose development of a still more powerful type with greater range and a velocity increase from the 265 feet per second of the M6A3 to 500 feet per second. The resulting T59 unhappily proved in tests to be dangerous to the user and quickly became a bone of contention between scientists of NDRC and the Ordnance Department. The former, having let considerable advance publicity concerning their new "super-bazooka" rocket reach the theatres, suspected that Ordnance men were needlessly delaying its production and issue. But postwar developments were to vindicate the Ordnance Department when more than six years' work still failed to remove the bugs from the rockets.[38] Work upon the T59 nevertheless led to investigation of the possibility of a larger antitank rocket, which, like the 2.36-inch, could be projected from a shoulder launcher.[39] While development of a 3.5-inch Navy rocket for air-to-ground fire had begun in February 1944 only to be dropped in March 1945, a 3.5-inch antitank rocket was still wanted.[40] The project was initiated in August 1944. The first experimental model, the T80, was charged with 1.9 pounds of cyclotol. Though it obtained longer range and higher velocity than the standard bazooka rocket, it fell short of that achieved by the T59 with its eight pounds of pentolite. Yet the cyclotol in the T80 would, research men believed, ensure penetration of 8-inch homogeneous armor plate. Static, flight, and penetration tests in March supplied data on which to base a revised design, but V-J Day arrived before this was proved.[41]

Once the projectile had reached its target, the final job was to do the greatest possible damage. The rate of speed at which the projectile was traveling at the moment of burst was of course important, but the ultimate result was determined by the quality of the ammunition itself. Some German ammunition was of better quality than American because it was more perfectly fabricated. But it had to have more exacting machining and more careful heat-

[37] (1) OCM 24671, 10 Aug 44; 25125, 14 Sep 44. (2) Rocket Notes, pp. 17–23, OHF.

[38] Interv with Dr. Colin Hudson, 11 Sep 51.

[39] OCM 24666, 10 Aug 44; 25110, 14 Sep 44; 25252, 26 Sep 44.

[40] OCM 22884, 10 Feb 44; 27184, 5 Apr 45.

[41] (1) OCM 28409, 14 Jul 45; 28796, 8 Aug 45. (2) PSP 20, pp. 1–12, OHF. (3) For history of the project and postwar development, see OCM 32304, 5 Aug 48.

treating than U.S. mass-production requirements permitted. To increase fire power by otherwise improving the effectiveness of the projectile was a continuing problem for the Ordnance Department. Experts in terminal ballistics attempted to solve it in several ways. One was to improve the fuze. Another was to use a more powerful explosive in the warhead or to use an old explosive in a new way, applying the shaped-charge principle. And with specific targets in mind, designers devised special types of projectiles having the mass, size, and mechanical strength required to defeat different kinds of enemy defenses.

Fuzes

Artillery fuzes were likened by an NDRC scientist to "the old-time Army mule, ornery but indispensable." [42] The orneriness was inherent in their delicate and complicated mechanism, which was directed toward detonation at exactly the right time, not too early and not too late. Extensive work in the 1920's and 1930's had produced several families of fuzes adapted to use in any caliber artillery shell.[43] Designated point-detonating (PD) or base-detonating (BD) according to their position on the projectile, fuzes were further classified as "impact" or "time," depending on whether or not they functioned only when striking a target. Time fuzes did not require impact but were set by turning a time ring before firing. As the shell left the muzzle, a time element, either a clockwork mechanism or a slow powder train, began to work, and the fuze functioned at the moment it had been set for. Time fuzes were valuable for fragmentation effect, for smoke or illuminating shells, and especially for antiaircraft fire. Impact fuzes, used against targets of varying degrees of resistance, were of several types: supersensitive, superquick, nondelay, delay, or a combination of these. Supersensitive action was necessary against insubstantial targets such as airplane fabric. Against more solid targets, superquick fuzes were used when penetration was not desired, nondelay for detonation at the moment of penetration, and delay—usually of .05, .15, or .25 seconds — when penetration in varying degrees was wanted.

Fuzes need not be single purpose, though many were. Selective-type fuzes could be adjusted in the field for more than one kind of action, such as superquick and delay, or time and superquick. For example, the M48 fuze, used with the 75-mm., 3-inch, and 105-mm. high-explosive shell, and the M51, its counterpart for larger calibers, could be set to function immediately on impact or with a delay of .05 or .15 seconds. In all fuzes, mechanical safeguards restrained the firing pin until the right moment for detonation arrived. When the gun fired, the sudden and violent forces arising from acceleration removed one set of safeguarding devices. In flight the centrifugal force of the shell as it rotated about its longitudinal axis removed the last set of safeguards and the fuze was armed, that is, free to function.[44]

Engineers strove with some success to adapt the fuzes developed before 1940 to the tactical situations of World War II. The chief problem, determining the most effective delay times, was difficult to solve because the resistance of targets varied greatly.[45] On the whole, troops in all the-

[42] Burchard, ed., *op. cit.*, p. 104.

[43] See Ch. VII, above.

[44] (1) TM 9-1900, pp. 107-10. (2) Catalogue of Standard Ord Items, 1944, II, 651-65. (3) OCM 22839, 10 Feb 44.

[45] (1) OCM 22272, 2 Dec 43; 22839, 10 Feb 44. (2) OCO Tech Div, Rpt of FY 1943-44, pp. 22-24.

atres preferred the combination to the single-purpose fuze.[46] One important requirement for use in air-burst neutralization was an accurate, long-delay time fuze with a superquick functioning feature. The M67 mechanical time fuze could be set for a delay of 75 seconds, but as it depended on the turning of gears in flight and had no provision for detonating on impact it was unsatisfactory for neutralization.[47] One possibility for development was the M54, a powder-train type of time fuze with the desired superquick action. But the maximum range of the M54 was only 25 seconds. The problem of how to triple that range was not fully solved when the war ended.[48]

The most important point-detonating fuze developed during the war was a radical departure from other types, as it had a steel nose that adapted high-explosive ammunition to concrete-piercing uses. Since 1940 designers had been trying to find a way to destroy fortifications made of concrete reinforced with steel bars, such as the Siegfried Line. Against such targets, standard high-explosive shells would throw the fuze and become duds. Armor-piercing ammunition, based-fuzed, though better, lacked enough power to remove earth or sandbags placed in front of the concrete, to blow the reinforcing bars and debris from the impact area, or to cause large enough craters to make successive hits effective. The best solution was a completely new high-explosive shell with a base-detonating fuze. But that meant a new round for each weapon, further complicating the already complicated ammunition situation, and long delay in getting ammunition to troops. A more expedient answer was a steel nose fuze that could be attached to high-explosive rounds already in the field. Col. George G. Eddy began the development at Aberdeen in the summer of 1943. Tests against prototypes of West Wall fortifications showed the most practical design to be a fuze body made of molybdenum steel, heat treated for greater strength, with the delay assembly of the M48 and M51 fuzes and a modified booster. Developed in a matter of weeks, the steel nose fuze, standardized as the M78, was rushed to General Devers in Africa and successfully tried out at Cassino. Later it helped to breach the Siegfried Line and the log-and-earth bunkers encountered in the Pacific.[49]

The concrete-piercing fuze and the long-delay superquick time fuze were examples of developments to meet new tactical conditions and new targets. Fuzes for rockets, on the other hand, presented still another problem. Conventional artillery fuzes were not suitable because, thanks to the comparatively long burning time of rocket propellant, the rocket reached its maximum velocity much more slowly than the artillery shell, had virtually no setback force, and attained very much lower velocities. With these differences in mind, engineers designed new fuzes for the 2.36-inch bazooka rocket and the 4.5-inch, the models chiefly employed for ground fire in World War II. The bazooka rocket, pri-

[46] OCM 21680, 30 Sep 43; 24288, 6 Jul 44; 28145, 28 Jun 45.

[47] (1) OCM 22839, 10 Feb 44. (2) Borden Rpt, Ord Annex, p. 2, OHF. (3) Eddy Rpt, p. 2, OHF.

[48] Min Joint A&N mtg on Army Ord R&D, 1 Oct 45, p. 31, A&N Mtgs, Barnes file, OHF.

[49] (1) Ltr, Chief of FA to CofOrd, 10 Jan 40, sub: Military Characteristics of Weapons of Greater Power, and ind, 26 Apr 40, OO 472/3631, DRB AGO. (2) OCM 16366, 27 Dec 40. (3) Standard Artillery and Ammunition Against Reinforced Concrete Pillboxes, First and Second Progress Rpts, 5 Jan 44, 15 Feb 44, OCO Tech Div, OHF. (4) R&D Serv, Ann Rpt FY 1945, p. 26, OHF. (5) Barnes, *op. cit.*, p. 130. (6) Eddy Rpt, p. 4, OHF. (7) Ltr, Brig Gen George G. Eddy to Gen Ward, 26 Feb 52, OCMH.

marily an antitank weapon with an armor-piercing head, used a base-detonating fuze. When the first fuze proved prone to function prematurely, designers found that a bore-riding pin provided greater bore safety. The pin, held in place by the wall of the launcher while the rocket was traveling through the launching tube, was released at the muzzle and the fuze was then armed. Later simplification of design reduced the number of parts from thirteen to seven. The new fuze, the M400A1, combined with the metal parts adopted for the M6A3 bazooka rocket, gave the M6A5 rocket greater plate penetration and sensitivity than that of any earlier model.[50] Instead of the base-detonating fuze of the 2.36-inch, the 4.5-inch was equipped with a point-detonating fuze. Though two fuzes were at first thought to be necessary, one with superquick action, another with a short delay to permit airburst from ricocheting rockets, preliminary studies indicated that the two requirements could be combined successfully in one fuze, the setting of which could be adjusted for either superquick action or a delay of .10 second. The fuze embodying these features was standardized in the summer of 1943 as the M4. Used not only with rockets but also with mortars, it was especially valuable in the South Pacific. The 4.5-inch rockets, particularly when launched in rapid succession from multiple-tube projectors, had a high-explosive effect peculiarly useful for dispersed fire against enemy concentrations and area targets.[51]

But barrage fire depending for effect on saturating an area rather than on placing shots squarely on a particular target was frequently futile. With time-fuzed fire, relatively few bursts could be properly placed, and because the many shots needed to get on target destroyed the element of surprise, the enemy would have warning and could seek shelter. What was needed was a fuze that would operate not by time but by proximity to the target, for airbursts occurring at just the right distance would make foxholes useless and divest revetments and trenches of means of providing shelter from attack. Development of that kind of fuze occupied some of the best scientific brains of America and Britain and became one of the technological triumphs of the war.

The Navy had been considering the possibility of devising an influence fuze even before the National Defense Research Committee was established in June 1940. Hence, this project was the first that the Navy asked NDRC to study. In September the Tizard Mission to the United States made available to American scientists the fruits of British research upon the problem, data of great value in advancing American work. The British had been focusing attention upon fuzes for bombs and antiaircraft rockets. For shells, British physicists had regarded the difficulties as virtually insuperable. The Army request for NDRC help on proximity fuzes came in mid-January 1941. NDRC assigned the research on bomb, mortar, and rocket fuzes to a division under Dr. Alexander H. Ellett, and shell fuzes to a section headed by Dr. Merle A. Tuve.

Though sometimes popularly assumed to stand for "variable time" or "vacuum tube," VT was merely a code name. The means of operating VT fuzes to detonate without regard to time but rather at a given distance from the target could conceivably be several. NDRC began inves-

[50] OCM 28141, 28 Jun 45.

[51] (1) OCM 20830, 24 Jun 43. (2) Burchard, ed., *op. cit.*, p. 105. (3) R&D Serv, Ann Rpt FY 1944, p. 23 and FY 1945, pp. 59–60, OHF.

tigation of each method that appeared even remotely feasible—acoustic, photoelectric, radio and, after consultation with the British, radio-pulse fuzes triggered from the ground. The characteristics listed as essential by the Ordnance Committee for bomb and rocket fuzes give some idea of the complexity of the problem; in artillery and mortar shells space limitations and the violence of setback made a solution even more difficult than in bombs. The first stipulation was that the fuze must function when passing within effective fragmentation range of the target, whether in daylight or darkness, and in any kind of weather. Secondly, there must be a self-destructive feature to prevent injury of Allied troops and damage to equipment in case of missing the enemy target.[52] Separate storage of the power unit, presumably batteries, was also required, so that fresh units could be attached shortly before use. And, lastly, the mechanism must have sufficient ruggedness to withstand the rotational and setback forces of conventional artillery.[53]

The answer NDRC finally came up with was a radio-operated fuze triggered by reflection from ground, aerial, marine, or submarine target. The underlying principle was simple enough. Anyone familiar with electronics would immediately comprehend it, for it was essentially an application of short-wave transmission and reflection from the target, with use of the so-called Doppler frequency. Contained within the fuze was a miniature transmitting and receiving oscillator, an amplifier, an electrical firing circuit, and electrical and mechanical safety devices. The radio transmitter broadcast a continuous signal that was reflected back to the fuze as it approached its target. As the oscillator received the signal back, an interference, the Doppler frequency, was set up, which, when intensified sufficiently by the amplifier, passed a signal through to set off the firing circuit and detonate the projectile. If this sequence was simple to understand, fitting the mechanisms into the confined space of a fuze was complicated in the extreme. Several nations had issued patents for proximity devices, but no patent explained how the mechanism was to be made. By the end of the war Germany had in production a radio-operated fuze for rockets and had made some progress in design of acoustic fuzes. None of these saw service, presumably because production problems had not been solved satisfactorily.[54] The triumph of American research lay in successfully designing a fuze that could be manufactured by assembly-line methods.

As was true of fuzes operating on time or impact, VT fuzes were a considerable family. Each weapon had to have its own fuze, differing in particulars from that designed for every other weapon. The intensive study and elaborate, ingenious testing that produced effective, safe proximity fuzes for bombs, rockets, antiaircraft and field artillery shells, and, by the very end of the war, for 81-mm. mortars must command the utmost admiration. The technical research was chiefly the work of NDRC and its contractors. Three universities, the Department of Terrestrial Magnetism of the Carnegie Institution, the Bureau of Standards, and some twenty commercial companies all contributed. Infinite patience and wide scientific knowledge went into development of the proximity fuze, but without the experts of the Army and Navy who supplied the es-

[52] See below, Ch. XIV.

[53] NDRC Liaison, Project OD-27, OHF.

[54] Baxter, *Scientists Against Time*, p. 222.

VT FUZE. *Air burst of a 105-mm. HE shell and dust rising as shell splinters strike the ground in the impact area.*

sential data to make the elaborate electronic device practicable in ammunition, the laboratory achievement must have counted for little. The first fuzes were far too big and clumsy to be useful in combat. And after gradual, step-by-step corrections of that obstacle, the models hand-made at laboratory bench by skilled technicians had still to be adapted to mass production. Success in the end was the result of the full collaboration of civilian scientists, Army and Navy ordnance specialists, and experienced industrial engineers.[55]

The first VT fuzes used in combat were fired in January 1943 from Navy guns on the cruiser *Helena* to bring down a Japanese plane. For the next eighteen months use was restricted to the U.S. and British Navies, lest the enemy salvage enough pieces to copy the design. In the summer of 1944 Army antiaircraft batteries in England fighting off the German buzz bomb attacks were issued some of the new fuzes and employed them with effect, but their widest and most deadly application was against enemy ground troops. In October 1944 the Combined Chiefs of Staff approved preparation for release of VT fuzes for ground warfare in Europe. From stockpiles that had been accumulating since the fall of 1943, shipments to Europe built up ample supplies. Teams of officers sent to instruct ETO artillerymen in the proper use of this new killing device had the scene set to put it into action on Christmas Day

[55] (1) Barnes, *op. cit.*, pp. 115–16, 221–42. (2) Interv with Samuel Feltman, 15 Sep 50.

1944.[56] Generalfeldmarschall Gerd von Rundstedt's sudden stealthy move to cut the supply lines of the U.S. First Army in the Ardennes hastened the day. Though only 3,000 VT fuzes were issued to the VIII and V Corps stemming the enemy advance, and though the wooded terrain reduced the effectiveness of the fuzes, the surprise produced was considerable. Here was a truly secret weapon. After the Battle of the Bulge, Allied ground forces used VT fuzes in dozens of actions. In interdictory fire the effect was to deny the enemy use of key bridges and roads, for, as General Eisenhower's headquarters cabled, "by the unprecedented effectiveness of unseen fire at all hours of day and night, the enemy has been severely upset . . . ."[57] Introduced nearly simultaneously into the Pacific theatre, there also the "funny fuze" in rockets and bombs disrupted the enemy.[58]

High Explosives

Increasing the destructive effect at the target meant not only using suitable fuzes but also the most powerful explosive consonant with safety and dependability. The explosive in the warhead of an artillery shell had to be able to stand the shock of setback when the projectile was fired and the shock of impact against steel or concrete. That is another way of saying that it had to be obedient to the fuze. Trinitrotoluene, commonly called TNT, possessed this essential quality to a gratifying degree. It would not explode until the initial weak impulse from the detonator had set off a booster charge consisting of a small amount of a highly brisant explosive such as tetryl or PETN.[59] Considerable power combined with insensitivity, which made for easy loading, stability, and safety in handling and transport, made TNT and amatol, a mixture of TNT and ammonium nitrate, the preferred fillings for most high-explosive artillery shells at the outset of World War II. That they remained so was largely due to their availability in large quantities. As the war progressed and ammunition in general became more complex in design and more specialized in function, demand arose for improved explosives. This demand could not be met to any extent because the explosives developed between wars did not get into large-scale production in time. Nevertheless, throughout the war the Ordnance Department sought both to find ways of using more powerful new explosives and to adapt old ones to special purposes.[60]

There were at hand several explosives of higher shattering effect, or brisance, than TNT. The most important were, first, cyclotrimethylene-trinitramine, which the Americans called cyclonite and the British called RDX, "Research Department Explosive"; second, pentaerythritol tetranite or PETN; and third, ethylenedinitramine or EDNA, later named haleite. RDX and PETN were far too sensitive to be used in the pure state in a shell. It was therefore necessary to mix them with oils or waxes, or with other explosives, to form usable compositions. The British had managed to desensitize RDX by mixing it with 9 percent beeswax to form Composition A, for press-loading into shells; with 39.5 percent

[56] (1) Col. C. H. M. Roberts, Text of Broadcast for State Department "University of the Air" on the Proximity Fuze, 23 Apr 46, OHF. (2) Barnes, *op. cit.*, pp. 86–87.

[57] Quoted in Joseph C. Boyce, *New Weapons for Air Warfare* (Boston, 1947), p. 159.

[58] Barnes, *op. cit.*, p. 88.

[59] L. R. Littleton, The Bursting Charge Explosive Train, OHF.

[60] (1) R&D Serv, Ann Rpt FY 1943, p. 75, OHF. (2) Barnes, *op. cit.*, p. 73.

TNT and 1 percent beeswax to form Composition B, chiefly for bomb loading; and with 11.7 percent of a plasticizing oil to form Composition C, for demolition work.[61] These formulae were brought over by the Tizard Mission in 1940. In America development of Compositions A, B, and C was undertaken by the DuPont Company under contract with NDRC. Because the Ordnance Department wanted Composition A in granular form instead of the lump form specified by the British, DuPont produced a granular mixture designated Composition A3; but it had low priority in the very tight RDX program and played little part in ground warfare.

More promising than RDX for shell loading was haleite. From the 1920's onward chemists at Picatinny had been trying to find a compound that would have the high brisance of RDX without its sensitivity to friction and impact. Research on this problem, principally by Dr. George C. Hale, chief chemist, led to the discovery of ethylenedinitramine, or EDNA, the first entirely American high explosive. More powerful than TNT, it was slightly less powerful than RDX but was less sensitive. Its stability gave it an important advantage in considerations of manufacture, loading, storage, transportation, and use in the field. This advantage was offset in prewar days by the high cost of manufacture of one of its intermediates, ethylene urea. But, by the combined efforts of NDRC and the DuPont Company, the obstacle was removed, and in the late spring of 1943 EDNA was adopted for testing purposes. Designated haleite in honor of Dr. Hale, this new explosive could be press-loaded into small shells without a desensitizing agent, and its derivative, ednatol, a mixture containing 42 percent TNT, could be melt-loaded into large shells as easily as was amatol. Delay in solving manufacturing problems, however, prevented haleite from getting into combat.[62]

The most sensitive of all high explosives was PETN, which was even more readily detonated by fuze-booster systems than was RDX. It was desensitized by mixing it with TNT to form a composition named pentolite, which was extensively used in detonators, bazooka rockets, rifle grenades, boosting devices, and in the shaped charges of high-explosive antitank shells.[63]

Much of the work of improving high-explosive compositions was directed at finding the most efficient filling for antitank shells. For armor-piercing projectiles, relatively insensitive ammonium picrate, "Explosive D," had long been preferred. As it was not likely to detonate on impact, the shell could penetrate the tank before exploding. But experience with German heavy tanks in North Africa showed that something more was needed in the way of power and fragmentation, coupled with greater incendiary effect within the tank. Chemists at Picatinny accordingly tried several expedients. In armor-piercing shell, addition of a small amount of powdered aluminum to cyclotol—a mixture of RDX and TNT—to ednatol, or to TNT produced more brisance than Explosive D and increased sensitivity to impact. In high-explosive antitank shell fillings, conversely, the difficulty was the exact opposite. The high sensitivity of pentolite made it liable to detonation by target impact so

[61] Dr. R. O. Bengis, Super Explosive Program RDX and its Compositions A, B and C, PSP 16, I, 41, OHF.

[62] (1) PSP 16, I, 53–57, 65, 74–75. (2) Baxter, *op. cit.*, pp. 256–57. (3) OCM 20757, 17 Jun 43; 20021, 25 Mar 43. (4) Hist of Picatinny Arsenal Tech Group, III (April–May 1943), pp. 36–38, OHF.

[63] Barnes, *op. cit.*, pp. 73–74.

291064 O—55——25

that the problem was to tone it down to the proper degree of insensitivity. Among several possibilities considered were the addition of wax to the pentolite, the reduction of the PETN content, and the substitution of ednatol or Composition B. None was entirely satisfactory.[64]

The search for an explosive composition of the greatest possible power and brisance took a new turn after analyses of foreign explosives at Picatinny during 1943. Hitherto, research had been concentrated on two-explosive compositions such as pentolite, Composition B, or ednatol. The examination of a Soviet 76-mm. high-explosive armor-piercing round suggested the possibility of employing ternary mixtures. Tests revealed that castable ternary explosive mixtures such as RDX-Tetryl-TNT and Haleite-PETN-RDX offered great promise not only for armor-piercing projectiles but as fragmentation ammunition for weapons designed to produce blast and for demolition charges. Further study showed that the haleite ternaries were unstable. The best combination seemed to be 28 percent PETN, 43.2 percent RDX, and 28.8 percent TNT, a mixture designated PTX-2 (Picatinny Ternary Explosive). More brisant than any of the binary compositions, it was more stable than 50/50 pentolite, and less sensitive to impact. Preliminary firings at Picatinny indicated that it would be particularly adapted to shaped-charge ammunition. At V-J Day, PTX-2 was still in the testing stage.[65]

In spite of intensive effort, chemists at Picatinny and NDRC's laboratories failed during the war to develop any new explosive composition for shell loading that was wholly satisfactory and readily available in quantity. The obstacles were often disheartening. The characteristics of an explosive might be considerably affected by impurities existing in the raw material to begin with or admitted in manufacture; the instability of PETN, for example, was probably due to impurities in its raw material, pentaerythritol. Other variables that had to be taken into account were the different methods of testing and differences in interpreting results. Assuming that a composition had been hit upon that promised to combine greater brisance with less sensitivity, there was still the question whether it could be economically manufactured, safely handled, and made unchanging in character in temperatures ranging from arctic cold to tropical heat. In the search for explosives with special properties, much work had been done in the field of aluminized explosives, but, although aluminized TNT (tritonal) was used in bombs, much remained to be done. At the end of the war the Ordnance Department felt that deeper study of the fundamental properties of all high explosives was essential to effective development in the future.[66]

If no new explosive for artillery shell came into use during the war, a new way of employing explosives nevertheless did. The effect of a hollow-charge or shaped-charge projectile against armored targets was first successfully demonstrated by the bazooka and the rifle grenade. The intense forward jet of the charge, serving to focus part of the energy of the explosion in a limited area, gave to the light-weight low-velocity rocket the armor-piercing advantages hitherto possessed only by high-velocity artillery. The antitank rifle

[64] OCM 18386, 22 May 42; 20757, 17 Jun 43; 23762, 11 May 44; 23846, 18 May 44; 30120, 31 Jan 46.

[65] OCM 24213, 22 Jun 44; 25099, 14 Sep 44; 30120, 31 Jan 46.

[66] OCM 30120, 31 Jan 46.

RIFLE GRENADES. *M9A1 rifle grenade and launcher (left); rifle grenade, adapted from the 60-mm. mortar shell (right).*

grenade, containing only four ounces of pentolite, would penetrate up to four inches of homogeneous armor plate at a normal angle of impact. If not so powerful as the antitank rocket, which had equal penetration at angles of impact as great as 50 degrees,[67] the M9A1 rifle grenade still did excellent, albeit less publicized, work not only against tanks but against bunkers and pillboxes, where its good fragmentation characteristics were especially valuable. There were times when the infantryman preferred it to the bazooka because the grenade launcher could be fitted on the rifle he already had and did not involve carrying an extra weapon.[68]

Application of the shaped-charge principle to artillery naturally proceeded also. The choice of howitzers was logical because their low velocity made conventional types of armor-piercing projectiles ineffective, whereas for a shaped charge low velocity was an advantage. Before Pearl Harbor in an atmosphere of great secrecy, work began upon a shaped-charge shell, the "HEAT," for the 75-mm. howitzer. The designers, paying careful attention to the length of the ogive, the filler, and the striking velocity, came up with a 13.5-pound shell of the same length as the corresponding high-explosive round. The high-explosive, antitank shell, containing a filler of 50/50 pentolite, at a muzzle

[67] (1) Antitank Weapons, pp. 1, 4, OHF. (2) OCM 16374, 30 Dec 40. (3) Baxter, *op. cit.*, p. 260.

[68] (1) Barnes, *op. cit.*, p. 2. (2) Barnes Diary, 29 May 43; 5 Jun 43; 7 Aug 43; 9 Aug 43; 8 Jan 44; 30 May 44; 31 May 44, OHF. (3) Borden Rpt, Observations, p. 7, OHF.

velocity of approximately 1,000 feet per second would penetrate 3 inches of homogeneous armor plate. A similar shell for the 105-mm. howitzer appeared simultaneously.[69] Standardized in late 1941, HEAT shells were produced in time to take part in the North African tank battles early in 1943. The Ordnance Department had high hopes that they would succeed in penetrating the German heavy armor plate that had defeated solid armor-piercing ammunition.[70] But though sometimes successful, performance of shaped charges was not dependable. When they worked they worked like a charm, but they were ineffective disconcertingly often. In an effort to find out why, the Ordnance Department, with the help of NDRC and the Navy, intensified its research. In some cases observers in the field had blamed faulty manufacture, but investigators proceeded on the assumption that design of the round and the principles of operation needed improvement. Because of the difference in behavior of the nonrotated rocket and the rotated shell, the effect of spin was carefully studied as well as the method of fuzing. One of the most important discoveries was that increase in plate penetration was directly proportional to increase, up to approximately three calibers, in "stand-off" distance, that is, the distance from the base of the cone to the target at the moment of detonation. Yet this finding was only a beginning, and the solution to the puzzling behavior of hollow-charge projectiles was not found during World War II.[71]

Special Purpose Projectiles

Shifting conditions of battle in a war on many fronts and the constant demand for greater fire power against all kinds of targets spurred development of new projectiles and the adaptation of old ones to new purposes. In addition to changing the method of fuzing or using different fillers, the size, shape, and weight of the warhead itself, and the material of which it was made, had to be studied carefully with special targets in mind. The shell directed against troops or lightly armored defenses was necessarily different from that fired at tanks or concrete fortifications. Still another type would be required for smoke screening or signaling. And within these categories, a shell that might be effective in the European theatre might be unsuited to the jungle and cave warfare of the Pacific. Thus, the 105-mm. howitzer alone fired some thirteen different types of ammunition, delivering to the enemy projectiles that varied in persuasive power from the shaped charge to the propaganda leaflet.[72]

Of ammunition employed primarily against troops, perhaps the most interesting development was the adaptation of canister to modern warfare. This ancient type of projectile was the simplest imaginable, a cylindrical sheet-metal can filled with small steel shot set in a matrix of resin. But in jungle warfare canister proved surprisingly effective for stopping massed Japanese attacks and for clearing

[69] OCM 17638, 19 Dec 41; 17639, 20 Dec 41.

[70] (1) Barnes Diary, 18 Jan 43, OHF. (2) Barnes, *Weapons of World War II*, p. 82.

[71] (1) OCM 23765, 11 May 44; 23846, 18 May 44; 24214, 22 Jun 44; 27628, 10 May 45. (2) Barnes Diary, 18 Feb 43, OHF. (3) Memo, Col Zornig for Gen Barnes, 24 Nov 42, sub: British Development and Use of Shaped Charges, OO 350.05/1850, DRB AGO. (4) Min, Joint A&N mtg on Army Ord R&D, 1 Oct 45, p. 28, A&N Mtgs, Barnes file, OHF. (5) Min, Joint A&N mtg on Army Ord R&D, 26 Jun 46, p. 34, A&N Mtgs, Barnes file, OHF. (6) Development and Proof Services, APG, Vulnerability of Armored Vehicles to Ballistic Attack, Sep 50, p. 75, OHF.

[72] Barnes, *op. cit.*, pp. 77, 119.

jungle undergrowth. Containing neither fuze, ogive, nor bursting charge, it depended for operation on the shock of discharge, which ruptured the case and scattered the shot forward. The canister most used was the M2, containing 122 steel balls, which was fired from the 37-mm. antitank gun. Larger rounds containing 390 balls were developed for the 75-mm. and 105-mm. howitzers as a part of the extensive program for jungle weapons begun in the fall of 1943.[73]

Aside from canister, departures from prewar design were few in projectiles for use against troops and light emplacements. Developments were chiefly concerned with fuzes calculated to give greater range and more effective burst, and with providing terminal ballistic data to enable field commanders to make optimum use of the weapons. At the Ballistic Research Laboratory, in the course of intensive basic research on fragmentation, ultra-high-speed X-ray equipment was developed that enabled technicians to make radiographs showing what happened to a shell immediately after detonation. These remarkable pictures gave more insight into the nature of fragmentation than any yet attained and offered much promise for future development.[74]

Similar in ballistics to the high-explosive shell was the chemical shell. The filling, whether gas or smoke, was the responsibility of the Chemical Warfare Service, but the Ordnance Department supplied the case, the burster—a tube containing tetryl running down the center of the cavity—and the fuze, usually a superquick or combination time-and-superquick type. As gas was not used in combat, Ordnance concentrated on developing various types of smoke shells. Some had no burster. For example, the base-ejection type depended on an expelling charge of black powder that forced the smoke canister out of the base of the shell. It could lay down a smoke screen, or signal with colored smoke, but its construction made it useless for certain weapons. Of all smoke ammunition, the older and more versatile burster shell filled with white phosphorus turned out to be the most useful in combat. It was valued not so much for its screening ability, which was limited, as for its good qualities both as a spotting agent for signalling to aircraft observers and as a means of producing casualties and demoralization among enemy troops.[75] Phosphorus caused severe burns that were slow to heal. The white phosphorus (WP) shell developed for the 60-mm. mortar in the fall of 1943 was immediately popular in the theatres and brought about a demand early in 1944 for WP shells in calibers from 75-mm up.[76] A favorite with the infantryman was the WP rifle grenade, which was extremely useful in cleaning the enemy out of open trenches or smoking him out of bunkers and foxholes.[77]

Of necessity, Ordnance Research and Development Service focused much of its work in terminal ballistics on developing

---

[73] (1) Loading and Assembling Artillery Ammunition, Oct 45, PSP 18, OHF. (2) Barnes Diary, 11 Oct 43, OHF. (3) Barnes, *op. cit.*, p. 122. (4) Weapons for Jungle Warfare, 1 Nov 43, pp. 61–63, OHF. ,

[74] (1) Min, Joint A&N mtg on Army Ord R&D, 1 Oct 45, p. 28, A&N Mtgs, Barnes file, OHF. (2) Barnes, *op. cit.*, pp. 304–06.

[75] (1) OCM 23319, 30 Mar 44; 26098, 21 Dec 44. (2) Barnes Diary, 27 Apr 43; 28 May 43; 24 Aug 43. (3) Min A&N mtg on Army Ord R&D, 15 Sep 44, p. 15, A&N Mtgs, Barnes file, OHF.

[76] (1) Eddy Rpt, pp. 4, 21, 39–40, 54, OHF. (2) Borden Rpt, Observations, p. 13, OHF. (3) OCM 26323, 11 Jan 45. (4) Weapons for Jungle Warfare, 1 Nov 43, p. 50, OHF.

[77] (1) OCM 23532, 20 Apr 44; 23758, 11 May 44; 23868, 18 May 44. (2) Barnes Diary, 8 Jan 44, OHF. (3) Barnes, *op. cit.*, p. 93.

projectiles able to penetrate the heavy tank armor, pillboxes, log bunkers, and strong concrete fortifications that opposed the American advance from 1942 on. Reports from North Africa early in 1942 of tests on captured German tanks showed that under existing conditions American armor-piercing shot usually failed to penetrate German face-hardened armor. At the ranges required in desert fighting, this was true even of high-velocity weapons such as the 90-mm. gun. When shot did penetrate, fragmentation was insufficient to wreck the tank interior. To increase the armor-piercing quality, Ordnance engineers added to all calibers of armor-piercing shell a device already developed for the less powerful 37-mm. antitank shell, a steel armor-piercing cap with a windshield affixed for improved ballistics. To increase the destructive effect after penetration, these armor-piercing-capped—APC—projectiles were provided with a small cavity containing a bursting charge of Explosive D and with a base-detonating fuze. With these improvements, the 90-mm. APC M82 projectile, for example, would effect a deeper penetration of face-hardened armor plate at a thousand yards than the 90-mm. armor-piercing.[78] American 75-mm. APC ammunition, though then made without an explosive charge, was credited with saving the day in Libya, as British uncapped ammunition was ineffective against German face-hardened plate. APC projectiles with the explosive charge were late getting into production, partly because the base-detonating fuze was not available.[79]

Hardly had the new APC high-explosive ammunition reached the battlefields when the even more heavily armored Panther and Tiger tanks made their appearance. They could not be knocked out even by the 90-mm. M82 or the M62 APC provided for 3-inch and 76-mm. guns. This new threat called for a shell of radically different design. The Ordnance Department's answer was "HVAP." The principle underlying the effectiveness of HVAP—hypervelocity armor-piercing ammunition—was that the energy of a projectile is a function of the square of the velocity. Light-weight, hard-cored projectiles could attain hypervelocities, that is, from 3,000 to 4,000 or more feet per second, and thus have more than double the energy and hence penetrating power of those fired at ordinary velocities, which seldom exceeded 2,600 feet per second. Study of captured ammunition for the German tapered bore gun established the possibilities of the German design.[80] It had a core of tungsten carbide, a material of such density and hardness that it would not shatter on impact at high speeds, as steel was likely to do. To adapt this projectile to standard cylindrically bored weapons, the best method appeared to be to use a lighter weight shell made with an aluminum alloy jacket. Testing of a first experimental model, the T24, designed for the 37-mm. gun, began at Aberdeen in the spring of 1942. That summer NDRC, at Ordnance request, undertook basic research on the behavior of hypervelocity projectiles at the target.[81]

Despite the approximately 50 percent greater penetration of this new type of projectile as compared to that of standard armor-piercing ammunition, no 37-mm. HVAP was made for service use, nor was

[78] (1) Barnes Diary, 4 Apr 42, 18 Jan 43, OHF. (2) OCM 18340, 21 May 42; 18386, 22 May 42. (3) Catalogue of Standard Ord Items, III, 531–32.

[79] (1) Barnes Diary, 18 Jan, 18 Feb 43, OHF. (2) OCM 18340, 11 Jun 42.

[80] See above, pp. 348–50.

[81] (1) OCM 17188, 25 Aug 41. (2) Hypervelocity Development, Guns and Ammo, pp. 3–16, OHF. (3) Barnes Diary, 6 Apr 42; 20 Apr 42, OHF. (4) Burchard, ed., *op. cit.*, p. 277.

HVAP for bigger shells pushed until 1944. Before that time the Ordnance Department considered the existing 75-mm. and 3-inch armor-piercing projectiles capable of defeating any enemy tank so far met on the battlefield, and tungsten, imported from China, was in critically short supply.[82] But after D Day U.S. commanders in France cabled urgent appeals for weapons of high velocity to use against the German heavy tanks, more heavily armored than anticipated. The Ordnance Department then went quickly into action. Thanks to the earlier development work, the HVAP shot T4 for 76-mm. and 3-inch guns was in the field by September. This achievement was close to a record for speed. Unfortunately, the T4, although an improvement over any preceding armor-piercing ammunition, failed to solve the major problem, for it did not successfully penetrate the glacis plate of the Panther tank at practical ranges.[83] Continued development produced an improved design, the T4E20, standardized early in 1945 as the M93. By then a 90-mm. HVAP round had been developed which, following combat tests, was standardized as the M304 in June. Containing an 8-pound core of tungsten carbide as opposed to the 4-pound core of the 76-mm. HVAP shot, and at the same time attaining a muzzle velocity about 400 feet per second greater, the 90-mm. shot could destroy the German Panther and Tiger tanks at ranges up to 2,000 yards. Against the King or Royal Tiger it was only partially effective.[84] Foreseeing future need for penetrating even thicker armor at more difficult angles of presentation, the Ordnance Department carried an extensive HVAP development program into the postwar period.[85]

Breaching the heavy concrete obstacles and massive masonry walls encountered by the American forces in Europe required the utmost in explosive power, much more than most armor-piercing or semi-armor-piercing ammunition could deliver. The Engineers' demolition blocks, and notably shaped-charge blocks, were effective when fighting was at close quarters,[86] but at long ranges the problem remained of getting a high-explosive shell that would penetrate and not break up on impact. The best solution found was a special steel fuze that could be used with high-explosive ammunition of 75-mm. to 240-mm.[87] A still sturdier fuze together with an explosive more brisant than TNT promised even better results. In the interim, the Ordnance Department pushed work on ammunition for the 914-mm. mortar then under development. Though the shell for the Little David with its 1,584 pounds of high explosive proved in tests to have far more destructive capacity than any projectile ever previously conceived, at the end of the war its accuracy was still unsatisfactory.[88]

[82] (1) Barnes, *op. cit.*, p. 88. (2) Barnes Diary, 5 May 42, OHF. (3) Burchard, ed., *op. cit.*, pp. 281, 320–21.

[83] (1) Burchard, ed., *op. cit.*, p. 319. (2) OCM 24680, 10 Aug 44. (3) Barnes Diary, 25 Jul 44; 10 Aug 44; 11 Aug 44, OHF. (4) Ltr, Gen Holly, Hq Communication Zone ETO, to Gen Borden, 7 Sep 44, Overseas Letters Misc, Barnes file, OHF.

[84] (1) Tabulation prepared by Ballistics Sec, R&D Div, 13 Sep 51, OHF. (2) OCM 26551, 1 Feb 45; 28147, 28 Jun 45. (3) Armor-Piercing Ammunition for Gun, 90-mm. T15, Jan 45, OHF.

[85] Min, Joint A&N mtg on Army Ord R&D, 26 Jun 46, p. 28, A&N Mtgs, Barnes file, OHF.

[86] Weapons for Jungle Warfare, 1 Nov 43, pp. 30–32, OHF.

[87] See above, p. 362.

[88] (1) Barnes, *op. cit.*, p. 174. (2) Min, Joint A&N mtg. on Army Ord R&D, 26 Jun 46, p. 29, A&N Mtgs, Barnes file, OHF. (3) Interv with Col Rayle, 10 Mar 52.

CHAPTER XIII

The Development of Better Protection

Just as armies needed mobility and fire power in modern warfare, so, if they were to survive to achieve victory, they had to have the best possible protection from enemy fire. Inasmuch as no war in history has ever been won by defensive tactics alone, the age-old formula decreeing offense to be the best defense still obtained in World War II. But military men recognized that in both offense and defense armor plate on tanks, sheathing on aircraft and helmets and other kinds of body armor were likely to provide valuable safeguards to fighting men. There were, of course, various other ways of reducing combat hazards for troops. For example, the discovery that tank crews were subject to fire within the fighting compartment caused by exploding of shells resting in the ammunition racks led the Armored Force toward the end of the war to develop so-called wet packs, a system of ammunition stowage that surrounded the racks with water. The search for smokeless, flashless propellants for artillery was aimed at preventing battery crews from exposing themselves to counterfire. Simpler protective measures were the camouflage painting and netting for gun emplacements developed by the Corps of Engineers, the Ordnance Department's non-light-reflecting finishes for weapons, and, above all, for infantrymen, intrenching tools for digging foxholes. More revolutionary was the increased use of mines to halt enemy attacks. Mines, to be sure, might be listed as weapons, but as their primary purpose was defense, they fell also into the category of protective devices. Besides these means of giving what might be called passive protection, there were the developments of matériel to provide added protection to troops in an advance. Use of smoke shell to screen movements was a familiar method, whereas mine exploders to clear paths through enemy mine fields were a distinct innovation.

Armor Plate

Of all the problems involved in giving fighting men the utmost protection possible, the optimum thickness, quality, and shape of armor plate for combat vehicles was one of the most difficult. When doctrinal change at the end of the 1930's decreed that tanks must be invulnerable to more than small arms fire, the Ordnance Department quickly had to find ways of giving additional protection. Armor was essential not only to safeguard tank crews but also to prevent damage to an expensive piece of equipment. Yet to sacrifice mobility and fire power by affixing excessively heavy armor plate would be to make the tank unsuited to its combat mission. While armor as such was far from a new device for protecting troops and equipment from enemy explosives and missiles, the race between offensive effectiveness of armor-defeating weapons and defensive effectiveness of steel plate reached an unprecedented pace between 1940 and 1945. Since military operations had become highly mobile, neither men nor equipment could seek safety in the ground as in the years of position warfare in World War I. Combined with the speed of fighting vehicles in evasive action, armor spelled the difference between combat utility and worthlessness and also between life and death for the crews.

At the outbreak of World War II American experience in the manufacture and application of armor was extremely limited. Private manufacturers had virtually no background in the production of steels for armored ground weapons. Inasmuch as Army contracts for this product had been infinitesimal during the frugal interwar decades and public sentiment discouraged research and development on war matériel, Ordnance know-how was similarly restricted. Before Hitler's steel-clad legions demonstrated otherwise, the users of armored vehicles in the U.S. Army had accepted the theory that armor was meant to stop only small arms fire. Conforming to that concept, protective plate on American tanks, combat cars, and armored cars until 1941 measured a maximum of 1.25 inches in thickness, as contrasted with more than 4 inches at the end of World War II.[1] In order to save money, the large majority of vehicles built before 1941 carried not armor but merely mild steel plate. Research and development in the field of armor protection against large-caliber, high-velocity missiles and high-power explosives therefore dated only from the time that United States participation in the war was imminent.

To protect occupants and functional mechanisms of combat vehicles against attack, armor had to possess two principal characteristics: the ability to defeat hostile projectiles, and the capacity to absorb the impact energy of projectiles without rupturing. The two types of armor in use during World War II, face-hardened and homogeneous, had these qualities in different degrees.

Face-hardened armor had primarily a high degree of hardness. As its name implies, it consisted of alloy steel hardened on only one side—the one facing enemy attack. Beneath the hardened outer surface face-hardened plate was relatively soft. While it had the advantage of lending itself readily to the production of a large range of surface hardnesses, it had the drawbacks of being expensive to manufacture, difficult to weld, and requiring from 3 to 5 percent nickel, a material in critically short supply. Rolled alloy steel of this type was used as armor on light combat vehicles and for outer stations on aircraft. But face-hardened plate was unsuitable for large sections such as castings. Against capped projectiles it was ineffective. Furthermore, its toughness factor was relatively low, a characteristic resulting in a tendency to spall—to tear, splinter, or throw off lethal fragments on the inside of the surface under attack. Although specifications for face-hardened armor were changed in late 1942 in an effort to obtain

[1] Medium tank T5, Phase III, built in 1938, carried 1 7/16 inches of armor on its turret but only 1¼ inches on its hull. Plate of 1¼-inch thickness likewise constituted the maximum protection of medium tank M2A1, the immediate forerunner of the General Grant. R&D, Tanks, OHF.

greater toughness and to limit back-spalling tendencies, subsequent tests showed that under arctic conditions the product was still unsatisfactory in those respects.[2]

Homogeneous armor had above all a high degree of toughness. Unlike the face-hardened type, it was essentially uniformly hard throughout its depth. It was more quickly manufactured than face-hardened armor and more easily machined and welded. In addition, homogeneous armor could more easily be produced in any desired shape. It could be rolled in the form of plate or cast in the form of complete components such as turrets, gun mantlets, hulls, and rear-drive casings. Because mass production of vehicles in wartime prohibited using the materials, man-hours, and machine-hours needed for processing face-hardened armor, homogeneous armor, which previously had been used only experimentally, came to be adopted as the primary protective material for American combat vehicles. Beginning with the authorization in June 1940 for procurement and test of a cast homogeneous upper hull for the General Grant medium tank, both cast and rolled homogeneous armor replaced the face-hardened type.

Firing experiments showed that at angles upward of 30 degrees homogeneous armor offered substantially the same protection against armor-piercing high-explosive shell that face-hardened plate gave, but the latter was somewhat superior against armor-piercing shot. The contours of castings could readily be made to follow the most favorable ballistic lines, whereas curved surfaces produced by welding segments of flat plate would always offer certain straight expanses more vulnerable to attack. Perhaps even more significant, particularly during the early war years when production was the watchword, was the time saved in the assembly of vehicles. A tank embodying cast major components, such as a turret, could be turned out in materially less time than one in which those components had to be fabricated by welding.

Among the foremost problems in armor research and development during World War II was that of arriving at specifications that guaranteed a satisfactory product without delaying production, the paramount consideration in America's armament program. Specifications in use between January 1939 and September 1940 contemplated the use of rolled armor plate only. Alloy contents of steel, heat treatment, and methods of fabrication were at the option of the manufacturer, who had to submit to the Ordnance Department samples of each lot for two ballistic tests, one determining resistance to penetration and the other determining resistance to shock. Both tests consisted of firing .30-caliber, .50-caliber, and 37-mm. armor-piercing shot against the sample plates. While the Ordnance Department considered using both rolled face-hardened and rolled homogeneous plate, the penetration requirements set forth in the specifications were so high that only face-hardened armor met them. By the autumn of 1940 the rapidly changing picture of American needs in fighting vehicles introduced elements necessitating a radical departure from prevailing practices and standards.

America's new tanks were designed for tactical roles in which they would have to withstand large-caliber artillery projectiles, so that toughness and resistance to back spalling assumed much greater importance than theretofore. Homogeneous

[2] R&D Serv, Armor Plate, Development and Production 1940–45, OHF. Unless otherwise stated, all material in this section is from this manuscript.

armor consequently came to be used in increasing quantities. Yet because requirements for armor steel increased a thousandfold with the rapidly mounting production of weapons, shortages in alloy metals forced the development of new analyses that markedly reduced the content of critical materials such as nickel, chromium, and vanadium.[3] Specifications governing armor steel began to be written not with a view to obtaining a product ideal in every respect, but with the intent of getting the best possible result consistent with the limitations inherent in mass manufacture.

Between 1940 and the end of World War II little in the American armor program remained static. Changes in the composition of armor steels, improvements in obtaining the desired physical properties with the requisite degree of uniformity, and novel testing procedures expediting acceptance of the finished product were introduced whenever and wherever they promised to further the purpose of providing U.S. and Allied troops with better protection. Following experience gained at Camp Shilo, Manitoba, during the winter of 1942–43, for example, the Ordnance Department in co-operation with industry devised two entirely new acceptance tests.

Experiments at Shilo showed that current methods of acceptance-testing armor by means of ballistic attack under normal conditions gave no assurance of satisfactory performance in subzero temperatures. In fact, the very validity of those tests as criteria of good armor became questionable. Face-hardened plate, for instance, turned out to behave unsatisfactorily in extreme cold, and, while homogeneous armor preserved its shock properties fairly well, it likewise revealed an increased tendency toward cracking and back spalling. Ballistic tests, though necessary for accumulating design information, were patently wanting in accuracy for acceptance testing of armor. What were needed were qualitative tests applicable to production inspection.

Early in 1943 the so-called fracture test for steel soundness was developed and eventually became mandatory for determining the acceptability of armor steels. In this test, plate specimens from every heat were hardened and then slowly broken in a press, thereby revealing the presence and frequency of laminations—characteristics conducive to back spalling. A material advantage of this test lay in the fact that it could be applied early enough in the treatment of steel to reject whatever was unfit for high-quality armor. Another test, the fibre fracture test developed by Watertown Arsenal, was made on specimens of plate as well as production plate for the purpose of controlling processing and heat treatment. The specimens were broken with a sharp blow and acceptance or rejection was determined by the structure revealed by the fracture. A fracture dull or fibrous in appearance indicated adequate heat treatment and high absorption of energy before failure. A fracture crystalline in appearance, on the other hand, indicated either unsatisfactory heat treatment or excessive hardness, either of which was indicative of low absorption of energy before fracture.

Other important work on armor and allied problems was done in the field of welding. Because of the wide use of face-hardened steel, which lost its hardness at places subjected to the heat of welding, the interwar years had seen little progress in this method of fabricating combat vehi-

[3] See Ch. XVIII, below.

cles. Armor was commonly joined by riveting, but riveted joints had a number of weaknesses. Studies and test firings at Aberdeen Proving Ground at the outbreak of World War II, for example, showed that heavy machine gun fire drove rivets into the fighting compartments of tanks and there created a hazard fully as lethal as shell fragments. Furthermore, bullet splash entered through riveted joints, and, under the impact of armor-piercing projectiles as small as 37-mm., the joints parted at the seams. Although some of these shortcomings were corrected in ways such as seal-welding rivet heads to the interiors of vehicles, the greater strength of welded joints as well as the time saving in production soon led to the wholesale adoption of welding.[4]

Only tremendous progress in the development of new materials and techniques—the result of Ordnance teamwork with expert groups such as the Subcommittee for the Welding of Armor of the Ferrous Metallurgical Advisory Committee—made that changeover practicable and successful. An obstacle such as the difficulty of welding face-hardened plate was overcome by devising a method of joint construction that eliminated the necessity of welding directly to the hard surface of the armor. Even better results were obtained in later work with face-hardened armor when its edges were protected during the hardening process, so that welding the edges was similar to welding homogeneous plate. The need for conserving critical alloying metals was met by the development of low-alloy electrodes. Production speed-ups were made possible by the development of an automatic process of submerged-arc welding. The utility of all these advances in the fabrication of armor steel, as well as those in the development of higher-quality steels proper, depended in the final analysis, however, on two cardinal elements—structural design and its applicability in practice.

Even the thinnest coat of armor added substantial weight to any combat vehicle and thereby impaired its mobility, the principal asset of motorized equipment. Invulnerability against attack from all varieties of explosives and all types and sizes of projectiles would have required a prohibitively heavy covering of armor. In practice, therefore, a compromise between optimum protection and weight requirements was reached. Sloping the surfaces exposed to attack increased the effectiveness of a given layer of armor in two ways: it increased its thickness when measured from a horizontal plane, a measurement known as armor basis, and it offered a less favorable surface for attack because projectiles were more likely to bounce off than to penetrate. The value of sloped surfaces on armored vehicles was dramatically illustrated by tests which proved that at identical optimum obliquities the average resistance to penetration of purposely selected plates of good and poor quality varied little. Some experimental work on use of spaced armor also proceeded, both in the United States and in Germany, in an attempt to safeguard against shaped-charge attack by causing the energy of the charge to exhaust itself against an outer sheath of armor or of low-density material attached to the armor plate proper. But while various methods of applying the principle of an insulating space or material were tested, neither the enemy nor the Allies arrived at a satisfactory answer.[5]

[4] APG Development and Proof Services, The Vulnerability of Armored Vehicles to Ballistic Attack, 1950, p. 145, OHF.

[5] *Ibid.*, pp. 34, 75–77.

Wartime improvements in design, the work of the Armor Branch at Aberdeen Proving Ground, were manifold. The sloped, streamlined surfaces of American tanks of late wartime vintage, for example, bore little resemblance to the boxlike hulls of prewar vehicles. Desirable features found in enemy equipment were promptly adopted. Thus, the sharp-nosed bow of the German Panther tank, which the Germans had copied after their unpleasant experiences with the similarly shaped Russian T34, made its appearance in the General Pershing. Invisible but no less vital design changes added to the protection of U.S. and Allied tank crews. Doors and escape hatches were modified for greater resistance to shock; ventilating devices were redesigned to provide more positive protection against bullet splash; gun shields were improved so that projectiles and fragments were less likely to impair the functioning of guns through burring or damage to trunnions. If not yet ideal, American vehicular armor plate by the end of World War II was not only producible in quantity but also gave troops and equipment far greater protection than that deemed attainable in 1940.

Body Armor

Armor for aircraft was a problem in which the Ordnance Department became involved because of its experience in establishing specifications for tank armor, but the task was largely one for aircraft designers, and Ordnance participation was chiefly advisory. Development of body armor, on the other hand, grew into a job of considerable proportions.

For ground troops the principal article was the helmet, a high-manganese steel cap designed to afford greater protection by fitting further down over the ears and neck than did the old "tin hat" of World War I. The new model was standardized in 1941 and produced in great quantity, some 22,000,000 before the end of the war. Though eventually armored vests were also standardized for the ground forces, it was body armor for flyers that engaged most attention. The unit of the Small Arms Division of Research and Development Service, to which this development project was assigned in the summer of 1943, soon found occasion to consult the armor workshop of the Metropolitan Museum of Art, where experts were familiar with every kind of armor in existence, from Roman cuirasses down through the medieval knight's chain mail and the gold-inlaid steel plates of the sixteenth century grandee. Study of the strong points and weaknesses of these centuries-old samples aided in the development of armor for the most modern of all soldiers, the flyer.[6] In the fall of 1943 Ordnance specialists devised an extremely useful new method of testing the protection afforded by various types of material. This so-called 20-mm. triangulation fragmentation test utilized the static detonation of 20-mm. high-explosive incendiary projectiles at a distance close enough to the armor under test to attack it with fragments of the size and velocity that caused most combat casualties. Examination of the materials after fragments had penetrated permitted a comparative evaluation based on the "retained casualty producing power" of the

[6] (1) R&D Serv, Body Armor, OHF. (2) Development of Body Armor, Chs. 1–4, preliminary draft MS prepared by Engineering Experiment Station School of Mechanical Engineering, Purdue University, OHF. (3) OCM 21021, 15 Jul 43; 21350, 19 Aug 43; 21525, 9 Sep 43; 27904, 7 Jun 45.

BODY ARMOR *of the type used by members of the U.S. Army Air Forces.*

fragments.[7] Tests of fabrics, laminates, steels, aluminum, and composites of metals and fabrics showed the best material to be a combination of aluminum and nylon. Flyers' full-armored vests, half-armored vests, aprons, groin armor, and neck armor were then made of this material exclusively.

Toward the end of the war the superiority of this light-weight material led to its adoption for helmets for all soldiers. While the sacrifices of mobility entailed by wearing any kind of armor raised the question of its utility for most ground troops, for airmen it was of great value. Of the ground forces, only Engineer units assigned to mine clearance had greater need of protection than of mobility. As the effects of exploding antipersonnel mines—*Schuetzenminen* and "S" mines—were severe, and as crotch armor promised to give useful psychological as well as physical protection, an adaptation of flyers' armor was worked out in the fall of 1944. Some 4,000 pieces were issued to the Corps of Engineers.[8]

Land Mines

Armor provided passive protection for equipment and troops at all times, but against an enemy advance protection could be supplied not only by fire power but also by land mines strewn in his

[7] Min, Joint A&N mtg on Army Ord R&D, 1 Oct 45, pp. 8–9, A&N Mtgs, Barnes file, OHF.

[8] (1) *Ibid.* (2) Development of Body Armor, Ch. 5, OHF.

path. While the War Department was slow to endorse a vigorous program of mine development, combat experience soon showed that heavy antitank mines and smaller antipersonnel mines had come to be essential munitions in warfare. Useless if an army were moving forward, they gave very real protection to troops in retreat or units stalemated before an aggressive enemy force. Reports from France in 1940 and from Russia in 1941 had carried indications of the importance of mines as a cheap and effective means of stopping tanks. The evidence multiplied when the great tank battles in North Africa began. Sown by the hundreds of thousands over the desert, the Germans' flat, deadly "Teller mines" protecting Rommel's army were a major obstacle to the British Eighth Army in Libya and later to the Americans in Tunisia. Though not wholly ignored by the U.S. Army before the North African campaign, antitank and antipersonnel mines alike were only then recognized as vital. A tour of North Africa after the victory in May 1943 convinced General McNair that the land mine was "almost a new arm of warfare."[9]

From 1926 to 1937 the Chief of Engineers had had responsibility for antitank mine development. Progress had been slow. From time to time the Engineer Board manufactured experimental models, simple metal boxes containing TNT and a contact fuze made by Picatinny Arsenal, but it was not until the fall of 1936 that steps were taken leading to active development. At that time the trend was toward a design that should be a standard item of issue to all ground combat troops—infantry, cavalry and mechanized—as well as to the engineers. Because the mine would no longer come under the general category of demolitions and because its most complex part was a fuze, manufacture of which was properly an Ordnance function, the Chief of Engineers recommended that responsibility be transferred to Ordnance. The transfer was authorized by the War Department early in 1937, and development work began at Picatinny.[10]

The Infantry Board wanted a mine strong enough to disable a medium tank and yet light enough to be carried by a foot soldier. It must function under light tanks weighing about three tons, must be capable of being immersed in water for several hours, must be easily armed and disarmed in daylight and darkness by men with little training, must operate above ground as well as below, and must have two fuzes. The board suggested that it contain 5 or 6 pounds of TNT or the equivalent and that it not exceed one foot 2 inches in length, 6 inches in width, 5.25 inches in height, and 19 pounds in weight when loaded.[11]

The mine designed by the Picatinny Technical Group was made of steel and was circular in form rather than rectangular, because by methods of manufacture then current a cylinder was easier to make. It was about 7.25 inches in diameter, 3.25 inches high, weighed approximately 10 pounds, and contained about 5.5 pounds of TNT. It had one fuze, inserted in a well at the top, instead of two; but a cover plate extended the full diameter of the mine would work the fuze if a vehicle ran over any portion of the plate. Thus, one fuze served the purpose of two. Pressure on the plate crushed a thin collar between the

[9] (1) *The New York Times,* May 16, 1943. (2) Barnes Diary, 14 Dec 42–31 Jan 43, OHF.

[10] (1) Ammo Development Div, R&D Serv, Land Mines, Aug 45, pp. 6–9, OHF. (Hereafter cited as Land Mines.) (2) Hist of Picatinny Arsenal Manufacturing Group, Explosives Dept, Vol. I, Pt. 1, p. 376, OHF. (3) Hist of Picatinny Arsenal Tech Group, II, 28A, OHF. (4) OCM 13428, 11 Feb 37; 13502, 4 Mar 37; 14665, 1 Sep 38.

[11] OCM 13428, 11 Feb 37.

striker head and the fuze body, broke two shear pins, and operated a spring-loaded firing pin that functioned the detonator. When service tested early in 1940, this experimental model revealed defects that necessitated modifications. The fuze was unsafe for handling, and the solid pressure plate was susceptible to blast, so that the mines could not be placed close together. The fault in the fuze was corrected by inserting between the striker head and the body of the fuze a safety fork that had to be removed by hand. The defect in the mine case was corrected by substituting for the cover plate a "spider" consisting of a steel rim around the perimeter of the mine with crosspieces intersecting at the fuze. Tests showed that the mines thus modified would stop a light tank and, thanks to the spider design, could be placed as close as eighteen inches apart. The mine was standardized in late October 1940 as the antitank mine M1, the fuze as the M1 antitank mine fuze.[12]

Yet even at the time of standardization there were intimations that the M1 was inadequate. Shortly after the fall of France, Engineer and Ordnance officers had obtained from an officer of the French Corps of Engineers, Maj. Pierre Delalande, an accurate description of the Germans' powerful Teller mine, which contained twice as much explosive as the M1 and which had impressed Major Delalande with its effectiveness. After discussions with him, the Chief of Engineers asked Ordnance to develop a heavy deliberate antitank mine that would contain from fifteen to twenty pounds of explosive. The Chief of Ordnance objected. He considered the use of the M1 in pairs to be a better solution, because of the supply problem. As the Engineers did not agree, Ordnance made an M1 model with the body deepened to permit fifteen pounds of TNT. In tests it blew a hole through the floor of a light tank and hurled the cupola five feet. Then the Engineers decided that after all no military requirement existed for so large a mine. The project was canceled.[13]

A more productive result of early reports from Europe and conversations with Major Delalande was the beginning of antipersonnel mine development. The antipersonnel mine had been in the fall of 1939 a secret weapon of the Germans. Buried in great quantities between the Siegfried Line and the Maginot Line, the mine was first discovered in the Arndt Forest in Lorraine by French patrols who nicknamed it the "Silent Soldier." It was a bounding device that projected a delayed-action shell. In co-operation with Major Delalande, Ordnance engineers constructed a model; from this and from a British copy of the Silent Soldier, they developed a mine consisting of a tube containing a mortar projectile, connected at the tube's lateral end with a smaller tube containing a fuze and propelling charge. Pressure on the fuze pressure button or a pull on the fuze pull ring set off the charge at the base of the larger tube, projecting a shell that exploded when it was two to six feet from the tube. The first model, the M2, was cleared for procurement in April 1942.[14] But it was difficult to manufacture, had an erratically functioning fuze, and was unsatisfactory when buried in the

[12] (1) OCM 15453, 9 Nov 39; 15504, 7 Dec 39; 16165, 10 Oct 40; 16204, 24 Oct 40. (2) Land Mines, p. 22, OHF. (3) Hist of Picatinny Manufacturing Group, Explosives Dept, Vol. I, Pt. 1, p. 416, OHF.

[13] OCM 16585, 8 Mar 41; 17909, 1 Mar 42; 17959, 14 Mar 42.

[14] (1) Lt. Col. Paul W. Thompson, "Mines by the Millions," *Infantry Journal,* LI, 6 (1942), 14. (2) OCM 16585, 8 Mar 41; 17587, 17 Dec 41; 18013, 2 Apr 42; and 18060, 10 Apr 42. (3) Land Mines, pp. 61–64, OHF.

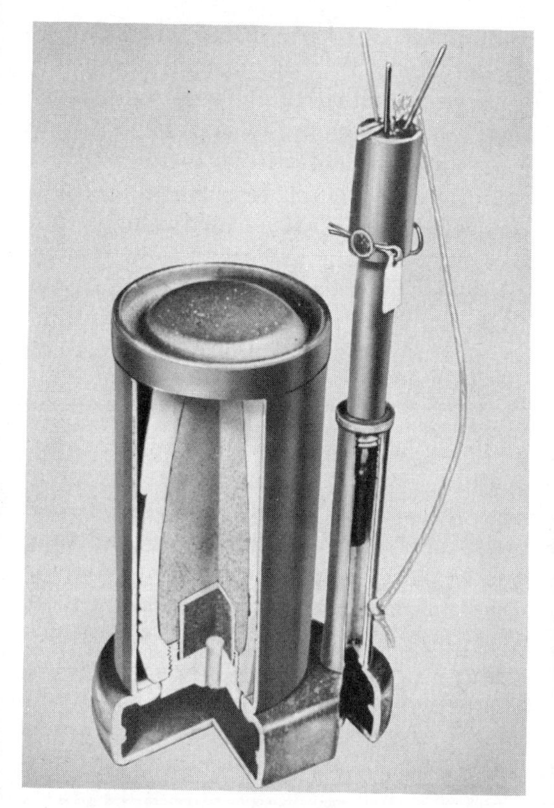

LAND MINES. *The U.S. bounding antipersonnel mine (upper left); the German "S" mine, nicknamed "Bouncing Betty" (upper right); and the U.S. antitank mine M6 (below).*

291064 O—55——26

ground since it was not waterproof. In an effort to make it waterproof, designers made model after model. Finally, the tubes and base were welded together and in this form the M2A4 and M2A4B2 were standardized. In operation they were the same as the M2 except for the fuze; the new and safer fuze had a three-pronged top similar to that on the German successor to the Silent Soldier, the "S" mine.[15] In addition to the bounding mine, Ordnance and the Corps of Engineers developed a fragmentation mine that inflicted injury by bursting into pieces. This consisted of a small hollow cast-iron block filled with TNT and equipped with wells for receiving a fuze similar to that used in the M2A4 mine. This mine was developed in a few months and standardized in August 1942 as the antipersonnel mine M3.[16]

In 1941 Ordnance engineers began the search for satisfactory nonmetallic mines. This trend resulted from a report that the British had a detector for metallic mines. A nonmetallic antitank mine, developed by the Onandaga Pottery Company, was standardized in the spring of 1943 as M5. Not unlike the German *Topf* mine, it consisted of an inverted ceramic bowl separated from its ceramic base by a rubber cushion that activated a plastic plunger. The fuze was also nonmetallic: the plunger forced a piston to break a glass ampule containing a reactive primer mixture. The mine was too heavy in proportion to its explosive power; with about the same amount of explosive as the M1, it weighed three pounds more and took up 64 percent more shipping space. For this reason, Ordnance requested the Department of Agriculture's Forest Products Laboratory to develop plywood and plastic mines—types extensively used by the enemy. But the experimental models were neither powerful enough nor very safe. Field requirements for a nonmetallic mine were never very large and lessened after the United States took the offensive since, after an advance, troops had difficulty in locating their own mines. Early in 1945, at the request of Army Ground Forces, Ordnance began work on a heavy nonmetallic mine but canceled the project after V-J Day. At that time a project for a nonmetallic antipersonnel mine requested by AGF in the summer of 1944 was also canceled.[17]

Throughout World War II the most important mine development continued to be the metallic antitank mine. The model standardized in October 1940 as the M1 was followed by a slightly modified mine, the M1A1. Just when a further and even slighter modification, the M4, was nearing standardization in the spring of 1943, the entire subject of land mines was brought sharply into focus by the events of the North African campaign. At that time the M1A1 was being procured in great quantities, in spite of the fact that it had never been tested against anything stronger than a light tank. By 1943 there were powerful

[15] OCM 21880, 21 Oct 43; 24160, 22 Jun 44.

[16] (1) Land Mines, pp. 69–71, OHF. (2) OCM 17698, 29 Jan 42; 18041, 8 Apr 42; 18521, 23 Jul 42.

[17] (1) OCM 19807, 25 Feb 43; 25596, 2 Nov 44; 26069, 14 Dec 44; 28794, 20 Aug 45; 29073, 13 Sep 45; 29153, 20 Sep 45. (2) Land Mines, pp. 27–31, 33–34, OHF. (3) Catalogue of Standard Ord Items, III, 595. (4) Picatinny Arsenal Manufacturing Group, Explosives Dept, Vol. I, Pt. 1, p. 417. (5) Ltr, Gen Campbell to Mr. H. Leroy Whitney, Chairman WPB, 9 Aug 44, sub: Tests by Forest Products Laboratory, OO 476/1192, DRB AGO. (6) Baxter, *Scientists Against Time,* pp. 102–03. (7) Memo, CG ASF for CofOrd, 25 Aug 44, sub: Non-Metallic Antitank Mines, OO 476/1200, DRB AGO. (8) Ltr, CG AGF to CG ASF, 1 Sep 44, sub: Military Characteristics of Non-Metallic, Antitank and Antipersonnel Mines, OO 476/1261, DRB AGO. (9) Ltr, CG ASF to CofOrd, 5 Sep 44, sub: Non-Metallic Antitank Mines, OO 476/1226, DRB AGO. (10) Barnes Diary, 16, 17 May 44, OHF.

arguments for a heavier mine: the effectiveness of Teller mines in North Africa, the appearance of the huge German Mark VI tanks, and the example of the British who in the fall of 1942 had increased the charge of their antitank mine from five pounds to ten. The Engineers, pointing out that Ordnance had no officer assigned solely to antitank mines, asked for more vigorous development and, backed by the Army Ground Forces, requested that a thorough test program be put into effect.[18] Consequently, at Aberdeen in April the M1A1, M4, and M5 were tested against the Teller mine. Mine for mine, the German model came off best, but the final conclusion of Aberdeen's commanding general was that when greater strength was needed, the M1A1 should be used in multiples. In this solution General Barnes, who had made a tour of North Africa late in December 1942 and was still convinced that "we do have a satisfactory mine," concurred.[19]

The Ground Forces and Engineers out of their combat experience, especially with Rommel's employment of mines at Kasserine Pass, thought otherwise. Under battle conditions, the use of small mines in pairs presented problems of concealment, excavation, and emplacement. When General McNair went to North Africa in mid-May to evaluate certain types of training and weapons, the use of land mines was one of two important points of controversy uppermost in his mind.[20] General Bradley wrote General Marshall, "Unless we can immediately develop mines better than the German 'S' and German Teller types, I would suggest that we adopt them both and start production immediately."[21] Ordnance officers in NATOUSA tested the M1 mine against captured enemy tanks and found that it would not stop the Mark VI. They proposed an explosive charge of ten or fifteen pounds and a mine case like the Teller mine's. Of the antipersonnel mines, the Infantry thought the M2 as good as the "S" mine. Both Infantry and Engineers wanted, in addition to a large deliberate mine, a hasty light antitank mine. Moreover, General McNair recommended more extensive use of mines by all branches of the Army.[22] The recommendations coming from North Africa were bolstered by a survey of all theatres made by ASF and by further and more comprehensive tests at Aberdeen, where the M1A1, M4, and M5 were again compared with Teller mines, and a British hasty mine, the Hawkins grenade, was also carefully studied.[23] As a

[18] (1) Land Mines, pp. 16–26, OHF. (2) OCM 16204, 24 Oct 40; 19903, 11 Mar 43. (3) Ltr, President Engr Bd to CofEngrs, 19 Feb 43, sub: Development of Antitank Mines, Data for Reopening Project DM 294, and ind, 5 Mar 43, OO 471.6/524, DRB AGO. (4) Barnes Diary, 23 Jun 43, OHF. (5) Message W-1528, Eisenhower to AGWAR, 28 May 43, OO 386.3/359, DRB AGO.

[19] (1) OCM 20649,3 Jun 43. (2) Barnes Diary, 6 May 43, and 22 Jun 43, OHF.

[20] (1) *The New York Times,* May 16, 1943. (2) Land Mines, p. 19, OHF. (3) *Time,* XLI, 13 (1943), 14.

[21] Ltr, Gen Christiansen, CofS AGF, to CG ASF, 16 Jul 43, sub: Development of Deliberate Antitank Mine, OO 476/313, DRB AGO.

[22] (1) *Ibid.* (2) Message, AGWAR to Crawford for Hall, 11 May 43, CM-OUT 7765, OO 386.3/349. (3) Message W-1419, Eisenhower to AGWAR, 26 May 43, OO 396.3/357. (4) Message W-1528, Eisenhower to AGWAR, 28 May 43, OO 386.2/359. (5) Memo, Maj David F. Shepherd, Ammo Off NATOUSA, for Chief Ord Off NATOUSA, 14 Jun 43, sub: Report of Tests of Antitank Mines versus Armored Vehicles, and ind, 21 Jun 43, OO 350.05/4508. All in DRB AGO.

[23] (1) OCM 19903, 11 Mar 43; 20649, 3 Jun 43, 23463, 13 Apr 44; 20423, 13 May 43; 20163, 4 Apr 43. (2) Ltr, CofOrd to Dir Proving Center, APG, 10 May 43, sub: Mines, Antitank, U.S. and Foreign—Tests to Determine Characteristics and Effects Produced by, and ind, 11 Apr 44, OO 471.6/568, DRB AGO. The Hawkins grenade is not to be confused with standard American grenades.

result of these investigations the Ordnance Department immediately began development of a heavy mine as destructive as the Teller mine, and of a light one for convenient and versatile use in multiples against tanks and singly as booby traps. And notwithstanding the Infantry's favorable report on the M2 antipersonnel mine, Picatinny Arsenal was instructed to study the German "S" mine and work on a new design.[24]

Designers of the heavy mine attempted to correct faults both of the M1A1 and of the German mine. Used above ground the M1A1, because it was too tall, tended to tip when a tank ran over its rim; when it was buried, earth and rocks would work into the space between spider and mine and prevent the fuze from functioning. The new mine was low and, instead of a spider, had a pressure plate like that of the Teller mine, but covering only about half the area of the mine. This corrected a defect of the Teller mine No. 1, the pressure plate of which covered it entirely and made it subject to detonation from blast. In Teller mine No. 2, the Germans reduced the area of the pressure plate. Teller mine No. 3 had a covering pressure plate with radial flutings that gave maximum area with minimum susceptibility to blast. In Teller mine No. 4 a mushroom-head type that screwed into the main igniter socket replaced the pressure plate.[25]

By late August 1943 the Ordnance Department had four pilot models ready for test. Both the Ordnance Technical Division and the Engineer Board's Technical Staff preferred the one designated T6E1. This had a thin metal shell, weighed twenty pounds, and contained twelve pounds of TNT, thus fulfilling the Ground Forces requirement that the mine be 60 percent explosive. Offering the greatest possible area to tank tracks, the mine case was about three inches high and thirteen in diameter, and had activating wells in the sides and bottom for booby trapping. Inside, a stack of four Belleville springs supported the pressure plate and provided the tension fixing the 350-pound load under which the fuze would function. The fuze well in the center was closed by a reversible plug that could be screwed down in either a safe or an armed position. This feature met the important requirement that arming be the last step in mine laying. The fuze was chemical, similar to that of the nonmetallic mine.[26]

The light hasty mine had the same general shape as the British Hawkins grenade mine but was more powerful. The body was a flat metal can—readily available commercially—loaded with tetrytol, an explosive 20 percent more effective than TNT. The same chemical fuze used in the heavy mine was inserted in the flat side of the can and covered by a pressure plate shaped to the contour of the mine body; it would function under a load of approximately 200 pounds. Loaded, the mine weighed only about four pounds. It was pre-eminently an infantry mine. It could be carried in the cargo pocket of combat trousers and was therefore available wherever men on foot could go. The Infantry Board was enthusiastic about it.[27]

A new antipersonnel mine under development at Picatinny resembled the Ger-

---

[24] (1) R&D Serv, Antitank and Antipersonnel Mines, Introduction, OHF. (2) Land Mines, pp. 36–43, OHF. (3) Hist of Picatinny Arsenal Tech Group, V, 36, OHF. (4) OCM 26024, 14 Dec 44.

[25] Middle East Tech Intel Summary 101, 30 Jun 43, Apps. B and C, Ord Tech Intel files.

[26] OCM 21730, 7 Oct 43.

[27] (1) OCM 21551, 16 Sep 43; 25174, 21 Sep 44. (2) R&D Serv, Antitank and Antipersonnel Mines, pp. 8–12, OHF. (3) Hist of Picatinny Arsenal Tech Group, IV, 43, OHF.

man "S" mine rather than the American two-tube M2A4. Within a canister about 4 inches in diameter and 4.5 inches high was a cast-iron projectile loaded with .7 pounds of TNT, propelled by a charge of black powder set off by a three-pronged fuze in the canister's top. This model was more compact than the two-tube bounding mine, easier to manufacture, and much more nearly waterproof. It was also a good deal heavier: three pounds had been added to the projectile and bursting charge to produce more than double the number of effective fragments of the M2A4. Tests were encouraging, and on V-J Day the new model was about to supplant M2A4.[28]

Because of the urgent need in the summer of 1943 for the heavy antitank mine and the hasty mine, procurement began that fall before either was standardized. After correction of minor defects in the T6E1, notably a tendency to leak, it was standardized in September 1944 as the M6. At the same time the hasty mine was standardized as the M7. Thanks to the early procurement program, which constituted a tooling-up for full-scale production, at the end of 1944 2,500,000 M6 mines and 750,000 M7's were on hand in the zone of the interior. There were none in the European theatre. General Barnes, who considered the M6 a much more effective antitank mine than any other in existence and the M7 very valuable, tried in vain to get both mines used in the theatres.[29] Overseas, stocks of M1 and M1A1 mines were excessive, and operational requirements for land mines were lessening. While General Barnes' faith in them appears to have been justified, the new mines came too late. Except for the brief German break-through in the Ardennes in December 1944, U.S. forces were on the offensive from D Day on and had only restricted need for field fortifications and obstacles.[30]

Mine Exploders

Whereas mines diminished in importance as the United States and Allied armies advanced, the problem of neutralizing enemy mine fields became increasingly pressing when the United States began to plan its offensive in Europe and the Pacific. Mines had worked so well for the enemy in North Africa that they were used even more widely in Italy. The German antipersonnel mine, sown in belts and patches, would take a man's foot or leg off. Especially dangerous was the *Schuetzenmine* that appeared for the first time in Italy. The antitank mine, buried by the thousands, row upon row, would disable a tank by shattering the track and suspension components. The five or six million mines that Rommel laid in his defense of the coast of Europe, not only in mine fields but in holes cut in paved roads, slowed the American advance and caused considerable losses in men and equipment.[31] In the

[28] OCM 25913, 30 Nov 44; 26024, 14 Dec 44; 28794, 20 Aug 45; 29073, 13 Sep 45.

[29] (1) Ltr, Gen Barnes to Gen Simpson, 3 Jan 45, sub: [M6 and M7], OO 476/1340, DRB AGO. (2) Barnes, *Weapons of World War II*, p. 94.

[30] (1) Memo, CG ASF for CinC SWPA, 14 Sep 44, sub: Mine, AT, Light, T-7, and ind, 14 Dec 44, OO 476/1348, DRB AGO. (2) Final Report of the Chief Engineer European Theater of Operations 1942–1945 (hereafter cited as Rpt of Chief Engr ETO), p. 162, copy in OHF. (3) Barnes Diary, 16 May 44 and 17 May 44, OHF.

[31] (1) Barnes Diary, 14 Dec 42–31 Jan 43, OHF. (2) Baxter, *op cit.*, pp. 100–103. (3) Harrison, *Cross-Channel Attack*, p. 164. (4) Eddy Rpt, pp. 31–32, 70, Missions, Barnes file, OHF. (5) Rpt of Chief Engr ETO, pp. 163–64, OHF. (6) Mine Exploder Mission to European Theater of Operations, U.S. Army, 4 April 1944 to 19 October 1944 (hereafter cited as Mine Exploder Mission ETO), p. 32, OHF.

use of mines the Japanese were not far behind the Germans. At one point in the Okinawa Campaign mines held up a U.S. division for more than a week.[32] From all theatres came urgent requests for an effective mine clearing device.[33]

Mine fields could be cleared by removing the mines by hand. The NDRC had designed detectors for both metallic and nonmetallic types, although they were not infallible, especially those for the nonmetallic. When detectors were not available or were not trusted, a man crawling on his knees and probing carefully into the ground ahead of him with his bayonet could dig up a mine safely if he were careful enough. But because of booby-trapping, this hand method was risky and at best was time consuming. The safest and quickest way to clear a path was to detonate the mines, either by blast or by pressure. For sympathetic detonation the Engineers used some of the devices employed to blast openings through wire entanglements, such as demolition snakes and Bangalore torpedoes, that is, tubes filled with high explosive. At various times other devices were considered—artillery fire, aerial bombs, hoses filled with liquid explosive, and rocket-propelled charges.[34] The Ordnance Department supplied the Bangalore torpedo, an old siege weapon, and a few other items, but in general mine clearance by explosives was the responsibility of the Chief of Engineers. To the Chief of Ordnance were assigned development projects for mine field clearance by pressure. The pressure method grew in importance as experience revealed serious drawbacks to the use of explosives. Bangalore torpedoes, demolition snakes, and other detonators would clear lanes in mine fields but would leave along the edges "tender" mines, with partially sheared pins, that would go off at the slightest touch; furthermore, as the war progressed, new blast-resistant Teller mines appeared. These considerations stimulated the search for an effective mechanical mine exploder.[35]

At the outset no belligerent had much experience that the Ordnance Department could tap. In the winter of 1941 the Russians cleared a German mine field south of Leningrad by marching over it tightly closed columns of soldiers shoulder to shoulder.[36] This method could hardly be recommended. The first mechanical mine exploder reported to the Ordnance Department was one developed by the French. A drawing sent in a Corps of Engineers memorandum in 1940 showed a tank propelling three sets of roller disks, two mounted on the front and one on the

[32] Baxter, *op. cit.*, p. 102.

[33] Mine Exploder Mission to Southwest Pacific Area and United States Army Forces in the Far East, 28 March 1945 to 1 June 1945, p. 11, OHF.

[34] (1) OCM 18484, 16 Jul 42; 19663, 4 Feb 43; 26022, 14 Dec 44; 26810, 1 Mar 45. (2) Ltr, CG Armored Force to CG AGF, 6 Oct 42, sub: Transmittal of Rpt, and 5th Ind, 30 Dec 42, OO 471.6/307, DRB AGO. (3) Ltr, Engr Bd to CofEngrs, 17 Mar 43, sub: Plan for Mine Field Clearing Tests, OO 471.6/558, DRB AGO. (4) Ltr, Engr Bd to CofEngrs, 7 Jul 44, sub: Vehicle for Snake, Demolition, Liquid Filled, OO 476/1151, DRB AGO. (5) Memo, CG ASF to CofOrd, 18 Sep 44, sub: Rpt on Bombing as a Method of Clearing Mines and Barbed Wire, OO 476/1245, DRB AGO.

[35] (1) Catalogue of Standard Ord Items, III, 598. (2) Rpt of Chief Engr, ETO, p. 163, OHF. (3) Baxter, *op. cit.*, p. 102. (4) Ltr, Deputy CofOrd to OCO, 9 Feb 43, sub: Mine Sweepers, General Development of; Characteristics of Land Mines of the United States and of Foreign Countries, OO 471.6/399, DRB AGO. (5) Middle East Tech Intel Summary 101, 30 Jun 43, Apps. B and C, Ord Tech Intel files. (6) Memo, CofEngrs for CG ASF, 12 Jun 44, sub: Development of Project DM 506, Equipment for the Passage of Enemy Minefields, and 3d Ind, 25 Jul 44, OO 476/1108, DRB AGO.

[36] "Peculiarities of Russian Warfare," German Report Series MS # T-22, Department of the Army, Hist Div, Rev. ed., 1949, p. 46.

rear. The T1, the American model adapted from the drawing, had steel disks 2.25 inches thick and 40 inches in diameter. Each of the three units mounted four disks and the units front and rear were spaced so as to clear a path slightly wider than the tank. Tests of this crude rig at Aberdeen early in 1942 showed that it would detonate mines, but it fell far short of possessing the other characteristics desired in a mine exploder: indestructibility, maneuverability, and simplicity of design. Yet, since the multiple-disk principle seemed sound, Ordnance engineers continued development on the French type of exploder.[37]

In the next important model the Ordnance Department strengthened the disks against mine injury by making them of armor plate, and improved control of the disk units by moving the rear unit to the front. The three units, which now consisted of six disks each, were supported loosely on a shaft to permit movement over uneven ground, and were mounted on a tank recovery vehicle, the hoist of which could lift them out of mine craters or ditches. The disk assembly alone weighed about eighteen tons and the whole contraption was nicknamed the "Earthworm."[38] Obviously something was still to be desired in the way of maneuverability and simplicity. The next development was a simpler model with two roller units instead of three. It depended for full ground coverage on two tanks operated in tandem. This transitional model led to a third, the T1E3 or "Aunt Jemima," similar in design but equipped with enormous disks eight feet in diameter. Instead of being pushed, these disks were driven through a chain drive taken from the sprockets of the tank. Driving the disk units increased maneuverability since they could be extracted from mine craters or ditches without a hoist. The disks, with large oval holes that dissipated high-explosive pressure, were less liable to damage by Teller mines than anything yet devised. The oval holes also somewhat reduced the weight but, even so, the assembly weighed nearly thirty tons.[39]

The promise displayed by the driven-disk exploder did not halt investigation of other types. Early in 1942 Ordnance engineers experimented with use of heavy steel slabs hanging from a boom fastened on the front of a light tank. These slabs, pushed over the ground ahead of the tank, would detonate mines, but tests of the pilot model showed that the explosions damaged the exploder. The drag-weight method was soon abandoned.[40]

Another early device was the well-publicized flailing exploder, copied from one designed by the British in North Africa. Hastily improvised at the Eighth Army Cairo base, the British "Scorpion" used steel chains attached to a revolving roller to beat the ground in front of a tank. On the basis of drawings sent to the United States in the summer of 1942, the Lamson Corporation began the manufacture of an American model, the T3. Before it was

[37] OCM 16285, 8 Nov 40; 20847, 24 Jun 43. For a general discussion of this and other mechanical mine field clearance devices, see: (1) Minefield Clearance Devices, 10 Dec 43, Kangaroo Folder, OHF; and (2) W. P. Wood, Mine Exploders and Excavators, Record of Army Ord R&D, August 1945 (hereafter cited as Mine Exploders), MS, OHF.

[38] (1) OCM 20847, 24 Jun 43. (2) Ltr, Maj Arra S. Avakian to Chief Ord Off NATOUSA, 2 Jul 44, sub: Mine Exploders T1E1 and T1E3, OO 476/1137, DRB AGO.

[39] (1) OCM 22128, 18 Nov 43. (2) Memo, Maj Brooks Walker, OD, for Mr. William Beasley, Ord R&D Serv, 4 Sep 44, sub: Mine Exploders, OO 476/1208, DRB AGO. (3) Barnes, *op. cit.*, p. 96.

[40] (1) OCM 18069, 16 Apr 42. (2) Wood, Mine Exploders, pp. 61–70, OHF.

completed, General Barnes in December 1942 visited the Eighth Army tank school in North Africa and witnessed a demonstration of the Scorpion. It whipped up dust that clogged the tank engines and was too slow; nevertheless, General Sir Harold R. L. G. Alexander and Maj. Gen. D. J. R. Richards so impressed General Barnes with the possibilities of their admittedly crude Scorpion and with the urgent need for an American mine exploder to combat German mines that he recommended to General Devers the manufacture of at least fifty T3's for immediate shipment overseas. Thirty were pushed to completion and shipped in the spring of 1943. They were the first mechanical mine exploders sent overseas. Unhappily, they did not fulfill the promise of their British prototype. Installation in the American model of a hydraulic system to raise and lower the boom made the unit heavier and less maneuverable than the original Scorpion. The flails threw mud and debris against the tank and were often broken off by mine explosions. Twelve T3's used by a mine field clearing company of Engineers in Italy were discarded as unsatisfactory.[41]

When clearing mine fields became an urgent necessity early in 1943, many novel devices were proposed. General Barnes suggested mounting a bank of machine guns high on the top of a tank and shooting into the ground.[42] The John Deere Company submitted the T7, consisting of hollow rollers to be filled with dirt or gravel. Col. Allison R. Williams, an Army Service Forces officer, designed a unit depending on a series of hydraulic shock-absorbed plunger rods that could be raised and lowered rapidly to pound the ground ahead of a tank. The York Safe and Lock Company made a pilot model, the T8.[43] Another proposal was for a very heavy studded drum, the T9, to be rolled ahead of a tank.[44] As the Engineer Board had enlisted NDRC aid, NDRC sponsored a design of a self-propelled device, consisting of two wheels eight feet in diameter, that contained gasoline engines and supported large disks between them; the device was steered by remote control.[45] The Ordnance Committee also considered a device for excavating mines from mine fields without detonating them. It had been under development, mainly by the Engineers, since October 1942. From a simple bulldozer blade attached to the front of a tank, a V-shaped moldboard had been evolved with teeth extending forward and downward that could dig up buried mines and throw them out of the path of the tank. In the summer of 1943 when mine-excavator development was taken from the Engineers and assigned to the Ordnance Department, the most promising model appeared to be a combination of several types.[46]

Because of the demand from the theatres, all mine-clearance models were pushed to completion and tested throughout the summer and fall of 1943 at Aberdeen and at the Armored Force Board's

---

[41] (1) Barnes, *op. cit.*, p. 96. (2) Ltr, Deputy CofOrd to OCO, 23 Nov 42, sub: Mine Detonating Device—Lamson Corporation, OO 471.6/325, DRB AGO. (3) OCM 20966, 8 Jul 43. (4) Barnes Diary, 14 Dec 42–31 Jan 43, OHF. (5) Eddy Rpt, p. 70, OHF. (6) Ltr, Maj Avakian, Ord Sec Hq NATOUSA, to OCO, 24 May 44, sub: Mine Exploder, T1E3; First Interim Report on Field Test of Two in NATOUSA, OO 476/1083, DRB AGO.

[42] Barnes Diary, 16 Apr 43, OHF.

[43] (1) OCM 20862, 24 Jun 43; 21268, 12 Aug 43. (2) Barnes Diary, 5 Apr 43 and 1 Jun 43, OHF.

[44] OCM 21443, 2 Sep 43.

[45] Ltr, Col Karl B. Schilling to Exec Off Engr Bd, 30 Jun 43, sub: Mechanical Devices for Clearing Minefields, OO 476/340, DRB AGO.

[46] OCM 20862, 24 Jun 43; 21394, 26 Aug 43; 21577, 16 Sep 43.

MINE EXPLODERS. *The driven-disc type T1E3 (above), and the "Scorpion" type (below).*

testing ground at Fort Knox, Kentucky. By December some evaluation was possible. The driven-disk exploder seemed to fulfill the requirements most nearly, with the pushed-disk exploder as second choice.[47] The automatic plunger type was impractical for use on uneven ground and its indestructibility was doubtful. The roller drum was acknowledged to be "relatively indestructible," [48] but it was also relatively immovable. It weighed 42 tons and could hardly be budged, even with the aid of a second tank. A lighter, 32-ton version was ineffective and not much more maneuverable. A modification of the T3 flail exploder was ineffective over uneven ground because, in an effort to make the device lighter, the hydraulic boom-lowering system had been eliminated. Inasmuch as the NDRC exploder and the T7 proved susceptible to damage by mines, work on these devices was early abandoned. The mine excavator seemed practical only for use in loose beach sand.[49]

Early in 1944 the Ordnance Department recommended procurement of 75 driven-disk Aunt Jemima T1E3 exploders. At the request of Army Ground Forces 75 Earthworms were added, in spite of Ordnance engineers' belief that the model would not stand full mine detonation. Four of the first production T1E3's were shipped overseas in May, two to England to be used in a test and demonstration mission, and two to Italy. After the tests, Ordnance officers reported that the exploders were satisfactory except for a tendency in very hard soil to bridge, or cross without detonating, a buried mine.[50] After the invasion, field tests in Normandy of both types of disk exploder showed other defects. The Earthworm, as Ordnance engineers had predicted, was susceptible to damage by mines. Aunt Jemima sometimes broke down and was too slow to head an advance. In operation over average soil it could do only three miles an hour; on roads its best speed was twelve. One irate division commander described it as the most effective roadblock his troops encountered in Europe. As the ground of Europe began to freeze, the tendency to bridge mines manifested itself. The Engineers preferred the flail exploder, despite its defects.[51]

Yet one important characteristic of a good mine exploder, indestructibility, had been demonstrated by the Aunt Jemima time and again. After field tests in Normandy, the officer in charge suggested that a different tactical use might increase its effectiveness. He recommended two categories of mine exploders, the first to include highly mobile devices that could move rapidly with an armored spearhead, the second to include slower and heavier exploders that could be loaded on tank transporters and taken wherever mine field resistance was severest or where special conditions obtained. Along with the T1E3 in the second category he placed the newest type of mine excavator, the T5E3, which had proved valuable as a beach clearer in the invasion of southern France.[52]

---

[47] (1) Ltr, CofOrd to Chief, Detroit Tank-Automotive Center, 18 Mar 43, sub: Mine Exploder Developments, OO 471.6/527, DRB AGO. (2) Ltr, Col Gerald B. Devore, President Armored Force Board, to CofOrd, 8 Apr 43, sub: Request for Personnel for Test of Mine Removing and Detonating Devices, OO 471.6/563, DRB AGO. (3) OCM 22509, 30 Dec 43.

[48] OCM 25160, 30 Aug 44.

[49] (1) *Ibid.* (2) OCM 22509, 30 Dec 43; 23837, 18 May 44.

[50] (1) OCM 22509, 30 Dec 43; 23837, 18 May 44. (2) Barnes Diary, 21 Apr–13 May 44, OHF. (3) Mine Exploder Mission ETO, OHF. (4) Ltr, Maj Avakian to CofOrd Off NATOUSA, 2 Jul 44, sub: Mine Exploders T1E1 and T1E3, OO 476/1137, DRB AGO. (5) See also n. 40(6).

[51] (1) Rpt of Chief Engr ETO, p. 164, OHF. (2) Baxter, *op. cit.*, p. 102. (3) Barnes Diary, 14 and 15 Feb 44, OHF.

[52] (1) Mine Exploder Mission ETO, pp. 34–35, OHF. (2) OCM 23744, 11 May 44.

In the first category he suggested the T12, a newly developed device to clear mine fields by exploding bombs over them, and one old device, the flail exploder. Interest in the flail exploder had been revived by the performance of the British "Crab," successor to the Scorpion, in Normandy. Development of the T12, a medium tank on which a platform for launching spigot bombs replaced the turret, was the major Ordnance contribution to schemes of mine clearance by detonation. Renewed interest in the use of explosives was the result of the conclusion reached by the Eddy mission that explosives, because they were quicker, were better than mechanical exploders for clearing mine fields.[53] The advantage of the T12 over the Bangalore torpedo lay in its bombs exploding over the mine field rather than along the ground. An early report of German success in exploding mines by setting off a 200-kilogram charge placed 14 centimeters above the ground had suggested the efficiency of this method. It was the only way to detonate the new blast-resistant Teller mines.[54]

Combat experience perpetually sharpened awareness of the need not only for a satisfactory means of destroying antitank mines but also for a mechanical exploder for antipersonnel mines. In one theatre troops had to be carried over a mine field on a large platform mounted on sled runners spaced to conform with the tracks of a towing tank. The problem was especially serious in France where the rapidity of the American advance did not permit the time-consuming method of hand removal. In the November battle for Metz, for example, one company ran squarely into a mine field containing about twelve thousand mines and was forced to attack straight through, taking its losses.[55] A mechanical antipersonnel mine exploder consisting of two rows of small concrete disks towed behind a tank had been under development at Aberdeen for some time, but had not progressed beyond the experimental stage when in the fall of 1944 theatre demands became urgent. The outcome was the completion of the T13, an armor-protected cargo carrier pushing a series of lightweight rollers.[56]

During the fall of 1944, when combat troops and Ordnance Department recognized the vital necessity of finding answers to the problem of mine fields, engineers at Aberdeen tried out several new devices. High in favor was a new disk type of antitank mine exploder submitted by the Chrysler Corporation. Another was a modification of the driven-disk Aunt Jemima, incorporating improvements recommended in theatre reports. A third, a series of rocket launchers mounted on a trailer towed behind a medium tank, was tested by the Engineers and found to be more effective than the T12 as a detonating device. Development on the T12 was discontinued, and the Ordnance Committee, concluding that the flail exploder was unsatisfactory, recommended that it also be dropped. Meanwhile, tests were made of an improved flail exploder, the "Rotaflail," which NDRC had designed. It was still under development in the summer of 1945.[57] Perhaps the most promising new

[53] (1) Wood, Mine Exploders, pp. 159-63, OHF. (2) Eddy Rpt, p. 11, OHF. (3) OCM 23097, 9 Mar 44. (4) Memo, CofEngrs for CG ASF, 12 Jun 44, sub: Development of Project DM 506, Equipment for the Passage of Enemy Minefields, OO 476/1108, DRB AGO.

[54] (1) OCM 19663, 4 Feb 43. (2) Ltr, Engr Bd to CofEngrs, 22 Aug 42, sub: Antitank Mine Field Clearing Device, OO 471.6/316, DRB AGO. (3) Ltr, CofOrd to Hq ASF, 16 Dec 43, sub: Clearance of Mine Fields, OO 476/1001, DRB AGO.

[55] (1) Baxter, *op. cit.*, pp. 100, 102. (2) Cole, *The Lorraine Campaign*, pp. 401-02.

[56] OCM 24822, 24 Aug 44; 26036, 14 Dec 44.

[57] (1) OCM 26036, 14 Dec 44; 27570, 10 May 45. (2) Barnes Diary, 6, 7 Dec 44, OHF.

development was a mine-resistant vehicle. The idea was not new; Colonel Bouchier of the British Army Staff had suggested it in the summer of 1943, but at that time the Tank-Automotive Center had rejected it in favor of a self-propelled exploder of the NDRC type. A year later interest was revived by the discovery that the enemy was using coupled and delayed action mines that would immobilize the vehicle propelling a mine exploder. Acting on suggestions of Colonel Williams, the Research and Development Service began strengthening the tracks and suspensions on the M4 tank and adding armor plate under the floor. Since preliminary tests were encouraging, development on the mine-resistant vehicle continued into 1945, but the war ended before the Ordnance Department had found any wholly satisfactory way of protecting troops from enemy mines.[58]

Controlled Underwater Mines

A further protective device, a controlled underwater mine system for harbor defense, became an Ordnance responsibility in 1942. Though differing in character from the task of providing protection for troops in combat, the development, procurement, and maintenance of equipment to safeguard the home front from attack by enemy ships assumed almost equal importance, particularly during the first half of the war. Underwater mines used as weapons of offense were the responsibility of the Navy but, used defensively as part of the defense of harbors in the United States and its territories, were the responsibility, first, of the Army Corps of Engineers and then, from 1901 to 1942, of the Coast Artillery Corps. When the reorganization of the War Department transferred the responsibility to the Ordnance Department, the Coast Artillery Corps Submarine Mine Depot at Fort Monroe, Virginia, was assigned to the Artillery Division of Ordnance Industrial Service. The word "Depot" is misleading, for storage was a minor function. Indeed, a few of the heavier parts of the controlled mines were shipped directly from manufacturers to harbor defenses. Ordnance specialists not only designed and supervised procurement, inspection, and repair of all parts but also trained technicians in operating and maintaining the electrical control units for the mines. Underwater matériel required to plant a single group of mines weighed approximately fifty tons, and there might be six to thirty groups in a large harbor.[59]

The kind of controlled mine developed in 1869 has been used in United States harbors ever since. It required an electrical connection through a cable to a shore control station or "mine casemate" from which the operator could manually control the firing or nonfiring of a mine that had been struck or influenced by a passing ship. The system standard in March 1942 was designated the M3. Underwater were buoyant mines in groups of 19; for each group of 19 there was a selector box housed in a watertight distribution box and connected with the shore station by a cable. The selector assembly in the box provided a means of

[58] (1) Baxter, *op. cit.*, p. 103. (2) Ltr, Chief of Tech Div OCO to Chief of Tank-Automotive Center, Detroit, 17 Jul 43, sub: Mine Exploders, OO 476/357, DRB AGO. (3) Memo, Col Colby, Tank-Automotive Center, for OCO, 4 Aug 43, sub: Antitank Defense; Mine Exploders, Suggestions of Col Bouchier, OO 476/357, DRB AGO. (4) Memo, William Beasley, Chief of Tank and Motor Transport Div, R&D, to CG OCO Detroit, 3 Aug 44, sub: Exploder Mines, T14, and inds, 11 Aug 44 and 2 Sep 44, OO 476/1068, DRB AGO. (5) OCM 25031, 7 Sep 44; 26036, 14 Dec 44.

[59] (1) WD Cir 57, 2 Mar 42. (2) Ord Off Memo 602, 28 Mar 42, OHF. (3) Submarine Mine Depot, Hist of Controlled Submarine Mines, 1943, pp. 6–8, OHF.

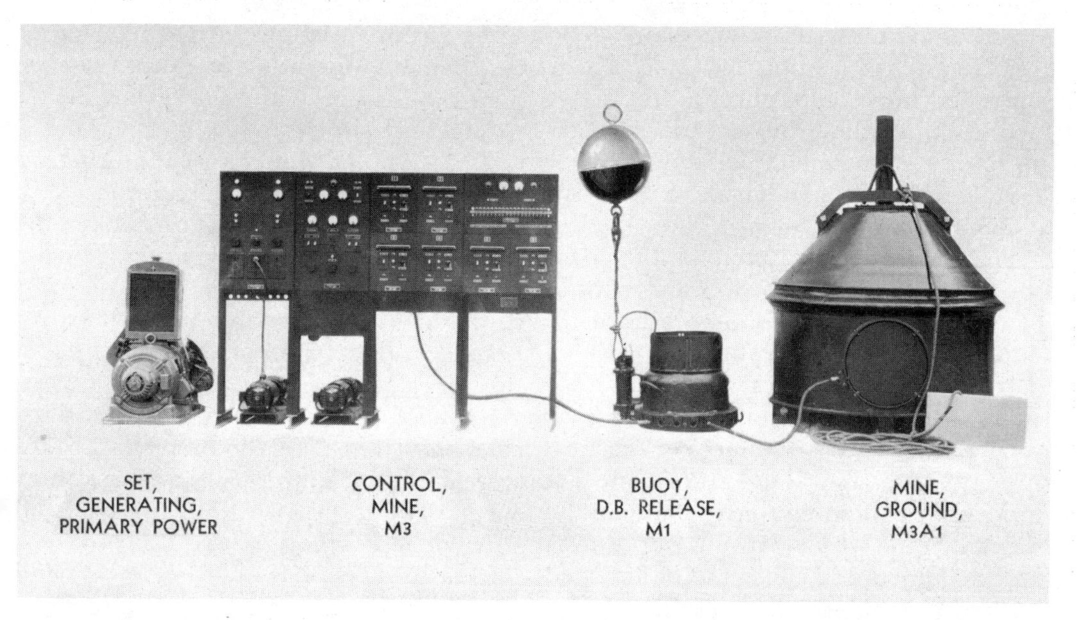

CONTROLLED MINE SYSTEM AND THE M3A1 MINE

electrically selecting, testing, or firing any mine in the group it controlled. The buoyant mine cases, which were connected by wire rope and electrical cable to cast-iron anchors, contained from 300 to 500 pounds of granular TNT and housed a firing device that was actuated by the impact of a vessel. When a ship struck a buoyant mine, a signal appeared on the mine control panel in the casemate ashore and the mine could then be fired by closing the proper firing switch. The shore installations consisted of the mine casemate, a storehouse, a loading room, a cable tank for storage of cable, a mine wharf and derricks, trackage or roads, a group commander's station, base end stations, a plotting room, and cable terminal huts.[60]

The greatest advantage of the M3 system over European systems was in firing single mines rather than whole groups. This method left small gaps of less than 300 feet in a line of mines, instead of 500 yards or more.[61] Most British harbors used the loop system, consisting of a loop of electric cable in which a current set up by a passing steel ship would be carried to shore by a "tail" cable. The loop enclosed a row of moored mines, the sinkers of which were also connected to the shore by the tail cable. All mines in a group had to be fired simultaneously, leaving a large gap in the defenses.[62] The Germans did not employ controlled mines until after the raids at Dieppe on 19 August 1942 and at St. Nazaire on 27 March 1943 had demonstrated the weakness of net and boom defenses. Thereafter, they converted offensive magnetic needle mines into defensive mines, connecting them to a shore station by cable. The short-

[60] (1) Catalogue of Standard Ord Items, II, 231–54. (2) Morland King, Submarine Mines, Record of Army Ord R&D, September 1945 (hereafter cited as Sub Mines), p. 22, OHF.

[61] Rpt, Col H. C. Reuter, A Summary of Historical Information Pertaining to Controlled Submarine Mining, 5 Sep 49 (hereafter cited as Reuter Rpt), filed at Submarine Mine Depot, Fort Monroe, Va.

[62] J. S. Cowie, *Mines, Minelayers and Minelaying* (London, 1949), pp. 103–05, 138.

age of submarine cable in Germany, however, limited the number and size of their controlled mine fields considerably. The Japanese throughout the war used a buoyant mine system generally similar to that of the United States, and it was a deterrent to U.S. submarines.[63]

The United States system of mine control was capable of improvement both in its underwater and its shore equipment. Under water, the buoyant mine with its large steel mooring ropes was a hindrance to the operation of friendly vessels, and to restrict huge fleets to narrow channels through the mines was not practicable. For this reason, it was desirable to supplant the buoyant mine with a large ground mine that would not need contact to be actuated but could be influenced by a magnetic device. Development along these lines had been under way at the Submarine Mine Depot since 1938.[64] Ashore, the mine casemate was vulnerable to enemy action; therefore the Coast Artillery Corps had been developing a small portable system operable at any point where 110 volts, 60 cycle, single phase A.C. of 2 kilowatt capacity was available. A pilot model of such an emergency control system, constructed by the Submarine Mine Depot before November 1941, was under test at the time the Ordnance Department took over the submarine mine projects from the Coast Artillery Corps.[65]

Of the two problems, the development of an effective ground-mine system was at once the more pressing and the more difficult. By 1944 Ordnance engineers had evolved from the experimental model of 1941 the desired portable shore installation, which was standardized, with a few changes, as emergency mine control M4. It was a compact unit for the control of 10 groups of 19 buoyant or 13 ground mines, designed either for parallel operation in mine casemates along with the M3 or for independent operation on landing boats, mine planters, or in any emergency shelter the tactical situation required.[66] That a tactical situation would arise requiring the use of an emergency mine control in U.S. harbors early in 1942 was possible but did not seem likely. On the other hand, enemy submarine activity off the Atlantic coast throughout 1942 rendered more than ever urgent a satisfactory replacement for buoyant mines. It was not generally known at the time, but some of the German submarines operating along the Eastern seaboard were mine layers: they closed Chesapeake Bay to traffic for two days in June and three in September, bottled up New York harbor for three days in November, and for brief periods closed Jacksonville, Florida, Charleston, South Carolina, and Wilmington, North Carolina.[67] Use of mine sweepers to remove mines planted by the enemy was impossible in harbors where buoyant mines were present; when ground mines were present, such sweeping was possible. German development of influence-operated mines that German submarines or airplanes could sow in American harbors was a primary reason for accelerating the development in the United States of a controlled ground mine system.[68]

In other respects also, submarine warfare dictated the turn submarine mine research was taking. Buoyant mines planted

[63] Reuter Rpt, pp. 7–8, Fort Monroe, Va.

[64] (1) *Ibid.* (2) Ord Off Memo 602, OHF. (3) OCM 18588, 6 Aug 42.

[65] (1) OCM 18576, 30 Jul 42. (2) Sub Mines, pp. 7–8, OHF.

[66] (1) Sub Mines, pp. 7–8, OHF. (2) Catalogue of Standard Ord Items, II, 255. (3) 1st Ind, ltr, Col R. E. Dingeman to Col D. S. Lenzner, CO Sub Mine Depot, 5 Nov 47, sub: Hist of Development of Submarine Mines, 14 Nov 47, OO 314.7/13, DRB AGO.

[67] Baxter, *op. cit.*, p. 39.

[68] (1) OCM 18571, 30 Jul 42. (2) Sub Mines, p. 23, OHF.

at 100-foot intervals were originally designed for protection against enemy surface vessels. They were a poor screen against submarines whose beams approximated 25 feet. During experiments conducted in the Philippines, a submarine actually navigated through a buoyant mine field without arming a single mine.[69] Summing up the situation in July of 1942, General Barnes wrote, "The maintenance of an effective buoyant mine defense has been found impracticable in approximately 50 percent of United States harbors." [70]

Until 1943, when nearly 4,000 buoyant mines were replaced by ground mines, the Research and Development Division of the Submarine Mine Depot centered attention on devising an influence-operated ground mine that could be controlled by the standard M3 system. The mine case presented no special difficulty. It required a watertight container for 3,000 pounds of granular TNT, a firing device, and a detector. It should be capable of submersion in 100 feet of water, able to withstand the shock of explosions occurring 150 feet away, and usable with existing planting facilities. Under development since May 1941, the case in July 1942 had a flat base and a welded steel cylindrical body with a cone-shaped top. In the lower part of the case, a firing device labelled the M5 was located with the booster charge electrically connected to it. A bail was attached to the top for raising or lowering the mine.[71] In operation, the magnetic field of an approaching vessel induced a minute current in the windings of a coil rod which caused a series of relays to operate, enabling the mine control system to select the mine.[72] When this experimental case showed no appreciable deterioration after nine months' submersion, the model was standardized as the M3. Tests in October 1942 led to modifications—the addition of 400 pounds weight in the bottom of the case to improve stability of the mine on the sea bottom, greater strength of construction, and a rigid bail that could not be moved by tidal action to arm the mine. This case became the M3A1.[73]

Mine case M3A1 had to be loaded with granular TNT and the electrical detection and operating units installed at the harbors where it was to be planted. Early in 1944 the Joint Army-Navy Ammunition Storage Board recommended to the Secretary of War that submarine mines be loaded at Ordnance depots instead of at the place of use. This led to the construction by the Submarine Mine Depot of two mine case models that were loaded with cast TNT—the T1, made of ⅛-inch and 3/16-inch plate and having no base weight, and the T2, made by conversion of the M3A1 mine case. Firing tests of these and of the Navy Mark 18 mine, which was under consideration as a cast TNT preloaded mine of lighter weight, were conducted in the Chesapeake Bay. Only the T2 proved able to stand the shock of 3,000-pound TNT explosions at 125 feet. Loaded with cast TNT, flat on top, and low in height, this model exerted much more pressure per square foot on the bottom of the sea than the M3A1 and presented only half as much area to wave action. These stability characteristics were of special interest because of unsatisfactory performance by a group of thirteen M3A1 mines that had been planted in San Francisco Harbor in April 1944 on a rocky bottom where water current velocity as high as five miles an hour was encountered. Apparently because of mine case movement, nine of the thir-

[69] Sub Mines, p. 23, OHF.

[70] OCM 18571, 30 Jul 42.

[71] (1) Sub Mines, p. 17, OHF. (2) OCM 18588, 30 Jul 42.

[72] Catalogue of Standard Ord Items, II, 254–55.

[73] Sub Mines, pp. 18–19, OHF.

teen were spuriously armed nearly every day between April and August. False armings made the operation of the M3 control system unreliable. Consequently, the Coast Artillery Board recommended in October 1944 that the T1, the T2, and the Navy mine be tested for stability under the severe hydrographic conditions prevailing in San Francisco Harbor. The test was deferred, however, pending the outcome of tests of new firing devices then being conducted at the New London submarine base.[74]

A sensitive firing device for use in the ground mine had been the subject of considerable research since 1942. The task, begun by NDRC, was carried on by the Submarine Mine Depot in co-operation with the Navy and by several private laboratories.[75] Firing device M5 was not satisfactory against small submarines of the "O" type in water more than 80 feet deep. The problem was to develop a firing device that would be sensitive enough to detect small submarines of the latest type running at 5 miles an hour or less in 100 feet of water and yet would be sufficiently stable to avoid false armings. With regard to the sensitivity requirement, the main difficulty lay in the M3 mine control system itself, which did not permit transmission of electric power from shore to mine. Power was necessary to operate equipment that would amplify the very small currents generated in firing devices by influence detectors.[76]

Development of an effective firing device, therefore, was carried on simultaneously with development of a revised mine control system, and models of one were tested with models of the other. By December 1943 firing device T5E22, employing an electronic amplifier, was ready for test. When planted against "O" and "R" type submarines at New London, it demonstrated sensitivity at a depth of 100 feet. It was tested with a model of the new mine control system, T7. Because of instability and limitations imposed by mine control T7, the Coast Artillery Board disapproved the T5E22, but its basic principle was employed in a later model, firing device T5E23, developed at the Submarine Mine Depot. The T5E23 provided means both of sending a signal ashore for interpretation and of testing the device, including the detector, from shore. Operated with an improved mine control, the T8, in tests at New London, it gave high-actuation effect against "O" and "R" submarines.[77]

An improved mine control system was needed not only in order to transmit power to operate each mine but also because soon after Pearl Harbor the Japanese had probably captured a complete M3 system installed at Corregidor.[78] By February 1944, four types of mine controls were under development. One employed a separate test, selection, and firing for each mine; a second, a simplified version of the first, had a single indication frequency system; a third used bypass equipment with the M3 to supply small amounts of power to magnetic amplifiers in each mine; and the fourth, the T7, was a modification of the M3 that permitted powering the electronic firing devices from shore. Each of these

[74] (1) Sub Mines, pp. 20–21, OHF. (2) Ltr, CO Sub Mine Depot to CofOrd, 20 Sep 44, sub: Mine Cases T1 and T2, and inds, 27 Oct 44 and 3 Nov 44, OO 400.112/193, DRB AGO. (3) Memo, CofS for CG AGF, 23 Nov 44, sub: Service Tests of Mine Cases T1 and T2 in the Harbor Defenses of San Francisco, OPD 476.1 (20 Sep 44), DRB AGO.

[75] (1) OCM 18571, 30 Jul 42; 18609, 18610, 18611, and 18614, 6 Aug 42. (2) Sub Mines, pp. 26–31, OHF.

[76] (1) Sub Mines, p. 8, OHF. (2) OCM 18575, 30 Jul 42.

[77] (1) Sub Mines, pp. 32–33, OHF. (2) OCM 27390, 19 Apr 45. (3) 1st Ind, ltr, Col Dingeman to Col Lenzner, 14 Nov 47, sub: Hist of Development of Sub Mines, 314.7/13, copy in Sub Mine Depot files, Fort Monroe, Va.

[78] OCM 18575, 30 Jul 42.

four types of control had some insuperable disadvantage. On 23 February 1944 the commanding general of Army Service Forces approved a project for developing a scanner type of control, the T8, combining the best features of the four controls under study and at the same time simplifying the circuits so that bulk was reduced about one half. The Rudolph Wurlitzer Company of Tonawanda, New York, suggested the system and the Submarine Mine Depot developed it.[79] It was an electromechanical control, each basic unit of which would supply power and operate up to ten groups of thirteen mines, with each group operated over a single shore cable. It consisted of three units—one centralized control cabinet; ten group cabinets, one for each group of thirteen mines; and one selector assembly for each group. Because of the power equipment necessary for the mine electronic detectors, the T8 weighed more than twice as much as the standard M3 system and was more than three feet longer. It required one man per ten-group control as compared with one man for all groups in the M3, and there might be from one to four ten-group control units in a casemate. The increased personnel requirement, however, was considered offset by the additional information gained by continuous surveillance of the signal influences of every mine in a mine field, in contrast to the single mine actuation possible with the M3 control.[80]

From mid-October 1944 until January 1945, mine control T8, with the T5E23 firing devices and mine cases M3A1 and T2, was under test at the New London submarine base. It demonstrated the soundness of its design and its reliability under field conditions. Results were also satisfactory with the T5E23 firing device. Within a three-week period twelve mines with T5E23 firing devices in depths between 95 and 110 feet missed only 4.4 percent of 226 courses by "O" and "R" types of submarines that passed within 100 feet of a mine. Some of the firing devices were found to be unstable, but the feasibility of interpreting the signals decreased materially the effect of instability and permitted study of its causes. The tests indicated that mine case motion was probably the major cause.[81]

The original plan was to include pilot models of the mine control T8 and firing device T5E23 in the test of T1, T2, and the Navy Mark 18 mines to be conducted in San Francisco Harbor. The test was to be in two phases, the first to determine how much the effectiveness of existing mine fields, using the standard firing device M5, could be increased by the substitution of different mine cases, and the second to determine the suitability of the T1, T2, and Mark 18 mines when employed with the new, highly sensitive firing device T5E23 and mine control T8. In late January 1945 the Submarine Mine Depot began a program, involving all departments of the depot, to construct experimental matériel and ship it to the Harbor Defenses of San Francisco. The coming of V-E Day put a stop to those preparations. The equipment for the San Francisco test "sat on the shelf" until 1946, when tests resumed.[82]

Next to the development of an effective

[79] (1) Ind cited n. 77(3). (2) OCM 22912, 17 Feb 44. (3) Sub Mines, pp. 5–6, OHF.

[80] OCM 23471, 13 Apr 44; 24081, 8 Jan 44.

[81] (1) Ltr, CO Sub Mine Depot to CofOrd, 4 Jan 45, sub: Summary of Development Projects for Month of December 1944, OO 400.112/109, DRB AGO. (2) 8th Ind, Coast Artillery Board to CG AGF, 25 Jan 45; sub: Service Tests of Mine Cases T1 and T2 in Harbor Defense of San Francisco, to basic memo, CofS for CG ASF, 23 Nov 44, both in OPD 476.1 (20 Sep 44). (3) OCM 26960, 15 Mar 45. (4) Sub Mines, pp. 33–34, OHF.

[82] (1) OCM 27668, 17 May 45. (2) Historical Rpt, Submarine Mine Depot, First Quarter 1945, Navy

ground mine system, the most important single project was the search for a suitable mine fire control system to provide information on enemy approach as far ahead of the mine field as practicable. The need for such a listening device was emphasized in a report of 4 May 1942 from the commanding general of Harbor Defenses of Manila and Subic Bays, Corregidor, P.I., requesting some method of determining whether mines were being armed by shell bursts and bombs or by an approaching hostile vessel. The characteristics desired in such a device were to provide early information regardless of the size of the vessel and to indicate the class of the vessel and probable speed. Projects set up at the Submarine Mine Depot used such varied devices as hydrophones, magnetic loops, a sonic barrier, and a microphonic cable.[83] The system employing hydrophones was the most satisfactory. After extended tests at Fort Monroe and San Francisco, it was standardized in July 1943 as audio reception system M1. The underwater equipment consisted of two hydrophones, covering four groups of mines, connected together and to the shore equipment by single-conductor submarine cable; the shore equipment consisted of a preamplifier, an amplifier, and a sound recorder. The operator could hear vessels at distances of from five hundred feet to two miles, depending on hydrographic conditions, and could distinguish between mines being armed by underwater explosions, wave action, and the approach of a vessel. In San Francisco Harbor, where fogs and bad weather were frequent, the system reported 87 out of 92 submarine test-crossings. An improved audio reception system, designed to filter out fish noises and provide vastly better acoustic detection of midget submarines, was standardized in 1945.[84]

Between 1942 and 1945 redesign of mine system equipment, such as distribution boxes, selector boxes, and cables, eliminated critical materials and expedited production. With these minor changes, mine control system M3, using ground mines instead of buoyant mines after 1943 and aided by the audio reception system, remained in operation throughout World War II. Its tactical operational effectiveness in the defense of United States harbors was never put to the test; at least no confirmed report ever came in of the destruction of any German or Japanese submarine by United States controlled mines. On the other hand, they unquestionably prevented enemy submarines from seeking entrance to American harbors, for the Axis Powers knew of the presence and fire power of these controlled mines. Testimony to the strategic importance of the system lies in the fact that no German submarine was known to have attempted entry into United States harbors and that all enemy mines were laid at least 3,000 yards seaward of the line of controlled mines.[85]

Bureau of Ord Harbor Defense files. (3) Interv, 20 Nov 50, with Col Reuter, Chief of R&D, Sub Mine Depot, 1939–48. After the war the prompt return to private life of many scientists delayed for some three years the completion of new mine controls.

[83] (1) OCM 18572 and 18574, 30 Jul 42; 18831, and 18832, 3 Sep 42. (2) Submarine Mine Depot, Hist of Controlled Sub Mines, 1943, p. 43, OHF. (3) Sub Mines, p. 36, OHF.

[84] (1) Sub Mines, pp. 36–39, OHF. (2) OCM 18573, 30 Jul 42. (3) Catalogue of Standard Ord Items, II, 252. (4) Ind cited n. 77(3).

[85] (1) Reuter Rpt, p. 9, Fort Monroe, Va. (2) Sub Mines, pp. 40–55, OHF. (3) Submarine Mine Depot, Hist of Controlled Sub Mines, 1943, p. 16, OHF.

CHAPTER XIV

Antiaircraft Defense: Ground-to-Air Weapons

Developments in aircraft design following World War I opened up prospects of a type of warfare that would dwarf in significance all air operations of the 1914-18 period. The Italo-Ethiopian War and the Spanish Civil War amply confirmed the importance of defense against bombing raids and focused attention of the United States Coast Artillery Corps and Ordnance Department upon the need of long-range, accurate, powerful antiaircraft guns. Though the Air Corps, tutored by Brig. Gen. William L. Mitchell, the famous Billy Mitchell, for a decade had nursed the belief that well-armed fighter planes would make antiaircraft guns superfluous, Ordnance officers foresaw the need of antiaircraft artillery as well as fighters.[1] The 3-inch antiaircraft gun standardized in 1927 was a good weapon for use against aircraft of the 1920's but had neither the range to be effective against planes flying at the heights attainable by 1937 nor the fire control mechanisms needed to track accurately enemy craft flying at the greater speeds of the more modern planes. Even before the outbreak of war in Europe, American preoccupation with defense made logical the dedication of utmost effort to design of improved antiaircraft weapons. Later the Battle of Britain and realization of the overwhelming advantage that clearing the skies of enemy craft would give, when the time came for a full-scale offensive against the Continent, further stressed the wisdom of perfecting antiaircraft equipment of every kind—guns, mounts, tracking devices, and ammunition.

The problem of reaching targets flying at great heights did not loom large for antiaircraft batteries in World War II. Most enemy planes operated at not more than 10,000 feet and the 3-inch antiaircraft gun M3 had a slant range of 15,000 feet. Newer guns had much greater range.[2] Command of necessary range by no means solved the problems of effective antiaircraft fire. It is important to remember that because airplanes, unlike ground equipment, operate freely in three dimensions, accurate fire control is as much more complex for antiaircraft guns than for ground weapons as solid geometry or spherical trigonometry is than plane geometry or trigonometry. Add to that complexity the factor of the speed at which modern planes fly—whereby the fourth dimension of time is introduced—and success in destroying

[1] Interv with Gen Barnes, 13 Jun 51.

[2] (1) Catalogue of Standard Ord Items, II, 209. (2) Interv with Gen Barnes, 13 Jun 51. (3) Interv, 5 Jul 51, with Samuel Feltman, Associate Chief of Resources and Materials Br, R&D Serv. (4) Barnes, *Weapons of World War II*, p. 149.

enemy planes by ground fire might appear to become a matter of luck. To convert chance into some predictable proportion of destructive hits to number of targets fired at was a challenge that the Ordnance Department faced through much of the war.

Of the various ways of meeting the challenge, a steady barrage of fire was one. Against low-flying craft, use of guns with rapid cyclic rates would increase the chances of a strike by sheer volume of fire. A machine gun, or better still batteries of machine guns, could saturate the path of the enemy plane with a rain of bullets, provided the gunners had estimated range, height, and direction correctly. But that method, necessarily employed under some circumstances, was extravagant of ammunition inasmuch as fire control on a machine gun could consist only of sights. Against high-flying planes machine gun fire was too short-ranged to be reliable. Furthermore, even a direct hit might lack destructive power if the energy of the bullet were nearly spent upon impact, if the plane's armor plate were so heavy as to prevent penetration, or if upon penetration the projectile did little damage. Special ammunition was required to forestall those contingencies. Artillery, on the other hand, though having long range, power, and shell bursts covering a considerable area, could not fire fast enough to blanket the skies, even if guns were equipped with automatic fuze setter-rammers. As the skies are wide and a plane at any distance is a mere speck, the saturation technique manifestly was useful only for defense against close-in attack. In fact, every shot against moving planes, Ordnance experts had long realized, must be an aimed shot, whether fired from a machine gun or a larger weapon. British experiments in defending the Channel and London by sending up barrages of rockets were spectacular and thus helped civilian morale, but were of doubtful value because of rockets' inaccuracy at that time. Since General Barnes considered antiaircraft rockets useless unless accuracy could be improved, the Ordnance Department abandoned its rocket development plans as soon as sufficient antiaircraft artillery became available.[3]

A more efficient way of improving antiaircraft fire, in the opinion of Army Ordnance, was to develop and employ ammunition and weapons of very high muzzle velocities. The greater velocity would flatten the trajectory of projectiles' flight and, by lessening time of flight, insure a larger proportion of hits. Supervelocity, however, introduced the problem of excessive barrel erosion, and, as antiaircraft artillery shots, regardless of velocity, had to be aimed properly to be effective, tracking devices were essential. They might be electromechanical systems that computed firing data and directed the gun's fire on the basis of optical observation, or they might employ radar linked with an electronic computer that transmitted the data to electric controls on the gun's mount. Both types of director would greatly assist in keeping on the target. Finally, fuzes calculated to function only when within a given distance of the enemy craft would guarantee a large number of lethal strikes regardless of the plane's speed. Use of all these means in combination promised the

[3] (1) Interv with Gen Barnes, 13 Jun 51. (2) Interv, 25 Jun 51, with Dr. Colin Hudson, Guided Missile Br, R&D Serv. (3) Memo, CofS for Gen Barnes, 15 Aug 41, OO 334.9/705, DRB AGO. (4) OCM 16336, 19 Dec 40. (5) Col Borden, Summation of Observations in North Africa and United Kingdom, 15 Apr 43 to 22 May 43, p. 6, Misc Missions, Barnes file, OHF.

most nearly foolproof system of antiaircraft defense conceivable, and before the war was won employment of that combination brought deadly results. Whereas one hit in every 2,500 artillery shots was average in 1940, that ratio in some engagements was reduced to about one in every 300 by late 1944.[4]

Volume of Fire for Defense Against Low-Flying Aircraft

Machine Guns

For saturating fire against strafing attacks the .50-caliber machine gun was regarded by both the Ordnance Department and the using arms as a satisfactory weapon. The .30-caliber machine gun was too light to serve under most circumstances, though for training it answered as well as the .50-caliber and was cheaper to use. In the 1930's the Coast Artillery, then the arm concerned with antiaircraft defense, preferred the .50-caliber water-cooled gun, the basic M2 equipped with an outer water-filled jacket and a water pump for cooling the barrel. Yet because a water supply might be hard to maintain under some combat conditions, an air-cooled heavy-barreled model was also designed for ground use where long bursts of fire might be necessary. The added amount of metal in the barrel absorbed heat just as water-cooling dissipated it. To increase velocity and accuracy and to reduce flash and smoke, the barrel was lengthened from 36 to 45 inches for the heavy-barreled and the water-cooled models in 1937 and 1938, respectively.[5] The former, firing 400 to 500 rounds a minute, the latter, 500 to 650, had both proved their dependability, and attempts to increase greatly those cyclic rates threatened to impair efficiency and durability. Though early in the war the rate on each type was successfully pushed about 50 rounds a minute higher, and increase in belt-lift capacity was achieved in 1944, most improvements were minor. Smoother functioning also resulted from improved manufacture, as producers learned how to provide better finishes and eliminate interferences between moving parts. In the last months of the war an experimental barrel lightened from 28 to 20 pounds permitted considerably faster rates of fire. But by that time the danger from enemy aircraft had so lessened that the Ground Forces believed the added wear on the barrel too great to warrant establishing a requirement for the faster-firing gun.[6]

If .50-caliber antiaircraft machine guns themselves required few changes after 1940, their mounts were another story. The tripod mount adopted in the 1930's had been designed for a different tactical use from what the changes in air warfare demanded in 1940. By then, the Chief of Coast Artillery labelled existing mounts too heavy, too hard to transport, and having insufficient elevation to be suited to close-in defense against low-flying, high-speed targets. Complex sighting devices for tracking at ranges beyond a thousand yards were no longer necessary for machine guns. A mount capable of being transported in and fired from a ¼-ton or 1½-ton truck would have to be consider-

---

[4] (1) Intervs, 5 Jul 51, with Samuel Feltman and with Dr.. Wilhelm Jörgensen, Chief of AA Fire Control Sec, R&D Serv. (2) Barnes, *op. cit.*, p. 158.

[5] OCM 10717, 25 May 33; 10787, 22 Jun 33; 14187, 13 Jun 38; 15314, 31 Aug 49.

[6] (1) OCM 15314, 31 Aug 39; 20774, 17 Jun 43. (2) Machine Guns, PSP 36, pp. 24–26, 42–57, OHF. (3) Hist of Springfield Armory, Vol. II, Book II, pp. 137–38; Book III, pp. 263–64, 529–30, 707–10, OHF. (4) Interv, 17 May 51, with Paul W. Welsh, Jr., Machine Gun Sec, R&D Serv.

ably lighter than the 500-pound mount then standard. Upon the basis of two designs prepared after careful study by Rock Island Arsenal, the Heintz Manufacturing Company of Philadelphia in 1942 built an acceptable model which was standardized as the M3. The new mount weighed 380 pounds including the armor-plate shields for the gunner, had the desired elevation of –15 to 90 degrees, and a simple ring sight. Early in 1943, before the M3's were available, the need for antiaircraft equipment became so urgent that some improvisation was imperative. Specially designed elevator cradles that could be affixed to existing ground mounts permitted using for antiaircraft defense the thousands of heavy barreled caliber .50's in the hands of troops in all theatres. The cradle, standardized in August 1943, was light, sufficiently stable, and readily attached to the tripod ground mount. Though these elevator cradles were a makeshift, the 80,000 put into service before midsummer of 1944 supplemented the supply of antiaircraft mounts at a time when strafing planes were a threat in every theatre of operations.

Meanwhile, the Airborne Command requested mounts that could be put into action faster than the standard M3. Search for a mount weighing less than 160 pounds, transportable by two men, and possessing good stability, went forward during 1943 and culminated in a satisfactory model, the M63, in May 1944. The M63 was based on a Heintz Manufacturing Company design that Maj. John H. Kochevar of the Airborne Command modified by supplying a quadruped base with horizontal legs and a folding, T-shaped trigger extension attached to the cradle. It weighed only 144 pounds. Nearly 48,000 were produced before V-J Day and filled the need for mounts that could be airborne, landed from small boats, or carried into places inaccessible to vehicles.[7] For protection to ships and landing craft, mounts were assembled with pedestal bases that could be bolted to the deck. The Army for the most part adopted Navy models for use on tank lighters and similar craft needing antiaircraft machine guns.[8]

As volume of fire could be increased not only by more rapid rates of fire but also by multiplying the number of guns trained upon a target, multiple mounting of caliber .50's was recognized early in the war as a sound method of adding to the protection of moving convoys. The first multiple machine gun carriage completed in 1942 was a 4-wheeled trailer on which 4 heavy-barreled caliber .50's were placed on a power-driven armored mount having a self-contained power unit. A turret, resting on a steel base plate anchored to the floor of the trailer, provided 360 degrees traverse. The turret could also be emplaced in a half-track to make a self-propelled unit. A centrally located gunner's seat was situated between two trunnion sectors, each of which supported two guns and two 200-round ammunition chests. A sight base with a reflector sight, the ME IX developed by the Navy, moved with the trunnions. The guns were normally fired electrically but, in event of power failure, could be fired by a hand mechanism. In 1943 a variation of this M51 carriage was designed for airborne use. A portable 2-wheeled trailer mount, light

[7] (1) SA and SA Ammo, Book 3, Machine Guns and Related Items, pp. 120–27, OHF. (2) OCM 16305, 16 Nov 40; 18103, 21 Apr 42; 18192, 7 May 42; 21349, 19 Aug 43; 22846, 10 Feb 44; 23769, 11 May 44; 24319, 6 Jul 44. (3) Machine Gun Mounts, PSP 43, pp. 18–19, 25–26, 36–37, OHF. Hereafter cited as PSP 43.

[8] PSP 43, pp. 27–29, 33–35, OHF.

and compact enough to be stowed in a C6–4A glider or a C–47 transport plane, was equipped with mechanical jacks permitting rapid emplacement and leveling for firing once the trailer wheels had been removed. In most features identical with the mount of the M51 carriage, the mount on this M55 model provided a special armor shield and a handlebar control of turret movement and firing.[9] Still more effective for some purposes than quadruple .50-caliber mounts was a combination of two water-cooled machine guns and a 37-mm. automatic gun in a special cradle mounted on a half-track.[10] This mount, standardized as the 37-mm. antiaircraft M15, was appraised in a report from North Africa.

The proficiency of this mobile weapon can be attributed to three characteristics: its mobility enabling it to work well in close support of combat troops in forward areas and also to effectively patrol roads over which heavy traffic must travel under constant threat of bombing and strafing; its flexible fire power combining the volume of caliber .50 with the knocking power of the 37-mm.; and the facility with which its fire is controlled by using the tracer stream of one caliber .50 to bring it on the target before opening with the full volume of its armament. Numerous cases are cited where a 'mouse trap' effect has been obtained when enemy planes came in much closer on the initial caliber .50 fire than they would on light cannon and are caught by the 37-mm.[11]

Improved Ammunition

The destructive effect of antiaircraft machine gun fire depended quite as much upon the type of ammunition used as upon velocity or volume. Though there was some difference of opinion about the value of tracer, the using arms tended to believe it was an aid to accuracy. Certainly penetration could be improved by use of armor-piercing ammunition, and deadliness by employment of incendiary. A cartridge embodying all those features could be the most desirable of all. Between 1940 and 1942 Ordnance experts investigated the possibilities of explosive bullets but development of better types put an end to this work.[12] Thanks to an Ordnance development program of the 1930's, one kind of tracer armor-piercing cartridge was available for small arms in 1940. As the war progressed some work was expended on developing special .30-caliber ammunition for machine guns,[13] but most .30-caliber armor-piercing ammunition was used in rifles and carbines in place of ball ammunition. After mid-1943 antiaircraft batteries used the smaller weapon only rarely and the Army Air Forces never. Hence the discussion that follow deals largely with caliber .50's and artillery.

The most urgent requests for improved .50-caliber ammunition from 1940 onward came from the Air Forces.[14] But the Antiaircraft Command was also concerned, particularly after the Lend-Lease Act made British problems and experience in antiaircraft defense a strong consideration.

[9] (1) Catalogue of Standard Ord Items, II, 153–54. (2) OCM 17969, 26 Mar 42; 18020, 4 Apr 42; 18845, 3 Sep 42; 18963, 1 Oct 42; 19140, 5 Nov 42; 20025, 25 Mar 43; 21241, 22 Apr 43; 22117, 18 Nov 43; 22521, 30 Dec 43.

[10] OCM 17313, 10 Sep 41.

[11] Quoted on pp. 141–42, *Weapons of World War II*, Gen. G. M. Barnes, 1947, D. Van Nostrand Company, Inc.

[12] SA and SA Ammo, Book 2, pp. 64–71, 190–96, OHF.

[13] For example, a project authorized in April 1945 called for development of a .30-caliber tracer with preliminary dim trace, followed by a bright trace up to 1,000 yards, which would provide "sufficient observability for tracer-controlled antiaircraft fire." This was to be a long-time, continuing, peacetime development. See SA and SA Ammo, Book 2, pp. 88–90, OHF.

[14] See Ch. XVI, below.

British faith in tracer ammunition fortified the belief of the American Antiaircraft Command in the usefulness of tracer to guide machine gun fire. The trajectory of a tracer bullet is visible for a given distance because a chemical element incorporated in the cartridge provides a trail of flame or smoke. Consequently, in response to a series of requests, throughout the war Ordnance technicians undertook dozens of research projects on various types of tracer to supplement the one kind available in 1940. But lack of agreement among the using arms about what characteristics were essential resulted in the Ordnance Department's spending much money and effort to produce a great number of types, many of which were never adopted for combat. Though down into 1944 the Antiaircraft Command used the .50-caliber M1 tracer, standard in 1940, late in 1942 the command headquarters requested a cartridge with a bright trace increased from 2,000 to 2,500 yards. The argument of the Antiaircraft Board was that the greater length of trace would enable the .50-caliber machine gun used as a subcaliber weapon on 37-mm. and 40-mm. guns to duplicate more nearly the effect of fire of the larger guns. The desired features of lengthened trace and minimum flash at the gun were successfully achieved in a cartridge standardized in July 1944 as the M17. This replaced the M1 for antiaircraft use until March 1945, when a still better cartridge, the M20, was available. The M17 continued to be used for training even after the war.[15]

Whatever its value for improving accuracy, tracer alone lacked power to pierce armor plate and therefore was ineffective against the armored planes and the self-sealing fuel tanks employed by the Axis Powers. Even armor-piercing cartridges frequently failed to do much damage. Thus, the need for ammunition of greater lethal effect was apparent a year before the United States became a belligerent. British experience pointed to the usefulness of incendiary. The first .50-caliber incendiary, the M1, was designed for air combat, but antiaircraft batteries also used it for a time while awaiting development of an armor-piercing-incendiary bullet requested in the fall of 1942 for ground use. Study of a Soviet 13.2-mm. and an Italian 7.7-mm. armor-piercing-incendiary assisted Frankford Arsenal in devising a cartridge with an armor-piercing core inserted into the M1 incendiary bullet jacket. The bullet weighed 649 grains, and 14 grains of a special incendiary mixture were added in the bullet jacket. Tests during 1943 proving it satisfactory, the new armor-piercing-incendiary cartridge was adopted under the designation M8.[16] Thereafter the Ground Forces used a linkage of four M8 cartridges to one tracer.

A single cartridge incorporating armor-piercing, incendiary, and tracer characteristics had not yet been evolved. The Ordnance Department began experimenting with a modification of the M8 late in 1943. By omitting the lead base filler used in the M8, adding several more grains of incendiary mixture, and inserting in the base of the core a new tracer mixture, Ordnance experts had an armor-piercing-incendiary tracer model ready for service tests by June 1944, when the Air Forces established a requirement for ammunition

[15] SA and SA Ammo, Book 2, pp. 73, 80, 91, 103–04, OHF.

[16] *Ibid.*, pp. 35–36.

of this kind. While preparations were under way for manufacturing a large quantity for combat test, the Ordnance Department furnished samples to the Antiaircraft Board as well as to other boards of the services and to the Navy. For aircraft use, this T28 had indisputable value, but whether it would meet the needs of the Ground Forces was uncertain. The findings were universally approving. The Antiaircraft Board pronounced the trace features superior to those of the M1 tracer, because the initial trace was dimmer and the smoke along the trajectory less. Since the armor-piercing-incendiary characteristics added deadliness, the Commanding General, Army Ground Forces, recommended standardization. The cartridge was designated the caliber .50 armor-piercing-incendiary tracer M20. Its drawbacks were two: the complexity of design made manufacture difficult, and the chemical composition of the ammunition led to rapid deterioration in storage. The second fault was common to all tracer ammunition, and the demand for the M20 was so great that no problem of prolonged storage arose during the war. The hitch was rather one of keeping supply somewhere near the level of demand, a problem rendered acute by the difficulty of manufacture. But the M20 gave both Ground and Air Forces a tracer cartridge with ballistic performance identical with that of the round for which the tracer served as fire control. Time of flight of the M20 was exactly that of the M8 armor-piercing-incendiary at all points of the trajectory.[17] The adoption of the armor-piercing-incendiary tracer marked the peak of accomplishment in machine gun ammunition used against aircraft during the war.

Artillery Fire for Defense Against Close-in Attack

37-mm. Guns

The limitations of machine guns made light artillery essential for defense against relatively close-in attack. Light artillery could be equipped with fire control mechanisms that could not be used on machine guns; and an artillery projectile, if only because of its far greater mass, could destroy a target that machine gun bullets might hit without seriously damaging. After World War I, by general agreement, a project was given high priority to develop an antiaircraft gun of about 37-mm. caliber to fill the gap between machine guns and comparatively slow-moving intermediate and heavy artillery. Ordnance designers, assisted by John Browning of machine gun fame, and later by the Colt's Patent Fire Arms Company, pushed forward work upon a 37-mm., and, after standardization of a model in 1927, Watertown and Frankford Arsenals carried on development of a carriage and sighting system. Yet progress was slow, particularly on the fire control and sighting devices, which were of considerable complexity and not very satisfactory in operation. Nevertheless, by the fall of 1938, as the war was drawing closer, a carriage, standardized as the M3, and a sighting system, M2, coupled with a so-called control equipment set, the M1, were put into production, while orders for the gun itself went to Watervliet Arsenal and Colt.

The next two years saw numerous modifications. The muzzle velocity of the gun was lowered to prevent premature bursts

[17] *Ibid.*, pp. 107–08.

from new self-destroying tracer ammunition and to lessen barrel erosion; and before 1940 was out, the sighting and control system was scrapped in favor of a British development, the Kerrison predictor and "oil gears." The latter were electrohydraulic power-control units mounted on the carriage and linked by an electrical data transmission system to the mechanical director; the separate, off-carriage Kerrison predictor computed the firing data as it tracked the target.[18] This British remote control system, originally designed for use with 40-mm. Bofors guns, was so undeniably superior to the American that the Ordnance Technical Committee recommended adopting the British type for all new 37-mm. carriages. So equipped, the carriage was designated the M3A1. While tracer shell alone was a poor substitute for an accurate tracking system, a tracer element was incorporated in all 37-mm. ammunition. If the director failed to work, the tracer would still provide some fire control, and at all times would provide a check upon the accuracy of the tracking mechanism. Moreover, when the combination mount M15 was put into service, its two .50-caliber machine guns helped to keep the 37-mm. on the target as well as to increase volume of fire.[19]

40-mm. Bofors

Meanwhile the 40-mm. Bofors had shown its capabilities. The carriage of the Bofors differed little from the American. The gun itself, in the opinion of many experts, was a better weapon than the 37-mm. in several respects. The British strongly advocated adopting the 40, and it was obvious that manufacturing facilities were too few to produce both 37's and 40's in quantity. The Swedish Bofors gun and carriage together weighed some 575 pounds less than the 37-mm. mounted on its carriage. The Bofors was somewhat similar in design, fired a projectile half again as heavy at 270 feet per second higher muzzle velocity, and had a slightly faster cyclic rate than the 37-mm. An automatic loading mechanism fed cartridges into a loading tray from which they were pushed into the chamber by a mechanically operated rammer. Though the 40-mm. barrel when fired at a rate of 140 rounds per minute tended to overheat, a new barrel could be emplaced in about two minutes. The 4.3-mile range of the foreign weapon exceeded the 6,200-yard maximum range of the American, but use of the director actually limited effective range of the Bofors to about 3,000 yards. Still, in many situations the advantages of the director more than offset the reduction of range.[20]

Endeavors in 1937 to purchase Bofors for test had come to nothing, owing to a series of mishaps.[21] Not until the fall of 1940 did the United States obtain models, the Navy one in October, the Army one in December. Only close collaboration between the Army, the Navy, and the British enabled the United States to hasten negotiations for manufacturing rights and the Ordnance Department to get drawings and construction of two pilot models

[18] See below, pp. 38ff.

[19] (1) OCM 12664, 20 Feb 33; 13766, 1 Jul 37; 13796, 15 Jul 37; 14738, 13 Oct 38; 14912, 1 Mar 39; 15811, 17 May 40; 15908, 27 Jun 40; 16309, 20 Nov 40. (2) Design, Development and Production of 37-mm. and 40-mm. AA Guns, PSP 29, OHF. (3) Interv, 27 Jun 51, with Granville Taliaferro, Artillery Ammo Br, R&D Serv.

[20] (1) Catalogue of Standard Ord Items, II, 203–06. (2) Interv with Gen Barnes, 13 Jun 51, and with Samuel Feltman, 5 Jul 51.

[21] The misunderstandings with the Bofors Company that halted purchase in 1937 and 1938 are described in PSP 29, pp. 22–23, OHF.

ANTIAIRCRAFT GUNS. *37-mm. (above) and Bofors 40-mm. (below).*

started even before contracts with the Swedish company were formalized. The Army officially adopted the air-cooled Bofors as the 40-mm. automatic antiaircraft gun M1 in April 1941, with the explicit statement that as soon as quantity manufacture was achieved, the 40-mm. was to supersede the 37-mm. antiaircraft gun.[22] That moment was not reached until the summer of 1943, a delay that had been prolonged by the necessity of transposing the metric measurements of the foreign drawings to United States Ordnance standards. Minor changes resulted from tests in the summer of 1942. The most important was the decision to follow British practice and the original Bofors design of increasing the twist of the rifling from one turn in 45 calibers at the breech to one turn in 30 at the muzzle. The increasing twist lengthened accuracy life from 4,200 service rounds to approximately 6,000.[23]

All Bofors ammunition was in the form of fixed rounds, either armor-piercing with tracer or high-explosive shell. Before midsummer 1943 American manufacturers found it hard to make. The British percussion fuze, in particular, was so complex that as early as January 1942 the Ordnance Technical Committee recommended substitution of a simple plunger type of point-detonating fuze similar to those the Ordnance Department had long used. Before this PD fuze M64 got into quantity production, the Navy was turning out its Mark 27 PD fuze which answered the same purpose. Consequently the Army also used the Mark 27 with high-explosive shell, though in the interests of more economical manufacture, the Ordnance Department developed another PD fuze, the M71.[24]

Both mount and carriage also were somewhat modified, partly to ease manufacture and maintenance, partly to improve performance. The Firestone Tire and Rubber Company, who accepted the contract for the first pilot models, succeeded in producing a welded frame to replace the riveted construction of the original mount, a far more efficient and easily fabricated bearing for the traverse mechanism, cheaper and more easily installed bushings for bearings, and steel tubing instead of forged and machined axles. The carriage was modified by adding four-wheel electric brakes and a few other improvements. Some slight differences between the model manufactured for the British and that for the U.S. Army led to assigning the nomenclature M2 to the latter carriage, M1 to the lend-lease model. To increase the tracking rate in following a high-speed target approaching from an unexpected direction at short range, new gears with a higher gear ratio were installed in the carriage, now labeled the M2A1. Addition of "cartwheel" sights was another improvement. The diameter of the forward ring was first increased to provide for leading a target traveling at 300 miles an hour at a 1,000-yard range and later was increased to cover targets moving at 400 miles an hour.[25]

As combat experience in North Africa emphasized the need of combining maximum fire power and mobility with a minimum number of vehicles, in 1943 various combination mounts on both half-tracks

[22] The Navy adopted a water-cooled model, many parts of which were dissimilar to the Army Bofors.

[23] (1) OCM 16647, 24 Apr 41. (2) PSP 29, App. D, and p. 36, citing Ord Program 5444, 30 Jul 42, OHF.

[24] (1) OCM 17703, 26 Jan 42. (2) Interv, 6 Jul 51, with Robert Cuthill, Ammo Br, Ind Serv. (3) Ltr, Gen Crain, London Munitions Assignment Bd, to Gen Campbell, CofOrd, 14 Jun 43, OO 350.05/3676, DRB AGO.

[25] (1) J. E. Trainer, "Antiaircraft Gun Carriages," *Army Ordnance*, XXII, 130 (1942), 543–44. (2) OCM 17499, 4 Dec 41; 21027, 15 Jul 43; 21098, 22 Jul 43; 21639, 23 Sep 43; 22378, 16 Dec 43. (3) Catalogue of Standard Ord Items, II, 206.

and tank chassis were tried out—twin 40-mm. guns, a 40-mm. gun together with two .50-caliber machine guns, and twin 40-mm. with twin machine guns. Any of these promised to increase volume of fire considerably. The most satisfactory proved to be two 40-mm. antiaircraft guns mounted on the chassis of the light tank M24, in 1944 designated the M19 twin 40-mm. gun motor carriage.[26] Experiments with mounting a 75-mm. antiaircraft gun on this carriage began early in 1945 but were incomplete by the end of the war. For airborne use, a somewhat lightened 40-mm. carriage, the M5, was developed. The gun barrel and detachable outriggers had to be removed before loading into a transport plane but, after landing, three men could emplace the carriage in five minutes.[27]

At one stage of the war, after manufacture of 37-mm. antiaircraft guns had stopped, the question arose of whether a weapon between the .50-caliber machine gun and the 40-mm. gun would not be an advantage. Both the Germans and the Italians used 20-mm. ack-ack, but always with ammunition containing a self-destroying feature which neither British nor American 20-mm. ammunition possessed. The danger of serious casualties to Allied troops, unless fire were only over water, was too great to risk. Furthermore, theatre reports in 1944 indicated no real need for an antiaircraft gun at once more powerful than a caliber .50 and lighter and smaller than the Bofors.[28]

Defense Against Fast-Flying Aircraft at High Altitudes

Longer Range: Rockets

High-flying enemy bombers and protecting escort planes had if possible to be brought down before crews unloaded the bombs. For that purpose light artillery such as the 37-mm. and 40-mm. guns had insufficient range and power. Powerful ground fire, as both American and British Ordnance experts knew, was a vital supplement to Allied fighter craft, particularly early in the war when American, British, and Russian planes were outnumbered by enemy. In the spring of 1941 the Ordnance Department requested NDRC to investigate the use of jet propulsion for antiaircraft projectiles in order to shorten time of flight, increase vertical range, and simplify the projecting weapon. Work on the fundamental research this project involved had not gone far when it got fresh impetus from Dr. Lauritsen, vice chairman of one of the NDRC divisions. The British had invested a great deal of effort and money in getting antiaircraft rockets into action because, after Dunkerque, artillery was in extremely short supply, and 3-inch unrotated rocket projectiles and launchers had been developed to the point where they could be used. British "UP–3's" when fired with time fuzes had a ceiling of about 22,000 feet. Because the potentialities of these antiaircraft rockets greatly impressed

[26] (1) 1st Ind, Col Gerhardt for NATOUSA, Attn Col David J. Crawford, 6 Apr 43, sub: Changes of Design of Certain Items of Ord Equipment, OO 350.05/2501, DRB AGO. (2) Memo, Col Crawford, Theatre Ord Off NATOUSA, for CofOrd, 6 May 43, sub: New and Proposed Mountings for Automatic Weapons, OO 350.05/3284, DRB AGO. (3) Memo, Col Francis A. Englehart, OCO, for Col Crawford, 21 Jun 43, sub: Automatic AA Weapons, OO 350.05/3851, DRB AGO. (4) Memo, Barnes for Campbell, 26 Jun 43, sub: Col Thomas H. Nixon's Letter, Barnes-Campbell Correspondence, Barnes file, OHF. (5) OCM 23746, 11 May 44.

[27] (1) OCM 26544, 1 Feb 45. (2) Catalogue of Standard Ord Items, II, 107.

[28] Memo, Col Englehart for CG Hq AAF, 10 Jan 44, sub: Artillery Opns, New Georgia Campaign, and 1st Ind, Col H. C. Porter, Actg Field Dir Ammo Plants, for OCO, 19 Jan 44, OO 350.05/8721, DRB AGO.

90-MM. ANTIAIRCRAFT GUN *during a practice alert in Iceland.*

Lauritsen, the NDRC representative in London in the summer of 1941, the American armed services after study of Lauritsen's report contracted with the California Institute of Technology to carry this development further. The resulting work upon rocket propellants was valuable for other purposes but was not put to use for antiaircraft rockets since, by the time the necessary preliminaries were finished, powerful long-range artillery was available in quantity. The greater accuracy and higher velocity of rifled guns made antiaircraft rockets needless. From the California Institute of Technology, however, did come the data that enabled the Ordnance Department to produce the 3.25-inch target rocket which was of help in training antiaircraft gunners.[29]

Longer Range: The 90-mm. Gun

Long before the United States had so much as considered antiaircraft rockets, the Ordnance Department had been working upon powerful long-range artillery. Though the 3-inch gun M3 did in fact command adequate range for most World War II antiaircraft defense, and though it served the U.S. Army well on Bataan, its muzzle velocity of only 2,600 feet per second and its light, 12.8-pound projectile were drawbacks. Aware of these shortcomings, in 1938 the Coast Artillery had requested a larger-caliber gun, with a higher muzzle velocity, capable of firing a 21-pound projectile to a greater height than the 3-inch could reach. Since a Coast Artillery Board report of 1939 spoke of bombers flying at 250 miles per hour at an altitude of 32,000 feet and of even faster craft under design which could operate at a ceiling of nearly eight miles, 1939 saw the start of work upon a still longer-range gun calculated to reach planes at heights of 56,000 feet.[30]

The 1938 project, a 90-mm. antiaircraft gun, was rushed to completion in 1940. The selection of that caliber had been determined by the weight of a shell that could be hand loaded; anything in excess of forty pounds for a complete round would be too heavy for men to handle for more than a few minutes at a stretch, and mechanical loading systems up to that time had not been reliable. To obtain greater stability and a self-cocking firing mechanism, several changes in the original design of both mount and gun were effected in late 1939 and early 1940. As tests showed the modifications to be adequate, gun and mount were standardized in February 1940.[31] Almost at once, however, a fuze setter and spring rammer was hurried into production to facilitate ammunition loading. In the field, gunners usually disconnected it, as crews thought hand-ramming faster and considered the spring rammer dangerous because it sometimes struck the loader or mashed his fingers. The spring rammer was admittedly a stop-

[29] (1) NDRC Liaison, Project OD-26, 8 Apr 41, OHF. (2) Memo, Dr. Lauritsen, Vice Chairman Div A, NDRC, for Dr. Bush, 1 Aug 41, sub: Expansion of Program of Rocket Developments, quoted in Burchard, ed., *Rockets, Guns and Targets,* pp. 24–28. (3) Burchard, ed., *op. cit.,* pp. 89–92. (4) 1st Lt Edward G. Uhl, Rpt on British Rocket Development, 24 Sep 42, OHF. (5) Rpt on U.S. Tech Mission, 26 Aug 42, Barnes file, OHF. See also n. 3.

[30] (1) Ltr, OCO to Henry Dreyfus, 29 Jun 42, OO 350.05/1056, DRB AGO. (2) Memo, Capt D. W. Hoppock, Development Analysis Sec, OCO, for Col Seleen, 11 Jul 42, sub: Weekly Performance Rpt of Ord Manufactured Materiel in Action, OO 350.05/1100, DRB AGO. (3) Coast Artillery Bd Rpt, Project 1153, 8 Mar 39 and Project 1116, 8 Feb 38, cited in Design, Development, and Production of 90-mm. and 120-mm. AA Guns, PSP 29, OHF. (4) OCM 14531, 9 Jun 38.

[31] (1) OCM 15641, 23 Feb 40; 15688, 21 Mar 40. (2) PSP 29, pp. 7, 10, OHF.

gap until a better, albeit more complicated, mechanism could be perfected. An electrically controlled rammer and fuze setter required linkage with mechanical or electric directors.

When the automatic fuze setter-rammer developed by the United Shoe Machinery Company was accepted by the Ordnance Department, the potential rate of fire of the 90-mm. gun increased. But it never got above 27 shots per minute, even in practice firing. This electrically controlled fuze setter-rammer, designated the M20, was ingenious. The crews fed a complete round of ammunition into slowly rotating ramming rolls that drew the round into the fuze setter jaws. There it stopped until the jaws received the position signal from the remotely located electric director and then rotated the fuze to set it as directed. Thereupon the jaws opened and the round was automatically rammed into the breech, the breech closed, and the round was fired. This decreased the "dead time" between setting the fuze and the moment of firing. As a fast-flying plane could move a considerable distance in that interval, use of the automatic fuze setter-rammer notably improved accuracy.[32] Only hypervelocity, largely a matter of ammunition with flatter trajectory, could further multiply efficiency of the gun itself.

The Search for High Velocity

The 90-mm. was to have been a high-velocity gun and, at its inception in 1938, its proposed 2,800 feet per second might have been called high velocity. The German 88-mm. *Flak 36* had a muzzle velocity of 2,690 feet per second. Unhappily, the walls of the first shell designed for the 90-mm. proved to have insufficient strength to withstand the pressures upon them when the rotating bands engaged the rifling. Special heat treating would give the needed strength, but in 1941 manufacturing capacity for that process was too limited to count upon. The alternative was to increase the thickness of the shell walls, a change that increased weight and reduced the amount of explosive charge, thereby decreasing muzzle velocity to 2,700 feet a second. When the German 88-mm. *Flak 41* gun with its velocity of 3,280 feet per second and its high-explosive ammunition appeared, the American 90 was outclassed in that particular. Unlike field guns, antiaircraft artillery never fired in direct competition with enemy ack-ack. If the American gun brought down its target, it mattered little that the gun was less powerful than its German counterpart. Yet the challenge of the German guns remained.[33] The 90-mm. M2 was, to be sure, so mounted as to enable it to fire at tanks and other ground targets, a versatility that won it the label of "triple threat" gun. But it was the 90-mm. M3, designed specifically for antitank use, that was pressed into use as a field gun. Velocity of the AA gun never got above 2,700 feet per second.

The difficulty for the U.S. Army was partly logistical. Increased velocities spelled excessive barrel wear unless erosion resistant gun tubes could be developed or powders combining high-potential with a cool-burning, noneroding chemical composition. For Germany, with her interior lines of supply, barrel replacement was

[32] (1) PSP 29, pp. 14–22, OHF. (2) Catalogue of Standard Ord Items, II, 210–11, 213–15. (3) OCM 17213, 11 Sep 41; 19946, 15 Jan 43; 20401, 13 May 43.

[33] (1) OCM 21269, 12 Aug 43. (2) PSP 29, pp. 12–13, OHF. (3) Barnes, *Weapons of World War II*, pp. 88–89. (4) The War Office, *Illustrated Record of German Army Equipment, 1939-1945*, Vol. II, *Artillery*, Pt. 2, MI-10 (London, 1948), copy in Ord Tech Intel files.

GERMAN 88-MM. AT PORTE FERRAIO, ELBA. *This was the multipurpose artillery piece of the German Army.*

very much easier than for the Allies, whose matériel had to be shipped from the States. The official German weapons handbook gave an estimated life of 1,500 rounds to the 88-mm. *Flak 41* gun, 2,000 to 2,500 rounds with supercharges to the *Flak 36* and *37*.[34] Life of the 90-mm. antiaircraft guns was limited to about 1,600 rounds because the mechanical time fuzes ordinarily used failed to function properly after the barrel was somewhat worn. Yet in firing against German V–1 missiles in the summer of 1944, experience showed that, with VT fuzes, life of barrels might be extended to 1,900 rounds, depending upon how rapid the rate of fire was and how long sustained. On the problem of achieving hypervelocity without creating an impossible maintenance situation, the Ordnance Department and its contractors throughout the war expended much time, effort, and money.[35]

Inasmuch as practicable solutions would depend upon considerable basic research into the mechanics and chemistry of barrel erosion, the Ordnance Department requested NDRC to undertake a comprehensive study of the problem. The work, under the guidance of Dr. L. H. Adams,

[34] (1) Ord Handbook, German Army Weapons Office, H15/27, GMDS DRB AGO. Yet after V-E Day American interrogation of Hauptdienstleiter Saur, one of the heads of German war production, elicited the statement: "Gun erosion was never a problem. In the L/56 the metallurgical qualities of the steel had worsened three times during this war. The 8.8cm guns did not only do their 5000 but 8000 rounds, 8.8cm 41 L/74 should take 500 rds, did 1800." Interrogation of Hauptdienstleiter Saur by Dr. Henry B. Allen, 2 Jul 45, Ord Tech Intel files.

[35] Intervs, 17 Jul 51, with Bruce Anderson, Artillery Ammo Br, R&D Serv, and Paul Netzer, Artillery Br, R&D Serv.

was primarily important because of the solid foundation of knowledge it laid down upon the causes of erosion. But NDRC's sixteen contractors on this project—research institutions and private companies—also contributed by exploring various applications of this knowledge. While NDRC success in developing liners for machine gun barrels[36] was not duplicated for artillery, some inconclusive experiments were tried: using replaceable steel liners for artillery, employing pre-engraved projectiles so as to lessen the friction between the projectile and the lands of the rifled bore, and a protecting metal sleeve to be fitted over the junction of the cartridge case and the projectile. More promising were the studies of erosion-resistant materials, notably molybdenum and hot-hard alloys, and the sabot projectile developed for the 90-mm. gun. But as the NDRC project was concerned with the over-all problem of hypervelocity, in May 1944 the Ordnance Department began work on hypervelocity specifically for 3-inch, 90-mm., and 105-mm. antiaircraft fire.[37] V-J Day arrived before this development program had made much headway.

Indeed, the only high-velocity American antiaircraft gun, the 120-mm., saw little action, partly because its development and production lagged by more than a year behind that of the 90-mm., and partly because its weight made transport difficult. Nevertheless, even in 1939 the Ordnance Department had been convinced that a more powerful antiaircraft weapon than the 90-mm. would in time be needed. Design of the 90-mm. was scarcely off the drawing boards when the Ordnance Department persuaded the Coast Artillery Board of the wisdom of having Ordnance develop a heavy antiaircraft gun. Whereas the limits of fire control in 1938 had precluded the use of a longer-range gun than the 90-mm., by 1939 developments in radar and electronics held out hopes of effectively reaching to greater heights. The project accordingly launched in June 1939, though modified somewhat during the next sixteen months, called for a gun with a muzzle velocity of 3,100 feet per second, and able to fire a 50-pound projectile to an altitude of 56,000 feet. The ammunition had to be semifixed, that is, the 50-pound projectile separate from the 51-pound sealed powder case. As 50-pound loads would be too heavy for hand loading, a power-operated ammunition tray and rammer was necessary. These characteristics were incorporated in the model standardized in 1944 as the 120-mm. AA gun M1. An automatic fuze setter to ease and expedite firing permitted a rate of 10 rounds per minute. Ordnance designers regarded the 120-mm. as the best gun the Allied armies had for bringing down enemy aircraft at high altitudes. The 61,500-pound weight of the gun and mount was one objectionable feature, and the 123.5-inch width was another. Only 550 guns were manufactured and none was shipped to Europe. The 90-mm. and lighter weapons served as antiaircraft defense against the Luftwaffe.[38]

Fire Control and Tracking Devices

Guns, ammunition, and firing mechanisms were by no means the only elements

[36] For a further discussion of this topic, see below, Ch. XV.

[37] (1) NDRC Liaison, Project OD-52, OHF. (2) OCM 23832, 18 May 44. (3) Interv with Paul Netzer, 17 Jul 51.

[38] (1) PSP 29, pp. 50–63, OHF. (2) Catalogue of Standard Ord Items, II, 216–17. (3) OCM 15059, 1 Jun 39; 19709, 11 Feb 43; 21389, 26 Aug 43; 22734, 27 Jan 44. (4) Interv with Bruce Anderson, 17 Jul 51.

to consider in making the best possible antiaircraft equipment. Sighting, traversing, and elevating mechanisms, and tracking devices were equally essential. Machine guns with their limited range required only simple sights, and only when multiple-mounted on power-driven turrets were the guns electrically traversed. Fire control for heavier, more powerful weapons naturally had to be more complex. In fact, because the speed at which dive bombers and low-flying strafing planes operated made effective close-in fire more difficult than at long-range targets, devising accurate fire control mechanisms for light antiaircraft artillery was one of the knottiest problems Ordnance faced in 1940. Hand-tracking and aiming were likely to be inaccurate; the mechanical controls developed in the 1930's for the 37-mm. gun were clumsy and slow. The most satisfactory answer was found in the adoption of a British mechanical director linked with gears on the gun that automatically elevated and traversed the gun as the director transmitted its computations. The Kerrison predictor, named for its British inventor, Col. K. E. Kerrison, was somewhat modified for use with American guns, a task undertaken by NDRC. Later, addition of a stereoscopic range finder, an altitude converter, and an electric mechanism for setting slant range into the director's multiplying mechanism produced the model labeled the M5A2 director. Improved oil gears to traverse and elevate the gun were also installed on the remote control system on the gun. Bofors sights on the 40-mm. and telescopes on the 37-mm. provided either for direct sighting or for use with the Kerrison predictor. On the 37-mm., one telescope to track in azimuth and one to track the target in elevation were attached to the top carriage and cradle so that each moved with the gun. Because the Kerrison predictors could not be mounted directly upon either the 37-mm. or 40-mm. carriage, they could not be used when the guns were moving to protect convoys or covering troops in forward areas. To permit aiming when the director was unusable, Frankford Arsenal developed a mechanical computing sight containing a mechanism by which the direction and speed of the target were set in. Parallel linkage of the two tracking mechanisms completed the computing sight.[39]

Directing fire of larger-caliber, heavier antiaircraft guns was only slightly less difficult. The original design of the 90-mm. lacked automatic controls. Manual operation of wheels to traverse and elevate rapidly a gun with a fifteen-foot barrel would require great exertion on the part of the gun crew, if indeed men at hand controls could keep on a fast-moving target at all. Consequently, though the Ordnance Department before 1940 had objected to automatic power controls as likely to be unreliable, it ran tests of a Sperry Gyroscope Company power system for the new 90-mm. gun during the summer of 1940. This first remote control system was, as Frankford Arsenal pointed out, "a complex combination of electrical, mechanical and hydraulic units," which would be expensive to build, difficult to maintain in the field, and would double the load on the gun's power generator.[40] Nevertheless, despite defects, the apparatus did work and did provide a method of relative accuracy in laying guns against targets moving at

[39] (1) Catalogue of Standard Ord Items, II, 329–33, 338–40, 345–47. (2) OCM 19539, 21 Jan 43. (3) For a general discussion of this problem of tracking, see Baxter, *Scientists Against Time,* pp. 212–17.

[40] PSP 29, citing memo, CG Frankford Arsenal for CofOrd, 8 Jan 40, sub: Power Control System for 90-mm. AA Gun, OHF.

FIRE CONTROL INSTRUMENTS. *Director T30 (above) and height finder M1 (below).*

high angular speeds as well as against targets at short ranges where manual tracking was extremely difficult. In February 1941 the Ordnance Committee therefore recommended standardization of the Sperry servo-system as remote control system M2. To simplify its installation and servicing, some redesign followed. Extensive redesign was necessary for the mount in order to accommodate the controls. The new mount embodying these changes was designated the M1A1.[41] It was a mobile unit resting on a single-axled, two-wheeled bogie drawn by a trail.

Sighting on the M1A1 mount was by elbow telescopes. Off-carriage equipment included a bore sight, as well as a height finder to determine the slant range or altitude of an enemy plane and to transmit the resulting data to the director. This telescopic device, largely perfected by the Eastman Kodak Company, was fundamentally a 13.5-foot stereoscopic range finder that converted slant range to altitude. The remote control system was linked by cable to an off-carriage mechanical director that computed the firing data continuously. Power was supplied by a separate generating unit located near by.[42] When the more elaborate fire control system for the 90-mm. gun M2 was developed, a good many changes in its mount were necessary, though it would have required some redesign in any case in order to install the fuze setter-rammer and the shields added to protect the gun crew. The gun itself differed from its predecessors only in minor details. The remote control system of the first 90-mm. models was replaced on the new mount by the M12 system, which permitted the gun to be depressed to −5 degrees so that it could be fired against ground targets and fast-moving torpedo boats. The greater weight of the M2 mount and gun, 32,300 pounds as compared to 19,000, demanded a two-axled trailer. The M12 remote control system operated on the same principle as the M2, from which it derived, but the M12 was connected with an electrical off-carriage director instead of with a mechanical director.[43]

The electric directors—the M9 series for the 90-mm. antiaircraft guns and the M10 for the 120-mm.—were extremely complicated devices. As they weighed about 3,500 pounds, they were installed in separate trailers. The major components of each director were a tracker, a computer, a power unit, and an altitude converter, all interconnected by a cable system. From the tracker, used only when the target was visible, data on range, elevation, and azimuth of the plane were transmitted to the computer. When the target was invisible, a radar system was used. The computer must seem to the layman to be a miraculous electric brain. The position of the target—its elevation, its azimuth, and its range at a given moment—was transmitted in polar co-ordinates to the computer, which transposed them to Cartesian, or rectangular, co-ordinates. As the speed at which the target was moving had to be taken into consideration to determine where to point the gun so that target and projectile would arrive at the same position in space simultaneously, the time element, introduced by velocity, had also to be figured. The computer mechanism made

[41] (1) PSP 29, citing memo, Col Alexander G. Gillespie for Tech Staff, OCO, 11 Jan 40, sub: Initiation of Project for Automatic Remote Control System for AA Guns, OHF. (2) OCM 16453, 6 Feb 41; 16755, 22 May 41; 16871, 21 Jun 41.

[42] Catalogue of Standard Ord Items, II, 211, 330–34, 338–41.

[43] (1) *Ibid.*, pp. 213–15. (2) PSP 29, pp. 17–20, OHF.

continuous automatic electrical computations of firing data and transmitted them continuously to the gun. The advantages of electric directors over mechanical directors were several: improved tracking; complete ballistical solutions for nonstandard meteorological conditions of wind, temperature, and air density; the elimination of some errors inherent in the mechanical prediction system; a much shorter minimum slant range; and nearly twice the maximum horizontal range.[44] Still the weight and bulk, as well as the complexity and cost, of this fire control equipment made it suitable only for big antiaircraft guns.

So intricate a device as the electric director did not, of course, spring like Athena whole from the head of Zeus. The proposal, conceived by Dr. D. B. Parkinson, came in June 1940 from the Bell Telephone Laboratories to the Chief of the Signal Corps who, after investigation of the rather detailed plan, pronounced it sound.

The story runs that Parkinson, who for some time had been interested in problems of fire control, dreamed one night of an electric computer that directed antiaircraft fire so exactly that as the "ping" of a fired shell sounded in the dreamer's ears down came a plane, another ping and another plane fell—always one shot to a kill. Fascinated by the somewhat fantastic idea his dream had given shape to, Dr. Parkinson described it to his chief, Dr. Lovell, who recognized more than fantasy in it and directed his young assistant to try working out details.

Meanwhile, the creation of NDRC led the Bell Telephone engineers to approach Dr. Warren Weaver's section, which was concerned with fire control. In September the enthusiasm over the plan evinced by members of the British Tizard Mission gave added impetus. As the problem involved automatic laying of the AA gun as well as use of radar for tracking the plane, the Ordnance Department took over from the Signal Corps. The specifications for a 90-mm. electrical director were worked out in the next six weeks, with the Ordnance Department, the Bell Laboratories, and NDRC collaborating. A year after formal initiation of the project, a first model was ready for the Coast Artillery test. NDRC's contribution lay principally in its careful analysis of the mathematical problems involved. Some modifications of the pilot model followed, in keeping with Coast Artillery Board recommendations, but upon incorporation of these changes the director was standardized as the M9 in February 1942, only nineteen months after the inception of the idea. Though mathematically complex, the director was far easier to manufacture than the mechanical director it superseded. Many of the parts of the M9 and its later variations were standard commercial apparatus, and only where commercial parts lacked precision were specially made parts needed.[45]

Proximity Fuzes

While all other methods of increasing the proportion of effective antiaircraft hits were under consideration, the question arose of whether a fuze could be developed that would operate not by time but by proximity to the target. Impact-detonating ammunition would have been ideal for most antiaircraft fire had cyclic rates of

[44] (1) Interv with Dr. Wilhelm Jörgensen, 13 Jul 41. (2) Catalogue of Standard Ord Items, II, 343–44.

[45] (1) NDRC Liaison, Project OD-28, OHF. (2) Baxter, *op. cit.*, pp. 212–15.

weapons been sufficiently high and fire control of greater accuracy. But early in the war the difficulty of computing the target's range exactly led to reliance on mechanical time fuzes. These, if correctly set with proper allowance for dead-time, might explode the shell at the exact moment when the plane was within the cone of flying fragments, but in practice the burst was likely to occur anywhere along several hundred feet of shell path.[46] Use of influence fuzes promised to improve the effectiveness of antiaircraft fire as much as any other single means conceivably could.[47]

For antiaircraft fire, two requirements of the proposed fuze were only less important than the primary stipulation that it function when passing within effective range of the target. Because antiaircraft batteries usually fired over friendly terrain, the fuze must have a self-destructive feature to guarantee that, in case of missing the target, no friendly troops or civilians would be injured or valuable equipment damaged. Secondly, the mechanism must have sufficient ruggedness to withstand the rotational and setback forces of antiaircraft weapons. Success in meeting these and the numerous other difficult requirements enabled the Army to issue proximity fuzes to AA batteries in the summer of 1944 when the German buzz-bomb attacks on England began. Forewarned of the impending attack, the Ordnance Department shipped the fuzes to the United Kingdom and stored them under guard until specialists had instructed AA gunners in use of what Lt. Gen. George S. Patton, Jr., later called the "funny fuze." The result of the last four weeks of the V–1 bombings showed mounting effectiveness: destruction of 24, 46, 67, and 79 percent of the targets fired at. The British credited the proximity fuzes, together with American antiaircraft artillery, radar, and fire control, with saving London from the buzz bomb.[48]

[46] Interv, 25 Jul 51, with S. Seymour Podnos, Fuze and Booster Sec, R&D Serv.

[47] See above, Ch. XII.

[48] (1) Barnes, *op. cit.*, p. 86. (2) Col. C. H. M. Roberts, Text of Broadcast for State Department "University of the Air" on the Proximity Fuze, 23 Apr 46, OHF.

CHAPTER XV

Aircraft Armament: Weapons for Air-to-Air Combat

The problems antiaircraft batteries had to deal with in countering the powerful attacks of Axis aircraft were matched, perhaps more than matched, by those the Army Air Forces encountered. Aircraft manufacturers in the United States during the 1930's had been building planes capable of ever-increasing speeds, but as specifications for military craft had slighted the concomitant developments—faster-firing guns, protecting armor, and self-sealing fuel tanks—these netted relatively scant consideration before 1939. Fuel tanks, as an integral part of the plane, were an Air Corps responsibility. Before 1940 the Air Corps had rejected the idea of armored planes, and only when General Henry H. Arnold insisted, after checking the reports of the Battle of Britain, was any attention given to use of protecting armor. Testing suitable materials and preparing specifications then fell to the Ordnance Department because of its experience in ballistics and knowledge of the behavior of plate on armored vehicles under fire.[1] But the major task of the Ordnance Department in developing matériel for the Army Air Forces was to design guns and ammunition for attack.

The Problem of Speed

When President Roosevelt in January 1939 requested of the Congress vast sums of money to produce 50,000 aircraft, only Ordnance experts and a handful of Air Corps officers fully appreciated the need of equipping these planes with very fast-firing guns, with more guns per plane, or with both, in order to score hits on enemy planes traveling at new high speeds. General Arnold, to be sure, as early as the summer of 1937 had requested the Ordnance Department to increase the cyclic rate of the .50-caliber aircraft machine gun, and the Springfield Armory and Colt's Patent Fire Arms Company had spent some time on study of the problem. But funds were skimpy, and progress had been proportionately slight. Furthermore, the Air Corps had submitted no list of required military characteristics.[2] Whether to add more guns to a plane to increase its volume of fire was a matter for the Air Corps to decide; the quality of those guns, in keeping with the user's specifications, was up to the Ordnance Department.[3]

American fighters in 1939 carried nothing heavier than .30-caliber and .50-cali-

[1] Interv, 26 Jul 51, with Col Quinn, Artillery Br, R&D Serv.

[2] SA & SA Ammo, Book 3, Machine Guns and Related Items, p. 25, OHF.

[3] During the war the number of caliber .50's per fighter was increased from four to six, and on bombers to fourteen and sixteen. Col René R. Studler, Air Craft Guns and Ammunition, MS in Machine Gun Sec, R&D Serv, OHF.

ber machine guns in multiple mounts on the wings, fuselage, and nose of the plane.[4] Though the standard .50-caliber Browning machine gun M2 of 1939 could fire 600 rounds a minute on a rigid test mount, in some planes that rate was reduced by about 100 rounds a minute, partly because of the aircraft mount's resilience and partly because of the heavy ammunition-belt loads on the gun's feed mechanism. The .30-caliber aircraft gun fired 1,200 rounds a minute, but its muzzle velocity was low and its bullet light.[5] Aircraft guns had to be mounted in confined spaces, so that any redesign or modification must, if possible, retain the external dimensions of the originals in order to minimize modification of the plane to accommodate the new models. Not until late September 1939 did the Air Corps establish the military characteristics wanted in a machine gun of cyclic rate rapid enough to be effective in the shortened "on-target" time of new planes. By then it was clear that what would suffice to hit a target moving at 200 miles an hour would not serve against aircraft flying at 300 to 400 miles an hour.

Higher Cyclic Rates

Accordingly, the Air Corps' major requirement for the new gun was a cyclic rate of at least 1,000 rounds a minute and as much more as other features would permit. The time of bullet flight was to be .7 second for 600 yards and at that range penetrations of .75-inch armor plate must be possible when armor-piercing bullets were used. The over-all length of the gun should be kept within 68 inches and weight as low as was consistent with efficient performance. Other requirements were full automatic fire, controlled by hand and by trigger motor, right-hand and left-hand ammunition feed, adaptability to mounting for either fixed or flexible use, and the least possible trunnion reaction, that is, the lowest possible strain on the shafts upon which the gun was mounted in the plane. Air-cooling the gun with an aerodynamic barrel jacket extending at least 20 inches aft of the muzzle was listed as essential. The Colt's Patent Fire Arms Company, which owned John Browning's patents, undertook design of a gun to meet these requirements, only to have each model tested during the next two years show such serious defects as to be wholly unsatisfactory. In 1940 engineers at the Springfield Armory, by lightening the barrel of the standard M2 machine gun and by substituting double driving springs for a single spring, pushed the cyclic rate up to 800 rounds a minute, but that was still far below the 1,000 rounds a minute the Air Corps wanted.[6]

Increasing the cyclic rate of a gun such as the .50-caliber M2, designed to fire at 650 to 800 rounds per minute, resulted in added stresses upon the barrel and all the moving parts. Even if other components were strengthened enough to avoid excessive breakage, the problem of barrel erosion would remain. The hot gases generated by the explosion of the powder charge softened the bore surface, the chemical composition of the powder attacked the metal, and the high temperature and pres-

[4] See above, Ch. VII, for the earlier history of machine gun development.

[5] (1) From 1930 on, the .50-caliber had gradually superseded the .30-caliber, and in 1943 the AAF discontinued use of the smaller gun altogether. SA & SA Ammo, Book 3, p. 53. (2) See also memo, AAF Ord Officer, Wright Field, for CofOrd, 2 Dec 42, sub: Extracts from Correspondence Between Bell Aircraft Co. and their Foreign Representatives, OO 350.05/1862, DRB AGO.

[6] (1) OCM 15382, 29 Sep 39; 15738, 4 Apr 40. (2) SA & SA Ammo, Book 3, p. 24.

sure tended to expand the bore in a very fast-firing gun. Inaccuracy would therefore soon develop unless barrel erosion could be lessened by cooling the barrel, by using a heavier barrel, or by improving the barrel's metallurgy.[7] In February 1942 the Ordnance Department requested NDRC to study the whole problem. NDRC let contracts to some twenty-six companies, universities, and other research institutions, each of which followed out a particular line of investigation. Two and a half years of work, notably that of the Crane Company and the Geophysics Laboratory of the Carnegie Institution, produced a liner of a special alloy which, fastened into the breech end of the barrel, greatly reduced erosion. Further experimentation showed that combining this material at the breech end with chromium plating extending to the muzzle end gave still higher erosion resistance and better general performance.[8]

In the interim, efforts to develop a machine gun of high cyclic rate had continued. Early in 1942 the High Standard Company of New Haven offered a promising design, though the models tested that summer at Aberdeen lacked both the strength and the reliability to be acceptable. Later models, built under a development contract with the Ordnance Department, showed marked improvements but still failed to meet all requirements. Throughout, High Standard worked on the basis of designing a high-speed gun in which changes from the M2 would be kept to a minimum. This came to be a big handicap. Consequently, in August 1943 the Ordnance Department entered into contract with the Frigidaire Division of General Motors Corporation, with the understanding that a gun be developed using the basic mechanism of the M2 aircraft gun but with no restrictions upon the number of changes that might be made. In short, the Ordnance Department abandoned any plan of having parts of the new gun interchangeable with those of the M2. Frigidaire's first model was ready for test in March 1944. It was essentially a new gun; only minor components were interchangeable with the standard M2. Numerous changes were still needed but, by adopting some features of the High Standard experimental models, Frigidaire succeeded by the fall of 1944 in producing a weapon, the T25E3, that had a cyclic rate of 1,250 or more rounds per minute and functioned well enough to warrant fabrication of a hundred for AAF and Navy service test. By the next April the guns that had been carefully service-tested at Wright Field were proving so far superior to the M2 that the Air Forces requested immediate standardization of the new model. The latter then became the .50-caliber aircraft gun M3, and the M2 was reclassified as limited standard.

Development of a machine gun with cyclic rate increased from 800 to 1,200 rounds per minute, at the cost of only a pound in weight and with no significant change from the over-all dimensions of the slower-firing M2, was so impressive an achievement as to merit some particulars. It was accomplished largely by twelve new

[7] (1) Div I, NDRC Summary Tech Rpt, Hyper Velocity Guns, *passim,* OHF. (2) Proceedings of a Symposium on Gun Barrel Erosion, 26 Apr 50, copy in Machine Gun Sec, R&D Serv, OHF.

[8] (1) NDRC Liaison Project OD-52, OHF. (2) SA & SA Ammo, Book 3, pp. 151–56, OHF. (3) OCM 26230, 4 Jan 45. (4) For discussion of the steps in this research program, see Burchard, ed., *Rockets, Guns and Targets,* pp. 370–93. Burchard, indeed, declared that the combination of special liner and plating gave resistance ten to fifteen times that of an ordinary steel barrel, but Ordnance specialists found this claim greatly exaggerated.

features. First was a bolt of improved metallurgy and design with holes drilled through to reduce weight. Second was an extractor with a reversible ejector which eased ammunition feeding. Third was the substitution of a pneumatic barrel buffer for the older oil buffer, a change that produced smooth operation regardless of extremes of temperature. Alteration of the curvature of the accelerator resulted in more effective use of the energy of the barrel and barrel extension to accelerate bolt recoil, while a Belleville spring back-plate buffer, using cupped steel washers, accelerated counterrecoil of the bolt. Rigidly mounted breech-lock depressers added to stability of the gun's components during operation. Redesign of the back-plate and of the breech-lock cam strengthened the construction and gave smoother functioning, and an improved firing pin provided about five times as long a life as that of the M2 firing pin. The two features incorporated from the High Standard guns were a special cover assembly to increase ammunition belt-life capacity and split belt-holding pawls to improve ammunition feeding. Use of the new erosion-resistant lining for the barrel, moreover, permitted firing long bursts without loss of accuracy or marked drop in velocity.[9]

Unfortunately, few M3's saw action in World War II, as only some 2,400 were completed before September 1945. Yet in the fall of 1944 Ordnance engineers perceived that some desirable proven features of the High Standard and Frigidaire high-speed models could be readily applied to the M2. Among the parts to be used were High Standard's extractor assembly, recoil booster, wide top-cover assembly and split pawls, as well as two parts designed by Frigidaire for the still unperfected T25E3 model. With improved metallurgy, use of a lined barrel, removal of the oil from the oil buffer, and one or two lesser changes, this modified M2 gun, the T36, could fire slightly over 900 rounds a minute. In October 1944 the Air Forces requested 31,336 of these, but rapid progress on the T25E3 limited output to some 8,000.[10]

Encouraging though these developments were, still faster-firing aircraft guns would clearly be advantageous. The Germans, indeed, believed that extremely high cyclic rates would offer the best possible method of combating high-speed craft. Toward the end of the war observers reported on a German development program to introduce aircraft machine guns with cyclic rates well beyond those under development in the United States. The object was to lay down a dense curtain of fire from a very short range. These experimental guns fired short bursts, with firing initiated photoelectrically when the plane was in the proper position.[11] From the American point of view the great drawback of the device was that it did not permit continuous or prolonged fire, a feature the AAF regarded as more important than a single, very fast burst. In 1945 the maximum rate the Ordnance Department set as its goal was 1,500 rounds a minute. Springfield Armory for a time worked on a design of a totally new mechanism suitable for high-speed operation, and Frigidaire designers continued efforts to increase the rate of the M3 to 1,500 rounds per minute, but the war ended before either type had reached the stage of extended testing.[12]

[9] (1) SA & SA Ammo, Book 3, pp. 25–39, OHF. (2) Hist of Springfield Armory, Vol. II, Book 3, pp. 263–64, 383–88, 529–32, 705–10, OHF. (3) OCM 25695, 14 Dec 44; 27496, 3 May 45.

[10] (1) SA & SA Ammo, Book 3, p. 43, OHF. (2) OCM 25399, 12 Oct 44; 28134, 28 Jun 45.

[11] Ordnance CIOS History, p. 11, OHF.

[12] (1) SA & SA Ammo, Book 3, p. 45, OHF. (2) OCM 28138, 28 Jun 45.

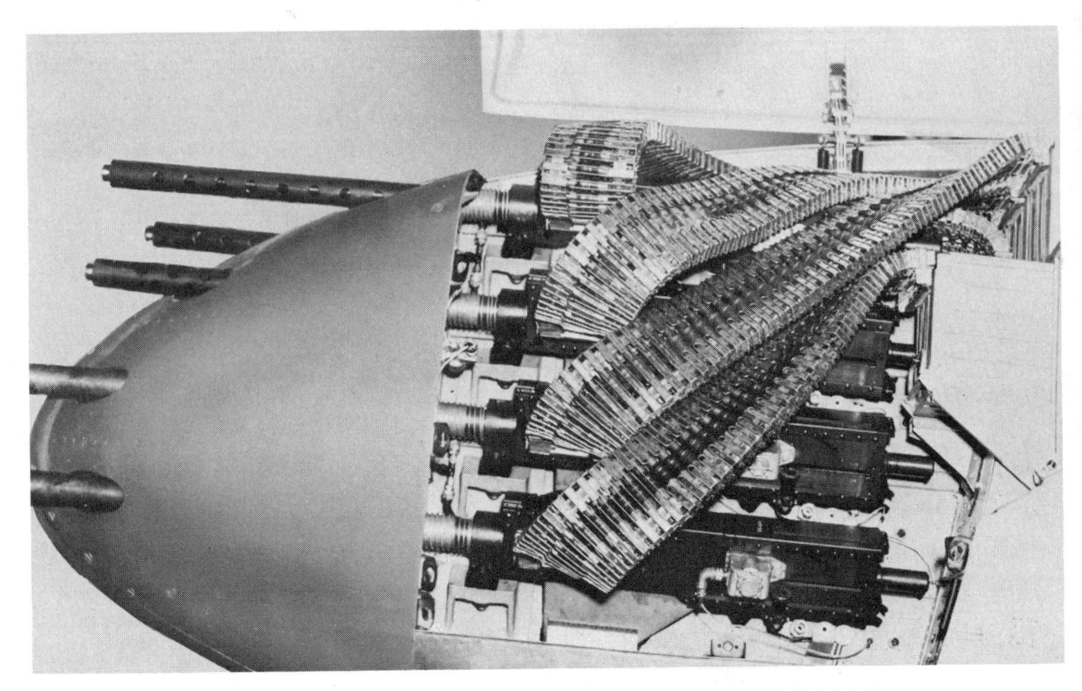

METALLIC LINK BELT *installation in the nose of a P–38.*

Improvement in the metallic link belts for aircraft machine guns was also needed to make them sturdier and flexible enough to use in restricted spaces such as the plane's tail. The complexity of the problem may be envisaged by study of the accompanying photograph of an installation. A project to improve the link began in the spring of 1940, and, while the Air Corps accepted a modified link early in 1941, search for a design still more serviceable and easier to manufacture continued throughout the war. If, in addition to getting a high degree of strength combined with great flexibility under strain, a lightweight link could be made, the advantages for aircraft guns would be important. Before V-J Day designers tried some twenty-eight variations of the standard one-piece link and several two-piece types. Not only design but also materials and heat-treating affected performance in all metallic links. As the light weight of aluminum and plastic suggested substitution of these materials for steel, considerable study of a nylon link went forward, but the effect of extremes of climate upon plastic links and the inelasticity of aluminum prevented development of anything as satisfactory as the steel types used in World War II. In these, lowering the hardness of the steel largely overcame brittleness.[13] Addition of a sprocket to serve as a booster to the feed mechanism also relieved strains.

Higher Muzzle Velocities

Faster-firing guns were not the only answer to the greater speeds of enemy air-

[13] (1) SA & SA Ammo, Book 3, pp. 128–45, OHF. (2) Metallic Link Belt, Fabric Ammunition Belt, PSP 36, OHF. (3) OCM 16396, 16 Jan 41; 16494, 20 Feb 41; 20031, 9 Mar 43; 21747, 7 Oct 43; 22073, 3 Nov 43; 26729, 15 Feb 45.

craft. Flatter trajectory of fire obtained by higher muzzle velocity was an even surer answer and was sought simultaneously. The NDRC study of hypervelocity noted at the end of the war that, in attacking targets moving in three dimensions, heightening the muzzle velocity of guns by 50 percent would more than triple the number of hits. In any given gun, unless the barrel were lengthened, thereby increasing the weight of the gun, or unless the metallic ammunition components were changed, the only way to increase muzzle velocity without adding to pressures was to use higher-potential powder. But higher-potential powders, like increased cyclic rates, spelled the probability of excessive barrel erosion. This could be avoided only by keeping the temperature of powder combustion low. Extensive experimentation, largely at Frankford Arsenal, produced .50-caliber ammunition with muzzle velocity heightened from 2,700 to 2,880 feet per second, but even with lined barrels the danger of "keyholing" after firing relatively few rounds forbade more powerful charges. As the interior surface of the barrel wore, the projectile tended to deform so that it lost velocity and tumbled in flight, and upon impact made a keyhole-shaped mark. If the barrel became excessively hot the bullet might even break through the wall of the barrel. At the very end of the war tests at the Ordnance research and development center indicated that a newly developed lighter-weight cartridge, the armor-piercing-incendiary T49, using a single-base powder, would give muzzle velocity of over 3,400 feet per second, but the erosion properties of the T49 were still a drawback.[14]

The German point of view on high muzzle velocities in aircraft weapons offers a contrast to the American concept:

> Investigation of German small arms development and production revealed that, as concerns automatic weapon design, the attainment of a high cyclic rate appeared to be a primary consideration. This was particularly true in the case of automatic weapons designed for aircraft use. Apparently German authorities believed that a relatively low muzzle velocity was acceptable if a high rate of fire could be obtained. High velocities required larger and heavier rounds with a consequent reduction of cyclic rate . . . .[15]

Training Devices for Bettering Marksmanship

Use of power-driven turrets developed by the Air Forces to enable the aircraft gunner to locate his quarry quickly and track him accurately was another means of dealing with the problem of hitting a target moving at high speed.[16] There remained the human factor in marksmanship. Whatever the perfection of gun mechanisms, Army and Army Air Forces both knew that soldiers must be well trained in their use; few weapons were highly effective in the hands of the inept or inexperienced. Where speed of hand and quickness of eye were so vital as to the aircraft gunner, his training became of more than usual importance. Skeet shooting, firing at a towed airborne sleeve or "drone," and shooting a camera gun were used in the early part of the war, but the shortcomings of those methods of training were so obvious that the Air Forces in September 1942 requested a conference with

[14] For exhaustive discussion of the research on this complex problem, see SA & SA Ammo, Book 2, Ch. 1, OHF.

[15] Rpt of CIOS, G-2 Div, SHAEF (Rear), The Intelligence Exploitation of Germany, 15 Sep 45, p. 44, OHF.

[16] All mechanisms that were integral parts of the plane were the responsibility of Army Air Forces. See above, Ch. VIII, section on military agencies.

the Ordnance Department to discuss ways of improving upon them. The Air Forces proposed that the Ordnance Department develop a projectile that would disintegrate upon impact without harm to the target or its crew, but a projectile with ballistics similar under training conditions to those of the service ammunition under combat conditions. The Air Forces, agreeing that a suitably armored target plane would be essential to successful use of a frangible cartridge, undertook to develop an armored plane. Two months later the Air Forces changed its mind about the armored target plane and informed the Ordnance Department that unless a bullet could be made that would shatter against an unarmored craft, the whole project must be abandoned. The Ordnance Department dropped it. Research men of NDRC later charged that "one or two willful men in the Ordnance Department nearly stopped the development altogether." The Ordnance staff averred that the Air Forces had tied its hands.[17]

At this point, one or two Air officers, convinced of the value of the idea, persuaded the Air Forces to turn the problem over to NDRC and approve a research contract with Duke University. Experiments were to be confined to work upon a .30-caliber bullet because, though .30-caliber machine guns were ineffective in combat against the armor plate of World War II planes, the firing characteristics were nearly identical with those of the more powerful .50-caliber, and the smaller-caliber ammunition was cheaper. In the course of the next year men at Duke and NRDC came up with a 90-grain bullet of powdered lead bonded with bakelite that, fired from a modified .30-caliber aircraft machine gun, at a distance of 50 yards disintegrated against a quarter inch plate of dural placed normal to the line of fire, or, if the bullet perforated the plate, caused little or no damage. This achievement was encouraging, though it still did not meet the Army Air Forces specifications. The Air Forces then requested the Ordnance Department to continue the development, but Maj. Cameron Fairchild, AAF, Professor Paul Gross and associates at Duke, members of NDRC, and the Bakelite Corporation, who had been the chief proponents of the program thus far, largely saw it through.

The technical difficulties were various. Beside making a frangible bullet with the proper ballistics and adapting the machine gun to firing ammunition with reduced powder charge, a plane had to be built, armored enough to be safe and yet able to fly. A hit indicator system had to be devised and a plan worked out for vectorial scaling of bomber and fighter velocities, for the bullet muzzle velocity, and for the ring sight size. The bullet T44, finally produced in some quantities and used at several training fields toward the end of the war, was slightly heavier than the first experimental type. The machine gun was satisfactorily modified and the scaling problem solved. The Air Forces did build an armored plane upon which hits were scored automatically by electrically amplifying the vibration caused by the bullet's impact and thus flashing a light on the nose of the plane. Yet in spite of these successful developments, only a small fraction of bullets manufactured were fired. After the war Air Forces psychologists concluded that trainees were prone to get false ideas of aiming and firing because the bul-

[17] For a detailed account of the conflict over the frangible bullet development see Burchard, ed., *op. cit.*, pp. 328–37.

let simulated too much. The frangible cartridge was then declared limited standard.[18]

Tracer Ammunition for Bettering Marksmanship

As an aid to accurate fire, tracer ammunition had long been held in high regard by the Air Corps. In 1924 an improved .30-caliber tracer cartridge was standardized as the M1, the combat characteristics of which remained unchanged until Pearl Harbor. But after the Battle of Britain in 1940 the British, though praising tracer as a medium of fire control, wanted a controlled length of trace and, in order to minimize the blinding effect upon the gunner, a delay of 150 yards before the bright-burning powder ignited. Satisfactory types were developed in the course of the next two years, but obsoletion of .30-caliber machine guns for Army aircraft resulted in limiting .30-caliber tracer to ground use and, in small quantities, to use by the naval air forces.[19] Caliber .50 tracer, on the other hand, mounted in importance as the war progressed. A type standardized in 1931 as the M1 formed the basis of the .50-caliber tracer most widely used by the Air Forces during the first two years of the war, though improvements were made in the original bullet by changing tracer and igniter mixtures, by increasing velocity 330 feet per second, and by developing clad-steel bullet jackets. Frankford Arsenal modifications of the M1 produced ammunition with a controlled bright trace of 550 plus or minus 50 yards, and later a type, standardized as the M10, which not only eliminated risk of blinding the gunner and gave a sufficient glow during the first moments of flight to permit him to retain trace image but also had ample intensity to enable him in daylight firing to follow the trace for the duration of the ignition. Thus, the M10 could be used in both night and day combat. It had, moreover, the advantage of longer life with less deterioration in storage than several other types of tracer ammunition.[20]

Another variation of the M1 tracer was developed between 1942 and 1944, a so-called headlight tracer, which gave a frontal visibility three times as bright as the M1. Initial reports from active theatres indicated that the psychological effect upon enemy pilots gave this bright-burning tracer particular value. The Tenth Air Force in December 1944 stated: "Preliminary reports indicated that they [caliber .50 headlight tracer cartridges] . . . make adjustment of fire easier. Enemy pilots seem to be less aggressive and show a tendency to break off combat at longer range than with standard ammunition . . . ."[21] And the Commanding General, Strategic Air Forces in Europe, cabled: "Brilliant tracer indicates enemy fighter to other gunners in formation, which enables our planes to spot enemy aircraft more effectively at greater distances. . . . [This] ammunition is an important factor in breaking up enemy fighter attacks at extreme ranges."[22] Furthermore, pilots at that time believed that this tracer used in ground strafing disturbed flak tower operations. It was therefore standardized as the caliber .50 headlight tracer M21. Only

[18] (1) OCM 24926, 31 Aug 44; 25101, 14 Sep 44; 28268, 5 Jul 45. (2) Baxter, *Scientists Against Time,* pp. 192–93. (3) Interv, 24 Oct 50, with Col Studler. (4) Interv, 3 Aug 51, with Dr. Frederick Carten, Ammo Sec, R&D Serv. (5) SA & SA Ammo, Book 2, Ch. 5, OHF.

[19] SA & SA Ammo, Book 2, pp. 80, 190, OHF.

[20] *Ibid.,* pp. 73, 91–103.

[21] Quoted in SA & SA Ammo, Book 2, pp. 100–103, OHF.

[22] *Ibid.,* p. 103.

after the war did the Air Forces conclude that enemy pilots had been less easily scared by this ammunition than first reports stated.[23] The M21 was then dropped.

The Problem of Effective Striking Power

Incendiary Ammunition

Rapidity of fire, flat trajectory, and accuracy of aim might solve the problem of scoring hits against enemy planes flying at high speeds, but if shots failed to disable the plane or crew, the effect of accuracy was lost. Greater striking power could be achieved by increasing machine gun muzzle velocities, by using air cannon that fired bigger projectiles, or by employing rockets. The threat of encountering enemy armor plate capable of withstanding .50-caliber machine gun fire did not actually materialize in World War II, but bullet penetration of the plane's armor did not necessarily knock out aircraft. Enemy use of self-sealing fuel tanks necessitated development of effective incendiary ammunition.[24]

A .30-caliber incendiary had been used in World War I but, because of difficulties in manufacture, was later discarded for tracer. When in 1939 and 1940 tests of incendiary characteristics of the tracer showed it to be unsatisfactory, search for suitable incendiary ammunition began again. The Chief of Cavalry and Chief of the Air Corps in July 1940 submitted requirements for incendiary .30-caliber and .50-caliber rounds that upon striking would ignite a gasoline or oil tank or pipelines from the tank. Time of flight was to be approximately that of standard ammunition and the center of impact was to be within twelve inches of the center of impact of standard Air Corps ammunition. Fortunately the British had made some progress with the problem. During the Battle of Britain in the fall of 1940 they had employed a .303-caliber incendiary cartridge that was effective against German bombers. But, like the World War I incendiary, its design was so complex that simplification was essential for quantity manufacture. Frankford Arsenal, assigned the task of redesigning the British .303 both to adapt it to mass production and to convert it to .30-caliber, succeeded in evolving a satisfactory bullet and cartridge by September 1941. This became the .30-caliber incendiary M1 and was issued linked in the ratio of two armor-piercing–two incendiary–one tracer, until in 1943 the Army Air Forces discarded .30-caliber machine guns altogether.[25]

More urgently needed was an effective .50-caliber incendiary. The first acceptable design was the work of the Remington Arms Company, whose staff had already had considerable experience in work on Swiss patents for incendiary ammunition. The Remington development was based upon the British .303 B Mark VI Z and was adopted in September 1941. The bullet was a flat-base type with lead base closure and steel body and was charged with 35 grains of incendiary mixture, 50 percent magnesium alloy and 50 percent barium nitrate. A few months later Frankford produced a type of .50-caliber boattailed bullet that equalled Remington's in performance and proved better adapted to mass production. The Frankford design was standardized and the Remington became the Caliber .50 Incendiary M1 Alternate.[26]

[23] (1) OCM, 27138, 29 Mar 45. (2) Interv with Dr. Carten, 11 Jul 51.
[24] SA & SA Ammo, Book 2, Ch. 1, OHF.
[25] OCM 20272, 26 Mar 43.
[26] SA & SA Ammo, Book 2, pp. 19–26, OHF.

By 1942 flyers had come to regard some type of incendiary as indispensable for air combat. "These pilots, who are in daily conflict with the enemy, swear by the effectiveness of the incendiary ammunition and would as soon go up without their machine guns as without this type of ammunition." [27] But the M1 incendiary did not serve every purpose. In the spring of 1943 the air forces were suffering heavy losses of B–17's in daylight bombing operations over Europe, partly because the M1 incendiary, though excellent against enemy fighters approaching from most angles, was ineffective against frontal attack.[28] The protection afforded by the engine of the enemy craft served to exhaust both the incendiary and the penetration energy of the projectile before it got to the fuel tank. Ordnance small arms ammunition specialists consequently suggested use of the M8 armor-piercing-incendiary developed for antiaircraft defense. The M8, when manufactured in relatively small quantities, proved more efficient than either armor-piercing or standard incendiary rounds, but, when manufactured by mass production methods with the types of powder then available, retention of its high velocity became impossible. Inasmuch as armor-piercing-incendiary with less velocity lost most of its penetrating and its incendiary properties, the Ordnance Department recommended that until something better could be perfected the M1 incendiary continue to be used for general air combat and straight armor-piercing for ground strafing.[29] The something better than either standard incendiaries or the M10 tracer emerged in the spring of 1944 in the T28 armor-piercing-incendiary tracer standardized in March 1945 as the M20.[30] Air Forces theatre commanders were authorized to request such quantities as they saw fit.

Meanwhile, in the winter of 1943–44, increasing German employment of jet-propelled aircraft burning kerosene created the need for .50-caliber ammunition capable of igniting aviation kerosene. Half a dozen different Ordnance plants worked on the problem. The Des Moines Ordnance Plant produced the most satisfactory model, a 500-grain bullet containing 90 grains of an incendiary mixture composed of 50 percent magnesium aluminum alloy, 40 percent barium nitrate and 10 percent potassium perchlorate. A single-base powder was used that was found to be superior to double-base powder for firing extended bursts. Quantities of the Des Moines cartridge, listed as the T48, were shipped to the theatres in the winter of 1944–45 and proved so effective that in May 1945 the T48 bullet was standardized as the .50-caliber M23 and the round as incendiary cartridge M23. A report of June 1945 from Headquarters, U.S. Strategic Air Forces in Europe, was enthusiastic: "Most pilots stated that aircraft burst into flames more readily when hit with this type ammunition in contrast to armor-piercing-incendiary ammunition. Many enemy aircraft burned after having been hit only two or three times. . . . One pilot destroyed 10 aircraft on a single mission by firing short bursts." [31] This testimony notwithstanding, design of incendi-

[27] *Ibid.*, p. 15, quoting from Military Reports on the United Nations, 15 Aug 43.

[28] See discussion in Wesley F. Craven and James L. Cate, eds., *The Army Air Forces in World War II:* Vol. II, *Europe: TORCH To POINTBLANK, August 1942 To December 1943* (Chicago, 1949) (hereafter cited as *AAF II*), pp. 321–43.

[29] SA & SA Ammo, Book 2, p. 41, OHF.

[30] (1) *Ibid.*, p. 107, citing Ord R&D Center Firing Record, S-41123 and S-42584. (2) OCM 27137, 29 Mar 45.

[31] Quoted in SA & SA Ammo, Book 2, p. 33, OHF.

291064 O—55——29

ary and armor-piercing-incendiary ammunition remained at the end of the war a problem requiring much additional study.[32]

Air-to-Air Cannon

To provide more destructive fire power, an alternative to the use of high-velocity machine guns and incendiary ammunition lay in mounting cannon in aircraft. Though the greater weight, heavier recoil, and smaller ammunition capacity were disadvantageous, the bigger guns would have longer range as well as greater striking power. The development of air cannon had had a considerable history before 1940. In World War I some 37-mm. guns had been mounted in planes, but in 1920 Ordnance Department engineers, believing it possible to design a gun better adapted to air combat, began work upon a fully automatic 37-mm. aircraft cannon. Though the project was suspended in 1925, some ten years later the question of the most effective type of air armament was reopened. During 1936 Aberdeen Proving Ground conducted a series of comparative tests of the destructive power of .50-caliber machine guns and 20-mm., 25-mm., and 75-mm. guns firing high-explosive instantaneous-fuzed projectiles against aircraft frames so loaded as to simulate the stresses of planes in flight. The outcome of these tests was an Air Corps request for development of three types of aircraft cannon, two automatic, one semiautomatic. Design of a high-velocity automatic gun was given first priority, its essential features to include a caliber of not less than 20-mm. or as much larger as would permit full automatic fire, weight not in excess of 300 pounds, a minimum muzzle velocity of 2,850 feet per second, a maximum of 4,000 pounds trunnion reaction, a magazine carrying at least 50 rounds, and a high-explosive impact-fuzed projectile. A lighter gun with a lesser muzzle velocity, 2,000 feet per second, was given second priority. The third type desired, a gun capable of firing a time fuze-impact shell at a muzzle velocity of 1,500 to 2,000 feet per second, was not to exceed 75-mm. in caliber.[33]

While some work proceeded simultaneously upon all three projects, it was the second that was first concluded when in December 1939 a Colt automatic cannon was recommended for standardization as the 37-mm. automatic gun M4. It was not an ideal weapon: it would not fire at an elevation of more than 70 degrees, muzzle velocity was just 2,000 feet per second, cyclic rate was only 150 rounds per minute, and weight without the mount and accessories was 213 pounds. But the Air Corps felt that the need was acute for some aircraft weapon more powerful than the .50-caliber machine gun, and the 37-mm. M4 would function in most positions irrespective of gravity.[34] Two and a half years later the Air Forces and Ordnance Department sponsored a modification of this cannon to provide a disintegrating link-belt feed, a device better suited to aircraft installation than the magazine of the M4. The resulting 37-mm. M10, fed from either the right or left side, was accepted in April 1944 chiefly for use in the nose of P-63's.[35] The weight was 18 pounds more

[32] See discussion, SA & SA Ammo, Book 2, pp. 46-48, OHF.

[33] (1) R&D Serv, Design Development and Production of 37-mm. Gun M4, PSP 30, pp. 1-6, OHF. (2) OCM 13366, 11 Jan 37.

[34] (1) PSP 30, pp. 7-10, OHF. (2) Incl 1 to ltr, CofOrd thru OASW to TAG, 4 Jan 40, sub: Standardization of Gun, Automatic, 37-mm. M4, OO 472.1/2483, NA.

[35] OCM 23477, 13 Apr 44.

than the 213 pounds of the M4, but cyclic rate reached 165 rounds per minute.

But any 37-mm. cannon was necessarily too heavy, too bulky, and too slow-firing to meet all the specifications listed for aircraft armament to supplement .50-caliber machine guns. As several 20-mm. cannon of foreign design had been tested in the mid-thirties without giving satisfactory performance, in the spring of 1937 Ordnance designers began work upon a new .90-caliber gun, that is, about 22.8-mm. If a suitable weapon of American design could be developed, the Ordnance Department could avoid all the complications inherent in the purchase of a foreign model. The .90-caliber project was eventually canceled because the urgent need of the Air Corps for a light cannon precluded taking time to get all the bugs out of the one experimental model completed.[36]

Instead, the Ordnance Department found a foreign weapon that in essential features would meet the immediate demand. In the very month that the Ordnance Committee had established the .90-caliber project, a report had arrived from Paris describing a new Hispano-Suiza 20-mm. gun made under Birkigt patents. This so-called 404 type promised to meet all American requirements. The Ordnance Department accordingly purchased one gun and 2,000 rounds of ammunition to study. While waiting for the shipment to arrive, Aberdeen tested a Danish Madsen 23-mm., a 20-mm. Rheinmetall, a 20-mm. Swiss Oerlikon, and a 20-mm. French Hispano-Suiza of earlier design, the last two guns borrowed from the Navy. Ample comparative data were therefore available against which to check the newer Hispano-Suiza model. Tests of the latter took many months. The gun was a combination gas-operated blowback type and fired 600 rounds per minute at a muzzle velocity of 2,850 feet per second. Weight was 137 pounds. Tests established accuracy life to be 10,000 to 12,000 rounds. The gun could be mounted in aircraft wing or fuselage or fired through the propeller hub but was not designed for synchronized fire between the propeller blades. It fired electrically by remote control. Though some uncertainty about its adequacy still endured, inasmuch as Air Corps and Ordnance experts agreed that the 404 type Hispano-Suiza appeared to have more desirable features than any other intermediate caliber cannon tested, in the spring of 1939 the Ordnance Department bought thirty-three additional guns from the French and began negotiations to secure American manufacturing rights.[37] A year later General Arnold, urging haste in procuring guns of this type, restated the need:

> . . . as a result of the recent developments in leakproof gas tanks, the caliber .50 may become ineffective against this component in the near future. The 37-mm. aircraft cannon has a somewhat limited application due to its bulk and comparatively slow rate of fire. Its application to the tail gun and engine nacelle mounts on bombers and wing mounts on pursuit airplanes is very difficult without compromising to an unwarranted extent the desirable performance of the airplane involved. It has, therefore, became apparent that a gun of greater power than the caliber .50 and of less power than the 37-mm. will be required to meet certain installations where the 37-mm. could not be effectively employed.[38]

[36] OCM 13515, 9 Mar 37; 13638, 26 Apr 37; 14766, 10 Oct 40. A model designed for antitank use was test fired in 1940, but the aircraft design was dropped in late 1939. See APG Rpt on Ord Program 5082, Ord Tech files.

[37] (1) R&D Serv, Hist of 20-mm. Guns, M1 and AN-M2, pp. 1-8, OHF. (2) Catalogue of Standard Ord Items, II, 377.

[38] Ltr, Gen Arnold, CofAC, to Gen Wesson, 11 Apr 40, OO 472.91/2101, DRB AGO.

20-MM. AIRCRAFT GUNS. *After cleaning the guns, British mechanics replace them in the nose of a plane.*

The option on manufacturing rights already obtained was then taken up and in May 1940 the gun was approved for standardization as the 20-mm. automatic gun M1. Watervliet Arsenal prepared drawings for contractors because the French drawings not only would be delayed in arrival but also would give dimensions computed in metric measurement that would have to be transposed into feet and inches. Some nine months later, when changes in dimensions of some parts were adopted, the M1 was made substitute standard and the newer model declared standard as the AN-M2. "AN" meant that the Navy as well as the Army had adopted the gun. Three types of ammunition were available by 1942, armor-piercing with tracer, which had a muzzle velocity of 2,563 feet per second; ball with a muzzle velocity of 2,820 feet per second; and high-explosive incendiary with muzzle velocity of 2,820 feet per second but effective range of only about 200 yards.[39]

Though, in the interest of saving time, the design of the 20-mm. automatic cannon was purchased, Ordnance engineers had to devise a number of modifications to make it fully satisfactory for air combat. Different planes required different types of adapters to control the gun's recoil, different kinds of firing mechanisms, and different types of loading devices or chargers. If with one type of adapter a 60-round magazine were used, a muzzle brake had to be screwed to the barrel to reduce recoil

[39] 2d Ind, CofOrd for CG SOS, 21 Mar 42, sub: Reply to Cablegram 723, 350.05/278, DRB AGO.

distance. If that same adapter were used with a disintegrating link-belt feed mechanism, the muzzle brake had to be replaced by a thread protector. The Navy demanded a hydraulic charger, the Army Air Forces a manual charger. The British wanted a sear mechanism instead of an electric trigger. Altogether there were seven different types of this 20-mm. aircraft gun in use during the war. In 1943, after prolonged tests, minor changes were introduced to reduce malfunctions. The dimensions of the powder chamber were slightly reduced, a new type of extractor spring replaced the original, the firing pin was transformed into a floating firing pin, and the breechblock slide springs were strengthened. The 40,000 guns already manufactured were altered in keeping with the last three of the four changes.[40] Toward the end of the war a faster-firing model, the M3, was developed. Weight of gun and feeder combined was reduced by one fifth, to 112 pounds; muzzle velocity was slightly lowered, but cyclic rate was increased to an average of 750 rounds per minute. Furthermore, use of new automatic belt-feed mechanisms notably increased pull.[41] Of the 134,633 20-mm. guns produced, over 26,000 were converted to the M3 models in the last fifteen months of the war.[42] Study of ammunition for these cannon went forward simultaneously with investigations of smaller caliber cartridges.

The third type of cannon the Air Corps requested in 1937 was to be approximately 75-mm. in caliber. Preliminary planning for developing such a weapon began the next summer and experiments started in 1939 with mounting a 75-mm. field gun in an airplane. The difficulties were far greater than with light cannon. The original 37-mm. gun of World War I had indeed been designed for aircraft, and the 20-mm. was not very much bigger or heavier than the .50-caliber machine gun. But no one had ever before attempted aircraft installation of so large a gun as a 75; no one could prophesy how its weight and recoil would affect flight; and no one could state authoritatively what type of fire control would serve best if so heavy a weapon were to prove feasible in aircraft at all. In view of these uncertainties, before plans had gone beyond the drawing board stage, the Ordnance Department persuaded Air Corps technicians at Wright Field that the first gun, mount, and fire control equipment should be the simplest possible. Firing at a predetermined distance from the enemy plane would simplify range finding and fuze setting, while a fixed gun with maximum recoil would reduce the stresses on the plane. After study of performance of this type installation, both Ordnance and Air Corps would have data on which to base further developments.[43] The Air Corps undertook to supply a B–18 Douglas plane for experimental mounting and firing of the gun, first at Aberdeen and then at Eglin Field in Florida.

In June 1940 the 75-mm. field gun with a special mount was fired from a B–18 against a towed target. An Air Corps pilot and co-pilot flew the plane, but no member of the Air Corps Board witnessed the tests. The Ordnance experts directing the test firings reported that, for a first phase

[40] (1) R&D Serv, Hist of 20-mm. Guns, M1 and AN-M2, pp. 37–40, OHF. (2) Catalogue of Standard Ord Items, II, 377–78.

[41] OCM 28717, 9 Aug 45.

[42] OMPUS, 1 May 47, p. 147, OHF.

[43] OCM 13366, 11 Jan 37; 13515, 16 Mar 37; 14807, 29 Nov 38. Copies of other important documents relating to the development and testing of the 75-mm. aircraft cannon are contained in OCO Tech Div, 75-mm. Aircraft Gun M4 and Airplane Gun Mount M6, MS, OHF.

development, the gun and stereoscopic range finder performed encouragingly well. A fourth shot fired at 1,500 yards was a direct hit, and range errors were not excessive. Nevertheless, the final section of the report submitted by the Ordnance officer in charge, Capt. Horace A. Quinn, foreshadowed abandonment of the project:

(1) The Air Corps Board, so far as I was able to determine from discussion, although admitting the effectiveness and accuracy of the 75-mm. gun in an airplane was not prepared to accept it as a standard weapon. Opinion was expressed that the .30 Cal. probably could still be used against aircraft although (based on trends abroad) they were recommending that it be replaced with the .50 Cal. gun. Interest was also expressed in antiaircraft bombing to accomplish the same result as would be accomplished with the 75-mm. gun. The board was also anxious to know if a small caliber gun, 50-mm. for example, would be just as effective as the 75-mm. However, as I understood their reactions they would recommend that the development continue.[44]

Yet to all intents and purposes, there the 75-mm. air-to-air cannon project dropped. General Arnold himself was reportedly impressed by the possibilities of a gun capable of hits at a 2,000 yard range, but otherwise the Air Corps of this period was dominated by small arms enthusiasts who pinned their faith to machine guns. Tactical need of the powerful 75, moreover, failed to materialize for air combat, and not until long after World War II did the Air Forces request such a weapon.[45] When in 1944 two successful models of 75-mm. aircraft guns were developed, they were designed for strafing.

Aircraft Rockets

A similar shift of original plans attended development of aircraft rockets. The comprehensive program, inaugurated jointly by Army, Navy, and NDRC in the summer of 1941, had stressed work upon antiaircraft and plane-to-plane rockets. Army Ordnance and Navy undertook work upon the latter. The Ordnance Department had built a 4.5-inch rocket, standardized in 1942 as the M8, for either a plane-to-plane or ground artillery fire, with the only differentiation the fuze. But, though the 4.5-inch was put to use in ground warfare and in ground strafing, it saw no service in air-to-air combat, in spite of three years of Ordnance and Air Forces experimentation with various applications.[46] American aircraft rockets used in World War II turned into weapons for ground strafing.

To fire rockets against aircraft effectively, planes would have to be built big enough to carry automatic launchers and fast enough and maneuverable enough to keep fire directed at the target. The launching installation, therefore, must not be so heavy as to retard that essential speed. A system of reloading the projector while the plane was in flight would also be highly desirable. Though the Air Forces postponed designing a special type of plane, in November 1942 a contract with the United Shoe Machinery Company called for building automatic projectors designed by Ordnance engineers and for studying a magazine installation suited to various types of

[44] Memo, Capt Quinn, thru Chief of Artillery Div, Tech Staff, for Chief of Tech Staff, 5 Jul 40, sub: Aerial Test of 75-mm. Aircraft Mount T1, copy in 75-mm. Aircraft Gun M4 and Airplane Gun Mount M6, OHF.

[45] Interv with Col Quinn, 13 Aug 51.

[46] (1) Memo, CofS for Gen Barnes, 15 Aug 41, OO 334.9/705, DRB AGO. (2) Min, mtgs of Sec H, Div A, NDRC, 19 Aug and 27 Aug 41, 334.9, DRB AGO. (3) Burchard, ed., *op. cit.*, pp. 24–25. (4) Interv, 11 Jul 51, with Dr. Hudson, Guided Missiles Sec, R&D Serv, in 1942–43 assigned to Wright Field Ord Sec. (5) OCM 18187, 24 Apr 42; 19022, 13 Oct 42.

planes. But the launchers when ground tested in the spring of 1943 were dubbed too heavy and too slow firing for air use and that phase of the project then lapsed.[47] Another scheme grew out of an Eighth Air Force request for an upward-firing rocket launcher to protect B–17 formations from planes bombing them from above. The development, known by the code name SUNFLOWER SEED, was worked out in England, using a special British rocket, and a B–17 so equipped was flown to the United States for study. At the same time technicians at Wright Field evolved a somewhat similar vertical-firing installation using the American M8 rocket; this was tested at both Aberdeen and Eglin Field during the spring of 1944. The rockets behaved as the designers hoped, but the low velocity of the projectiles and the lack of flexibility in aiming them led to the conclusion that neither SUNFLOWER SEED nor its American variant would serve the intended purpose. And by September 1944, with the cessation of overhead bombing attacks against Allied bomber formations, tactical need for such a weapon disappeared. Results generally similar to those obtained with the vertical-firing launchers followed when test data were assembled on a rearward-firing breech-loading 4.5-inch rocket launcher mounted in a B–17 bomber. Consequently, until scientists could develop rockets of higher velocity, even rockets with proximity fuzes promised little for defensive air combat.[48]

For fighter craft the problem was somewhat different. In the summer of 1943 the Germans employed aircraft rockets with some success against unescorted Allied bombers, but as soon as Allied fighter range increased so that fighters could provide cover for bombers, this threat subsided. The Army Air Forces found fighters equipped with conventional armament adequate to combat enemy rocket-carrying planes because, one explanation runs, the rocket installation created a drag that slowed the enemy plane enough to make it an easy mark.[49] For Allied fighters, which by then were operating far from their bases, plane-to-plane rockets, in Air Forces opinion, offered no advantage. Had these planes had to fight enemy craft over England or the United States, tactical need might well have dictated using American rockets in air-to-air combat. Toward the end of the war the Air Forces experimented somewhat with a scheme to fire an air-to-air bomb and asked the Ordnance Department to supply the explosive container and a special VT fuze, but the project was incomplete at V-J Day and canceled at the Air Forces' request in 1946.[50]

Ordnance Department interest in plane-to-plane rockets received fresh encourage-

[47] Hist Div Intel T2, Air Tech Serv Command, Wright Field, Aircraft Rockets, 14 Dec 45, filed in Office, Air Force Directorate R&D, Pentagon. To this study were appended blueprint copies of all documents cited: (1) memo, Col Franklin O. Carroll, Chief of Experiments Engr Sec, Wright Field, for CG Materiel Command, AAF, Washington, 25 Apr 42; (2) Ord Project (535) 43-13126-E, 21 Nov 42; (3) ltr, Col Quinn to CG AAF, 17 Mar 43, sub: 4½" Rocket Projectors T4 and T2; (4) memo rpt, Engr Div, Materiel Command, AAF, 2 Apr 43, sub: Status of Rocket Projects; (5) memo, Brig Gen Benjamin W. Chidlaw, Chief of Materials Div, AAF, for Robert A. Lovett, USW for Air, 29 May 43, sub: Rocket Developments. All in DRB AGO.

[48] (1) Interv with Dr. Hudson, 13 Sep 51. (2) Aircraft Rockets, 1st Ind, 15 Dec 43, Col Franklin C. Wolfe, Chief of Armament Laboratory, Wright Field, to memo, Col Turner A. Sims, Jr., Dept CofS, for Engr Div, 10 Mar 44, sub: Sunflower Seed Projects. (3) Memo, Lt Col Harry A. Donicht, CO 732d AAF Base Unit, for CG Materiel Command, AAF, 5 Sep 44, sub: CT1-1625. Last two in DRB AGO.

[49] (1) The Rocket Panel of the Joint Board on Scientific Information Policy, US Rocket Ordnance, Development and Use in World War II, p. 67, MS, OHF. (2) Craven and Cate, *AAF II,* pp. 678–79.

[50] OCM 26891, 8 Mar 45; 28794, 20 Aug 45; 31030, 19 Sep 46.

ment in June 1945 when American experts in Germany discovered that the Germans apparently had a fully developed powerful type ready for production. Colonel Simon, then on a special mission to investigate German research and development projects, at once dispatched to General Barnes a file of data on the German 55-mm. aircraft rocket "believed to be the hottest thing to come out of Germany." A sample of this rocket was found at a research laboratory in Luebeck. Colonel Simon wrote General Barnes:

> By actual trials, they had shown that when these rockets were fired from a jet-propelled plane, they were almost certain of at least one hit, and one hit is sufficient to effect the destruction of an airplane. The rocket has the right size, the right ballistics, a velocity of about 1700 feet per second. THIS LOOKS LIKE THE CHANCE FOR A QUICK PAY-OFF ON SHOOTING DOWN SUICIDE BOMBERS, AND YOU WELL KNOW HOW BADLY WE NEED SUCH A WEAPON NOW."[51]

V-J Day arrived before study of this rocket was far advanced, and only postwar tests proved it no better than American types equipped with influence fuzes.[52]

As American techniques in making rocket powders improved and velocities accordingly increased, the potential advantages of rockets for air-to-air combat became more evident. Though having lower velocity and lesser accuracy than projectiles fired from rifled bores, wing-mounted rockets had great power and no recoil, and the launchers, by comparison with conventional gun mounts, were simple and light.

The Problem of Functioning at High Altitude

Because progress in aircraft design by 1940 was enabling planes to fly at 36,000 feet or higher, study of the effects of altitude upon air ordnance was also essential. Engineers feared that the thinness of the atmosphere at great heights might make fuel-air mixtures in gasoline tanks too rich to be ignited by the incendiary ammunition that was effective at lower altitudes, and might even affect the flash properties and stability in flight of all types of ammunition. At the temperatures encountered at high altitudes, perhaps as low as 50° or 60° F. below zero, gun steels might become excessively brittle and oils in buffer mechanisms and lubricants too thick to function properly. Here were contingencies with which no ordnance designer at the beginning of World War II was familiar.

Testing at high altitudes and subzero temperatures was not easy to arrange. Making a series of controlled recordings necessitated working on the ground rather than in the air, and no laboratory facilities existed in the United States at the altitude desired. In the late fall of 1943, therefore, experts from the Ordnance Research and Development Center at Aberdeen Proving Ground were sent to Mount Auconquilcha in Chile to conduct tests at some 19,000 feet above sea level. The outcome of tests of the .50-caliber incendiary cartridge M1 and of the armor-piercing-incendiary M8 showed ignition efficiency of the former unimpaired and of the latter somewhat decreased. Camera films proved both types able to destroy enemy aircraft at 36,000 feet. Study of the effects of severe cold on gun steels and oils was part of the mission of the Winter Detachment sent to Camp Shilo in Manitoba in December 1942. All air ordnance tested there performed satis-

[51] Ltr, Col Simon to Gen Barnes, 8 Jun 45, Zornig Mission, Barnes file, OHF.

[52] Interv with Dr. Hudson, 15 Oct 51.

factorily if lubricated with suitably thin oils.[53]

Nevertheless, inasmuch as improved oil buffer assemblies in machine guns would minimize oil leakage at high temperatures and congealing at low, during 1943 Springfield Armory experimented with use of new synthetic packings, new finishes, and design modifications, until the Frigidaire Division of the General Motors Corporation evolved the pneumatic type buffer that used no oil at all. Two helical springs absorbed the recoil and functioned so well in tests in the fall of 1944 that this mechanical buffer was incorporated as a feature of the M3 aircraft machine gun. Not only did the air-and-spring type buffer dispense with the use of oils, the spring action allowed markedly increased rates of fire. Furthermore, in the modified M2 aircraft gun, engineers found it possible to use the oil buffer without oil.[54]

The problem of powerful, dependable armament for air-to-air fighting thus emerged as one of balancing the gains against the drawbacks of every given type or combination of types of guns. To cope with the speed of an enemy plane, Allied aircraft could saturate the path of flight with fire by sheer number of guns. But as air drag increased with every additional gun mounted and, more important, as the weight of guns and ammunition belts and the limited space in aircraft for stowing ammunition put a ceiling upon numbers, the AAF installed not more than eight .50-caliber machine guns per fighter and sixteen per big bomber. Considerably heavier guns had greater range than .50's but necessarily had a lower cyclic rate, could fire fewer rounds, and suffered the handicap of pronounced recoil. The advantage of the heavy powder charges of rockets and the lack of recoil was obvious, but the weight of rockets and the impracticability of carrying more than 14 on a plane constituted equally clear disadvantages. And for air-to-air fighting, rockets were virtually still untried. Experience taught the Air Forces that the .50-caliber machine gun was an eminently reliable weapon for the combat conditions of World War II. The 1,453,829 .50-caliber aircraft guns produced testifies to their usefulness.[55] Nevertheless, by V-J Day indications pointed to the probability that more powerful, bigger guns would be employed increasingly as aircraft structures became heavier and stronger and their speeds still greater.

---

[53] (1) SA & SA Ammo, Book 2, Ch. 1, OHF. (2) Shilo Camp Winter Detachment, pp. 5, 11, 17, 19–21, 36–38, OHF.

[54] (1) Hist of Springfield Armory, Vol II, Book III, pp. 705–06, OHF. (2) SA & SA Ammo, Book 3, p. 43, OHF.

[55] OMPUS, p. 153, OHF.

CHAPTER XVI

Aircraft Armament: Guns and Rockets for Air-to-Ground Attack

Air-to-air fighting in World War II ordinarily took place to prevent enemy craft from reaching their ground or naval objectives, to forestall enemy reconnaissance, and to ward off attacks upon Allied bombers and strafing planes. Clearing enemy planes from the skies to give the Allies air superiority was an essential preliminary to employing Allied air power for offense. But because men live on the earth, not in the air, air offensives ultimately had to be directed at ground targets. Inevitably air combat and air-to-ground offensives were not wholly separable. Yet aircraft designed for use in strategic and tactical bombing missions or in close support of ground forces were usually equipped with ordnance somewhat different from that mounted on escort fighter planes. The machine guns employed on fighters were effective for strafing infantry, but for knocking out armored forces or for destroying fortifications, ships, and submarines, other weapons were needed.

Air Cannon

Use of aircraft cannon was naturally one method of achieving the power required for heavy strafing. Early in 1943, therefore, the Air Forces requested a high-velocity fully automatic cannon capable of firing a 1.92-pound armor-piercing projectile at 2,900 feet per second and a 1.34-pound high-explosive shell at 2,600 feet per second. Though the gun was to be usable in air combat, it was wanted primarily for strafing mechanized ground forces. Consequently, it was to function at positions of elevation from plus 35 degrees to minus 75 degrees, mounted either in normal position or on its right or left side. It must fire at temperatures as low as −52° F. On the other hand, for air-to-ground fire a cyclic rate of only 120 rounds per minute would be satisfactory, and weight of gun tube and feeding device might run to as much as 400 pounds. Trunnion reaction was not to exceed 10,000 pounds. The Oldsmobile Division of the General Motors Corporation undertook this project, basing design upon the standard 37-mm. antiaircraft gun M1A2, modified for aircraft installation. The pilot model failed to meet fully every specification—trunnion reaction was 13,000-pound maximum instead of 10,000, and the mount limited gun rotation to 45 degrees from the normal vertical position, instead of permitting 90 degrees, but operation was sufficiently satisfactory to make the design acceptable. Standardized in January 1943 as the M9, the gun had an average cyclic rate of 140 rounds per minute. Muzzle velocity with armor-piercing ammunition reached 3,050 feet per second, and, most important of all, a shot fired at a 500-yard range could penetrate 3.1 inches of homogeneous armor plate.[1]

Meanwhile, long before work on the M9 37-mm. cannon began, Ordnance engineers had been trying to develop a still more powerful strafing weapon. The 75-mm. field gun tested in plane-to-plane fire in the summer of 1940 had established the feasibility of mounting a big gun in aircraft. Though further work on that first development project had lapsed, the Air Corps had evinced some interest in a scheme to install a 75-mm. in a plane built to mount it for fire against ground targets. In mid-1941 the Douglas Aircraft Company, instead of using the B–18 first tried, undertook to adapt a new medium bomber to take a specially designed cannon and mount. Though a Douglas XA26B did mount a 75 and fire it successfully in June 1942, the bomber that eventually carried the 75-mm. into action was the B–25 made by the North American Aviation Corporation. In 1941 Ordnance engineers to whom design of the gun, mount, and fire control system was assigned had for guidance only the knowledge that the job was possible. It meant a completely fresh start, for the field gun tried as an air-to-air weapon could not readily be modified to meet the new requirements for air-to-ground fire. In one respect only was the designers' task simplified: impact fuzes and aiming by ordinary gun sights would suffice for effective strafing of stationary or slow-moving ground targets, whereas proximity fuzes or preset fuzes and elaborate range finders would have been needed against aerial targets.[2] Still the problems were peculiarly difficult.

The 44-inch recoil mechanism of the ground-mounted gun was impossible to use in the confined space of a plane. Shortened recoil would increase trunnion reaction, and mounting the conventional hydromatic recoil and counterrecoil cylinders above or below the gun tube would make the gun silhouette too large. Ordnance engineers found the answer in step-by-step modification of the 75-mm. M3 tank gun and in development of a new mount. The single-shot, hand-loaded weapon with its vertical sliding, automatically operated breechblock was fired electrically. An ejector mechanism spewed out the shell case after the round was fired. A hydro-spring recoil mechanism using two cylinders mounted above and below the gun barrel reduced the silhouette somewhat. The stronger construction of the newer bombers enabled Ordnance engineers to let the plane absorb part of the recoil shock and thus limit the recoil stroke to the 21-inch length of the round, a space needed in any case to load the gun. In the first models an automatically functioning muzzle cover that opened when the breech was closed and closed when the breech opened was provided to prevent fumes from pouring into the gunner's compartment after firing and to ease ammunition loading, but this feature was found unnecessary and later dropped.

---

[1] (1) R&D Serv, Design, Development and Production of 37-mm. Gun M9, OHF. (2) Catalogue of Standard Ord Items, II, 380. (3) Ltr, Gen Barnes to TAG, 5 Mar 42, sub: High Velocity 37-mm. Gun in Aircraft, OO 350.05/207, DRB AGO.

[2] (1) OCM 16188, 24 Oct 40; 18145, 20 Apr 42; 18699, 1 Aug 42. (2) Interv, 13 Aug 51, with Victor A. Lucht, engineer in charge of 75-mm. aircraft gun development in 1942.

The model accepted in the summer of 1942 was designated the 75-mm. aircraft gun M4, and its mount the M6. Gun and mount together weighed 893 pounds. Muzzle velocity with high-explosive ammunition averaged 1,974 feet per second, with armor-piercing-capped ammunition, 2,024.[3] The ammunition was the same as that standard for ground guns, a considerable advantage in procurement. Moreover, on at least one occasion, this interchangeability was of importance in the field. Maj. Gen. Claire L. Chennault in his memoirs described how one of his officers saved the day for Chinese troops equipped with three old French 75-mm. field guns but no ammunition. Sacrificing some of his cherished supply of 75-mm. aircraft shell, the pilot dropped enough to the Chinese to put their guns into action. From the Pacific theatres after 1942 came testimony to the effectiveness of the gun for strafing. Its fire destroyed pillboxes and sank naval vessels. In July 1943, for example, two B–25 bombers mounting 75-mm. air cannon attacked a large Japanese destroyer off the coast of Cape Gloucester and in two runs, firing seven shots on each run, riddled the ship from stem to stern and left it sinking.[4]

Even before the 75-mm. M4 was standardized, Ordnance engineers began work upon a light-weight, mechanically-loaded air cannon. An entirely new recoil mechanism in which the cylinder was concentric about the gun tube reduced both silhouette and weight. By using a new high-strength alloy steel having an elastic limit of 130,000 pounds per square inch, the designers lowered the weight of the gun alone to 406 pounds. When metallurgical tests at Watertown Arsenal and firing tests at Erie Proving Ground established the greater strength of hollow quenched over solid quenched gun tubes and breechblocks, the former method of manufacture was included in the specifications. An automatic fuze setter-rammer saved the space required for manual loading and permitted firing at a rate of 30 rounds per minute. Two models of this light-weight cannon varying from each other only in minor details were standardized in 1944 as the 75-mm. AN-M5A1 and the M10.[5]

Early in 1943 the 37-mm. M9 for strafing mechanized ground troops and the 75-mm. M4 for destroying heavily armored ground targets were serving their purpose well enough to inspire work upon a still more powerful gun. Tests at Eglin Field, Florida, comparing the effectiveness of existing rockets and air cannon pointed to the superiority of the latter. Development of a 105-mm. aircraft gun, therefore, was started in July 1943 with endeavor to adapt a 105-mm. howitzer to use for air-to-ground attack. A year later numerous changes necessitated by the excessive blast of the first models led to making a new approach. The resulting T7 105-mm. aircraft gun was test fired late in 1944 only to show that the feed mechanism required further study. Before the changes were completed the war ended and the project was canceled.[6]

[3] (1) R&D Serv, 75-mm. Automatic Guns and Material, pp. 1–17, OHF. (2) Catalogue of Standard Ord. Items, p. 381. (3) OCM 19025, 15 Oct 42.

[4] (1) See Ch. IX, Charles F. Romanus and Riley Sunderland, Stilwell's Command Problems, a volume in preparation for the series UNITED STATES ARMY IN WORLD WAR II, MS, OCMH. (2) Barnes, *Weapons of World War II,* p. 70.

[5] (1) R&D Serv, 75-mm. Automatic Guns and Material, pp. 12–23, 44–45, OHF. (2) OCM 22659, 20 Jan 44; 23727, 4 May 44; 25652, 2 Nov 44; 24945, 31 Aug 44. (3) OCO, Monthly Rpts, R&D Projects, Progress Rpt on 75 mm. Feed Mechanism T13E1, 13 Nov 44 and 10 Jan 45, OHF.

[6] (1) OCM 23117, 9 Mar 44; 23348, 30 Mar 44; 24296, 6 Jul 44; 29264, 4 Oct 45. (2) Interv with Victor Lucht, 16 Aug 51.

Rockets

More than a year before any model of cannon for ground strafing was approved, the drawbacks of mounting heavy guns in aircraft were recognized. This knowledge intensified the search for other types of powerful air armament. Accurate bomb sights would increase the effectiveness of bombs, and airborne homing torpedoes better the percentage of hits in antisubmarine warfare. But neither of these was the direct responsibility of Army Ordnance, although work of the Ballistic Research Laboratory at Aberdeen in compiling a complete set of ballistic tables for use with the Norden bomb sight contributed greatly to more effective bombing. Rockets, on the other hand, were the immediate concern of the Ordnance Department, as well as of the Navy Bureau of Ordnance and the Air Corps. If accurate rockets could be launched from aircraft, the problem of strafing might be largely solved. In December 1940 the Ordnance Department requested NDRC's assistance in developing a 4.5-inch rocket primarily for use in aircraft. The fruits of British research on rocketry, in 1940 far in advance of American and promptly put at the disposal of the United States, greatly expedited progress on adaptation of this ancient weapon to conditions of modern warfare.

British research before 1942 had been directed at developing rockets for antiaircraft and plane-to-plane fire, but in the United States the Army's attention early centered upon other phases. The bazooka was the first Army device to use a rocket in combat. Yet an Ordnance officer had fired an experimental 4.5-inch aircraft rocket before anyone had seriously considered the application of rocket propulsion to an infantry weapon. This 4.5-inch rocket, though originally designed for either ground or plane-to-plane use, was in actuality employed in the latter capacity in China, and then only experimentally. For strafing, however, it came to be a valuable weapon, adding to the fears of "the American harassment" repeatedly expressed by German ground troops.

To produce dependable, powerful rockets involved solving innumerable new engineering and ballistic problems. Motor tubes strong enough to withstand the high pressures of the propellent powders must be as light as possible, particularly for aircraft rockets. Propellants must create pressure high enough to attain the desired range but must be safe to handle, easily manufactured, and of composition to burn readily at a wide range of temperatures. Getting suitable even-burning powder was, in fact, the biggest poser of all. Nozzles to reduce the rate of flow of propelling gases must not raise internal pressures to the point of bursting the tubes. Traps and cages, by which to suspend the propellant sticks in the motor tubes, must be so designed as to retain the powder in the tubes until the sticks were completely burned, but without permitting the traps to interfere with the even, quick burning of the powder and without adding excessive over-all weight or reducing the rockets' pay load. A safe reliable ignition system was essential. Some means of stabilizing the rocket in flight and fuzes that would function properly with low-velocity projectiles must be devised.

Despite these obvious difficulties, development of a 4.5-inch rocket for air use initially proceeded with deceptive rapidity. Tentative military characteristics were agreed upon in the summer of 1941 after Ordnance ammunition experts had had opportunity to study samples of British rockets. That fall, Maj. Leslie A. Skinner, the only Ordnance officer to work on rocketry during the 1930's, successfully made a few 4.5-inch rockets, using old fire-extinguisher cylinders as casings. This caliber appeared to be the smallest that could contain a reasonable-size burster tube and warhead and enough propelling charge to give about 1,000 feet-per-second velocity. Fired at Aberdeen in December 1941 these rockets, for all their crudity, were stable in flight and performed fairly well. They weighed about 33 pounds apiece and carried 3.8 pounds of explosive. Redesign for production began at once. Before the war was over, considerable criticism was directed at the Army and Navy for developing two separate rockets for essentially the same purpose but with a difference of half an inch in diameter. The sheer chance of having old fire extinguisher tubes available had determined the size of the Army models.[7]

By April 1942 both the Ordnance Department and the laboratory staff at Wright Field dared hope that a usable aircraft rocket was about ready. Aberdeen firings from the ground had indicated reasonably satisfactory accuracy of the redesigned 4.5-inch model and the probability of no damage to the plane structure. Fins that unfolded after the projectile left the tube gave adequate stability in flight.[8] Wright Field designed a mount for a launching tube under the wing of a P–40, while plans got under way for installation of projectors in the bomb bay of an A–20A plane to permit reloading while the plane was in flight. The chief of the Experimental Engineering Section at Wright Field, considering the rocket project vital, urged the Commanding General, Materiel Command, AAF, to inform the Chief of Ordnance of its importance. "In view," he wrote, "of the rapid progress which has been made and the information available on its employment abroad, particularly by the Russian Air Forces, it is suggested that the military characteristics for such a weapon be reviewed."[9] The Ordnance Department needed no prodding. Confidence in the 4.5-inch model ran so high that the Ordnance Committee had already recommended standardization and limited procurement of some 3,500.[10]

Six weeks later belief still endured that the difficulties so far encountered could be overcome quickly "if vigorously prosecuted."[11] Better ammunition, namely propellent powder of uniform thickness or "web" having neither internal fissures nor external cracks to interfere with even burning, was a problem the Ordnance Department hoped to have answered by midsummer. Maj. Gen. Millard F. Harmon, Chief of Air Staff, on 10 June set 1 October as the goal for having rockets available for the AAF in TORCH, the invasion of North Africa. Delivery of 15,000 for testing to

[7] (1) OCM 17047, Jul 41. (2) R&D Serv, Rocket Development, PSP 20, pp. 1–2, 14, OHF. (3) R&D Serv, Rockets, Development, Production and Performance, 1940–1945, Project Paper 20, pp. 8–9, OHF. See also testimony of Robert Patterson at *Hearings* on H Res 465, 26 Apr 44, p. 82.

[8] Historical Office, Air Materiel Command, Wright Field, Ohio, Aircraft Rockets, 1945, and attchd memo, Col Clyde H. Morgan, Ord Off, Wright Field, for Chief of Experimental Engr Sec, Wright Field, 3 Apr 42, sub: Installation of Rocket Gun in P-40 Airplane. Unless otherwise noted, with the exception of references to OCM's, copies of all documents hereafter cited on aircraft rockets are contained in blueprint copy form in this Wright Field compilation, on file in Hq USAF, Office of DCofS for Development.

[9] Memo, Col Carroll, Chief Experimental Engr Sec, AAF Materiel Command, for CG, Materiel Command, AAF, 25 Apr 42, sub: Rocket Development for Aircraft Armament.

[10] OCM 18187, 24 Apr 42.

[11] Memo rpt, Experimental Engr Sec, AAF Materiel Command, 8 Jun 42, sub: The Four and One-Half Inch Aircraft Rocket.

begin in August was requested. On 6 July a 4.5-inch rocket was successfully fired from a P-40E plane in flight without injury to the plane, a performance that fortified faith in the future of aircraft rockets.[12] Procurement then was raised to 600,000. But there the project bogged down because of the powder bottleneck. General Barnes wrote that the first 15,000 rockets could not be shipped until further experimentation and tests established the safety of the propellant and the rocket tubes. That moment arrived only seven months later, in March 1943. Overoptimism earlier, plus premature notices of prospective availability of rockets for the combat zones, made the unavoidable delays hard to explain to men who failed to comprehend the magnitude of the task.[13] Even Dr. Bush, Chairman of the Office of Scientific Research and Development, protested the slowness of progress. Maj. Gen. G. E. Stratemeyer, Chief of Air Staff, assured Dr. Bush in January 1943:

> Realizing the many problems confronting the development section of the Ordnance Department, we have no criticism of that Department for not having had everything connected with this program available and in order "for a long time." Personally, I feel that splendid progress has been made by the different groups concerned with various phases of this program, considering the complexity of the problems, dealing as it does with new propellants, new fuzes and new types of launching equipment.[14]

How to obtain suitable propellant was the first question, and the second was how to hold multiple small grains in the rocket motor. The Ordnance Department's answer to these problems fortunately could be one and the same for aircraft rockets and ground-launched rockets.[15] The plan to develop a single type of 4.5-inch rocket for Air Forces and Ground Forces alike permitted the Ordnance Department to dedicate far greater resources in technical talent and testing facilities, and, later, in production and inspection, than would have been possible otherwise. Most problems were common to the two applications.[16] The differentiation of aircraft rockets from ground rockets was to be solely in the fuze. To develop the best kind suited to air use required extensive experimentation. For some types proximity fuzes were to be tried, for others impact fuzes. When in June 1943 impact-fuzed high-explosive rockets were test fired at Eglin Field against water targets, observers reported functioning satisfactory and the splash pattern of fragments effective. Proximity fuzes, on the contrary, when tested both then and at intervals later, gave many duds and some prematures. Consequently VT fuzes were not employed.[17] Their use-

[12] (1) Memo, Gen Harmon, Chief of Air Staff, for CG Materiel Command, 10 Jun 42, sub: Rocket Projectiles. (2) Memo rpt Experimental Engr Sec, AAF Materiel Command, 15 Jul 42, sub: Air Firing of 4½ Inch Rocket from P-40E Airplane—AAF No. 41-25008.

[13] (1) Memo, Col John T. Murtha, Jr., Chief of Armament Sec, AAF Materiel Command, for CofOrd, 24 Aug 42, sub: Rocket, 4½" and 2.36" for Test by the Army Air Forces, and 1st Ind, Col Scott B. Ritchie, Deputy Chief of Tech Div, 9 Sep 42. (2) Memo for record, Col William H. Joiner, ACofS AAF, 10 Sep 42, sub: Rocket Program-Conference at Pentagon . . . 9 Sep 42.

[14] (1) Ltr, Dr. Bush to Lt Gen Henry H. Arnold, 8 Jan 43. (2) Ltr, Gen Stratemeyer to Dr. Bush, 29 Jan 43.

[15] See above, Ch. XII.

[16] OCM 19022, 13 Aug 42. The Ordnance Committee at this meeting recommended one designation, M8, for both air and ground 4.5-inch rockets. In April 1943 AGF established a requirement for 11,000,000 of these.

[17] (1) Memo, Col Carroll for CG Materiel Command, AAF, 26 Oct 42, sub: General Status Information. (2) Memo, Brig Gen Benjamin W. Chidlaw, ACofS AAF, for Gen Arnold, 3 Jan 43, sub: Current Status of Rocket Projectile Div. (3) Comment 2, Gen Chidlaw for ACAS Materiel, Maintenance and Dis-

fulness would have been chiefly for air-to-air combat, and by mid-1944, with enemy air power on the wane, the Air Forces had largely discarded plans for special new air-to-air weapons. Some work on influence fuzes for rockets continued down to V-J Day, but it was aimed at a long-term development rather than at one for immediate use.[18]

Projectors were still another feature of aircraft rocket installation that proved to be troublesome. In March 1943, after successful ground tests at Aberdeen, the Ordnance Department dispatched two experimental launchers to Wright Field. These were admittedly too heavy but were to be followed by aluminum alloy tube models, which would be very much lighter. They were designed for mounting in bomb bays to permit reloading while in flight. Though the models of this design were never air-tested, one sample of a redesigned lighter-weight automatic launcher was eventually shipped to Burma, where firing established the soundness of its principle of operation. After the war this launcher supplied the basis of an extensive development project.[19] But in World War II, after mid-1943, the "rocket gun" gradually dropped out of sight in planning, for at that point the Air Forces turned attention to jettisonable three-tube steel or plastic clusters to be mounted under the wings of aircraft.[20] Such a device precluded the possibility of reloading in flight, but omission of a reloading feature permitted more rapid completion of safely usable launchers. The three-tube plastic clusters, in fact, appeared to be sufficiently satisfactory to warrant an initial Ordnance procurement order of 5,000, and in October 1943 the AAF asked for 10,000 more. Soon after delivery of the first 5,000 in December, the AAF pushed its requirements for 1944 to nearly 200,000, far more than could be manufactured with the limited supply of plastic. Since magnesium-alloy tubes met all essential requirements, they were manufactured in considerable numbers to supplement the plastic. Though the combat theatres used some of both types of launcher, thousands were stored in the United States by the spring of 1945, literally an unwanted, obsolescent commodity.

This accumulation of large stocks was due partly to the unexpectedly long life of tube launchers in service, and partly to the small number jettisoned in action. But the principal reason was the lack of proper aircraft mountings for the clusters. The Navy "zero rails," short simple posts beneath the wings from which the rocket could be suspended and launched without using tubes at all, were proving perfectly satisfactory. The speed of the aircraft gave sufficient directional stability to fixed-fin rockets to make needless any guide rail. Easy to manufacture and install, the zero rails had the further advantage of creating less drag

tribution Div, 26 May 43, sub: Rockets. (4) Comment 3, Gen Coupland for same, 22 Jun 43, sub: Aircraft Rockets. (5) Col Joiner, memo rpt for record, 7 Jun 43, sub: Trip to Eglin Field in Connection with 4.5″ Rockets.

[18] Memo, Col James F. Phillips, CG Materiel Command, AAF, for Brig Gen Edward M. Powers, Deputy ACAS Materiel and Services Div, 7 Jun 45, sub: Rockets.

[19] (1) *Ibid.* (2) Interv with Dr. Colin Hudson, 11 Sep 51. (3) Air Technical Serv Command, Instructions to Procurement Div, 2 Apr 45, sub: Cancellation of Procurement for 4½″ Rocket Launchers.

[20] (1) Memo, Col Quinn, OD, for CG Materiel Command, AAF, 17 Mar 43, sub: 4½″ Rocket Projectors T4 and T2. (2) Memo, Gen Chidlaw for Director Military Requirements, 18 Mar 43, sub: 4½″ Rockets. (3) Memo, Gen Chidlaw for CofOrd, 17 Apr 43, sub: Procurement of 4.5″ Rocket Launcher Clusters. (4) ATSC, memo rpt, 27 Nov 44, sub: Closeout of Expenditure Order 552-452 (Development of a Rocket Gun).

AIRCRAFT ROCKET INSTALLATIONS. *Typical installations on Air Forces and Navy aircraft.*

291064 O—55——30

than tube launchers. By the time mounts were available for the latter, the Army Air Forces had adopted both the zero rails and the Navy 5-inch rockets. Still, because of the large quantities of 4.5-inch rockets available, commonsense dictated using them. Installation of adapters, which include a large fixed fin, a bayonet type of igniter, and lugs, permitted firing the smaller rocket from the zero-length launcher designed for the 5-inch. Used with these adapters the 4.5-inch, the Ninth Air Force reported, then compared favorably in accuracy with the 5-inch and were an acceptable substitute until the 5-inch were in larger supply.[21]

The AAF switch from the Army 4.5-inch rocket to the Navy 5-inch high-velocity aircraft rocket, HVAR, nicknamed "Holy Moses," grew out of delay in Air Forces procurement of mounts, impatience over the slowness of Ordnance developments, and discovery in the summer of 1944 that some HVAR's were immediately obtainable. Six months earlier Maj. Gen. Barney M. Giles, Chief of the Army Air Staff, had written the commanding general of the Army Service Forces listing the shortcomings of Army Ordnance rocket development. Stating that the 4.5-inch types were inaccurate, subject to fuze trouble, limited by extremes of temperature, and lacking in adequate velocity, Giles concluded:

> The Ordnance Department personnel have repeatedly stated that they were working on these difficulties, and that before winter the Air Forces would have another improved rocket. To date no recent improvement in the rockets that are being furnished to the Army Air Forces has been noted; in fact present tests underway at the Proving Ground on a current lot of ammunition indicate less satisfactory operation than previous lots tested at that station.
>
> 7. The experience of the Navy and of our Allies establishes the rocket as a weapon of prime and possibly decisive important [sic]. . . .
>
> 8. It is requested, therefore, that the Ordnance Department redouble its efforts to furnish the Army Air Forces a rocket suitable for combat use.[22]

Up to the fall of 1943, the 4.5-inch rocket, it is true, had had a checkered career. The mass production begun the preceding spring had been halted in June when service tests showed that motor tubes and some other components failed to function properly in extreme temperatures. Reducing the propellent charge in rockets already manufactured, though shortening effective range, made them safe to use at high temperatures, while strengthening the motor tube and redesigning the warhead partly corrected the weakness of the new rockets. Later, a slight modification of the fin blade produced a model labeled the M8A3.[23] But some months before General Giles aired his concern, the Ordnance Department itself had taken steps to "redouble its efforts" to speed rocket work. A separate Rocket Development Branch, created within Research and Development Service in September, expanded rapidly from a staff of 2 officers and 13 civilians to 15 officers and 31 civilians. Larger sums of money allotted to rocket projects enabled the chief of the branch, the gifted

[21] (1) Memo, Col Donald B. Diehl, Chairman Armament Sec, Materials Div, for CG Materiel Command, Wright Field, 31 Jul 44, sub: Aircraft Rockets. (2) Memo rpt, 21 Feb 45, sub: Monorail Type Rocket Launchers. (3) Memo, Maj J. K. Sun, Assistant Ord and Chemical Off, Hq Eighth AF, for Ord and Armament Off Eighth AF Div, 30 May 45, sub: Aircraft Rockets. (4) Rockets, Development, Production and Performance, 1940–1945, Project Paper 20, pp. 20–21, OHF.

[22] Memo, Gen Giles for CG ASF, 18 Dec 43, sub: Aircraft Rockets, 4.5-inch.

[23] (1) Rocket Development, June 1945, pp. 17–19, OHF. (2) OCM 20555, 27 May 43; 22778, 3 Feb 44.

TABLE 12—COMPARISON OF 5-INCH AND 4.5-INCH ROCKETS

	5″ HVAR Rocket	4.5″ M8 Type Rocket
Total weight	140 pounds	40 pounds.
Maximum velocity	1,300 feet per second	865 feet per second.
Weight of high explosive	7.8 pounds	5.1 pounds (M8A3). 4.3 pounds (T22).
Maximum accurate range	1,000 yards	800 yards.
Approximate penetration of Class A armor	1.75 inches	1 inch.
Good reinforced concrete	3 feet	1 foot.
Operating temperature range	0° F to 120° F	−10° F to 105° F (M8A3). −20° F to 120° F (T22).
Weight of plane mounting installation	15 pounds (16 mounts)	196 pounds (with 2 cluster launchers).

Source: Memo, Lt Col J. W. Gruitch for C. W. Bunch, Office of Commitments and Requirements Div, 15 Aug 44, sub: Comparison of 4.5″ Type and 5″ HVAR Rockets, Hq USAF file, Office of DCofS for Development.

Col. Gervais W. Trichel, to intensify and widen the program and to establish closer ties with research groups of the Navy, NDRC, and AAF units at Wright Field and Eglin Field. As the AAF also enlarged its research and testing staff and opened Muroc and the Dover Air Bases, Army aircraft rocket developments moved more rapidly.[24]

Dissatisfaction with the first modifications of the M8 rockets revealed the necessity of designing motor tubes strong enough to withstand an internal pressure of 10,000 pounds per square inch. Experimentation proved that heat-treated alloy-steel seamless tubing gave the desired strength and extended the rockets' temperature range from −20° to 120° F.[25] The Ordnance Technical Committee designated this high-strength rocket the T22.[26] By August 1944 a comparison of these new types of 4.5-inch with the Navy HVAR 5-inch rockets showed that the latter was by no means superior in every respect. (*Table 12, above.*) While the HVAR thus carried about 50 percent more high explosive, had considerably greater muzzle velocity, and was equipped with both a nose and a base fuze, the 4.5-inch was so designed that it could be fired from an automatic launcher and could be launched in other directions than in the line of flight of the plane. The fact that the HVAR had an excellent underwater trajectory, which the 4.5-inch lacked, constituted no particular advantage of HVAR for Army Air Forces use inasmuch as the AAF had ceased to participate in sea search and antisubmarine warfare in July 1943, and Wright Field investigation of rocket launching devices for vertical bombing of submarines had faded out thereafter.[27] Moreover, a comparison tabulated after zero rails and adapters for the 4.5-inch rocket had come into use

[24] (1) 1st Ind, Gen Styer, CofS ASF, for CG AAF, 23 Dec 43. (2) Ltr, Col Joiner to Col Diehl, 5 Nov 43. (3) Ltr, Col Joiner to Col Bogert, Wright Field, 10 Nov 43. (4) Tech Div Memo No. 22, 23 Sep 43, OCO. (5) Ord Department Organization Chart, 48, 1 Jun 44, OHF.

[25] See above, Ch XII.

[26] See discussion in Craven and Cate, eds., *AAF II*, pp. 321–43.

[27] Air Tech Serv Command, memo rpt, 6 Dec 44, sub: Retractable 7.2″ Antisubmarine Launchers.

might have made the lesser weight of the 40-pound rocket a more obvious asset. And finally, because the AAF employed rockets only for strafing, the 4.5-inch had an eminently desirable distinctive feature: its design enabled the pilot to fire both rockets and machine guns simultaneously by merely harmonizing with the gun sight.

Meanwhile, the existence of rather extensive facilities able to produce the thin-webbed wet-extruded powder grains used in Army 4.5-inch rockets, coupled with the relatively limited sources of supply for the thick-webbed dry-extruded powders needed for the 5-inch, pointed to the wisdom of designing a rocket at least nearly equalling HVAR in power, yet employing a solvent type of propellent powder. Early in 1944 the Ordnance Department requested NDRC to undertake the project, and by October experimental lots of the "H" 4.5-inch rocket were ready for test. Mounted on zero rails on P–47's and B–25's, these first "super 4.5-inch" rockets performed well. Damage to the planes was slight and easily preventable, and dispersion of fire was not excessive. Though the "H" rocket carried a 39-pound payload, HVAR a 48-pound, and though velocity of the former at long range was considerably lower than that of the 5-inch, the new rocket with its faster-burning propellant got up more speed quickly and, over short ranges, attained higher velocities. For many kinds of mission a weapon possessing these characteristics would be better than HVAR. A thousand of the "H" 4.5-inch rockets were accordingly made for further testing, but no production order followed, because as the tactical situation in the spring of 1945 altered, the probability shrank that any need would arise for this type of short-range rocket.[28]

Aircraft rockets played a smaller part in AAF combat than in naval air forces engagements, just as operations over Europe were different in character from those over the Pacific areas. Nevertheless, the knowledge gained in World War II about rocket design and performance was quite as valuable to the Army as to the Navy. An Army Air Forces officer prophetically summarized the importance of the Ordnance and AAF rocket developments when he wrote in 1943:

> In view of the potentialities of rockets as a new aircraft munition, . . . we should go after them hard, although I have never felt nor suggested that any of our "new weapons" would very strongly influence the outcome of the present war. My own view is that new weapons of one war become of real usefulness during the war after that in which they are introduced, and that we shall have to slug out this war for the most part with the guns, bombs and other munitions which we had or had in sight when we entered it.[29]

[28] (1) ATSC memo rpt, 18 Nov 44, sub: Preliminary Rpt on Launching of 4.5" Rockets from AAF Aircraft. (2) Interv with Dr. Hudson 20 Sep 51.

[29] Ltr, Col Joiner to Col Diehl, 5 Nov 43.

CHAPTER XVII

Bombs

Of all aircraft weapons of World War II, bombs were the most widely used in air-to-ground operations. Bomb design, unlike design of antiaircraft equipment and weapons for air-to-air combat, was little affected by the rate at which planes of the 1940's could travel. Though the speed of the modern bomber made accurate aiming difficult, the swiftness of the ship's flight concerned Ordnance ballisticians only in preparing appropriate bombing tables. Before the end of the war, progress in aeronautics did introduce changes in the development program when bombers appeared that were capable of carrying 10,000-pound bombs and bigger, and did present new problems of bomb ballistics when stratosphere flights became feasible. But through most of World War II the Ordnance Department's major difficulty in bomb development was in adjusting to the frequent changes of doctrine of air warfare. Yet no change in strategic or tactical planning lessened the importance of bombs; in relation to weight and cost, bombs had a higher destructive potential than any other one weapon. They required no complicated, heavy, launching devices as did air cannon, and, under favorable conditions of weather, could be dropped on the target from heights from which rocket fire became inaccurate. And before the war ended, the Allied air forces found that small bombs used to strafe in tactical support of ground troops were more effective than machine gun fire.

Developments to 1940

The bomb is the oldest aircraft weapon. The first ever dropped in combat from an airplane fell among a group of Arabs in a Tripolitan oasis on 1 November 1911. How the Arabs felt about it we do not know, but the bombardier, Lieutenant Gavotti of the Italian Army, reported that from his altitude of about 2,300 feet he saw a cloud of black dust and running men. The bomb he dropped was a round grenade, a little larger than an orange, filled with potassium picrate. Holding it between his knees, Lieutenant Gavotti fuzed it, armed it, and dropped it over the side with one hand, while he guided the plane with his other hand.[1] Military men everywhere were quick to perceive the promise of this new kind of warfare. Targets unreachable by other means now came within range.

World War I bombers carried grenades and small-caliber shells and before the war was over dropped bombs of 1,000 kilograms. In the United States three kinds of bombs were developed. The largest, weighing from 50 to 1,600 pounds, was the demolition bomb, a light steel case made

[1] Maj. J. A. Swaney, Bomb Development, Record of Army Ord R&D (hereafter cited as Swaney, Bomb Development), pp. 9–10, OHF.

of sections welded together and filled with TNT. Its purpose was to demolish buildings by blast, that is, the pressure or shock waves sent out by the explosion. The second type was the fragmentation bomb of about twenty pounds, consisting chiefly of rejected artillery shells, while the third type was the incendiary bomb, loaded with oil emulsion, thermite, or metallic sodium. The three types differed in kind and amount of filler and in thickness of case but had operational features in common. Fins designed to provide stability in flight usually extended almost half the length of the case. Shortly after the Armistice, Americans began work on a safety device, used by the French and British during the war, a mechanism that allowed the bomb to be dropped unarmed and to arm itself in flight. When the bomb left the airplane, a small wind vane in the fuze began to turn and after a certain number of revolutions armed the bomb. In the airplane the vane was restrained by an arming wire threaded through it; the wire was withdrawn as the bomb was released. The arming wire could be left on the bomb if it became necessary to unload over friendly territory.[2]

In 1921 the War Department convened a Bomb Board to conduct an extensive program for testing bombs against various kinds of structures and surfaces. The tests, running over a period of two years, provided data that guided the Ordnance Department and the Air Corps through the 1930's. Ordnance engineers strengthened demolition bomb cases by forging them as nearly as possible in one piece, with a minimum of welding, and substituted for the long fins of World War I short box fins that gave greater stability in flight.[3] Uniformity of fragment size of the fragmentation bomb was achieved by encasing the body in rings cut from steel tubing or in wound steel coil. For low-level bombing, experiments with means of delaying the action of the fragmentation bomb sufficiently to permit the airplane to get to a safe distance before the bomb detonated produced a parachute attachment in place of fins. The parachute slowed descent and caused the bomb to strike the ground with its axis nearly vertical so that the fragments tended to be scattered above ground instead of being buried. Collaboration with the Chemical Warfare Service developed bombs that could be filled either with a fire-producing substance or with gas or smoke. The filling was the responsibility of the Chemical Warfare Service, the case of the Ordnance Department. The case had thin walls like the demolition bomb but had a burster tube running down its center. Shortly before the United States entered World War II, development of the incendiary bomb became entirely the responsibility of the Chemical Warfare Service.[4]

The filling for demolition and fragmentation bombs was trinitrotoluene. TNT was eminently stable, capable of being stored for long periods of time without deterioration, and, as it was relatively insensitive to blows and friction, it could be safely handled and shipped. It was easily melted for casting into bombs. Another virtue was its ready susceptibility to detonation by tetryl or the other highly sensitive explosives used in boosters. At the beginning of World War II, shortage of TNT for a time necessitated substitution

[2] (1) Swaney, Bomb Development, pp. 11, 14, 112, OHF. (2) Gen. H. H. Arnold, "Wings, Bombs, and Bullets," *Army Ordnance*, XXV, 140 (1943), 317–18.

[3] (1) OCM 11476, 17 May 34. (2) Swaney, Bomb Development, pp. 295–99, OHF.

[4] (1) Min, Wesson Conference, 6 Oct 41, OHF. (2) Barnes Diary, 6 Oct 41, OHF. (3) Ltr, SW to Chief of Chemical Warfare Serv, 3 Sep 41, sub: Incendiary Bombs, AAF 471.6, DRB AGO. See also above, p. 259.

in large bombs of amatol, a mixure of TNT and ammonium nitrate. Amatol had slightly less shattering power—brisance—than TNT, and somewhat less sensitivity to detonation. Later, increased production permitted the use of straight TNT.[5]

Blast Versus Fragmentation, 1940–41

As World War II approached, the War Department, realizing the need for speeding the manufacture of demolition bombs and for making interchange of bombs possible between the Army and the Navy, called together a committee made up of representatives from the Navy Bureau of Ordnance, the Army Ordnance Department, and the Air Corps. On the committee's recommendation, the Army's 600-pound and 1,100-pound demolition bombs were discarded, and new 500-pound and 1,000-pound bombs that could be carried on aircraft of either service were standardized.[6] In determining basic policies, a further and more far-reaching step was taken early in 1941 with the creation of a subcommittee of the Joint Aircraft Committee. The latter had been established in September 1940 to insure systematic and equitable allocation of aircraft between the British and the U.S. Air Corps. The function of the special subcommittee, composed of members of the Ordnance Department, the Air Corps, the Navy, and the Royal Air Force, was to recommend standard types of aircraft bombs and test programs for developing them.[7] From this committee's discussions first emerged the arguments pro and con on whether blast effects of bombing were more destructive than fragmentation effects. Long after the committee ceased to be active, some controversy over this matter endured and, indeed, majority opinion swung back and forth several times during the war.

The findings of the subcommittee were initially influenced by the experiences of the British in the Battle of Britain. The British member, Group Captain Charles Crawford, thought American bombs too fragile and therefore likely to fracture on impact, becoming duds of a low order of detonation. Largely because of this opinion and Group Captain Crawford's report that fragment damage was in many instances greater than the blast damage inflicted by German bombs dropped on England, the subcommittee recommended that a series of bombs with walls thicker than those of the old demolition bomb be developed by the Ordnance Department in 250, 500, 1,000, and 2,000-pound sizes. They would be about 30 percent high explosive by weight, in contrast to the demolition bomb's 55 percent. Following British nomenclature, they were called general purpose bombs, since the burst of their thick cases into damaging fragments would make them effective against a variety of targets. For targets that general purpose bombs could not penetrate, such as concrete fortifications and the decks of most ships, the subcommittee recommended that the Ordnance Department develop 500-pound and 1,000-pound semi-armor-piercing bombs, the Navy armor-piercing bombs for use against the very heavily armored decks of capital ships and depth bombs to be used against submarines. Two types of special purpose bombs already in existence were recommended for standardization, the 20-pound

[5] H. S. Beckman, "High Explosive Bombs," *Army Ordnance*, XXXII, 164 (1947), 99.

[6] OCM 15079, 8 Jun 39. The 100-pound bombs of both services were already identical. The Army's 300-pound and 2,000-pound bombs were not used by the Navy.

[7] Rpt 1, Rpts of Joint Aircraft Committee (JAC) on Bombs, 3 Mar 41, copy in Demolition Bombs: Design, Development and Production, Vol. II, 1 Aug 44, OHF.

fragmentation bomb as the M41, and the 100-pound gasoline incendiary bomb as the M47. Early in March 1941 the subcommittee's final recommendations on the standardization of aircraft bombs, "Case 217," were approved by the Joint Aircraft Committee.[8]

The general purpose bombs, modeled on the British thick-walled bombs of low-explosive content, had been accepted with some reservations by the American members of the subcommittee. Tests of United States prewar demolition bombs, which had a 55 percent explosive charge, had not indicated any great degree of malfunction on impact.[9] Moreover, reports coming from London and Berlin indicated in the spring of 1941 that German bombs, with an explosive charge of about 50 percent and a case no stronger than that of the American demolition bomb, accomplished more by blast than did the British bomb by fragmentation. An observer in London reported: "The British have learned by bitter experience that the havoc caused by blast is far more destructive in towns and cities than the localized splinter effect and relatively little blast effect of small, thicker-walled bombs." [10] Finally, with a shift of earlier attitudes, the British themselves supported the case for blast. On 17 April 1941 the RAF dropped on Berlin the famous 4,000-pound blockbuster. Since it had a thin case, it could carry 2,990 pounds of high explosives and the blast effect was unlike anything seen before. The bomber crew reported that the shock could be felt in the aircraft as high as 14,000 feet and that flame, debris, and smoke were seen to spread over large areas.[11]

Impressed by the reports of the destruction inflicted by this tremendous bomb, General Arnold, Deputy Chief of Staff for Air, requested the Chief of Ordnance to develop a 4,000-pound light-case bomb not later than 1 July 1941. The bomb that resulted, developed on schedule and tested between 2 and 5 July, weighed 4,166 pounds of which 3,221 pounds was the weight of the explosive charge. Its performance was very satisfactory, but the Air Corps retreated from its position, stating that it would rather carry two 2,000-pound GP bombs than one 4,000-pound blast bomb. General Barnes and General Somers, then chief of the Technical Staff, also doubted whether the 4,000-pounder would be as effective as two 2,000-pound bombs. Nevertheless, Robert A. Lovett, Assistant Secretary of War for Air, sensed the importance of the larger bomb and, on a directive from the War Department, development continued. In August the 4,000-pound light-case bomb was standardized as the M56.[12]

A more immediately productive result of reports from abroad in 1941 was the de-

[8] (1) *Ibid.* (2) OCM 16358, 18 Dec 40; 16605, 1 Apr 41. (3) Min, Wesson Conference, 12 Mar 41, OHF.

[9] Rpt 2, Rpts of JAC on Bombs, 4 Aug 41, in Demolition Bombs, Vol. II, 1 Aug 44, OHF. See also n. 7, above.

[10] (1) Second wrapper ind, Dir Air Corps Bd to CofAC, 2 Oct 41, to ltr, Chief of AAF to CofOrd, 18 Aug 41, sub: Additional Types of General Purpose Bombs to be Tested for Determining Army-Navy-British Standard. (2) Ltr, Dir Air Corps Bd to CofAC, 14 May 41, sub: Sizes of British Bombs Used Against Germany, and ind, 5 Jun 41. All in AAF 471.6, DRB AGO.

[11] (1) Ltr, Air Marshal Arthur T. Harris to Recorder, JAC, 2 Oct 41, sub: Effect of Very Large Blast Bombs. (2) Ltr, Air Marshal Harris to Gen Arnold, 14 Jul 41 [sub: RDX as Bomb Filling]. Both in AAF 471.6, DRB AGO.

[12] (1) Min, Wesson Conferences, 3 Jul 41, 22 Aug 41, OHF. (2) Barnes Diary, 7 Jul 41, OHF. (3) Ltr, CofOrd to DCofS for Air, 17 May 41, sub: Development of Large Demolition Bombs, OO 471.62/714, DRB AGO. (4) Ltr, Robert Lovett to CofAC, 2 Jun 41, sub: Heavy Bombs, AAF 471.6 DRB AGO. (5) OCM 17071, 7 Aug 41; 17152, 20 Aug 41.

velopment of general purpose bombs containing a larger charge of explosive. The case strength of their thick-walled British prototype that carried only 30 percent explosive was partly a virtue of necessity: limited British forge capacity necessitated fabricating the bomb by casting. American manufacturers could spin and forge steel bombs equal to the English in case strength yet able to take explosive charges of 50 percent. Essentially a modification of the old demolition bomb with a stronger case, general purpose bombs in 250-pound, 500-pound, 1,000-pound, and 2,000-pound sizes were standardized in the fall of 1941.[13] The Army estimated that this series would fill about 90 percent of its requirements and could be used effectively against all land targets except those with armor or heavy concrete protection. For such highly resistant targets, the JAC subcommittee recommended a 1,500-pound solid-nosed bomb similar to the Navy's 1,600-pound armor-piercing bomb and containing about 15 percent explosive filler. As supply of this type could not possibly meet the combined demands of the Army, the Navy, and the British, the 500-pound and 1,000-pound thick-walled general purpose bombs originally authorized by the Joint Aircraft Committee, containing 30 percent explosive filler, were tested to see whether they would fill the requirement. They were found satisfactory and, provided with steel nose plugs instead of nose fuzes and with tail fuzes like those in general purpose bombs, they were standardized as SAP, that is, semi-armor-piercing bombs.[14]

Chemical Bombs

At the opposite extreme in case strength from the semi-armor-piercing bombs were the thin-walled chemical bombs. Except for photoflash and target-identification bombs for which the Ordnance Department had sole responsibility, development for chemical fillers was assigned to the Chemical Warfare Service. One bomb at first sufficed for incendiary, gas, and smoke purposes. Made of light sheet metal, it was about 70 percent filler. Its blunt rounded nose distinguished it from explosive bombs. Later somewhat modified, it was manufactured in large quantities. It was employed with excellent effect as an incendiary but as a gas bomb was unsatisfactory because its welded construction made it subject to leakage. This did not matter in the case of the incendiaries, which were shipped empty and filled in the field with a gasoline and rubber solution. But gas bombs had to be shipped loaded and then stored for long periods. An attempt to develop a leakproof, gas-filled bomb resulted in a slightly larger and heavier model made of 3/16-inch steel tubing, somewhat longer than the 100-pound general purpose bomb but of much the same construction.[15]

The trend toward larger chemical bombs with thicker cases continued. At the request of Chemical Warfare Service,

[13] (1) Min 10, Min of Committee on Aircraft Ord; 18 Apr 42. (2) Rpt 3, 25 Sep 41, and Rpt 4, 5 Nov 41, Rpts of JAC on Bombs. All in Demolition Bombs, Vol. II, 1 Aug 44, OHF. (3) OCM 17336, 9 Oct 41; 17490, 24 Nov 41. (4) Ltr, CofAC to CG Air Force Combat Command, 17 Oct 41, sub: Equipment, Miscellaneous, AAF 471.6, DRB AGO.

[14] (1) See n. 13(2). (2) OCM 17457, 12 Nov 41. (3) Swaney, Bomb Development, p. 262, OHF.

[15] (1) Swaney, Bomb Development, pp. 51-98, OHF. (2) Catalogue of Standard Ord Items, III, 581-82. (3) OCM 19301, 10 Dec 42. (4) Ltr, CG Air Tech Serv Command to CG AAF, 17 Feb 45, sub: Unsatisfactory Rpt re M47A2 H-Filled Bombs, and inds, 23 Mar 45 and 6 Apr 45, OO 471.2941, DRB AGO. (5) Baxter, *Scientists Against Time*, p. 289. (6) Interv, 17 Apr 53, with Joseph A. Llompart, Bombs and Pyrotechnics Sec, Ammo Br, R&D Serv.

BOMBS. *Lt. M. S. Crissy with the first bomb to be dropped from the air, San Francisco, California, January 1911. The Wright airplane pilot is Philip O. Parmalee (above). Bombs developed by the Ordnance Department (below).*

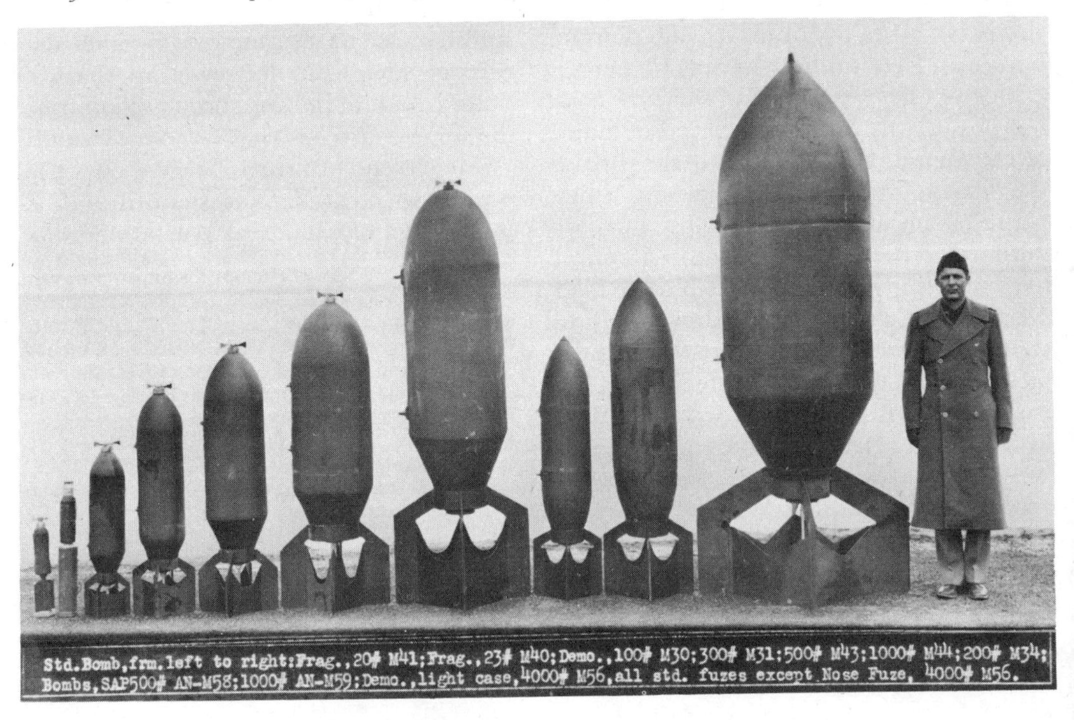

Ordnance later developed 500-pound and 1,000-pound sizes for different types of fillers, incendiary as well as gas. After experiments with several thin-case models, Ordnance engineers in the end simply converted general purpose bombs to chemical by welding in longitudinal burster walls and by making holes in the base plugs through which the cases could be filled. The designers took great care to avoid even the most minute crevices, especially at the filling hole, which was closed by a special plug and gasket. The burster, consisting of a waterproof fiber tube filled with about two and a half pounds of tetrytol, was given a tight seal. With these changes, general purpose bombs taken from existing production lines became chemical bombs. They proved strong enough to withstand shipment and rough handling and had much better ballistic characteristics than the first chemical bombs.[16]

Fuzes

The fuzes for all bombs were agreed upon by the Joint Aircraft Committee. General purpose bombs had both nose and tail fuzes. The nose fuze functioned when a striker head plunged a firing pin into an explosive train consisting of primer, detonator, and booster. The tail fuze, the purpose of which was to detonate the bomb if the nose fuze failed to function, was activated by a plunger operated by inertia and was the same for all bombs except for its arming vane shaft. The vane shaft varied in length according to the size of the bomb, so that the vane would be positioned sufficiently to the rear of the bomb body to be in the airstream. The tail fuze reduced the percentage of duds to about 0.1 percent. Another use for this fuze became increasingly important. In dive bombing, the bomb had to become armed in a hurry.[17] Designers reduced the revolutions of the arming vane from the 675 required in the earlier tail fuzes, to 175 in a new series, and then to only 18 revolutions. In addition, Ordnance developed for skip bombing or "masthead" bombing of ships a series of very sensitive fuzes that could delay explosion either from 4 to 5 seconds, from 8 to 11 seconds, or, later, 8 to 15 seconds, depending on the primer detonator used. These highly sensitive fuzes were produced in great quantities in 1943 and were popular in the theatres. Used with the 500-pound bomb they were credited with helping to sink the Japanese fleet. As the rapidity with which they became armed made them dangerous to use on carrier-based aircraft, at Navy request the Ordnance Department developed a series in which the arming time was increased from 18 to 150 revolutions.[18]

Early in 1943 an urgent requirement arose for bombs fuzed for a delay of from one hour to twenty-four hours. Maj. Gen. James H. Doolittle wanted them to hamper and restrain workers unloading ships at enemy dock installations in North Africa; Lt. Gen. Simon B. Buckner, Jr., needed them to keep the Japanese confined to their dugouts in the Aleutians.[19] At the time, the Ordnance Department was developing two types of long-delay

[16] (1) Swaney, Bomb Development, pp. 99–110, 131–36, OHF. (2) OCM 19442, 7 Jan 43; 23068 and 23072, 2 Mar 44.

[17] (1) Min 12, Min of Committee on Aircraft Ord and Armament of Working Subcommittee on Standardization, 19 Jun 42, in Demolition Bombs, Vol. II, 1 Aug 44, OHF. (2) Bomb Fuze Development, Record of Army Ord R&D, Nov 45 (hereafter cited as Bomb Fuze Development), pp. 8–15, 73–74, OHF.

[18] (1) Bomb Fuze Development, pp. 74–77, OHF. (2) Barnes Diary, 5 Mar 43, OHF.

[19] Barnes Diary, 4 Jan 43 thru 29 Mar 43 OHF.

fuzes. One with an adjustable clockwork mechanism proved unsatisfactory because the enemy could stop clock mechanisms with magnets or by injecting acid into them. The other, a chemical fuze, was still in the experimental stage when the sudden demand from the theatres made quick action necessary. A copy of the British No. 37 Mark IV pistol was hastily tested and standardized in three lengths. A celluloid disc restrained its cocked striker. When the fuze became armed an ampoule of acetone broke and dissolved the celluloid. The delay time could be varied from 1 to 144 hours by changing the concentration of the acetone or the thickness of the disc, or both. To prevent the enemy from withdrawing the fuze, it was booby trapped. This introduced a factor of unreliability and danger. The bomb could explode in midair if the downward flight unscrewed the antiwithdrawal feature and caused it to function. Modifications aimed at greater sturdiness and safety followed, but the Air Forces still raised objections, especially to the antiwithdrawal feature, which prevented the bombs from being defuzed if a bombing mission were canceled.[20]

The Ordnance Department also worked out countless variations of fuzes to meet the needs of the using services and to keep pace with bomb and aircraft development. In 1944 new high-level "stratosphere" bombing presented problems just as the early low-level bombing had done. For example, the B–29 bomber released many bombs simultaneously from a great height, so that with quick-arming nose fuzes they sometimes bumped into each other and detonated just below the ship. Increasing the number of threads on the fuze arming screw and striker gave a longer arming time. New delay elements were incorporated both in this nose fuze and in the standard tail fuze to adapt them to use with new types of bombs such as the VB–1 (Azon–1). For glide bombs, which approached the target at a flat impact angle and sometimes had shrouded noses and special tails, Ordnance engineers designed a fuze in which the arming screw, connected with an anemometer vane mounted on the side of the bomb, entered the striker at 90 degrees instead of the top. As the war ended work was proceeding on special fuzes with long arming distances for robot bombs.[21]

Of the specialized fuzes, one of the most significant was the diaphragm fuze that operated by blast to explode the bomb above ground. First considered for use in the 20-pound fragmentation model, it was copied from a British fuze that utilized the air blast from a preceding bomb or an air cushion effect from the ground. A very light firing pin was secured to a flexible, slightly convex metal diaphragm. When pressure snapped the diaphragm to a concave position, the fuze functioned. A number were tested in 20-pound fragmentation bombs, some dropped singly and some in

[20] Bomb Fuze Development, pp. 87–92, OHF.

[21] The Ordnance Department also supplied warheads and destructor sets for robot bombs and other kinds of guided missiles. The development of air-sustained guided missiles was an AAF responsibility. (1) See above, Ch. VIII, pp. 49–50. (2) Bomb Fuze Development, pp. 8, 24–25, 57–58, OHF. (3) OCM 26598, 8 Feb 45; 26683, 15 Feb 45. (4) Ltr, CG AAF to CofOrd, 6 Jan 43, sub: Destructors, Type T-4 for Glide Bombs, and ind, 16 Mar 43, OO 471.62/789, DRB AGO. (5) Ltr, Air Ord Off to CofOrd, 26 Jun 44, sub: Storage Classification of Kits, Accessory, Bomb, T2, T3, and T4, OO 471.62/2332, DRB AGO. (6) Ltr, CG AAF to CofOrd, 9 Aug 44, sub: Bomb, Flying, AAF 471.6, DRB AGO. (7) Ltr, CG AAF to CofOrd, 12 Dec 44, sub: JB-2 Bombs, OO 471.62/2783, DRB AGO. (8) Ltr, Gen Arnold to CG Materiel Command, 2 Aug 44, sub: Combining AAF and Ord Experience on Guided Missiles, AAF 471.6, DRB AGO. (9) Ltr, Howard Bruce, Actg Dir Materiel, to ACofS Opns Div, WDGS, 3 Mar 45, sub: JB-2 (Buzz Bomb), OO 471.62/2866, DRB AGO.

pairs, but the results were so disappointing that further development was abandoned. On the other hand, the British who early in the war had had the notion that a bomb burst in the air would be especially effective because of less shielding by buildings, began experiments with the blast-operated fuze in general purpose bombs and aroused the interest of U.S. Air officers. Consequently, at the request of the Army Air Forces, the Ordnance Department modified its earlier models for trial in general purpose bombs. The new type, incorporating features that made for greater safety and even more sensitivity, was tested with 100-pound, 500-pound, and larger GP bombs. So fuzed, 500-pound bombs dropped in threes would detonate at approximately 25 feet, vertically, from each other. The fuze was standardized late in 1944 as the M149 and, at the urging of Army Air Forces, the Ordnance Department gave it high priority.[22]

Except for fuzing, World War II saw few changes in the general purpose and semi-armor-piercing bombs that had been standardized in the fall of 1941. In order to make the 500-pound, 1,000-pound, and 2,000-pound sizes more effective against water targets, the Navy's Mark 30 hydrostatic fuze, which functioned by water pressure, was adopted for both Army and Navy use as the AN-MK 30. To accommodate it, the bombs were given a larger tail fuze cavity and assigned new designations.[23] Another minor change followed an AAF discovery that the antiwithdrawal feature of the long-delay tail fuzes could be circumvented by removing the base plate or adapter-booster. Ordnance engineers added locks for these parts.[24] In the first year of the war the Air Forces used in most operations the 500-pound and 1,000-pound general purpose bombs, which would destroy such vital targets as concrete docks, steel bridges, and light cruisers. The 500-pound was the bomb that General Arnold gave the credit for sinking about 39 Japanese ships in the Makassar Strait.[25]

The New Role of Fragmentation Bombs

When the United States forces began to move forward the need for a bomb to be used against troops became clear, and the theatres began to demand the 20-pound fragmentation bomb. Standardized in 1940 and adopted by the Joint Aircraft Committee early in 1942 as the AN-M41,[26] this small bomb weighed not more than 23 pounds, even with a parachute attachment. It was not dropped singly, but by sixes in a cluster that would fit in an airplane's 100-pound bomb station. Clustering was made possible by the use of an adapter consisting of a hollow rod to which the bombs were wired. When the adapter was released from the aircraft an arming wire was pulled, activating a cartridge with a steel slug that cut the wires holding the bombs. The bombs fell free, arming themselves with their own arming vanes. Later design modification eliminated the cartridge and substituted clamped straps

---

[22] (1) OCM 20017, 25 Mar 43; 25458, 19 Oct 44. (2) Burchard, ed., *Rockets, Guns and Targets*, p. 262.

[23] (1) Burchard, ed., *op. cit.*, pp. 3, 95. (2) OCM 18348, 6 Jun 42. (3) Rpt 10, Rpts of JAC on Bombs, 25 May 42, in Demolition Bombs, Vol. II, 1 Aug 44, OHF.

[24] OCM 22610, 13 Jan 44; 22731, 27 Jan 44.

[25] Gen. H. H. Arnold, "Wings, Bombs, and Bullets," *Army Ordnance*, XXV, 140 (1943), 319.

[26] (1) Barnes Diary, 4 Jan 43, OHF. (2) Arnold, *loc. cit.*, pp. 319–20. (3) Craven and Cate, eds., *The Army Air Forces in World War II:* III, *Europe: Argument To V-E Day, January 1944 to May 1945* (Chicago, 1951) (hereafter cited as *AAF III*), p. 106. (4) OCM 18187, 7 May 42.

THE PARAFRAG BOMB IN ACTION. *Old Namlea Airdrome, Boerce Island, Netherlands Indies, is shown during a low-level bombing attack by the U.S. Fifth Air Force.*

for the wires.[27] "Wicked little weapons," according to Brig. Gen. George C. Kenney, they proved their value in the battle for New Guinea and became increasingly popular. If accurately placed, they could harass front-line infantry and disrupt lines of communication far more completely than could machine gun fire. They were especially effective against parked aircraft, airdromes, supply trains, and encampments. By the spring of 1943 the effectiveness of fragmentation bombs was so well established that the Army Air Forces requested the development of new types, and before the war was over even fighter craft were supplied with them.[28]

The first new antipersonnel bomb was a 4-pounder copied from the German 2-kilogram "Butterfly" bomb. It got its name from two curved sections of its case that opened on release and formed wings that rotated in the air and slowed descent. It could be fuzed to detonate in the air, on impact, at any delay up to thirty minutes, or upon being disturbed. Delivered before an attack, it could deny the enemy use of his airdromes, antiaircraft installations, and supply areas. Butterfly bombs were dropped in clusters, either in a cluster of 24 bombs that fitted into a 100-pound station or in one carrying 90 that fitted in a 500-pound station. Engineers at Aberdeen made numerous tests to find the right timing and altitude for the release of the cluster from the aircraft and the opening of the cluster, in order to forestall excessive wind drift or damage to the butterfly mechanism. At the end of a year of tests, both bomb and cluster were standardized but, as the timing of the cluster opening was still not wholly satisfactory, testing continued into the summer of 1945. Fuze failures and the tendency of the cluster to open too soon after release sometimes made experience with the bomb in the field discouraging.[29]

Two fragmentation bombs developed in 1943 were like the 20-pound bomb but were five and ten times its size. The demand for such bombs came from the Mediterranean theatre, and urgently from the Southwest Pacific Area where Allied officers could testify to the effectiveness of Japanese 60-kilogram fragmentation bombs. As a counterweapon, General Kenney converted general purpose bombs into fragmentation bombs by wrapping them with heavy wire and used them effectively around Japanese airdromes and bivouac areas. In the summer of 1943 the Ordnance Department designed two sizes, a 90-pound model to be used in a cluster of six in a bomber's 500-pound station and a 260-pound model to fit in the 100-pound station. Both the lighter bomb, standardized as the M82, and the 260-pound, the M81, were similar to the 20-pound bomb, except for their fins. The cluster adapter for the M82 resembled that for the 20-pound except in size. Because one purpose of large fragmentation bombs was to reach

[27] (1) OCM 17049, 31 Jul 41. (2) Ltr, Gen McFarland, ACofOrd, to TAG, 21 Nov 41, sub: Adapter, Cluster, M2 and Cluster, Fragmentation Bomb M3, AAF 471.6, DRB AGO. (3) James A. Bradley, Fragmentation Bombs, Pt. II, pp. 1-5, OHF. (4) Interv, 23 Oct 51, with Harry S. Beckman, Bomb Sec, R&D Serv.

[28] (1) Arnold, *loc. cit.*, pp. 319-20. (2) Swaney, Bomb Development, pp. 165, 178, 206, OHF. (3) Ltr, CofOrd to CofS A-4, AAF, 28 May 43, sub: Comparison of Bombs with 50% and 30% Explosive Filler, OO 471.62/1156, DRB AGO. (4) George C. Kenney, *General Kenney Reports* (New York, 1949), p. 13. (5) Interv with Dr. H. M. Cole, 28 Sep 51.

[29] (1) Swaney, Bomb Development, pp. 205-50, OHF. (2) OCM 20957, 8 Jul 43; 24164, 22 Jun 44. (3) Ltr, CG AAF to CofOrd, 9 Jun 43, sub: Anti-Personnel Bombs, OO 471.6/742, DRB AGO. (4) Ltr, Lt Col William S. Cox, Jr., OD, to Ord Off AAF POA (Admin), 5 Mar 45, sub: Report on Use of Butterfly Bombs in Recent Operations, OO 471.62/3009, DRB AGO.

targets enclosed in revetments, the AAF wanted an above-ground airburst, but until proximity and diaphragm fuzes became available late in 1944, the standard nose fuze that functioned on impact had to serve.[30] Comparison tests of the single 260-pound M81 with the 20-pound M41 cluster proved that the large fragmentation bomb was better for destroying highly resistant and concentrated targets such as armored vehicles, parked aircraft, and PT boats, but that against unprotected troops and lightly armored vehicles and aircraft the cluster of 20-pound bombs was more effective. In the field, the AAF considered the 20-pound more versatile and useful than either the 260 or 90, so that a proposal of early 1944 to develop fragmentation bombs of 500 and 1,000-pound sizes was not pursued.[31]

Use of New Explosives

In the war-long argument over the relative merits of blast and fragmentation, the pendulum now began to swing back toward blast, partly because by 1944 the AAF would have aircraft capable of delivering larger and heavier loads. The heaviest bombers available in early 1943, the B–17 and the B–24, could carry bombs up to 4,000 pounds, but only on the wings. The B–29, expected to be ready early in 1944, was designed to carry 10,000-pounders in its interior. These considerations led the Army Air Forces officially to reverse the position taken in 1941 that no bomb larger than 2,000 pounds was required. Achieving greater blast meant renewed emphasis on large thin-case bombs of high explosive content. Reports from England in the fall of 1942 had stressed the effectiveness of such bombs. Hundreds of 4,000-pounders had been dropped over German cities and towns with such satisfactory results that the British were preparing bombs weighing as much as 12,000 pounds. Furthermore, the Air Forces had discovered from combat reports that 2,000-pound bombs had practically no effect against buildings adequately protected by sandbags. In spite of the earlier verdict, the Ordnance Department had already done some work on very large bombs. Mainly because of British interest,[32] the AAF had requested a limited number of a 4,000-pound light-case type standardized in August 1941, and early information from Wright Field about B–29 capacity had inspired a request for a 10,000-pound bomb. About 600 of an experimental model 10,000-pounder were actually manufactured before the project was canceled. When Air Forces interest in large bombs revived, tests of the 4,000-pound bombs at Aberdeen indicated that loading with new and more powerful explosives was the simplest means of increasing blast effect within size limitations.[33]

---

[30] (1) Barnes Diary, 12–14 Jan 44, OHF. (2) Ltr, CG AAF to CofOrd, 23 Apr 43, sub: Large Fragmentation Bombs, AAF 471.6, DRB AGO. (3) OCM 20617, 3 Jun 43; 22367, 5 Dec 43; 25955, 7 Dec 44. (4) Bomb Fuze Development, pp. 66, 105, OHF.

[31] (1) OCM 22367, 16 Dec 43. (2) Ltr, Air Ord Off to CofOrd, 29 Sep 44, sub: Operational Use of 90-lb and 260-lb Fragmentation Bombs, OO 62/2609, DRB AGO. (3) Bradley, Fragmentation Bombs, Pt. II, pp. 59–60, OHF. (4) Baxter, *op. cit.*, p. 257.

[32] See above, p. 454.

[33] (1) Memo, Lt Col Robert G. Butler, Jr., for Gen Barnes, 9 Sep 42, sub: Report of Trip to England, August 1942, Barnes file, OHF. (2) Memo, Col Carroll, Chief of Experimental Engr Sec, Wright Field, for Chief of Material Div, Office of CofAC, 9 Oct 41, sub: 4,000 Bomb Installation for Heavy Bomber (B–17 and B–24) Airplanes, AAF 471.6, DRB AGO. (3) Ltr, CG AAF to CofOrd, 8 Oct 42, sub: Relative Destructive Effect of Demolition Bombs of Various Sizes, and ind, 16 Oct 42, OO 471.623/41, DRB AGO. (4) OCM 22125, 30 Oct 43; 19594, 28 Jan 43. (5) Ltr, CofOrd to Hq AAF, 14 Jan 43, sub: Tests of Aerial Bombs—Summary of Notes of Conference Held on 11 Jan 43, and inds, 14 Jan, 6–18 Mar 43, OO 471.62/825, DRB AGO.

The earliest departure from TNT for bomb fillings was cyclonite or RDX, an explosive long known for its great power and brisance but generally considered too sensitive. The British had developed a method of desensitizing it by mixing it with beeswax and had used it with "terrible" effect [34] in the 4,000-pound bomb the RAF dropped on Berlin in April 1941. The following summer Air Marshal Arthur T. Harris had pressed for large-scale production of RDX in America. The United States Navy was also interested in the explosive because of its effectiveness underwater, especially in a mixture with TNT and aluminum called torpex. But the Ordnance Department, while willing to start production for the British and the Navy, held back until May 1943 on the use of RDX in its own bombs, and then adopted only a less sensitive mixture with TNT, known as RDX Composition B. This first significant change in bomb loading came about as a result of AAF insistence that the large fragmentation bombs developed in 1943 would need the greater power of RDX Composition B to burst their thick walls with the greatest effect. The loading, with TNT surrounds for greater safety, was authorized.[35] Though the Army Air Forces liked it and the Joint British-American Committee on Aircraft Ordnance and Armament approved it for all Army-Navy standard munitions, Composition B was used in only about 40 percent of the general purpose bombs. The reasons were two: first, the short supply caused by competition between it and high octane gasoline and synthetic rubber for production facilities and, second, the serious doubts of a number of Ordnance officers about the advisability of using it.[36]

Throughout World War II the Ordnance Department, believing itself in a better position to evaluate bomb fillings than were the using services, was "extremely cautious in its recommendations for any so-called improved explosive. . . ."[37] Much of this caution concerning RDX mixtures was justified. The most important weakness of Composition B was its tendency to detonate high-order without fuze action under the shock of impact. This made it undesirable for skip bombing. It was also more prone than TNT prematurely to deflagrate—decompose without detonating—when employed in delayed-action bombs dropped from high altitudes. Sensitivity to shock was not a consideration in the case of fragmentation bombs because they were not intended for delay fuze action on hard impact; but it was obviously a factor in the case of general purpose bombs. And the sensitivity of torpex-loaded depth bombs cost the Navy several serious accidents.[38] The problem might have been solved by the new American explosive ednatol, which was used in the blast tests of 1943–44, but by the time

[34] Ltr, Air Marshall Harris to Gen Arnold, 14 Jul 41 [sub: RDX], AAF 471.6, DRB AGO.

[35] (1) Baxter, *op. cit.*, pp. 253–59. (2) Ltr, CG AAF to CG ASF, 29 May 43, sub: Requirements for RDX, Large Fragmentation Bombs, OO 471.62/1183, DRB AGO. (3) OCM 22843, 10 Feb 44. (4) Memo, Group Captain Crawford, British Air Commission, for ACofS G–2, 7 May 42, OO 350.05/653, DRB AGO.

[36] (1) Min 19, Min of Committee on Aircraft Ord and Armament, 8 Apr 43, sub: Case No. 3021, Adoption of RDX Composition B, in Demolition Bombs, Vol. II, 1 Aug 44, OHF. (2) OCM 20021, 25 Mar 43.

[37] 1st Ind, CofOrd to CG AAF, 7 Mar 43, sub: Tritonal Loading for GP Bombs, to ltr, Air Ord Off to CofOrd, 6 Mar 45, OO 471.62/2919, DRB AGO.

[38] (1) Ltr, Air Ord Off to CofOrd, 17 Nov 44, sub: Bomb, G.P. 500 lb (RDX Comp filled) and inds, 5, 22, 26 Feb 45 and 7 Jun 45, OO 471.62/2710, DRB AGO. (2) Ltr, Hq AAF to CofOrd, 10 Sep 43, sub: Blast and Fragmentation Effect of Demolition and General Purpose Bombs, and ind, 22 Apr 44, OO 471.6/971, DRB AGO. (3) OCM 31926, 18 Dec 47.

291064 O—55——31

it was in production in any quantity, the war had ended.[39]

After 1943 of far greater interest than either RDX Composition B or ednatol were the new aluminized fillings. Until World War II the use of aluminum in explosives had not been extensive, and tests in England in 1941 had failed to indicate any significant difference between aluminized explosives and amatol or Composition B. In 1943 the discovery that German bombs containing aluminum were extremely effective spurred research and led to the development of minol, a mixture of aluminum with amatol, and tritonal, a mixture with TNT. For their 4,000-pound bomb the British favored Minol 2, a mixture 20 percent aluminum, 40 percent TNT, and 40 percent ammonium nitrate, and they requested that it be used in their 4,000-pound bombs being loaded in the United States. The British had learned, by using new methods of blast measurement and interpretation, that Minol 2 produced an area of demolition approximately 80 percent greater than the area obtained with a TNT filler. Ordnance technicians had independently arrived at a similarly high opinion of the blast effect contributed by aluminum by comparing the performance of 2,000-pound and 4,000-pound bombs loaded with minol, TNT, ednatol, and the RDX mixtures. As between minol and tritonal, they preferred tritonal, which contained no ammonium nitrate because, when even the slightest degree of moisture was present in the air, aluminum acted on ammonium nitrate and produced "spewing"—the evolution of hydrogen gas—and even explosions. Tritonal was much safer, and the British were won over to it.[40]

When reports on the successful loading of 4,000-pound British bombs with tritonal at the Nebraska Ordnance Works came to the attention of the Army Air Forces, a request followed for further testing of the new explosive, especially with a view to using it in large, light-case bombs for jungle warfare. Ordnance engineers, comparing tritonal with Composition B and TNT, found it almost equal to Composition B in peak pressure value, yet as insensitive as TNT, and hence safe to load and use. After these tests, the Ordnance Committee recommended that tritonal supplant TNT as a loading in all general purpose and light-case bombs.[41] Other bombs were filled with explosives suited to their particular purposes. For fragmentation bombs, RDX Composition B continued to be the preferred filling because it had more brisance than tritonal. The 2,000-pound semi-armor-piercing bombs developed early in 1944 were loaded with picratol, a mixture of TNT and ammonium picrate, or with Explosive D, which was of all explosives the least sensitive to shock and friction and was therefore the best to mix with TNT in a bomb that had to withstand severe shock and stress before detonating.[42]

Use of Air Bursts

Loading large, light-case bombs with the new aluminized explosives was one way to increase blast effect. Another way was air-burst fuzing. The idea that a bomb

[39] (1) See above, p. 368. (2) Hist of Picatinny Arsenal Tech Group, V, October–December 1943, 50–51, OHF.

[40] OCM 24163, 22 Jun 44.

[41] (1) OCM 24163, 22 Jun 44; 26023, 14 Dec 44; 26892, 8 Mar 45. (2) Ltr, AAF to CofOrd, 3 Jun 44, sub: Bombs, 2,000-lb, Tritonal Filled, and ind, 22 Aug 44, OO 471.62/2285, DRB AGO. (3) Ltr and inds cited n. 38(1). (4) Ltr, CG AAF to CofOrd, 4 Jan 45, sub: Bombs, General Purpose, Tritonal Filled, and ind, 7 Mar 45, OO 471.62/2919, DRB AGO.

[42] (1) OCM 26892, 8 Mar 45; 23255, 23 Mar 44. (2) U.S. Military Academy, *Explosives* (West Point, 1950), p. 23.

would be more effective if it were exploded in the air rather than on the ground grew out of abstract mathematical work carried on by NDRC on the theory of the interaction of shock waves: a special kind of nonacoustic reflection from the ground, known as the Mach effect, redistributed the energy of the explosive and widened the area affected by it. The theory was later supported by reports of observers in London who witnessed the great destruction wrought by German V-1 bombs that had struck the tops of trees and exploded above ground. Proximity fuzes promised to provide means of exploding bombs at roof-top level or above. As the VT fuze project got under way [43] Ordnance officers consulting with scientists of NDRC concluded that a tail proximity fuze for the large, light-case bombs could be developed in a fairly short time. This plan was soon shelved in favor of an effective nose proximity fuze that would either produce air burst of itself or activate a new, supersensitive tail fuze of the cocked-firing-pin type.[44]

From NDRC studies begun in 1941 several experimental types of nose proximity fuzes evolved, of which the most promising were the T50 and T51. They provided a burst height of 60 feet over water when released from 10,000 feet or less, and of 18 to 42 feet when released over ground, depending on reflectivity and terrain. Following NDRC's basic research, the Signal Corps, in co-ordination with the Ordnance Department, carried on work on these fuzes until late 1944, when Ordnance was given responsibility for the fuzes.[45] Development was slow, both because of the very nature of the device and because it had to be adapted to bombs of various kinds and sizes and to use in new high-altitude, high-speed aircraft. One of the most difficult problems was to allow for the correct timing between drop and arming, that is, the "minimum safe air travel" for use in various tactics such as high-level, low-level, and naval bombing. One answer was a new air-arming mechanism that was given a considerable range of safe air travel by making a simple adjustment at the factory or in the field. Without waiting for entirely satisfactory solutions to this and other problems, because of intense interest in the theatres, the War Department authorized limited procurement of the T50 in late 1943. Combat tests were postponed by a decision of the Joint Chiefs of Staff forbidding employment of the fuze over land until October 1944, and then AAF distrust of the fuze caused further delay. It was not employed until February 1945 when the Seventh Air Force dropped proximity-fuzed fragmentation, general purpose, and chemical bombs at Iwo Jima. Soon afterwards the T51 was also tested in combat.[46]

Of the two, the Ordnance Department preferred the T51, believing it more reliable than the T50 in producing the right height of burst and better functioning because less sensitive. It was also more versatile. Whereas the T50 was limited to

[43] See above, Ch. XII.

[44] (1) OCM 19939, 18 Mar 43; 22776, 3 Feb 44; (2) Min, Joint A&N mtg on Army Ord R&D, 1 Oct 45, pp. 33-35, A&N Mtgs, Barnes file, OHF. (3) Burchard, ed., *op. cit.*, pp. 259-62.

[45] (1) OCM 17715, 27 Jan 42; 21117, 17 Jul 43; 26444, 18 Jan 45; 28150, 28 Jun 45. (2) Ltr, CofOrd to Dir Camp Evans Signal Laboratory, 30 Sep 44; sub: Fuze, Bomb, Nose, T50 Series-Service Tests, and inds, 18 Oct 44, 9 Nov 44, 12 Dec 44, OO 471.82/3601, DRB AGO. (3) See George Raynor Thompson and Dixie R. Harris, Signal Corps: The Outcome, a volume in preparation for UNITED STATES ARMY IN WORLD WAR II, MS, OCMH.

[46] (1) OCM 21994, 4 Nov 43; 28150, 28 Jun 45. (2) Report of Activities of VT Bomb Fuze Team in Pacific Ocean Area, 10 January 1945 to 28 February 1945, OHF. (3) Baxter, *op. cit.*, p. 241. (4) Boyce, *New Weapons for Air Warfare*, pp. 212-16.

500-pound bombs, the T51 model would provide air burst on all bombs that normally took the AN-M103 nose fuze up to the light-case 4,000-pounder. Designated the T51E1 after minor modifications, the fuze was standardized in June 1945 as the M166.[47] The largest bomb for which it was adopted was the 2,000-pound general purpose AN-M66. It was tested with the 4,000-pound bomb but caused too high a burst.[48]

The Search for More Powerful Bombs

By September 1944 some of the 4,000-pound light-case bombs were loaded and in the theatres, but the Air Forces had made little use of them. No use whatever had been made of the 10,000-pound. With the appearance of the B–29, which could carry in its interior bombs 125 inches long and 50 inches in diameter, however, the Army Air Forces decided that very large bombs would be desirable. A request for 10,000-pound bombs of the light-case, general purpose, and semi-armor-piercing types to fit the B–29 bomb bay was followed by one for a 4,000-pound general purpose bomb to be used to penetrate the very thick bombproof structures that the Japanese were expected to erect to protect their main positions. Ordnance designers, having anticipated the need of a 4,000-pound general purpose bomb of this type, had a model ready by the end of the year. Concerning the 10,000-pound bomb of the general purpose type containing a 50 percent explosive filler, they had serious reservations, based on belief that the length limitation of 125 inches prohibited a true semi-armor-piercing bomb of more than 5,500 pounds, and that a heavier one would lack the flight or penetration characteristics to be expected of its weight. The same consideration applied to the general purpose 10,000-pound bomb. Ordnance Research and Development Service was willing to undertake the development of both types but pointed out to the AAF that neither would have characteristics anywhere near ideal. The truth was, the B–29 could not carry in its bomb bay an effective 10,000-pound bomb. This fact was admitted within the Air Staff itself, and for the time being the development of very large bombs was necessarily stalemated.[49]

Lacking "super-super" blockbusters and the airplanes to carry them, the Air Forces had to depend on the bombs already on hand to meet the tremendously increased requirements during and after the invasion of Europe. Improvisation had to serve. To increase payloads of all aircraft, as well as to fill efficiently the huge racks of the B–29, the Ordnance Department designed adapter clusters that would hold two or three bombs and fit in a station designed

[47] (1) Ltr, CofOrd to Office of Chief Signal Off, 19 Sep 44, sub: Military Characteristics of Fuze, Bomb, Nose T50 and T51, OO 471.82/3552, DRB AGO. (2) OCM 28150, 28 Jun 45.

[48] (1) Ltr, Air Ord Off to CofOrd, 23 Apr 45, sub: AAF Bd Rpt, Preliminary Guide to Tactical Employment of Airburst Fragmentation and General Purpose Bombs, Project 4324A471.6, and ind, 5 May 45, OO 471.62/3090, DRB AGO. (2) Burchard, ed., *op. cit.*, pp. 263–64. (3) OCM 28852, 23 Aug 45. (4) Interv, 24 Oct 51, with Hoyt W. Sisco, Fuze Sec, R&D Serv.

[49] (1) Min, Joint A&N mtg on Army Ord R&D, 15 Sep 44, A&N Mtgs, Barnes file, OHF. (2) Ltr, CG AAF to CofOrd, 27 Sep 44, sub: 4,000-lb. General Purpose Bomb, and ind, 29 Sep 44, OO 62/2602, DRB AGO. (2) Ltr, CG AAF to CofOrd, 17 Nov 44, sub: Bombs, 10,000 Pound Size, and ind, 24 Nov 44, OO 471.62/2702, DRB AGO. (3) Ltr, CofOrd to Office of ACofAS, Materiel, Maintenance, and Distribution, 6 Dec 44, sub: Development Status of Bombs, 10,000-lb Size—RMD-17, OO 471.62/2733, DRB AGO. (4) OCM 25519, 26 Oct 44. (5) Memo, Brig Gen Mervin E. Gross, Chief of Requirements Div, Office of ACofAS, for ACofAS, Opns Commitments and Requirements, 21 Nov 44, sub: Large Bomb Development, AAF 471.6, DRB AGO.

for one bomb. One model held three 100-pound GP bombs, another two of the 250-pound size, and another two 500-pounders. In this way, bomb loads were increased from 50 to 200 percent.[50] For low-level bombing the Ordnance Department supplied general purpose bombs with anti-ricochet devices—parachute assemblies and a prong or nose spike that stuck in the ground and kept the bomb from bouncing. But for the penetration of heavily fortified German defenses, such as concrete structures with roofs from 10 to 20 feet thick, something more powerful was needed than any bomb or rocket then in use. In this exigency Ordnance engineers pushed forward modifications of 2,000-pound GP bombs to incorporate the "shaped charge" or Munroe principle.[51]

Also called the "hollow charge" principle, it had been applied to small fragmentation bombs as far back as 1941. Ordnance designers, modifying the 20-pound M41 in this way for use against tanks, had obtained an intense forward jet along the longitudinal axis of the bomb, and had succeeded in penetrating 3.5-inch armor plate. But difficulty with the fuze made the model unacceptable.[52] Late in 1942 the Army Air Forces, having learned that the British had used the Munroe principle in a "CS" bomb designed to defeat capital ships, had asked Ordnance to develop a large shaped-charge bomb. But Air Forces interest in the project was short lived, and it was canceled less than a year after it had begun. In the interim Ordnance designers had produced two bombs that corresponded in size to 2,000-pound and 4,000-pound demolition bombs. Because of the difficulty of loading shaped-charge bombs to conform to those weights, they were designated not by pounds but by inches in diameter. The smaller was the 23-inch T1, the larger, the 34-inch T1. Four models of each, shipped to Aberdeen after the project was canceled, were there in May 1944 when the AAF asked for the reactivation of the 23-inch T1. Tests indicated need of further development. While that work was going on, the Navy Bureau of Ordnance asked the Army and NDRC to participate in a project to develop shaped-charge general purpose bombs. Development began on shaped-charge 100-pound, 500-pound, 1,000-pound, and 2,000-pound models, and, as the Army Air Forces also wanted these bombs, they were given an "emergency urgent" rating. Nevertheless, they did not get into combat. Testing continued into the summer of 1945.[53]

---

[50] (1) Ltr, CG AAF to CofOrd, 13 Jun 44, sub: Adapter Clusters for 100 lb, 250 lb, and 500 lb GP Bombs, OO 471.62/2279, DRB AGO. (2) Ltr, CG AAF to CofOrd, 26 Jul 44, same sub, and ind, 29 Jul 44, OO 471.62/2451. (3) Ltr, Gen Arnold to CG Air Materiel Command, 1 Sep 44, sub: Multiple Suspension of Bombs, AAF 471.6, DRB AGO. (4) Ltr, CG AAF to CofOrd, 17 Jun 44, sub: Immediate Increase in Bomb Tonnage, OO 471.62/2312. (5) Swaney, Bomb Development, pp. 310–14, OHF.

[51] (1) Ltr, CG AAF to CofOrd, 18 Nov 43, sub: Anti-Ricochet Devices, OO 471.6/1073. DRB AGO. (2) Ltr, Air Ord Off to CofOrd, 24 May 44, same sub, OO 471.62/2243, DRB AGO. (3) OCM 26459, 25 Jan 45. (4) Ltr, CG AAF to CofOrd, 24 Mar 45, sub: Anti-Ricochet Devices for Bombs, and ind, 5 Apr 45, AAF 471.6, DRB AGO. (5) Ltr, Gen Coupland, Air Ord Off, to Col Phillip Schwartz, Armament and Ord Off, USSAFE, 12 Dec 44 [sub: Shaped Charge Bombs], AAF 471.6, DRB AGO.

[52] OCM 20018, 23 Mar 43.

[53] (1) Ltr, Gen Chidlaw, ACofS, to CofOrd, 21 Dec 42, sub: Capital Ship Bomb, OO 471.62/734, DRB AGO. (2) Ltr, Dir AAF Bd to CG AAF, 13 Feb 44, sub: Shaped-Charge Bombs, and inds, 25 Feb 44, 4 Aug 44, AAF 471.6, DRB AGO. (3) Ltr, CofOrd to Dir Ord ResearchCenter, APG, 3 Jun 44, sub: Program for Hollow Charge Bomb, and ind, 2 Aug 44, OO 471.62/2140, DRB AGO. (4) Ltr, CofOrd to Dir Ord Research Center, 18 Apr 44, sub: Targets for Bombs, Shaped Charge 23" and 34" T1, OO 471.62/2161, DRB AGO. (5) OCM 24290, 6 Jul 44; 26549, 1 Feb 45. (6) Swaney, Bomb Development, pp. 308–10, OHF.

The Role of Pyrotechnics

In the last year of the war bomb development was affected not only by the need to overcome strong fortifications but also by changes in Air Forces doctrine. One example was the increased use of incendiaries. By August 1944 the AAF Board had come to the conclusion that "where there is vulnerability to fire, the damage by fire is greater than by demolition,"[54] a conclusion, to be sure, that an Ordnance observer had reached during the London blitz of 1940 but which the Ordnance Department had not acted upon. As primary responsibility was shifted to Chemical Warfare Service in November 1940, the decision in 1944 to increase the incendiary bomb program under the highest priority affected Ordnance very little. More important for the Ordnance Department was the change in AAF doctrine that initiated 24-hour bombing operations. Night bombing, always favored by the Royal Air Force but hitherto opposed by the United States, gave new importance to pyrotechnics. Flares and signals to be released or fired from aircraft or projected from the ground had been an Ordnance Department responsibility since 1920. The signals were cases filled with different kinds of compositions that would produce colored smoke or fireworks effects. Especially important were hand signals for downed fliers. Aircraft flares came closer to the usual bomb design. Aircraft flare AN-M26, designed to provide illumination for night bombardment, contained its illuminant in a round-nosed, finned-tail cylinder and developed 800,000 candlepower for a period of about three minutes. It had a drag sleeve that slowed its descent and a mechanical time fuze that functioned the illuminant at a predetermined time after release. A very much smaller parachute flare was employed for reconnaissance, and a tow-target flare towed by an airplane provided a practice target for antiaircraft gunners. The case designed for the M26 flare was versatile. It was modified at different times to drop "chaff" or "window"—metal straw for jamming enemy radar and thus protecting a bomber from flak—and propaganda leaflets, although for the latter the closed adapter clusters used for butterfly bombs eventually proved preferable.[55]

The most important developments in pyrotechnics concerned photoflash bombs for high-altitude night photography and markers to identify targets at night. The prewar M46 photoflash bomb had the round-nosed shape of a chemical bomb, weighed about 50 pounds of which half was the flashlight powder, and was functioned by a mechanical time fuze. It gave a light of 500 million candlepower. The powder consisted of an oxidant potassium perchlorate or barium nitrate combined with a fuel mixture composed of magnesium and aluminum. The Army Air Forces wanted a photoflash bomb that would give more light at high altitudes and that would be less susceptible to detonation by flak. The Ordnance Department attempted to meet the first requirement by furnishing two experimental large-sized models, one containing 50 pounds of flashlight powder,

[54] Ltr, Maj Gen H. A. Craig, ACofAS, to CofAS, 14 Aug 44, sub: Study of Employment of Incendiary Bombs, AAF 471.6, DRB AGO.

[55] (1) OCM 26238, 4 Jan 45; 27737, 24 May 45. (2) Catalogue of Standard Ord Items, III, 499–609. (3) Ltr, Maj Gen N. F. Twining, Hq Fifteenth AF, to CG AAF/MTO, 8 Aug 44, sub: "Chaff" Bomb, and inds, 21 Aug, 18 Oct 44, AAF 471.6, DRB AGO. (4) Ltr, Gen Arnold to President AAF Bd, 12 Aug 44, sub: Propaganda Leaflet Bombs, AAF 471.6, DRB AGO. (5) Ltr, CofOrd to Dir Ord Research Center, APG, 9 Aug 44, sub: M26 Flare Cases Modified for Propaganda Leaflet Bombs, OO 471.62/2494, DRB AGO.

and the other containing 100. To provide greater safety from flak, pyrotechnics experts tried two methods, a less sensitive powder and a bomb case with thicker walls. Loading a "safe photographic powder," developed by the British, into both the M46 case and the 250-pound general purpose bomb case failed to provide the answer, as the British powder gave less light, pound for pound, than the American. Hence the Ordnance Department concluded that solution of the problem lay in the heavy-walled case. Finally, NDRC was called in and established the relationship between case strength and charge weight and composition. Picatinny Arsenal experimented with different combinations of case, filler, and initiating system. The result was a photoflash bomb that produced approximately three times as much light as the M46. Because of urgent need for it in the theatres, its development was given an "A" priority late in December 1944, but further research was required and continued into the postwar period.[56]

Target identification bombs grew out of a technique evolved by the British to improve the accuracy of their night bombing. A "Pathfinder Force" equipped with special navigational aids flew over a target in advance of the attacking force and dropped various kinds of candles and flares, some to illuminate the general area and others to mark with color the special target. One munition designed specifically for this work was a stabilized bomb that ejected sixty-one pyrotechnic candles at a predetermined altitude. In the United States the earliest research on target identification markers produced five bombs of this kind. All were a modification of the 250-pound general purpose bomb and differed one from another only in the type of candle they contained. A mechanical time nose fuze caused the bomb to eject its candles at the moment when a mechanical time flare fuze ignited them. The candles were small flares, about a foot long and one and one half inches in diameter, that burned with either red, green, or yellow light for about three minutes. Each target identification bomb carried sixty-one of these signal candles, which together made a pattern of colored light approximately 100 yards in diameter around or on a target and were designed to be visible from altitudes as high as 35,000 feet. To keep the candles from being disturbed while they were on the ground, one type of candle had in its case a small cast-iron cylinder containing black powder that would ignite at the end of the burning time of the candle, that time being from one to two minutes. These sporadic explosions were intended to keep the enemy from disturbing the candles as they lay on the ground.[57] As the AAF extended its night operations, especially low-level bombing and strafing of illuminated targets by fighters and light attack bombers, need arose for ground-burning flares that would produce a minimum amount of smoke and thus leave the targets as clear as possible. For this purpose the Ordnance Department developed flare

[56] (1) Catalogue of Standard Ord Items, III, 600–601. (2) OCM 19651, 4 Feb 43; 22298, 9 Dec 43; 25381, 12 Oct 44. (3) Ltr, CG AAF Proving Ground Command, Eglin Field, to CofOrd, 22 Dec 43, sub: Oxidants for M-46 Photoflash Bombs, and ind, 30 Dec 43, OO 471.6/1003, DRB AGO. (4) Ltr, Air Ord Off to CofOrd, 20 Sep 44, sub: Bomb, Photoflash, M46, AAF 471.6, DRB AGO. (5) Ltr, Gen Arnold to President AAF Bd, 29 Dec 44, sub: Increased Priority on Photo Flashbomb Projects, AAF 471.6 DRB AGO. (6) Min, Joint A&N mtg on Army Ord R&D, 1 Oct 45, pp. 32–33, A&N Mtgs, Barnes file, OHF.

[57] (1) OCM 21439, 2 Sep 43; 26238, 4 Jan 45. (2) Ltr, CG AAF to CofOrd, 25 Oct 44, sub: "Pathfinder" Pyrotechnic Requirements, AAF 470.9, DRB AGO. (3) Ltr, CG AAF to CofOrd, 31 Oct 44, sub: Target Identification Bomb Development, AAF 471.6, DRB AGO.

bombs loaded with smokeless units.[58] At the end of the war Army and Navy experts agreed that future developments must be aimed at greatly increasing the candlepower, burning time, and visibility of all pyrotechnics, especially the photoflash bomb.[59]

Problems of High-Altitude Bombing

Meanwhile, the increased heights at which new types of aircraft could operate introduced a new problem in bomb design. "Stratosphere" bombing tests conducted at Muroc Army Air Base in the summer of 1944 profoundly affected the future of all air-to-ground munitions, bombs, and pyrotechnics alike. Ordnance ballisticians found that bombs dropped from 35,000 feet, the ceiling of the B–17's used in the test, behaved quite differently from those dropped at lower altitudes. The fin structures did not stand up well, and the bombs, especially the 1,000 and 2,000-pounders, were unstable in flight. This discovery led to the development of heavier fins as well as parts for strengthening the fins on bombs already in the theatres. A result more significant for the future was the decision of the Chief of Air Staff to enlarge and elaborate the stratosphere bomb-testing program in 1945. With the B–29's then available, the Ordnance Department was able for the first time to prepare bombing tables for altitudes above 35,000 feet. In the unusually clear air at Muroc the ballistic camera provided accurate data not only for extreme altitudes but for plane speeds faster than any previously known. The future design of both bombs and fuzes would have to be adapted to altitudes up to 60,000 feet, to plane speeds of 600 miles an hour, and to temperatures as low as $-65°$ F.[60]

The Development Program, 1945

With these adaptations in mind, the Ordnance Department directed its long-range program for fuze development toward more versatile fuzes, with the ultimate goal a single fuze that would serve every purpose by adjustment of arming times, delay times, sensitivity, and the like. The trend in bomb development generally was toward fewer but more effective and more accurate types for use in future airplanes of higher ceilings, faster speeds, and greater carrying capacity. Specifically, it was toward larger and more powerful bombs.[61]

In Lancaster heavy bombers, modified for the purpose, the Royal Air Force was, by June 1944, using a 12,000-pound bomb with tremendous effect. The blast bomb of this size, with approximately 75 percent explosive content, caused entire buildings

---

[58] (1) Ltr, CofOrd to Kilgore Manufacturing Company, 12 Dec 44 [sub: Bombs, Smokeless, T24E1], OO 471.62/2767, DRB AGO. (2) Ltr, CofOrd to CO Southwestern Proving Ground, 30 Mar 45, sub: Test of Target Identification Bombs, 250 lb T26, OO 471.62/2997. DRB AGO.

[59] Min, Joint A&N mtg on Army Ord R&D, 1 Oct 45, p. 32, A&N Mtgs, Barnes file, OHF.

[60] (1) *Ibid.*, p. 8. (2) Ltr, CG AAF to CofOrd, 13 Sep 44, sub: Bomb and Fuze Requirements for Future Development, OO 471.62/2578, DRB AGO. (3) Ltr, CofOrd to CG AAF, 14 Nov 44, sub: Planes for Stratosphere Bombing Trials, OO 452.1/302, DRB AGO. (4) Memo, Gen Barnes for Gen Campbell, 30 Nov 44, sub: Bombs for High Altitudes, Barnes-Campbell Correspondence fiie, DRB AGO. (5) Ltr, CG AAF to CofOrd, 7 Dec 44, sub: Bomb Fin Modifications, and inds, 12 Dec 44 and 16 Feb 45, OO 471.62/2730, DRB AGO. (6) Ltr, CG AAF to CofOrd, 18 Oct 44, sub: Bombs for Minimum Altitude Attacks, OO 471.62/2595, DRB AGO. (7) Ltr, CofOrd to CG AAF, 23 Feb 45, sub: Personnel for High Altitude Bombing Program at Muroc Army Air Field, OO 471.62/2936, DRB AGO. (8) Ltr, CG AAF to CofOrd, 14 Apr 45, sub: Stratosphere Bombing Program, OO 471.62/3068, DRB AGO.

[61] Min, Joint A&N mtg on Army Ord R&D, 1 Oct 45, p. 32, A&N Mtgs, Barnes file, OHF.

to disintegrate and collapse into rubble.[62] In addition to this giant, the British were preparing early in 1945 a new 12,000-pound bomb called "Tallboy," and a 22,000-pound bomb, the "Grand Slam," to destroy heavily fortified targets such as U-boat pens and underground factories. The 12,000-pounder and the 22,000-pounder were relatively heavy-walled bombs with approximately 43 percent explosive and were fuzed in the base only. The Army Air Forces saw the possibilities of huge earth-penetrating bombs of these sizes, envisaging them as large general purpose bombs to be employed for both blast and fragmentation effect, as well as to cause cave-ins and earth shock and to reach vital underground installations.[63] After a study of the so-called long bombs, the Air Forces Board asked the Ordnance Department, which already had drawings of the British bombs and fuzes, to hasten engineering studies on medium and large "pressure vessels," the 12,000-pound and 22,000-pound general purpose bombs. The models that resulted differed from their British prototypes in being made of steel forgings welded to rolled steel plate, instead of cast steel. The smaller, 21 feet long, carried about 5,600 pounds of explosive; the larger, 25 feet long, carried about 10,000 pounds. The main difference in the design of these bombs and that of the conventional aircraft bombs was in the tail-and-fin assembly, a slender, hollow cone that took up almost half the total length of the bomb and carried four radial airfoil fins. There were three tail fuzes, but no nose fuze. To save time, the test models were equipped with British fuzes and detonators, though the absence of an air-arming feature in the British fuze was a disadvantage. On V-J Day the bombs were still in the testing stage.[64]

The 22,000-pound British Grand Slam, termed "the most destructive missile in the history of warfare until the invention of the atom bomb,"[65] was the largest explosive bomb employed in World War II. By the end of the war the United States had a model nearly twice its size. It weighed about 44,000 pounds, of which 17,600 was high explosive. Though the ratio of explosive charge to weight was only about 41 percent, the Ordnance Department placed this colossus in the general purpose bomb category. It was loaded with tritonal. In design it resembled the Tallboy and Grand Slam, with a tail assembly that took up 122 inches of its total 322. By V-J Day several samples of the experimental model were ready for testing whenever the B–36 bomber became available.[66]

In the meantime Ordnance engineers, studying ways to correct the unsatisfactory features that had been of necessity copied from the British Tallboys, designed an air-arming fuze, and new fin assemblies made

[62] (1) Craven and Cate, eds., *AAF III*, pp. 531, 539. (2) Swaney, Bomb Development, p. 292, OHF. (3) Keith Ayling, *Bombardment Aviation* (Harrisburg, Pennsylvania, 1944), p. 191.

[63] (1) Ltr, CG AAF to CofOrd, 9 May 45, sub: Bombs, G. P., Large, OO 471.62/3162, DRB AGO. (2) Sir Arthur Harris, *Bomber Offensive* (London, 1947), p. 252.

[64] (1) Swaney, Bomb Development, p. 367, OHF. (2) Ltr, Air Vice Marshal R. B. Mansell, British Air Commission, to Office CofOrd, 22 Dec 44, sub: British "Tallboy" (Medium) and "Grand Slam"; American Pressure Vessel (Medium) and Pressure Vessel (Large), OO 452/78, DRB AGO. (3) Ltr, CG AAF to CofOrd, 3 May 45, sub: Bombs, Tallboy, 12,000-lb and 22,000-lb, OO 452/99, DRB AGO. (4) OCM 28279, 5 Jul 45. (5) Min, Joint A&N mtg on Army Ord R&D, 1 Oct 45, p. 32, A&N Mtgs, Barnes file, OHF.

[65] Harris, *op. cit.*, p. 252.

[66] (1) OCM 27278, 12 Apr 45. (2) Memo, Col Crosby Field, OCO Chicago, to Chief of Ammo Supply Div, FS, 4 Apr 45, sub: Storage of "Tallboy," OO 471.62/2972, DRB AGO. (3) Swaney, Bomb Development, pp. 370–71. OHF.

of steel instead of aluminum. As the extreme length of the British fins presented a problem of stowage as well as ballistics, the Air Forces suggested collapsible fins. The Ordnance Department objected on the grounds that they were not only liable to failure but would, by the necessary delay in opening, increase the range and deflection errors. On the whole, a long bomb tail was not economical from the standpoint of weight of explosives carried. Yet long fins gave the stability needed to place the bomb on the target. In efforts to solve the ballistics problem, Aberdeen engineers ran supersonic wind-tunnel tests of scaled-down Tallboy models to determine just what ballistic gain was present to offset the loss of space. The answer was not found before the end of the war. By that time the Ordnance Department had initiated a long-range project of research on very large bombs. Significantly for all bomb development, the project covered research on the best size and shape of bomb to fit in the bomb bays of the future. Henceforth there would presumably be a closer relationship between the weapon and its carrier.[67]

Testimony of the World War II Record

The largest bomb dropped by the AAF in World War II, the 4,000-pound blast bomb, would not fit in the bomb bay of the B–17 or the B–24, the heavy bombers employed in European operations, but had to be carried under the wings. The B–29 could carry the 4,000-pounder comfortably and in quantity, but as that ship did not get into combat until the late spring of 1944, it was pre-eminently a Pacific bomber. By the time the B–29 was operating in large numbers, incendiaries formed the greatest part of its load. The terrible effectiveness of incendiaries had been stressed in interim reports of the United States Strategic Bombing Survey (USSBS), a group of specialists who had been evaluating bomb damage in Europe since shortly after the invasion. Their findings showed that the M47 incendiary of about 100 pounds was twelve times as effective, bomb for bomb, as the 500-pound general purpose bomb against targets classified as readily inflammable, and one and a half times as effective against targets classified as fire-resistant. Another important conclusion of USSBS was that precision bombing of the "pin-point" or "pickle-barrel" type was a myth. Only about 20 percent of the bombs aimed at precision targets fell within the target area—a circle of 1,000-feet radius around the aiming point. The causes were various: weather conditions and enemy opposition, time limitations on training combat crews, and irregularities in equipment. The greatest promise for improvement in accuracy was the guided bomb, for whose development the AAF was responsible. Except for a brief and very successful experience with Azon bombs in Burma, Allied guided bombs had no influence in World War II.[68]

[67] (1) Swaney, Bomb Development, pp. 368, 370, OHF. (2) Ltr, Dir ATSC to CG AAF, 27 Feb 45, sub: Large Bombs in VHB Aircraft and inds 5, 13 Mar 45, OO 471.62/2933, DRB AGO. (3) Ltr, CG APG to CofOrd, 29 Jun 45, sub: Dispersion of Bombs, OO 471.62/3298, DRB AGO. (4) Min, Joint A&N mtg on Army Ord R&D, 1 Oct 45, A&N Mtgs, Barnes file, OHF. (5) Memo, Brig Gen Joe L. Loutzenheiser, ACofAS, Plans, for ACofAS, Opns, Commitments and Rqmts Div, 7 Dec 44, sub: Very Large Bomb Program, AAF 471.6, DRB AGO.

[68] The Azon bomb, developed by NDRC, was a 1,000-pound general purpose bomb with a radio receiver in its tail that enabled the bombardier to control its flight by radio. It got its name from the fact that it could be guided only to the right or left, that is, in AZimuth ONly. (1) Baxter, *Scientists Against Time*, pp. 198–99, 289. (2) *Third Report of the Commanding General of the Army Air Forces to the Secretary of War, November 12, 1945*, p. 41, Air Force Library. (3) Lincoln R. Thiesmeyer and John E. Burchard, *Combat Scientists* (Boston, 1947), pp. 195–201, 281–84.

The performance of the bombs developed by the Ordnance Department was difficult to evaluate, especially since bombers carried mixed loads that contained incendiaries as well as high explosives; but the record permits several conclusions. The semi-armor-piercing bombs encountered targets that defeated them. Fragmentation and general purpose bombs, on the other hand, generally possessed the four salient characteristics required: the ability to be carried by and launched from aircraft; proper flight characteristics under conditions of use; suitability of the design for mass production, handling, and storage; and, most important of all, adequate terminal ballistic effect at the target, that is, power to destroy the objective. Of these the first was largely a matter of aircraft design and thus an Air Forces responsibility. Destructive power also depended in part on the capacity of the bomber to carry a sufficiently big bomb. On the question of flight stability, Ordnance engineers admitted that several of the standard bombs were probably no more than marginally stable and needed more fin area. Production engineering problems were largely solved, especially for the general purpose bombs, the cases of which could be produced in quantity and modified to many uses. For example, the 250-pound size was adapted for pyrotechnics, the 500 and 1,000-pound cases were readily converted to chemical bombs, and the standard 1,000-pound general purpose bomb became an Azon bomb when fitted with a special tail. Toward the end of World War II the problem of fitting the proximity fuze into existing bombs led scientists of NDRC to urge that all bombs and fuzes be designed as an entity. For logistic reasons the Chief of Ordnance did not agree, and the newly established project was canceled in spite of NDRC's belief that it would lead to new weapons of significantly greater effectiveness. For the rest, the application of new principles of design, such as the shaped-charge bomb and the very large bomb, was delayed by the AAF's lack of interest early in the war. Most of the war was fought with the bombs standardized in 1941.[69]

Thus, bomb developments from Pearl Harbor onward suffered from want of a sound over-all scheme of employment determined in advance. Yet no nation at peace could establish any proved plan. World War I offered neither Air Forces nor Ordnance Department guidance in a development program for World War II, if only because the aircraft of the earlier period bore scant resemblance to the planes of the 1940's. Between wars no opportunity existed to appraise accurately the relative merits of blast and fragmentation under various circumstances, of blockbusters and showers of small bombs, of incendiaries and high explosives, of semi-armor-piercing types and shaped charges. Tests at Aberdeen during the 1920's and 1930's were at best simulations of combat, so that conclusions derived from that evidence were of necessity subject to frequent change when actual fighting and unanticipated tactical conditions showed earlier assumptions faulty. Hence, during the war, shifts in Air Forces doctrine canceled development projects half-

[69] (1) Craven and Cate, eds, *AAF II*, p. 245. (2) Ltr, Irvin Stewart, Exec Secy NDRC, to WD Liaison Off with NDRC, 10 Mar 45, sub: Cancellation of Project OD-190—Development and Design of Bombs and Fuzes as an Entity, and ind, 28 Apr 45, OO 62/3122, DRB AGO. (3) Ltr, Col Philip R. Faymonville, WD Liaison Off for NDRC, to NDRC, 4 May 45, same sub, OO 471.62/3149, DRB AGO. (4) Ltr, CG APG to CofOrd, 29 Jun 45, sub: Dispersion of Bombs, OO 471.62/3298, DRB AGO. (5) Baxter, *op. cit.*, p. 198.

way completed and substituted new ones that might in turn be quickly abandoned. Experience revealed that many of the numerous types of bombs on hand were not well suited to the purpose for which they had to be used, a purpose quite different from that for which they had been originally designed. Partial divorce of case design from fuze design, and, far worse, disregard in aircraft design of the shape and size of the bombs the ship might have to carry, tended to create confusion that could only be resolved by last-minute recourse to makeshifts. In fact, in the last year of the war improvisation came to be virtually the order of the day.

Still, however short of ideal as munitions, bombs were far and away the most important weapons of the Allied air forces throughout the war. Questioning of the ultimate value of bombarding cities behind the battle lines dropped out of sight. Not only did strategic bombing missions over Europe and, in the last months of the war, over Japan loom large in Allied operations, tactical bombing and strafing played an increasingly big part. In air-to-ground attack machine guns and cannon dwindled in importance as the war progressed, while rockets, though coming into ever-wider use, were still too new to rival bombs. And when the atomic bombs were dropped, most of the world concluded that bombs would henceforward be the single most valuable weapon a belligerent could employ.

CHAPTER XVIII

Conservation of Materials

Early Neglect of Conservation

Before World War II, conservation of materials was not a major consideration in the design of military equipment in the United States. In fact, extravagance rather than economy was the order of the day. Instead of carefully studying each part of a weapon or vehicle in terms of its military functions, determining the maximum strength or wearing quality required of it, and then manufacturing it of the most readily available material that provided the required strength plus a suitable margin for safety, Ordnance designers tended to specify the highest quality material available thus giving the part strength far in excess of maximum needs. In 1941 a survey of Ordnance items to discover ways of conserving critical materials revealed that, in a multitude of parts not subject to high stresses, alloy steel was prescribed when carbon steel would have been adequate, and that electric-furnace steel was specified for certain purposes even though open-hearth steel would have been just as satisfactory. This prodigality in the use of materials was not confined to the designers of military equipment but was common throughout American industry. Emphasis in military circles on high standards of performance under adverse conditions probably influenced military designers to be more wasteful than their counterparts in private industry, but openhandedness in employing material resources was so common before 1941 that it stood virtually as a national characteristic.[1]

The most obvious reason for this condition was the wealth of resources found within the United States or under the control of friendly, near-by nations such as Canada and Mexico. With an abundant supply of most essential minerals at hand there was no apparent necessity for parsimony in their use. For the Ordnance Department there were also other reasons for neglecting conservation, among them the national policy that envisaged mobilization in time of war of a comparatively small military force for defense only. To produce the munitions that might be needed by this small force in time of emergency, the resources of the United States, with a few exceptions, were certainly more than adequate. Under such circumstances there was no strong pressure for materials conservation, except for the few items on the War Department list of strategic materials, and even for those the emphasis

[1] (1) Ord Materials Br, Conservation of Materials, Rpt of Progress and Development, 15 Jun 42 (hereafter cited as Conservation of Materials), copy in Drawer T-237, Ord Exec Office file, DRB AGO. (2) Intervs, summer 1951, with Col Frye, wartime chief of Ord Conserv Br. (3) For a critical account of War Department prewar conservation policies, see Industrial College of the Armed Forces, Study R87, Conservation Within the ASF, particularly pp. 125ff, ICAF Library.

was on building up a reserve stockpile rather than on curtailing their use.[2]

In some instances, designers in the prewar years chose a critical material for a specific use without giving due consideration to the fact that some other, noncritical, material would have been just as satisfactory. Metallurgical developments in industry were proceeding so rapidly and along so many different lines that it was often impossible for Ordnance designers, who were not themselves metallurgists, to make intelligent choices among materials; and, since conservation of materials was not emphasized, metallurgists and production engineers did not normally participate in the process of selecting materials or designs for new items of equipment. Because of the high cost of experimenting and testing, and because of the insistent demand for dependability in weapons, designers generally took a conservative stand, reasoning that it was more economical, at least in the short run, to continue the use of tried and proven materials and manufacturing methods than to experiment with substitutes. "If our designs, as some people have said, were 'wrapped around a milling machine,'" General Campbell wrote, "it was because we simply could not afford production-engineering studies of our various models or pilots." [3] In some cases substitute materials and mass-production processes that would have saved critical materials, man-hours, and machine-tool time on quantity production were not used before the war because they could not be economically applied to the small-scale production of the peace years. In other cases, critical material needed in only one or two parts of a weapon was also specified for several other parts for the sole purpose of maintaining production of the small quantity actually required each year.[4]

This is not to say, however, that the Ordnance Department neglected metallurgical research before World War II. For many years, as the Army agency having primary interest in the use of metals, it had carried on intensive metallurgical testing programs at its arsenals and laboratories. As early as 1873 it had established a metallurgical testing laboratory at Watertown Arsenal, and during the years before and after World War I Ordnance pioneered in the development of molybdenum high-speed tool steel, in the use of macroetch-test and radiographic-inspection methods, in welding constructional steels, in determining the effects of cold working and low temperatures on the physical properties of steel, and in studying the causes of season cracking of brass.[5] There were laboratories at all the manufacturing arsenals where, within the limitations of the budget, metallurgical research pertaining to Ordnance materials was carried on. But the emphasis was not placed primarily on conservation.

The War Department had carried on continuous studies of sources of strategic and critical materials [6] for many years pre-

[2] For further information on prewar military conservation policy, see: (1) ASF Manual M-104, Strategic and Critical Raw Materials; (2) G. A. Roush, *Strategic Mineral Supplies* (New York, 1939); and (3) Significant Papers Expressing Stockpiling Policy of the Military Services, folder in ASF Resources and Production Div files, DRB AGO.

[3] Campbell, *Industry-Ordnance Team,* p. 292.

[4] Conservation of Materials, p. 2, DRB AGO.

[5] (1) Summary of the War Department's Metallurgical Research and Development during World War II, p. 13, OHF. (2) Armor Plate Development and Production 1940–45, pp. 43–45, OHF.

[6] The words "strategic" and "critical" were often loosely used as interchangeable in discussions of materials, but the Army and Navy Munitions Board in the prewar years defined the former as "those materials essential to the national defense for the supply of which in war, dependence must be placed in whole, or in part, on sources outside the continental limits of the United States, and for which strict control measures will be necessary." Critical materials were

ceding the outbreak of World War II, but not until the early months of 1941 did it issue specific instructions on conserving certain widely used metals. On 25 February 1941 the Under Secretary of War wrote to the chiefs of all the supply arms and services calling their attention to the need for conserving zinc, and during the next three months he issued similar memoranda on conserving aluminum, nickel, and tungsten. During this period the Office of Production Management, created in January 1941 and later replaced by the War Production Board, also took an interest in the matter and established a conservation section to promote the adoption by industry and government of measures to conserve scarce materials. Shortly after the President's declaration of a state of unlimited national emergency on 27 May 1941, the Under Secretary of War established a conservation section within his office headed by an Ordnance officer, Maj. Norris G. Kenny, and issued a directive to all the supply arms and services outlining the War Department conservation policy.[7]

Principles of the Conservation Program

Long before these steps were taken the Ordnance Department, on its own initiative, had organized a conservation section and had established the basic principles of its conservation program. In October 1940, as the multibillion-dollar defense production program was getting under way, Maj. John H. Frye, an industrial metallurgist in civilian life, was assigned to the staff of General Barnes to promote effective utilization of materials in Ordnance production.[8] Major Frye was soon joined by other officers and civilian specialists and during the early months of 1941 this small group initiated studies leading to the revision of many specifications for the purpose of conserving critical material. In February 1942 conservation sections were established in each operating branch of the Industrial Service, with over-all co-ordination of their efforts centered in Major Frye's section.[9]

The Ordnance conservation effort was born of necessity, and was intensely practical in nature. From its beginning in late 1940, the program was geared to the constant fluctuations in the supplies of a wide range of essential materials, and was designed to keep war production going in spite of shortages. When faced with inadequate supplies of various materials needed for the manufacture of munitions, Ordnance adopted the policy of economizing wherever possible to make its limited allocations of critical materials cover all essential requirements. It was recognized that too much devoted to one use would inevitably mean too little available for something else. "We were not saving materials just for the sake of saving them," Colonel Frye once remarked. "We were saving critical materials on items where they were not needed so we would have enough for other items where these materials were needed."[10]

Perhaps the most important principle underlying the Ordnance conservation activities in World War II was that substitu-

those that were expected to pose similar but less serious procurement problems. See statement by Col. Harry K. Rutherford, OASW, in *Hearings Before the Committee on Military Affairs,* HR, 76th Cong, 1st Sess, pp. 108ff.

[7] Memo, OUSW for Chiefs of Supply Arms and Services, 11 Jun 41, sub: Conservation of Certain . . . Materials, ASF Purchases Div 400.8, DRB AGO.

[8] (1) Hist of Materials Branch, Pt. II, OHF. (2) Interv with Col Frye, 18 Jul 51.

[9] Ord Office Memo 589, 12 Feb 42, OHF.

[10] Interv with Col Frye, 18 Jul 51.

tions were to be made only after a careful engineering analysis of each affected item of equipment. No attempt was made to introduce sweeping changes without taking into consideration the military functions of each item, and the Ordnance Department resisted efforts by higher headquarters to impose such changes. "It can readily be appreciated," General Barnes once wrote, "that mandatory edicts or wholesale substitutions are inconsistent with sound engineering design. Most war material was designed in times of plentiful materials. To change these designs now, it is necessary that the service functions and the nature of stresses involved be considered for each part." [11]

In this process of studying equipment with an eye to substituting less critical materials, Ordnance engineers were, of course, required to maintain unimpaired the military characteristics of each item. Conservation was not to be practiced at the cost of lowered efficiency, except in cases of dire necessity. The term "downgrading" was sometimes used to describe the substitution process, but it was not a fairly descriptive term. The purpose of the substitution was to eliminate waste caused by improper use of scarce materials; it was not a matter of lowering the quality of any item by making it of inferior material. When, to cite one simple example, the trigger guard of the .30-caliber M1 rifle was changed from chrome-vanadium steel to molybdenum steel, the rifle continued to be just as good as it ever was. Molybdenum steel provided all the strength required in a trigger guard; nothing was to be gained by making the guard any stronger, and critical materials were wasted when chromium and vanadium were used to gain unnecessary added strength.

Another guiding principle of Ordnance conservation activities was co-operation with industry. At virtually every step in the process, industrial specialists contributed to the solution of difficult problems. Hundreds of companies working on Ordnance contracts developed new designs or improved production methods to save labor, machine-tool time, and critical materials. Materials-saving suggestions from contractors and their employees were solicited by the Ordnance Department, particularly in the latter half of 1942, through publication of promotional literature that described the need for conservation and listed specific examples of design changes already adopted to save time and materials. [12]

In a more orderly manner, the resources of large sections of American industry were put at the disposal of the Ordnance Department through its day-by-day co-operation with trade associations and engineering societies. Through these organizations Ordnance was able to tap the best engineering talent in the country to aid in solving its problems. When, for example, need arose for developing a special kind of steel, members of the American Iron and Steel Institute were called upon for help; when the problem concerned trucks or combat vehicles, the Society of Automotive Engineers came to the rescue; when it concerned plastics, rubber, die-casting, metal-stamping, phenolic finishes, or any other

[11] Memo, Gen Barnes for Mr. Glancy, OUSW, 28 Feb 42, sub: Conservation . . . Materials, OO 400/4949, DRB AGO.

[12] The first pamphlet of this kind was "Tremendous Trifles," published by the Ordnance Department in August 1942. It was followed by two similar publications, "Metalurgency" in October 1942 and "Battlenecks" in January 1943. Copies are in History of Production Service Branch, OHF. One of the most energetic promoters of this suggestion program was Mr. George E. Whitlock, a prominent industrialist who received the first civilian award from the Army for his conservation efforts.

major material or industrial process, the appropriate industry association lent aid.

When Ordnance made its first monthly report to the newly formed conservation unit in the Office of the Under Secretary of War in August 1941, only four materials were separately reported on: silk, aluminum, chlorine, and zinc.[13] The report stated that Ordnance had taken steps to conserve silk by experimentally replacing it with cotton or rayon in powder bags, to conserve chlorine by changing the bleaching specifications for certain types of paper, and to conserve zinc by using porcelain-coated roofing and siding sheets in place of galvanized sheets and terne (lead-tin alloy) sheets. With aluminum, efforts were being made to substitute other materials wherever possible, and an investigation was under way to determine whether primary aluminum could be saved by manufacturing some items of secondary aluminum by using the die-casting process. In addition to these specific steps, the report declared that Frankford Arsenal had recently issued a hundred-page booklet entitled "Materials Specifications Handbook for Use of Design Engineers of Ordnance Equipment in Selecting Emergency Substitute Materials."[14]

Although it did not mention all the conservation activities that were under discussion or in progress at the time, the report clearly indicated that the Ordnance conservation program was just getting under way in August 1941.[15] A great deal of uncertainty was still in the air, both as to future production goals and as to the need for drastic conservation measures. Shortages had not yet become acute and the nation was still at peace. Plans for a huge munitions production program had been formulated, but everything was still on a more or less tentative basis.

With the attack on Pearl Harbor the whole situation changed overnight. There was uncertainty for a long time as to the precise requirements of the armed forces and as to national production goals, but everyone knew in December 1941 that war production would soon shift into high gear and that demands for critical materials would reach hitherto unheard-of proportions. The outbreak of war made the need for conservation of materials not only necessary but urgent, particularly for the Ordnance Department and its contractors.

The Ordnance conservation program encompassed an almost infinite variety of materials and manufacturing processes. In January 1940 the Army and Navy Munitions Board approved a list of fourteen strategic materials and fifteen critical materials, nearly all of them used in greater or less degree in the production or storage of munitions.[16] But the bulk of the Ordnance conservation effort was concentrated on four materials: alloy steel, copper, aluminum, and rubber. As efforts to conserve each of these materials were made more or less independently, although concurrently, they are here discussed separately.[17]

[13] Memo, CofOrd for Planning Br, OUSW, 11 Aug 41, sub: Conservation of Strategic Materials, OO 400/2221, DRB AGO. This memo was signed by Major Frye and Maj. W. P. Rawles, who were jointly responsible for maintaining liaison with the OUSW on conservation.

[14] This publication was also mentioned in the annual report for 1941 of the Assistant Chief of Industrial Services, Research and Engr Br, pp. 35-36, OHF.

[15] In comparison, see Conservation of Materials, the 165-page report of 15 June 1942, cited in footnote 1.

[16] The Strategic and Critical Materials, Army and Navy Munitions Board, March 1940, ASF Requirements and Production Div G-1927, DRB AGO.

[17] Much detailed information on the various conservation measures adopted by Ordnance is contained

291064 O—55——32

Steel and Its Alloys

During World War II no metal was more widely used by the Ordnance Department than steel. Literally hundreds of items ranging from small bullet cores to large bombs, heavy guns, trucks, and tanks were made primarily of steel. During 1942 and 1943 Ordnance used steel at the rate of more than one million ingot tons a month and took from 50 to 65 percent of all steel allotted to the Army. A conservative estimate of the total quantity of steel used for Ordnance production between 1940 and 1945 is 50 million tons.

Fortunately, the steel industry was one of the largest and most highly developed economic enterprises in the United States at the beginning of World War II and was able to supply the huge quantities needed for war production. In 1940 American companies produced over 65 million ingot tons of steel and productive capacity rose rapidly until by 1944 nearly 90 million ingot tons were produced, more than three times the annual German output. The Ordnance program was never seriously hampered by lack of steel, although occasional difficulties arose from faulty distribution. In 1942–43 sufficient steel was available to permit manufacture of steel cartridge cases when the shortage of brass became acute, the production of steel tank tracks to conserve rubber, and adoption of steel ammunition boxes when other materials proved unsatisfactory. As far as Ordnance was concerned, the pinch came only in certain types of steel for which the demand in war greatly exceeded normal peacetime production. These types possessed qualities of hardness, elasticity, toughness, or ease of fabrication that made them particularly valuable in the manufacture of munitions. Armor plate, for example, had to be hard enough to stop enemy projectiles; armor-piercing ammunition had to be even harder to penetrate enemy armor. The pins that held a tank track together had to have long-wearing qualities, while the steel used in truck cabs and fenders had to be soft and pliable enough to be formed between dies.

Long before World War II, metallurgists had succeeded in producing steels with these characteristics, but only by making liberal use of ferroalloys. After Pearl Harbor, and to some extent even before that date, this practice was threatened by a shortage of both alloys and electric-furnace capacity. At the time that military requirements were skyrocketing, the United States steel industry found itself cut off from most of its foreign sources of tungsten, chromium, vanadium, manganese, and other ferroalloys.[18] Even with the more accessible metals such as nickel and molybdenum the demand for a time greatly exceeded the capacity of existing productive facilities. To meet war production schedules under these circumstances, Ordnance and industry introduced a rigid conservation program guided by three fundamental principles: substitution of other materials for alloy steel; improvement of manufacturing processes to reduce waste; and more widespread use of low-alloy steels.

Even with plain carbon steel, which contained no scarce alloys and was relatively abundant, Ordnance engineers endeav-

in two sources: Conservation of Materials, DRB AGO, and Quarterly Review of Materials and Conservation Progress, prepared by the Materials Branch of the Technical Division, OCO (hereafter referred to as Quarterly Review), DRB AGO.

[18] For a detailed report on supplies of ferroalloys early in the war, see memo, USW for CofOrd, 19 Feb 42, sub: Conservation of Ferro-Alloy Metals, OO 470.1/8, DRB AGO.

CHART 10—PERCENT DISTRIBUTION OF STEEL USED, BY ARMY AGENCY: 3D QUARTER, 1942 AND 1943*

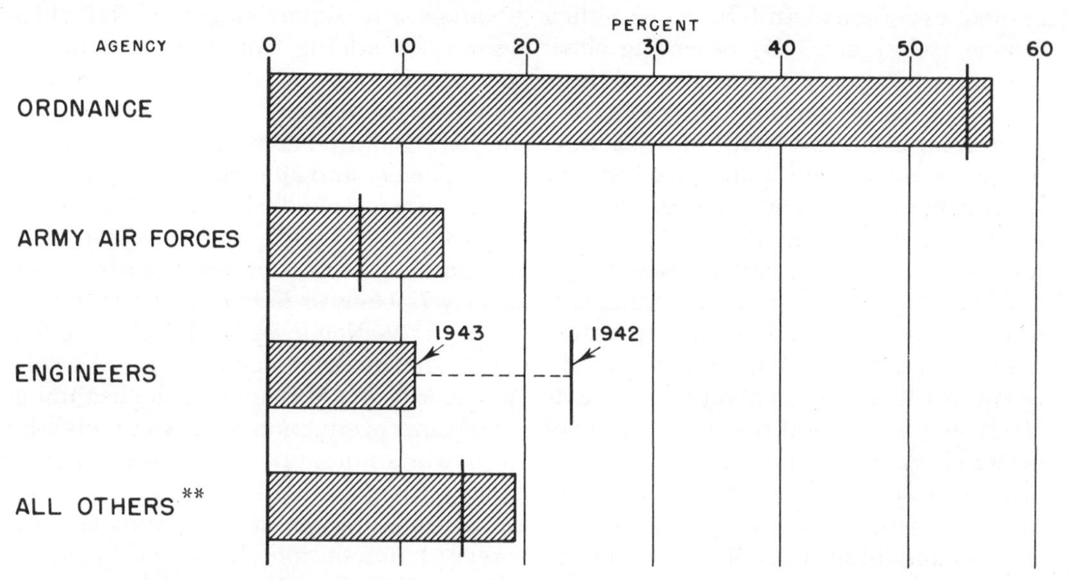

*Total Army monthly average use in 3d Quarter of 1943 was 1,834,000 ingot tons: 1942 was 1,930,000 ingot tons.
**Transportation, Quartermaster, and other Army agencies.
Source: Quarterly Review (December 1943), Charts 3–A and 3–B, DRB AGO.

ored to avoid waste, using equally satisfactory and more readily available substitutes when they could be found. But finding a suitable substitute was not always a simple matter. It involved careful consideration of many factors such as relative cost, ease of manufacture, and effect on production of conversion to the new material. The most outstanding example of this kind of substitution in Ordnance production during World War II was the use of wood to replace steel in truck and trailer bodies. The substitution of wood for steel in the 2½-ton truck reduced the number of pounds of steel per body from 1,700 to 700; in the 1½-ton truck the reduction was from 1,275 to 600 pounds per body. When multiplied by the thousands of trucks and trailers produced for the Army during the war, the savings were estimated at 75,000 tons in 1942 and more than 350,000 tons in 1943. Initiated by the Motor Transport Service of the Quartermaster Corps early in the war period, this project was continued after the MTS was transferred to Ordnance in August 1942 and proved to be the second largest source of steel conservation in the Ordnance production program.[19]

The measure adopted by Ordnance which ranked first as a steel-saver was not a matter of substitution or change in design but a refinement in the manufacturing process. Next to tanks and trucks, Ordnance used more steel for high-explosive shells than for any other class of items, and achieved its largest saving of steel by

[19] Quarterly Review (December, 1943), Chart 5, DRB AGO. See also *Army Ordnance*, XXIII, 135 (1942), 525.

the simple device of decreasing the weight tolerance of shell forgings as contractors gained experience and improved their forging techniques.[20] By observing closer tolerances, industry not only saved thousands of tons of steel in the course of a single year but also saved countless man-hours and machine-hours because the forgings required less machining.[21] Similar savings were made in hundreds of other instances. In the Birmingham District, for example, the 155-mm. shell-lifting plug was redesigned as a hollow cup rather than a solid block. The change cut the weight of the plug from about 28 ounces to 10. It saved over 300 tons of steel in the production of one million plugs and at the same time eliminated shrinks from the castings. With the 81-mm. mortar shell, large savings of steel resulted from a combination of a change in design and an improved method of fabrication. Instead of forming the hollow shell by machining from a solid forging, two drawn steel sections were welded together. The result was a saving on 1943 procurement of 6,000 tons of steel and 750,000 machine-hours.[22]

No matter what steps were taken, however, there was simply no substitute for steel in the great majority of Ordnance items. Scattered marginal savings were possible in all classes of munitions, but there could be no wholesale substitution of any other material. As a result, on a percentage basis the over-all conservation of steel by Ordnance was small—less than 5 percent of the computed requirement of 14 million tons for the year 1943. But that 5 percent amounted to 622,000 tons, roughly equal to the weight of finished steel in 13,000 medium tanks. During 1942, before steel conservation measures had become fully effective, the saving amounted to 96,000 tons.[23]

More important than the over-all saving of plain carbon steel was the saving of strategic alloys, particularly nickel, chromium, vanadium, tungsten, and molybdenum. Here the Ordnance Department made an impressive record. A comparison of 1943 requirements for nickel as computed before and after conservation measures were applied shows a drop from 40,000 tons to 14,000 tons; with vanadium the same comparison shows a drop from nearly 750 tons to 250 tons; with molybdenum a reduction from 10,500 tons to 8,000 tons. The saving of molybdenum was comparatively small because, at the beginning of the war production program, molybdenum was abundant and was freely used as a substitute for other ferroalloys. It was not until the summer of 1942 that this increased use of molybdenum caused a shortage for a few months and brought the need for conservation measures.[24]

Ordnance had two primary uses for tungsten—ammunition, and tool and die steels. As early as spring 1941 the arsenals were directed to reduce their use of tungsten in tools and dies wherever possible, but the savings in this area were necessarily limited.[25] It was in production of armor-piercing small arms bullet cores, and in certain types of artillery ammunition, that the greatest savings were made. At the beginning of the defense period an

[20] Conservation of Materials, pp. 131–32, DRB AGO. See also Barnes Diary, 28 Apr 42, OHF.

[21] Quarterly Review (December, 1943), Chart 5-B, DRB AGO.

[22] For these and many other examples, see "Tremendous Trifles," "Metalurgency," and "Battlenecks," Hist of Production Serv Br, OHF.

[23] Quarterly Review (December, 1943), Chart 5-A, DRB AGO.

[24] *Ibid.*, Charts 8, 9, and 10.

[25] Ltr, Barnes to Arsenal Commanders, 24 Apr 41, sub: Conservation of Tungsten, copy in Conservation of Materials, App. 24, DRB AGO.

electric-furnace steel known as WD 74100, containing up to 4 percent tungsten, was used for all armor-piercing small arms cores, although Frankford Arsenal and Watertown Arsenal had experimented with many other types of steel during the 1920's and 1930's and had found some to be nearly as good as the tungsten steel.[26] As the volume of small arms production rose steadily in 1940 and early 1941 and tungsten became extremely scarce, Ordnance switched from tungsten steel to manganese-molybdenum steel for armor-piercing cores. This effected an estimated saving of over 7,500 tons of tungsten in 1942–43 production.[27] When electric-furnace steel-making capacity became critical, Ordnance engineers discovered they could make satisfactory cores for both .30-caliber and .50-caliber ammunition from open-hearth manganese-molybdenum steel. Later, acceptable .30-caliber cores were made from high-grade carbon steel without the addition of any alloys at all. As a result of these efforts, satisfactory bullet cores were produced without using either critical alloys or electric-furnace capacity—and, in the process, the rate of production increased and the cost per unit decreased.[28]

Among the military agencies, Ordnance took the lead in conserving steel and its alloys, but the development of low-alloy steels was a broad national effort in which the Department was but one keenly interested participant.[29] The American Iron and Steel Institute, the War Production Board, and many other agencies, both public and private, co-operated in producing, testing, and cataloguing many types of steels using minimum quantities of scarce alloys, the so-called National Emergency (NE) steels. These steels not only used less of the alloying elements but were compounded with alloy scrap to save virgin alloy metals. Ordnance adopted and used these lower-alloy steels in thousands of items and parts of items without sacrificing performance capabilities. On a single piece of equipment the saving brought by the substitution was often small, but when multiplied by millions of items it added up to substantial quantities of scarce material. When, for example, a National Emergency steel was substituted for a chrome-vanadium steel in the operating rod handle of the M1 rifle, the saving in the course of a year amounted to several tons of chromium and vanadium on this one part alone. In the 90-mm. antiaircraft gun several parts were made of low-alloy NE steels and others of plain carbon steel with an estimated saving during 1943 of 150 tons of critical nickel. In breechblocks for the 75-mm. and 76-mm. guns the quantity of nickel required per thousand blocks was reduced from 3,500 pounds to 700 pounds, and proportionate reductions were made in recoil, recuperator, and counterrecoil cylinders. In the production of .50-caliber and .30-caliber machine guns, large savings resulted from the use of pearlitic malleable iron castings.[30] The ease with which this type of malleable iron could be fabricated made it particularly valuable for machine gun production and led to its substitution for alloy

[26] Ltr, CO Watertown Arsenal to CofOrd, 4 Nov 40, OO 470.1/130, DRB AGO.

[27] Conservation of Materials, p. 145, DRB AGO.

[28] Ord Materials Br, Summary of War Department's Metallurgical Research and Development during World War II, p. 29, OHF. See also Conservation of Materials, p. 145, DRB AGO.

[29] See Col. John H. Frye, "Development and Application of Military and Special Steels for Ordnance Purposes," a paper read before the General Meeting of the American Iron and Steel Institute, 25 May 44, OHF.

[30] Conservation of Materials, pp. 125–26, DRB AGO.

steel in the trunnion blocks and in the side, top, and bottom plates of the caliber .30 and caliber .50. Use of castings in place of machined steel forgings for each heavy-barrel .50-caliber weapon saved, in weight of material machined off, 37 pounds as well as considerable manpower and machine-tool time, both of which were critical.[31]

Important as such savings were, however, the greatest conservation of steel alloys was not made in small arms or artillery items but in tanks, trucks, and artillery ammunition. Ordnance used more steel of all kinds for tanks and trucks than for any other single purpose — approximately 7,000,000 tons during 1943. For artillery ammunition it consumed over 4,000,000 tons during that year as compared with less than 1,000,000 tons for artillery and approximately 1,550,000 for small arms.[32]

In tank production, the greatest savings of strategic metals were made by using low-alloy armor plate. At the start of the World War II production program it was not customary for the Ordnance Department to specify the chemical composition of the armor plate it purchased, nor to prescribe the processing methods used by manufacturers. The only requirement was one of performance. Each armor producer used a steel-making formula that differed in some respects from those used by other armor producers. But all the compositions had one characteristic in common: all were rich in nickel, chromium, and vanadium, some containing as much as 5 percent nickel.[33] "The main consideration," wrote the Ordnance Materials Branch, "was to produce good armor plate without regard to cost or strategic alloys." [34]

In 1941, when the Tank and Combat Vehicle Division of Ordnance surveyed the formulas used by manufacturers of armor plate and compared the quantities of ferroalloys required for each tank with the existing schedules for tank production, it became apparent at once that sufficient quantities of alloys would not be available to produce tanks with such steel. The same survey supported the idea that rather large reductions in the alloy content of armor plate could be made without lowering the ballistic quality. Shortly after Pearl Harbor, when the shortage of steel alloys became acute, Ordnance directed its armor producers to keep their use of alloys below certain percentages. At the same time, because there were not enough facilities to produce rolled armor in the enormous quantities needed for the tank program, Ordnance turned to the use of cast-steel armor. Thousands of ballistic tests proved that cast-steel armor was more than 90 percent as efficient as rolled armor, and that it had distinct advantages when the design called for curved surfaces. Acceptable cast armor was made without any vanadium and with only .5 percent nickel and .5 percent chromium.[35] Changes in armor composition brought the need for developing new welding materials and techniques, since low-alloy armor could not be successfully welded by the same

[31] (1) Small Arms Div Ind Serv, Hist of U.S. Machine Guns, Caliber .30 and .50, pp. 139–44, OHF. (2) Monthly Rpts of Maj Frye to Chief of Serv Br, Tech Div, OO 319.1, DRB AGO.

[32] Quarterly Review (December, 1943), Chart 5-B, DRB AGO.

[33] Conservation of Materials, p. 134, DRB AGO.

[34] Ord Materials Br, Summary of the War Department's Metallurgical Research and Development during World War II, p. 20, OHF. For a discussion of armor and its production, see Armor Plate, Development and Production, 1940–45, OHF.

[35] (1) Conservation of Materials, pp. 134–35, DRB AGO. (2) Ord Materials Br, Summary of the War Department's Metallurgical Research and Development during World War II, pp. 19–22, OHF. (3) Armor Plate, Development and Production, 1940–45, OHF.

CHART 11—STEEL ALLOYS REQUIRED PER MEDIUM TANK (M4) WITH AND WITHOUT CONSERVATION MEASURES

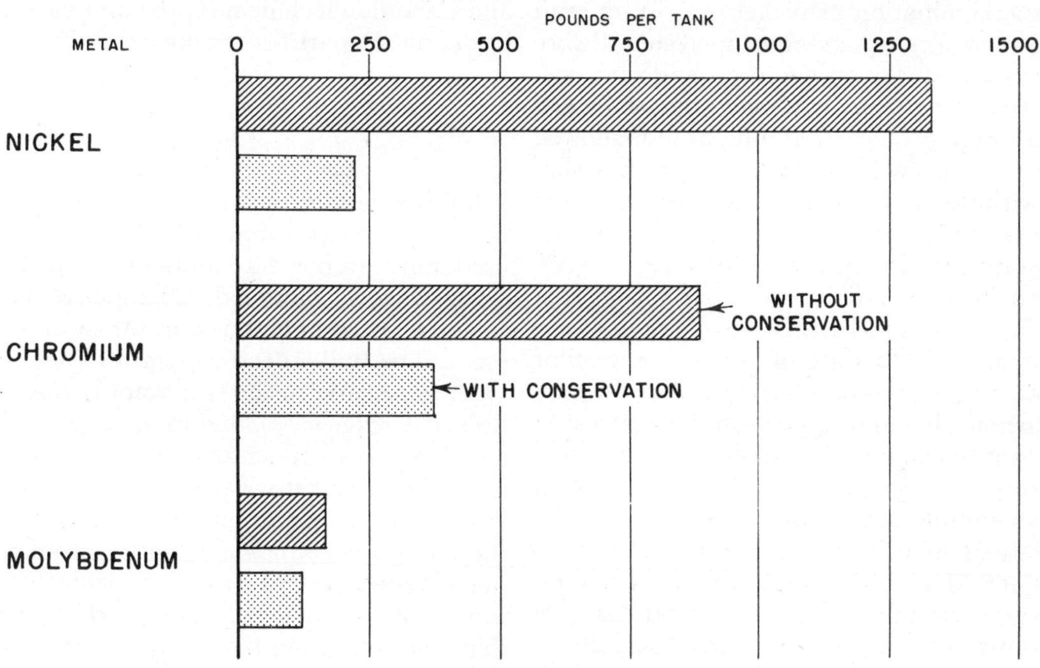

Source: Quarterly Review (December 1943), Chart 34, DRB AGO.

methods used with high-alloy armor.[36]

In analyzing the automotive components of tanks—the transmissions and differentials as distinguished from armor plate and guns—the Society of Automotive Engineers War Engineering Board gave invaluable assistance. This board was composed of top-flight engineers from all the leading automobile companies, and its purpose was to make available to the Army, without cost and with a minimum of red tape, the best technical advice on automotive engineering. Among scores of projects undertaken by this board for the Ordnance Department was one designed to reduce the quantities of critical materials used in tanks. In September 1942 the War Engineering Board appointed four subcommittees to study conservation of materials in the tank—one committee each for track, suspension, transmission and final drive, and miscellaneous (turret, gun mount, traversing and elevating mechanism).[37] Each committee determined the maximum stress to which each part would be subjected while in use and recommended that it be made of steel just strong enough to do the job required of it. In 1943 alone, it was estimated that the work of these committees on the M4 tank resulted in the saving of 3,500 tons of nickel, 1,000 tons of chromium, and 500 tons of molybdenum.[38]

[36] Arsenal Laboratory Research Record, Ch. IX, Welding, OHF.

[37] Unconfirmed Min of Mtg of Chairman's Steel Committee of SAE War Engineering Board at the Rackham Building in Detroit, 29 Sep 42, OHF.

[38] Ltr, Norman G. Shidle, Exec Ed of *The SAE Journal,* to Col Frye, 3 Aug 43, OHF.

In artillery ammunition, one of the earliest and largest savings resulted from the elimination of nickel in 75-mm. and 3-inch armor-piercing-capped shot. Before the war, shell manufacturers had used steel containing a high percentage of nickel, averaging 3.5 percent, but, as tests showed that nickel was not needed to produce shot with the required ballistic properties, the use of nickel steel in shot bodies was discontinued in April and May 1942.[39] According to estimates, during the next eighteen months this one change saved nearly 4,000 tons of nickel. A similar change was made in the smaller 37-mm. armor-piercing-capped shot bodies; a steel containing up to 4 percent tungsten was replaced by a chrome-molybdenum steel when tungsten became very scarce. In the latter half of 1942 the Ammunition Branch carried on an important project to conserve molybdenum in the production of bomb bodies. Ordnance engineers determined that, by using heat treatment, it was possible to make satisfactory bomb bodies from plain carbon steel, and after the first of May 1943 all bomb steel was of this type. The saving of molybdenum during 1943 exceeded 1,000 tons.[40]

The success of Ordnance efforts to conserve ferroalloys was officially recognized in the spring of 1943 by the commanding general of the Army Service Forces. In response to a memorandum from General Campbell outlining some of the achievements of the Department in conserving steel alloys, and reporting arrangements that had been made to place British and Canadian technical representatives on various Ordnance conservation committees, General Somervell wrote: "Congratulations on the splendid results achieved in conservation of critical materials by the Ordnance Department as outlined in your memorandum. . . . You are to be commended for extending these conservation activities to our Allies by placing British and Canadian technical representatives on Ordnance Department committees." [41]

Copper and Its Alloys

Of the nonferrous metals, Ordnance used more copper than anything else. It used more copper than all the other technical services combined, taking between 75 and 85 percent of the entire Army allotment. The bulk of the copper allotted to Ordnance early in the war went to make brass cartridge cases, and to make gilding metal, another copper-zinc alloy, for small arms bullet jackets. Early in 1942, as requirements for ammunition mounted into the billions of rounds, Ordnance production schedules called for the use of 800,000 tons of copper in 1942, and nearly twice that amount during 1943.

During the 1920's and 1930's copper and zinc had not been considered by the War Department as strategic materials that might be unavailable in time of war.[42] It was recognized that tremendous quantities of copper would be required for ammunition, naval vessels, and electrical equipment, but, as the United States was a leading producer of copper and South

[39] Conservation of Materials, pp. 149–50, DRB AGO. Copies of pertinent directives are in the appendix of this work.

[40] Memo, Col Frye for Chief of Serv Br, Tech Div, 10 Apr 43, sub: Report on Conservation, OO 319.1, DRB AGO.

[41] (1) Memo, CG SOS for CofOrd, 5 Mar 43, sub: Conservation of Critical Ferro-Alloys, OO 470.1/294, DRB AGO. (2) Memo, CofOrd for CG SOS, 6 Feb 43, sub: Conservation of Critical Ferro-Alloys, OO 400.12/3552, DRB AGO. Copies of both memos in Barnes file, OHF.

[42] See historical tabulation of strategic materials lists, Capt. G. K. Heiss, "Why a Raw Material Reserve?" *Army Ordnance*, XX, 115 (1939), 32.

CHART 12—PERCENT DISTRIBUTION OF COPPER USED, BY ARMY AGENCY: 4TH QUARTER, 1943*

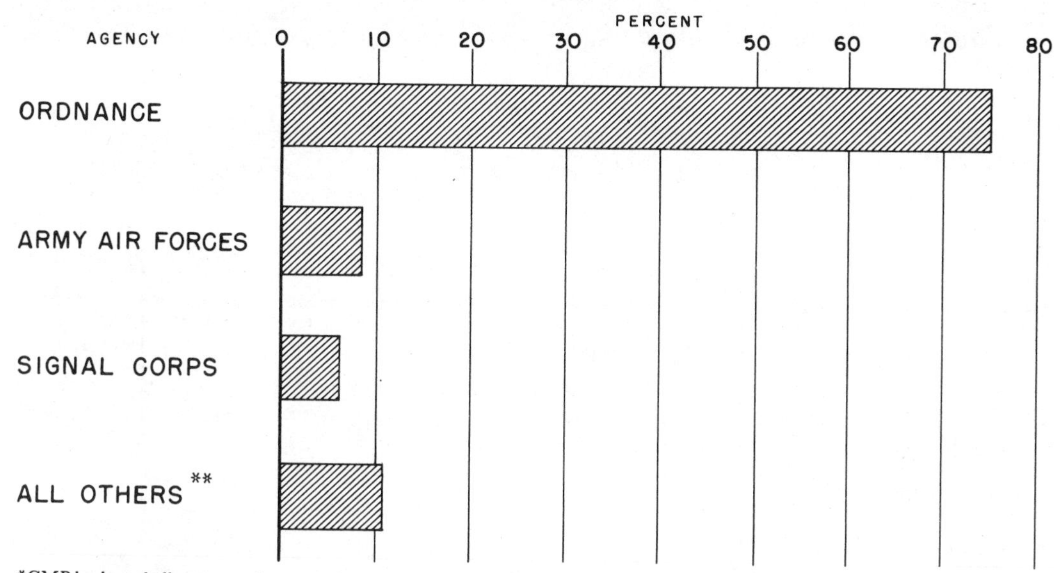

*CMP budgeted allotment to Army was for a monthly average use of 163,721 tons.
**Transportation, Quartermaster, and other Army Agencies.
Source: Quarterly Review (December 1943), Chart 18–B, DRB AGO.

America was a major foreign source of supply and one from which the United States was not likely to be cut off in time of war, the possibility of a crippling shortage seemed remote.[43] Even as late as January 1940 copper and zinc were not included on either the strategic or critical lists prepared by the Army and Navy Munitions Board, but after adoption of a multibillion-dollar munitions production program in the summer of 1940 the picture began to change. In the spring of 1941, with lend-lease requirements added to the needs of United States forces, Ordnance was informed that zinc was henceforth to be used only when no satisfactory substitute could be found, and during the summer the threat of an eventual copper shortage had to be considered.

The Ordnance program to conserve copper during World War II covered a wide front and involved innumerable substitutions and design changes. Some netted large savings while others brought only small reductions in requirements, but they all helped in some measure to stretch the available supply. A booster for high-explosive shells, for example, was converted from brass bar stock to a steel stamping with estimated savings of 83,000 tons of brass in 1943 production. Changing a gasoline tank cap and strainer from a machined brass casting to a low-carbon steel stamping for certain types of vehicles saved several hundred tons of brass, and substitution of steel for copper in radiators of trucks netted even greater savings.[44]

[43] Memo, SW for Secy Interior, 15 Feb 35, ASF Resources and Production Div 470.1/129.6, DRB AGO.

[44] (1) "Tremendous Trifles," OHF. (2) Quarterly Review (December, 1943), DRB AGO. (3) Hist of Development Br, OCO–D, IV, OHF.

CHART 13—PERCENT DISTRIBUTION OF COPPER USED BY ORDNANCE DEPARTMENT, BY TYPE OF MATÉRIEL: 4TH QUARTER, 1943*

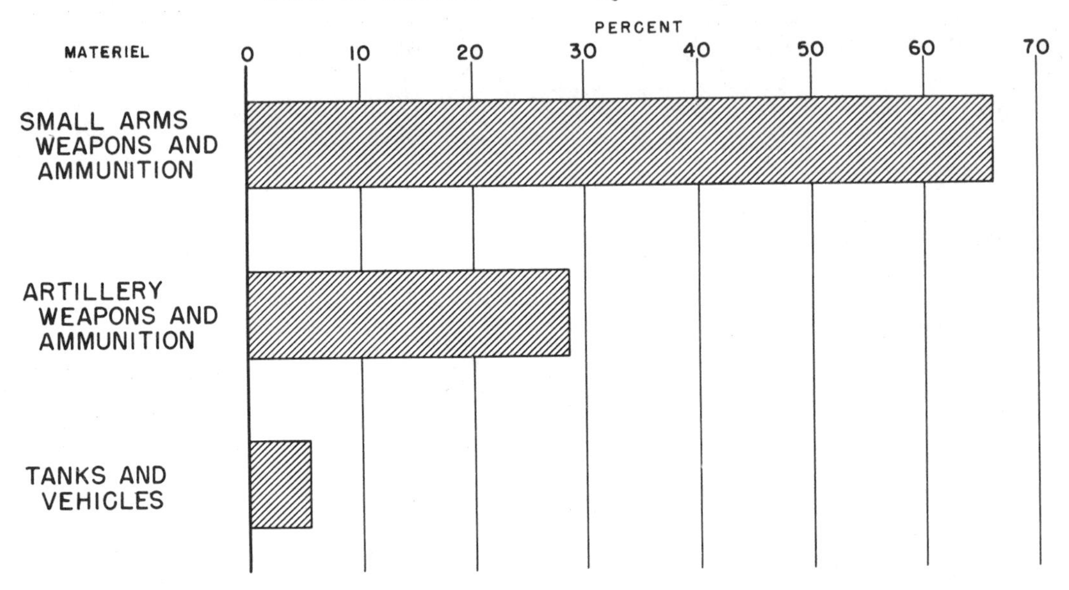

*CMP budgeted allotment to Ordnance Department was for a monthly average of 122,627 tons.

Source: Quarterly Review (December 1943), Chart 19–B, DRB AGO.

Steel Cartridge Cases

The Ordnance Department's most far-reaching effort to conserve copper was the program to manufacture cartridge cases of steel instead of brass. Before 1940 cartridge cases had been made almost exclusively of brass because only brass possessed the peculiar physical characteristics required. The wall of the case, for example, must be elastic enough to expand under pressure and then contract instantly when the pressure is released. The expansion is necessary to provide obturation during firing, that is, a tight seal against the breech wall of the weapon to prevent any gases from being driven back into the breech. After firing, the empty case must snap back to its original size so that it may be readily ejected from the gun. Because of the high pressures generated within the case when the powder ignites, the case must have great tensile strength at the head end, but the mouth must be annealed to much lesser strength to permit the necessary expansion. Cartridge cases made of brass not only met these exacting requirements but also possessed other advantages. They did not rust when exposed to the elements. After firing, brass artillery cases could be cleaned and used over and over again. Brass cases were relatively easy to manufacture and a well-established brass industry stood ready to supply the essential alloy stock for the purpose.[45]

The manufacture of steel cases was not

[45] For a description of manufacturing methods and requirements, see Charles O. Herb, "Steel Cartridge Cases from a Chase Brass Plant," *Machinery*, Vol. 50, No. 2 (October, 1943).

altogether new in 1941, but it was nearly so. A few steel cases for artillery ammunition had been made in the United States and Germany during World War I, but the results had not been altogether satisfactory in either country.[46] Because of the abundant supplies of copper and zinc available to the United States, and the many difficulties inherent in the use of steel cases, little attention was paid to the matter during the years between the wars. In 1939 and 1940 a few cases made of seamless steel tubing were submitted to the Ordnance Department by commercial producers for test but none proved satisfactory. As a result, when Ordnance engineers and representatives of industry were suddenly faced in 1941 with the problem of manufacturing steel cases they had to begin virtually from scratch.

The problems involved seemed at first to be insurmountable. It was, of course, essential that the steel case be just as effective as the brass. No substitution that impaired the performance of ammunition in combat could even be considered. Further, the steel case had to be perfectly interchangeable with the brass case in order to simplify its use on the battlefield. To achieve these results, it was necessary to develop a new type of steel with the elasticity required of cartridge cases—and do it without using appreciable quantities of critical alloying elements or scarce heat-treating equipment. New techniques for deep drawing steel had to be devised and tested, and a protective coating had to be developed for application to the finished case to prevent corrosion. Following the solution of these and other design problems it was necessary to devise manufacturing processes that would make the substitution of steel for brass feasible in terms of cost, machine tools, and manpower, and also in terms of volume production running into millions of rounds per month. Finally, it was highly desirable, if not actually mandatory, that the manufacturing techniques be of such a nature that the facilities already engaged in the manufacture of brass cases could be used, with a minimum of readjustment, to produce steel cases.[47]

Artillery Cases

Since the artillery cases appeared to raise fewer problems than did small arms cases, they were attempted first. After a period of unsuccessful experimentation with low-carbon steel, small quantities of acceptable artillery cases were produced by the fall of 1941 from heat-treated mild alloys.[48] Experimentation was then directed toward the production of cases from medium-carbon steel with only manganese added, and by January 1942 General Barnes was able to report to Mr. William S. Knudsen, cochairman of OPM, that the results of experimental work done up to that time indicated that artillery cases of all sizes from 20-mm. through 105-mm. could be made of steel, at least in small quantities.[49] When this report came to the

[46] Ord Materials Br, Summary of the War Department's Metallurgical Research and Development during World War II, pp. 29–30, OHF. For data on German conservation of copper in ammunition see report, Item 28, of Combined Intelligence Objectives Subcommittee, G–2 Div, SHAEF, sub: Reich Ministry of Armament and War Production, file XXVI–13, Ord Tech Intel files.

[47] (1) See CIOS rpt cited n. 46. (2) R&D Serv, Cartridge Case Development Project, OHF.

[48] See reports from Frankford Arsenal laboratory listed in R&D Serv, Cartridge Case Development Project, OHF.

[49] Memo, Barnes for Knudsen, 15 Jan 42, ASF Resources and Production Div 470.1/129.6(3), DRB AGO.

attention of the Under Secretary of War, he immediately directed the Chief of Ordnance to make plans for converting production of all artillery ammunition to steel on short notice. He mentioned the growing shortage of copper and cited the fact that the Ordnance ammunition program was at that time taking 86 percent of all copper allotted to the Army.[50]

All during the first half of 1942 Ordnance had to carry on its steel ammunition project under constant pressure to accomplish in a few months what normally would have taken years. Because of the activities of enemy submarines in the Western Hemisphere, the loss of Chilean copper imports was considered a possibility early in 1942; at the same time, the ammunition requirements for the United States armed forces and for the supply of friendly nations reached astronomical proportions. The situation became so critical that not only did Mr. Patterson and Mr. Knudsen take a keen interest in it but Vice President Henry A. Wallace also gave it his personal attention early in April.[51] In May 1942 the chief of the Small Arms Branch of the Industrial Service reported that both the Lake City and the Denver Ordnance Plants were operating with less than one week's supply of brass, and that it appeared probable that both would have to shut down before the end of the month for lack of material.[52] Under these circumstances the development process was streamlined, research and production being telescoped to a remarkable degree.

Because of the urgency of the situation there was a tendency to minimize the many technical difficulties inherent in the production of steel cases and to adopt an overly ambitious conservation program. Work was begun on all sizes of artillery cases from the 20-mm. up through the 105-mm., and in May 1942 a report to the ASF chief of staff stated: "Mass production of all cartridge cases (except 3-inch, 90-mm. and small arms) will be realized during 1942. . . . Steel cases are through the talking stage and are now production items."[53] But more than a year later the chief of the Ordnance Ammunition Branch had to report that, "with the exception of the 20-mm. cases, rejections are still running at rather high rates, indicating that there is still a large amount of development work to be completed before steel cartridge cases will be produced in sufficient quantities to meet the Army Supply Program."[54]

The Ordnance Department did not presume to carry on this project alone but enlisted the aid of private industry, particularly steel producers and steel fabricators. By May 1942 contracts had been let with many different companies for production of 20-mm., 37-mm., 40-mm., 57-mm., 75-mm., and 105-mm. cases, and a Cartridge Case Industry Committee had been formed to serve as a central clearing house of information on the manufacture of steel

[50] Memo, USW for CofOrd, 29 Jan 42, sub: Pilot Plant for Production of Steel Cartridge Cases, ASF Resources and Production Div 470.1/129.6(3), DRB AGO.

[51] (1) Memo, Mr.H. C. Peterson, Special Assistant to USW, for CofOrd, 2 Apr 42, and (2) Gen Wesson's reply, 9 Apr 42, both in OO 470.873/11115, DRB AGO.

[52] Memo, Chief of Small Arms Div for Asst Chief for Production, Ind Serv, 12 May 42, sub: Small Arms Ammunition Production, copy in R&D Serv, Development and Production of Military Small Arms Ammunition, OHF.

[53] Memo, Brig Gen Lucius D. Clay, Deputy CofS for Requirements and Resources, for CofS SOS, 8 May 42, sub: Report on . . . Steel Shell Cases, AG 471.87 (5-8-42) (1), DRB AGO.

[54] Memo, Brig Gen Rosswell E. Hardy, Ammo Br, for Chief of Production Serv Br, 20 Jul 43, sub: Increased Production of Artillery Ammunition Cases, OO 471.873/17788, DRB AGO.

TABLE 13—STEEL CARTRIDGE CASES IN WORLD WAR II

Weapons and Cartridge Case Models Attempted	Standardized	In Production
20-mm. Aircraft guns, M21A1B1 case	substitute	yes
37-mm. Subcaliber guns, MK 1A2B1 case	no	yes
37-mm. Aircraft guns AN–M10, MK III A2B1 case	substitute	yes
37-mm. Tank and AT guns, M 16B1 case	substitute	yes
37-mm. Aircraft AN–M9 guns and AA guns, M 17B1 case	substitute	yes
40-mm. AA guns, M 25B1 case	standard	yes
57-mm. AT guns, M 23A2B1 case	no	yes
57-mm. Recoilless rifles, M 30A1 case	standard	yes
75-mm. Howitzers, M 5A1B1 case	no	yes
75-mm. Field guns, M 18B1 case	substitute	yes
75-mm. Recoilless rifles M 31A1 case	standard	yes
3-inch AA and AT guns, MK II M 2B1 case	standard	yes
90-mm. AA and Tank guns, M 19B1 case	no	no
105-mm. Howitzers, M 14B1 case	substitute	yes
105-mm. M27 Recoilless rifles M32 case	no	no

Source: Ammo Br, Ind Div, OCO, OHF.

cases.[55] This group acted in an advisory capacity to all concerns engaged in cartridge case manufacture and helped solve technical problems as they arose. A similar committee was formed by the producers of the steel used in cartridge cases and another by the manufacturers of the finishes used to prevent corrosion. The members of these committees were representatives of companies that were normally competitors but they unstintingly shared their technical knowledge to advance the production program.[56] As a result of these efforts, thirteen types of steel artillery cases reached the stage of quantity production. (*See Table 13.*) Of this number, ten were given some degree of official acceptance by action of the Ordnance Committee. The cases for the 40-mm. AA gun, the 57-mm. recoilless rifle, the 75-mm. recoilless rifle, and the 3-inch AA and AT gun were accepted as fully standard while the other six were classified as substitute standard.

Small Arms Cases

The development of steel small arms cases was carried on concurrently with the development of steel artillery cases, but, with the exception of one caliber, progressed more slowly.[57] Because of the extremely high pressures generated in small arms cartridges, the substitution of steel for brass posed more difficult problems than it did in artillery cases. At the outset of the project a broad division of labor between

[55] For tabulation of numbers of contracts and quantities of steel cases on order in June 1942, see Conservation of Materials, DRB AGO.

[56] Campbell, *Industry-Ordnance Team,* p. 298. For similar testimony and the names of committee members and participating companies, see Lt. Col. H. R. Turner, "Steel Cartridge Cases," *Army Ordnance Report,* No. 5, 1 July 1944, published by Army Ordnance Association, Washington, D. C.

[57] For a detailed and technical exposition of the steel cartridge case project, see SA & SA Ammo, Book 2, Vol. 2, Ch. 15, OHF. This volume also devotes a chapter to the effort to make aluminum cases.

government and industry was agreed upon: development of commercial types of ammunition, such as shot-gun shells and the .22-caliber, was left largely to the commercial arms manufacturers while Ordnance facilities centered their attention on the .30, .45, and .50-calibers.[58]

Of all the small arms cartridges, the .45-caliber, a short, squat case, proved to be the easiest to convert to steel. Development work at Frankford Arsenal proceeded rapidly during 1941 and early 1942, and by the summer of 1942 the steel case went into production at the Evansville Ordnance Plant.[59] Other plants were soon added and by June 1943 over one billion cases had been produced. After thorough testing by the using arms, as well as by Ordnance, the .45-caliber steel case was accepted as standard in January 1943.[60]

Research on the .30 and .50-caliber cases was carried on at Frankford Arsenal and at four government-owned contractor-operated plants—Milwaukee, in Wisconsin, Lowell in Massachusetts, Denver in Colorado, and Twin Cities in New Brighton, Minnesota. A host of technical problems arose with these calibers. One of the most difficult resulted from the inelasticity of steel, which caused the cases to expand and stick in the chamber after they were fired. A great deal of effort still had to be put into development of a suitable protective finish for the steel cases. Nevertheless, by the spring of 1943 the Ordnance Department reported that .30 and .50-caliber ammunition was "passing from the research stage into the production development stage." [61] Several million .30-caliber steel cases and a quarter of a million .50-caliber cases had been produced, and schedules calling for the manufacture of 150 million rounds of .50-caliber and 210 million rounds of .30-caliber per month during the latter half of the year had been established. Arrangements were being made to submit both calibers to the using arms for test, with the expectation that they would be accepted first for training purposes and then, as improvements were introduced, for unrestricted combat use.[62]

At this stage in the process a sudden shift in plans occurred. In May 1943, at the recommendation of Brig. Gen. James Kirk, chief of the Ordnance Small Arms Branch, the scheduled production of .30 and .50-caliber steel cases was slashed from a total of 360,000,000 per month to 125,000,000. General Kirk reasoned that the new rate of production would be high enough to establish the feasibility of producing small arms ammunition with steel cases but low enough to eliminate the possibility of producing large quantities of ammunition that might, "because of the present state of the art, and lack of standardization, be a more or less complete loss." [63] This decision was the beginning of the end of the production of steel cases, both small arms and artillery, in World War II. A further drop in the production schedule occurred in July and by November 1943 all work on the .30 and .50-caliber steel cases was stopped except for experimental production lines at

[58] Lt. Col. Boone Gross, "Development of Steel Cartridge Case for Small Arms Ammunition," a paper prepared in the spring of 1943, ASF Resources and Production Div 471.87 Cartridge Cases, DRB AGO.

[59] For an informal account of this plant's operations, see W. W. Stout, *Bullets by the Billion* (Detroit, 1946).

[60] OCM 19493, 14 Jan 43.

[61] Gross, "Development of Steel Cartridge Case . . . ," ASF Resources and Production Div 471.87 Cartridge Cases, DRB AGO.

[62] *Ibid.* The .30-caliber carbine case was standardized in October 1945 by OCM 29368.

[63] Min of conference in Howard Bruce's office, 22 May 43, sub: Small Arms Ammunition with Steel Cases, ASF Resources and Production Div 471.87 Cartridge Cases, DRB AGO.

Frankford Arsenal. Three factors prompted this action: inferiority of most steel cases to brass cases, increased availability of copper resulting from greater production by copper mines and effective conservation efforts, and a sharp reduction in over-all requirements for small arms ammunition.[64]

Although a great deal of progress was made in converting cartridge cases from brass to steel, it was never possible to produce enough acceptable steel cases. The ambitious goals established for the steel-case project early in 1942 were not attained. To meet the requirements of the Army Supply Program, Ordnance had to continue the production of brass cases up to the limit of its brass allocation.[65] The value of the steel-case program was that it supplemented, rather than replaced, brass production. In addition, the wartime experience with steel cases led eventually to a fresh attack on the problem, in which Army and Navy co-operated, in the postwar years.[66]

Bullet Jackets

Another major step taken by Ordnance engineers to conserve copper was the substitution of clad steel for gilding metal in small arms bullet jackets. For many years before World War II, the lead or steel core in small arms ammunition was covered with a jacket of gilding metal composed of 90 percent copper and 10 percent zinc. The gilding-metal jacket was needed for two reasons: to provide a soft coat for the bullet core and to give the projectile the desired shape. A bullet hard enough to give good penetration of the target was too hard for the rifling in the bore of the weapon. In flight, a long slender bullet encountered less air resistance and was more stable, but a blunt-nosed bullet gave better penetration of the target. These conflicting requirements were met by forming the bullet core of hard steel shaped to give maximum penetration and then covering it with softer gilding metal shaped to give the best flight characteristics. Any space within the jacket not filled by the steel core was filled with lead alloy, partly for ballistic balance and partly for improved penetration.[67]

In searching for a substitute for gilding metal, Frankford Arsenal had produced steel jackets plated with cupro-nickel as early as 1898, and had tested various types of cupro-nickel-clad steel cases during the 1920's and 1930's, but without much success.[68] In 1941 experiments were made in the use of steel jackets coated with copper and others coated with gilding metal, and Ordnance engineers, working in close co-operation with metallurgists from private industry, soon developed a copper-plated steel jacket for .45-caliber bullets that went into production in the summer of 1942. The base material was a low-carbon steel with a very thin coating of electro-deposited copper on both sides. This copper-plated ammunition was promptly accepted by the using arms, and within a few months all .45-caliber ammunition in pro-

[64] See, for example, the statement in the Quarterly Review: "Copper is now available for all military and essential civilian needs and the probability is that the trend toward increased supply over demand will continue." Quarterly Review (December, 1943), DRB AGO.

[65] Memo, Gen Hardy for Chief of Production Serv Br, 20 Jul 43, sub: Increased Production of Artillery Ammunition Cases, OO 471.873/17788, DRB AGO.

[66] W. F. Stevenson, "Steel Cartridge Cases Advance toward Standardization," *Steel,* Vol. 129, 2 (1951), 72. A typographical error in the chart accompanying this article makes inaccurate the data presented in the lower third of the chart.

[67] For further technical details of this nature, see Hayes, *Elements of Ordnance.*

[68] SA and SA Ammo, Book 2, Ch. 16, OHF.

CHART 14—COPPER REQUIREMENTS FOR ORDNANCE MATÉRIEL: 1943

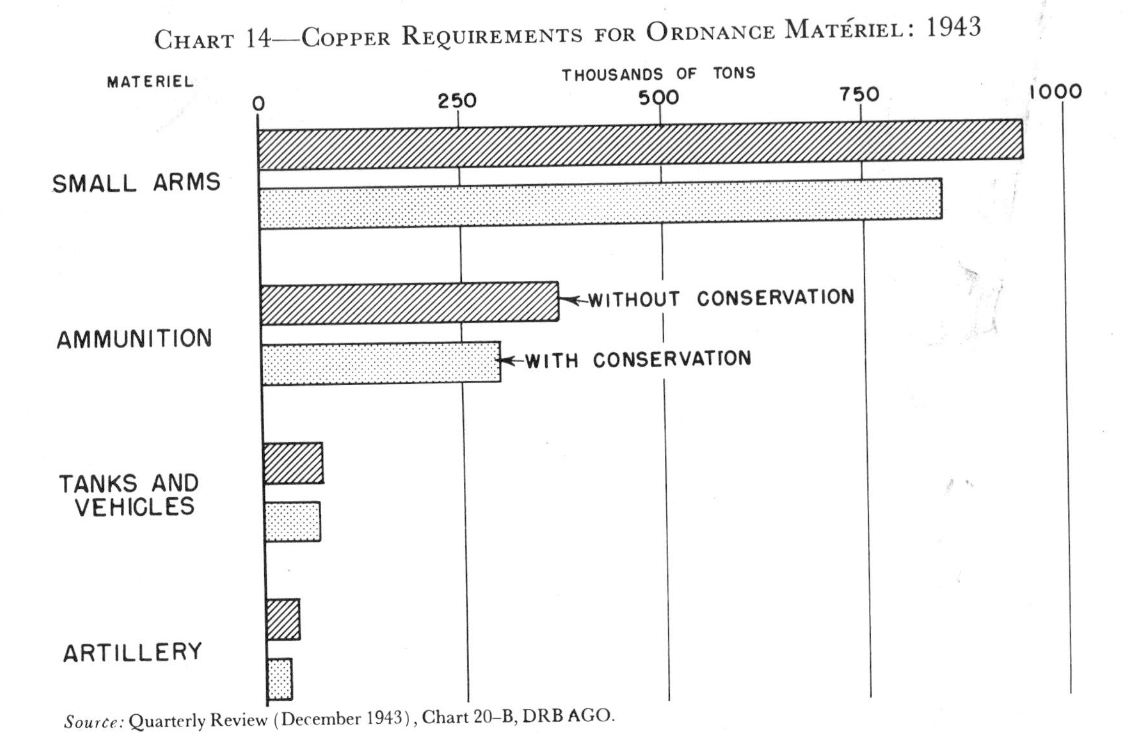

Source: Quarterly Review (December 1943), Chart 20–B, DRB AGO.

duction was copper plated.[69] For .30 and .50-caliber, progress was slower, but a satisfactory steel jacket coated with gilding metal was put into production in the fall of 1942. Both it and the copper-coated jacket could be made with 75 percent less copper than was needed for the solid gilding-metal jacket.

As the accompanying chart indicates, the greatest savings of copper in Ordnance production were made by the Small Arms Branch, which cut its consumption during 1943 by approximately 100,000 tons. This feat was achieved largely by the successful development of steel cartridge cases for .45-caliber ammunition and the conversion to steel or gilding-metal-clad steel for bullet jackets. The saving of copper in the artillery ammunition program was less, approximately 75,000 tons in 1943; the saving of copper in artillery and in tanks and vehicles was small chiefly because these classes of matériel were not large consumers of copper. The success of Ordnance efforts to conserve copper, coupled with increased production by the copper industry, resulted in a marked improvement in the copper supply picture in the fall of 1943. By December the Ordnance Materials Branch was able to report that it was "no longer necessary to use substitute materials for military applications where copper and copper alloys will provide better military characteristics and increase the useful life of materiel." [70]

[69] Memo, CofOrd for SOS, 10 Feb 43, sub: Combined Copper Committee Questionnaire, 470.1/291, DRB AGO. (2) Ord Materials Br, Summary of War Department's Metallurgical Research and Development during World War II, p. 40, OHF.

[70] Quarterly Review (December, 1943), Chart 20–B, DRB AGO.

CHART 15—PERCENT DISTRIBUTION OF ALUMINUM USED, BY ARMY AGENCY: 4TH QUARTER, 1942*

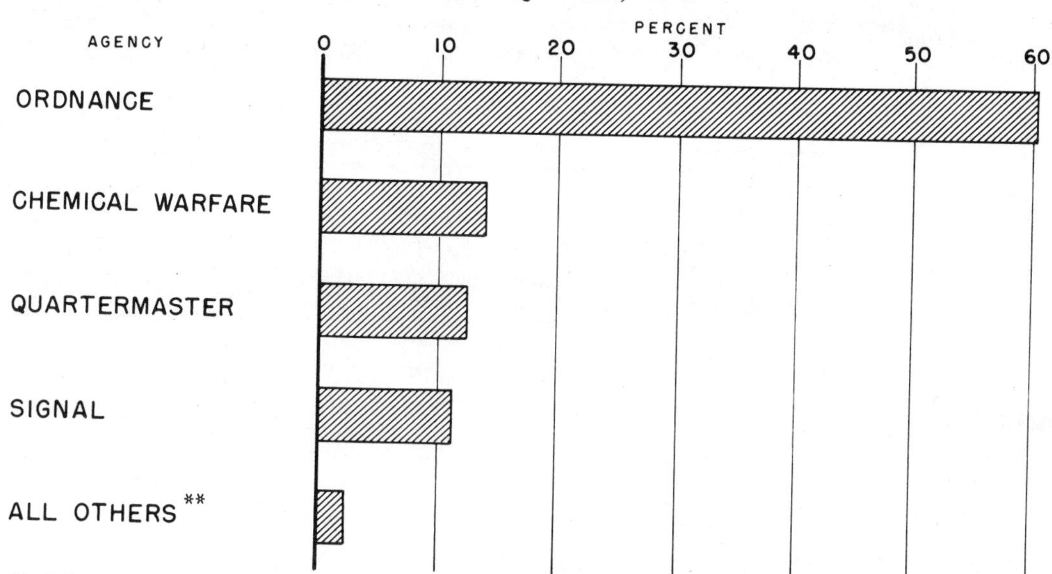

*Excludes Army Air Forces. Remaining Army monthly average consumption was 15,863,000 pounds.
**Transportation, Medical, and Engineers.

Source: Quarterly Review (December 1943), Chart 13–A, DRB AGO.

Aluminum

Aluminum did not appear on War Department lists of strategic materials until the year 1936, but after that date it rapidly came to the front as one of the most critical materials in the war production program.[71] In the fall of 1940 production of aluminum was barely sufficient to meet the demands for the aircraft program, which was given first priority for primary aluminum. In the spring of 1941 the Under Secretary of War and the Office of Production Management called the aluminum shortage to the attention of the supply arms and services and directed them to eliminate aluminum from their equipment wherever possible by substituting other less critical materials such as iron, steel, wood, and plastics.[72]

The Ordnance program to conserve aluminum actually began in the spring of 1941 when a survey of all Ordnance items containing aluminum or other critical material was undertaken. As a first step in the program, all aluminum parts were examined with a view to determining which could be made of some less critical material without sacrifice of military efficiency. When this study was completed shortly after Pearl Harbor, it revealed that such substitutions could be made without significant design changes in 337 aluminum parts with an estimated saving on planned production of 20,000 tons of aluminum.[73] Small arms ammunition chests, for exam-

[71] Capt. G. K. Heiss, "Why a Raw Material Reserve?" *Army Ordnance,* XX, 115 (1939), 32.

[72] Memo, OUSW for Chiefs of Supply Arms and Services, 15 Apr 41, sub: Conservation of Aluminum, ASF Purchase Div 400.8, DRB AGO.

[73] Memo, Barnes for Wesson, 4 Feb 42, sub: Pro-

291064 O—55——33

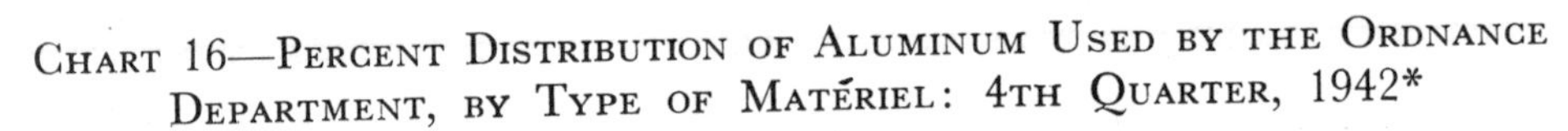

CHART 16—PERCENT DISTRIBUTION OF ALUMINUM USED BY THE ORDNANCE DEPARTMENT, BY TYPE OF MATÉRIEL: 4TH QUARTER, 1942*

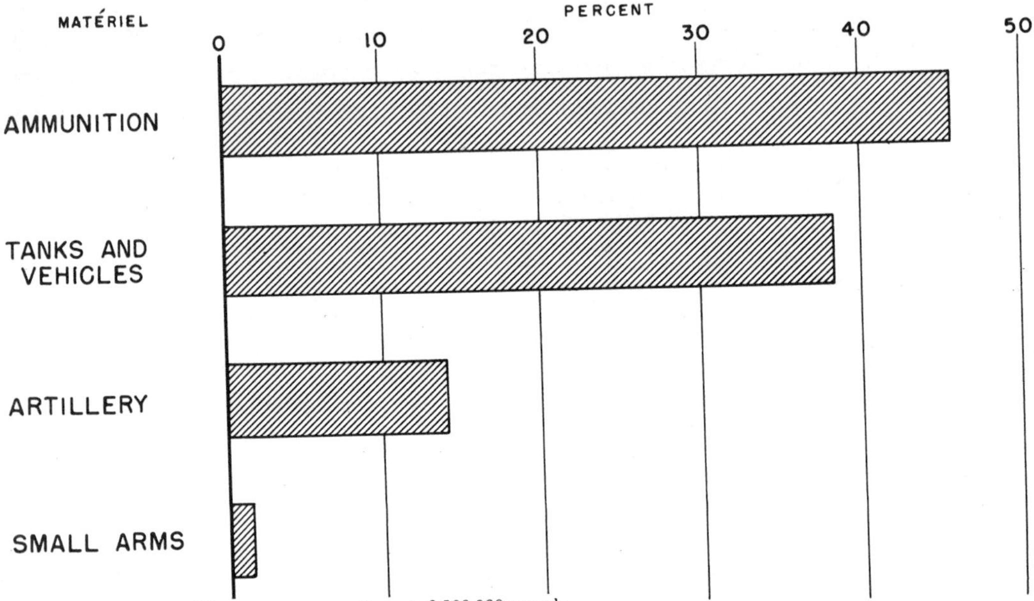

*Total Ordnance monthly average consumption was 9,500,000 pounds.

Source: Quarterly Review (December 1943), Chart 14–A, DRB AGO.

ple, could be of steel rather than aluminum; handles of inspection gages could be converted from aluminum to plastic; steel and plastic might be substituted for aluminum in parts of bomb fuzes and mortar fuzes; and malleable iron and steel used in parts of gun mounts and carriages.[74] By eliminating aluminum in the platform, handwheels, and miscellaneous parts of the 90-mm. gun mount, the quantity of aluminum required for this one item was reduced from over 400 pounds to about 25 pounds per mount.[75] The second step in the Ordnance campaign to conserve aluminum was to study those items in which substitute materials could not be used without significant design changes or elaborate tests. The items offering the least difficulty were to be investigated first and those that were expected to entail complications were left until later. As the two largest consumers of aluminum in the Ordnance Department were the Ammunition Division and the Tank and Combat Vehicle Division, efforts were concentrated on the items procured by these two divisions. By February 1942 General Barnes was able to report that aluminum had been largely eliminated from tanks and combat vehicles except for fans, transmission hous-

gram for the Conservation of Aluminum in Ordnance Material, ASF file 400.8, DRB AGO. See also the detailed list entitled "Aluminum parts for which alternate or substitute materials have become mandatory" in Conservation of Materials, pp. 27–50, DRB AGO.

[74] Conservation of Materials, pp. 22–26, DRB AGO. See also charts and text in Quarterly Review (December, 1943), DRB AGO.

[75] Quarterly Review (December, 1943), Chart 36, DRB AGO.

ings, and motors, and that new motors using less aluminum were under development. In artillery ammunition the situation was different. "Reductions of aluminum for ammunition will in general be difficult to make," General Barnes wrote, "since this metal was built into the designs of fuzes and other intricate parts of high explosives ammunition. Fuzes and similar components were developed only after years of experimentation. Considerable time will be required for tests of redesigned parts to determine whether the substitutions will be feasible." [76]

One of the earliest substitutions for aluminum in artillery ammunition was the adoption of the plastic M52 fuze for the 60-mm. and 81-mm. mortar shell. After extensive proof firings, the plastic fuze went into production early in 1942 with a saving of approximately one pound of aluminum for each fuze, or a total of 17,500 tons in 1942–43. The body of the M54 fuze was converted from aluminum bar to a forging with further substantial savings. The windshields of 75-mm. armor-piercing-capped shot M61, formerly made of primary aluminum, were converted to steel with estimated savings of 4,500 tons of aluminum during 1943. Steel also replaced aluminum in firing pins for artillery ammunition.

There were many other such substitutions, but the principal saving in artillery ammunition did not come from the substitution of some other material; it came from the use of secondary rather than primary aluminum. The use of secondary aluminum was made possible by application of the die-casting process by which the metal could be formed into intricate shapes needing little or no machining. Ordnance engineers encountered two major problems in adapting the die-casting process to munitions production. They had to modify the design of the items to make them suitable for die-casting, and they had to develop new casting alloys that could be made from aluminum scrap containing a high percentage of impurities. Experts from the die-casting industry co-operated with the Ordnance Department in solving both problems. One of these industrial experts, Mr. William During, initiated many design modifications while serving as a consultant on die-casting to General Barnes. An extensive experimental and test program had to be completed before a high-strength alloy capable of producing sound castings of intricate shapes and thin wall sections was developed. This alloy was used successfully from September 1942 until the end of the war, and in the postwar years became the standard aluminum alloy for industrial die-casting.[77]

As with all manufacturing processes that use dies, aluminum die-casting was not economically feasible for producing items in small quantities, but was well suited for the mass production required during World War II. Substitution of secondary aluminum die-castings for parts machined from primary aluminum bar stock netted a saving not only from the use of lower grade material but also from elimination of the scrap losses incurred in machining operations. "By comparison with screw machine procedure," the Ordnance Department reported in June 1942, "die-castings require only a 10 percent excess in raw material as compared to net weight of finished product, and half of this is ordinarily re-cast in subsequent operations. Bar stock scrap runs from 30 to 300

[76] Memo cited n. 73.

[77] (1) R&D Serv, Summary of War Department Metallurgical Research and Development, pp. 40–41, OHF. (2) Interv with Col Frye, 5 Jul 51.

percent, and this waste becomes secondary scrap and is lost to the virgin metal market."[78]

When aluminum requirements for 1942, computed before conservation measures were adopted, were compared with the quantity of aluminum actually used in Ordnance production during the year, the over-all saving was roughly 14,500 tons. (*See Chart 17.*) The same comparison for the year 1943 showed a saving of 62,500 tons, of which approximately 45,000 tons were in ammunition and 15,000 in tanks and other vehicles. Even these large figures do not indicate the full extent of Ordnance conservation of aluminum, for they do not show the saving of primary aluminum that resulted from the use of less critical secondary aluminum in die-castings. By the fall of 1943 nearly 60 percent of all aluminum used by the Ordnance Department was of secondary grade.[79]

While Ordnance engineers were doing everything possible to conserve primary and secondary aluminum, equally significant efforts were made by the aluminum industry to increase production. Total national production of aluminum more than doubled in the eighteen months between January 1942 and June 1943, from about 45,000 tons a month to nearly 95,000 tons a month, and further increases were made in the latter half of 1943. As a result, the aluminum crisis ended that summer. "The increased production of aluminum, combined with effective conservation," the Ordnance Department reported in September, "has resulted in aluminum becoming readily available and non-critical at the present. . . . Under these circumstances additional conversions and substitutions are unnecessary, although downgrading to the lowest purity limits practicable is desirable." [80]

Rubber

In terms of strategic materials, the most serious consequence for the United States of the outbreak of war with Japan and the subsequent Japanese advances into Malaya and the East Indies was the loss of crude rubber imports. Although the nation had on hand in December 1941 the largest stockpile of natural rubber in its history—about 527,000 tons—this reserve amounted to less than one year's supply. Small quantities of natural rubber could still be imported from Latin America, Liberia, and Ceylon; a certain amount of reclaimed rubber became available each year; and a few thousand tons of synthetic rubber could be produced by existing facilities. But none of these sources was more than a drop in the bucket when compared to the enormous military and civilian requirements for rubber in 1942.

The rubber crisis was of particular concern to the Ordnance Department because at the start of the war it was, among Army agencies, the second largest user of crude rubber, taking about 20 percent of the total Army allotment.[81] At that time it used rubber primarily for tires on combat vehicles, for track blocks, bushings, and bogies of tanks, and for hundreds of miscellaneous items such as gaskets, hoses, fan

[78] Conservation of Materials, pp. 114–15, DRB AGO.

[79] Quarterly Review (December, 1943), Chart 15-B, DRB AGO.

[80] Quarterly Review (September, 1943), Chart 16, DRB AGO.

[81] For further details on this and other aspects of the rubber problem see: (1) R&D Div, Rubber for Mechanized Warfare; (2) Lt Col Burton J. Lemon, OCO-D, Rubber, The Ordnance Story of Rubber, Its Problems and Solutions (hereafter cited as Lemon, Story of Rubber); and (3) Ord Dept FS, Requirements, Development, Production, Distribution and Conservation of Tires for Army Motor Vehicles, 1942–1945. All in OHF.

CHART 17—ALUMINUM REQUIREMENTS FOR ORDNANCE MATÉRIEL: 1943

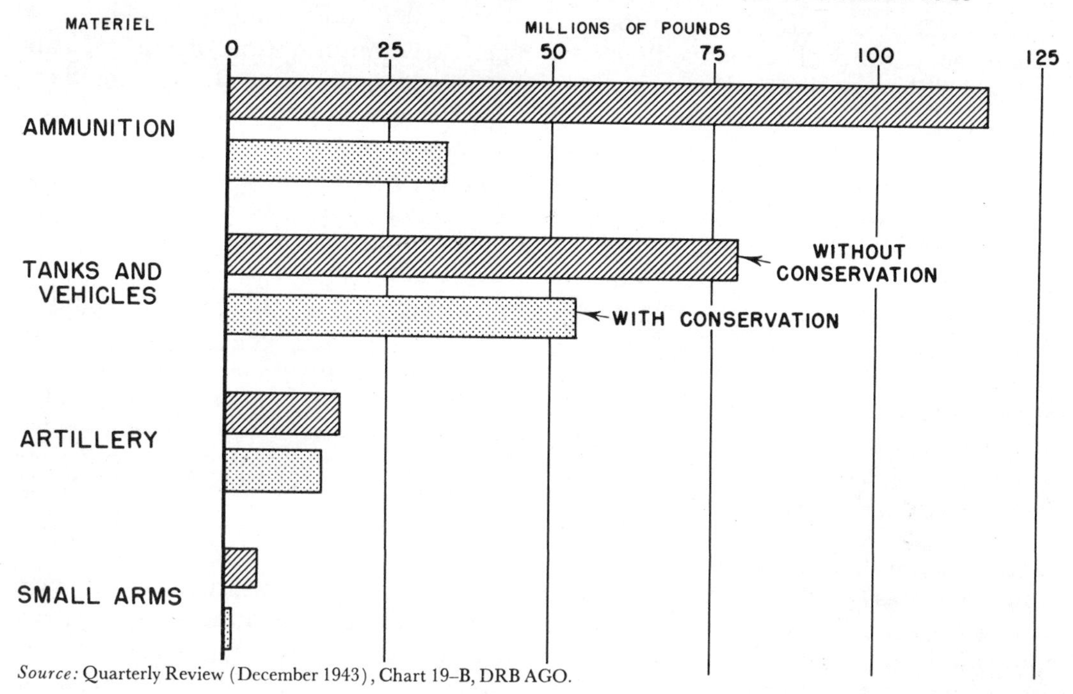

Source: Quarterly Review (December 1943), Chart 19–B, DRB AGO.

belts, and electrical cables. In the summer of 1942 when Ordnance took over from Quartermaster the responsibility for motor transport vehicles, including the procurement of millions of tires and tubes, it became by far the largest user of rubber in the Army, taking between 80 and 90 percent of the Army allotment.[82] Thereafter the task of conserving the Army's limited allotment of crude rubber was almost exclusively an Ordnance responsibility.

Both the Quartermaster Corps and the Ordnance Department had inaugurated rubber-conservation programs long before the attack on Pearl Harbor. As early as 1936 Ordnance had tested tires with synthetic tread for the 75-mm. gun carriage, and in 1941 had launched a survey of all Ordnance items made of rubber with a view to substituting synthetic rubber or some other material wherever possible. Late in 1941 the Quartermaster Corps had inaugurated a program for repairing and recapping all Army tires that were worn or damaged, and had taken steps to improve tire maintenance in the field. But an all-out effort to conserve rubber in military equipment did not begin until after Pearl Harbor. Then, under pressure of necessity, means were found to produce the essential tires, tank tracks, and other items needed by the armed forces before the national stockpile of crude rubber was exhausted.

There were many ways in which small savings of rubber could be made by changing the specifications for Ordnance equip-

[82] WD Cir 245. Responsibility for all replacement tires and tubes—except those for airplanes—was assigned to Ordnance by WD Cir 86, 27 Mar 43.

ment. In some parts, reclaimed rubber could be used instead of new rubber; in others the quantity of rubber could be decreased without serious loss of efficiency; and in still others some substitute materials such as felt or paper could be used in place of rubber. In April 1942, for example, the Small Arms Branch revised its specifications for recoil pads and water chest hoses to permit the use of reclaimed rubber in these items with estimated savings during 1942–43 of more than 1,000 tons of natural rubber. By reducing the amount of rubber in adhesive tape used for ammunition packaging, and at the same time using a higher percentage of reclaimed rubber, the Ammunition Branch reported in the spring of 1942 that it would save 800 tons of natural rubber. A steady flow of such conversions and substitutions continued throughout 1942 and 1943 until practically all the so-called mechanical rubber items were converted to some other material. While these measures helped to conserve the nation's stockpile of natural rubber, their total effect was small. They were undertaken because no one knew when the war would end, how long the stockpile of rubber would last, or when the day might come when the saving of even a single pound of crude rubber might be important.

Synthetic Rubber

Far more important in the long run was the conversion from natural to synthetic rubber, but this step could not be taken during 1942 because synthetic rubber simply was not available in large quantities. The synthetic rubber industry in the United States was still in its infancy and much remained to be learned of the physical properties of the various synthetic compounds. Annual production was only about 8,000 tons—roughly 1 percent of the yearly consumption of natural rubber—and large-scale production could not be achieved until new plants to produce the most promising types had been constructed.[83] After synthetic rubber became available, elaborate tests had to be made under simulated combat conditions to determine how it could best be used in military equipment. In this long and complicated process the rubber industry, various executive agencies of the government, and the Ordnance Department maintained the closest co-operation. In government-owned plants the rubber industry produced huge quantities of synthetic rubber. As far as Ordnance items were concerned, rubber companies manufactured the tires, tubes, and other synthetic products in their own factories and provided the laboratory test facilities; Ordnance supplied the test vehicles and proving grounds and bought the experimental products.

The four synthetic rubber compounds most widely used by Ordnance were GR-S (Buna-S), GR-M (neoprene), GR-N (Buna-N), and GR-I (butyl).[84] Each had many of the qualities that made natural rubber a useful industrial material, but none proved to be a perfect substitute. GR-M was more like natural rubber than any of the other synthetic materials, and

[83] In May 1941 the federal government authorized construction of plants with an annual capacity of 40,000 long tons of Buna-S. After Pearl Harbor this capacity was quickly raised to 705,000 tons of Buna-S, 132,000 tons of butyl, and 40,000 tons of neoprene. In 1945, production of synthetic rubber reached 820,000 tons. *Industrial Mobilization For War: 1940–1945*, I, *Program and Administration* (Washington, 1947), 377.

[84] The symbol GR-S stood for the words "Government Rubber-styrene," GR-M for "Government Rubber-monovinyl-acetylene," GR-N for "Government Rubber-acrylon-nitrile," and GR-I for "Government Rubber-isobutylene."

was, in addition, more resistant to oil and flame. But it had one serious defect—at extremely low temperatures it became hard and brittle.[85] When this fact was revealed by tests, further use of GR-M for tires was canceled, and it was thereafter limited to items such as V-belts, radiator and brake hoses, vibration insulators, fire control cables, and sponge rubber for seats and crash pads. Although GR-N was suitable for tires, it was used exclusively for mechanical rubber items because it could not be produced in the large quantities needed for tire manufacture. GR-S, made from petroleum and alcohol, was selected for tires and tank tracks partly because of its physical properties and partly because it could be manufactured more easily than any of the other compounds. During World War II about 90 percent of all synthetic rubber produced in government-owned plants was GR-S, but it was stiffer than natural rubber and when flexed rapidly and continuously it generated excessive heat. Tire tread made of GR-S was not only easily chipped by stony terrain but also required a thin layer of natural rubber between it and the carcass to provide proper adhesion. It tore too readily to be a good material for inner tubes, and was hard to repair because of its lack of adhesiveness. As the quality of GR-S was improved by industrial chemists, it came to be the standard synthetic for military tires and tank tracks, but as a material for inner tubes it was replaced in 1944 by GR-I, which held air even better than did natural rubber and could be patched more easily than GR-S.

Combat Tires and Tank Tracks

Before the transfer of motor vehicles to Ordnance in August 1942, Ordnance rubber-conservation efforts were centered mainly on combat tires and tank tracks. The combat tire was given particular attention because it used almost twice as much natural rubber as did the standard type of highway tire. Designed to run flat for 75 miles after being punctured, it had thick sidewalls that provided support for the vehicle while the tire was run flat. As a substitute for the combat tire, Ordnance experimented after Pearl Harbor with the use of so-called restrictor rings on standard tires. These were steel flanges which, securely fastened to the rim, partially encased the sidewalls of the tire. When the tire was punctured the restrictor rings gave enough support to prevent complete collapse of the tire, but their development was discontinued after tests showed that they caused steering difficulties, increased the danger of axle breakage, and made impossible the use of chains for driving on muddy ground.[86] Fruitless efforts were also made to conserve rubber by developing a tubeless combat tire. As a result, during 1943 it became necessary to sacrifice quality for quantity. The requirement that the tire run flat for 75 miles was cut to one of 40 miles, thus reducing substantially the amount of rubber needed for each tire.[87] About the same time, the number of combat tires to be manufactured was reduced when the War Department announced that such tires would no longer be required on various gun carriages. Toward the end of the year, when acceptable combat tires made of synthetic rubber came into production, the combat tire ceased to be a serious problem.[88]

[85] OCM 21222, 5 Aug 43.
[86] Lemon, Story of Rubber, pp. 35-37, OHF.
[87] OCM 22089, 11 Nov 43.
[88] Memo, Chief of Rubber Br ASF for Dir of Requirements Div ASF, 15 Nov 43, sub: Use of Combat Tires, and inds, OO 451.92/496, DRB AGO.

While these efforts went forward to conserve rubber in combat tires, Ordnance engineers also turned attention to the use of steel tracks to replace rubber tracks on tanks. Although steel tracks did not entirely eliminate the requirement for rubber, since they had to be fitted with rubber bushings, their use nevertheless brought an important saving of rubber. Steel tracks had disadvantages, however, and for some purposes were not as satisfactory as rubber tracks. They gave less protection to the suspension components, for example, and provided poorer traction on pavement and on ice and snow. These facts, coupled with the dwindling supplies of natural rubber, pointed inescapably to the conclusion that tank tracks had to be made of synthetic rubber.

During the winter of 1942–43, when improved synthetic rubber came into production, Ordnance launched an extensive program to develop and test synthetic tracks. By October 1943 the performance of the synthetic smooth block T16 for the light tank was so satisfactory that it was approved for use, and by May 1944 the synthetic smooth block T51 for the medium tank was approved. For half-track vehicles, one third of the production schedule was switched to synthetic in October 1943 and by May 1944 the proportion of synthetic production had risen to two thirds. When Allied forces in Italy reported their preference for steel rather than rubber tracks for use on rocky, mountainous terrain, Ordnance produced a rubber-backed steel track for medium tanks that helped reduce the wear on bogie wheels encountered in the use of all-steel tracks. Production of acceptable chevron-type tracks of synthetic rubber proved difficult and was not achieved until near the end of the war. The use of synthetic rubber for bogie wheel tires was also hard to accomplish, chiefly because of the heavy weights involved in tank suspensions. By October 1943 synthetic rubber was approved for the bogies of light tanks and half-tracks, and, beginning in January 1944, one fourth of the bogies for the medium tank were made of synthetic rubber. But by the spring of 1945 the bogie of the heavy tank T26E3 had not yet been converted to synthetic rubber.[89]

Truck Tires

Transfer to Ordnance of responsibility for motor transport vehicles in August 1942 opened an entirely new phase of the Ordnance rubber conservation program. Thereafter approximately 65 percent of the Ordnance rubber allotment went into pneumatic tires and tubes, as compared with only 35 percent used in tanks, mechanical rubber items, and self-sealing fuel tanks. When the Tank-Automotive Center was established at Detroit in September 1942, a Rubber Branch headed by Col. Joseph M. Colby, and later by Lt. Col. Burton J. Lemon, was made an integral part of the new headquarters.

Conversion of pneumatic tires from natural to synthetic rubber was a gradual process which began with the small tires, moved on to the mediums, and ended with the large tires only partially converted at the end of the war. The changeover had to be geared both to the gradually increasing supply of synthetic rubber and to the results of tests under field conditions. There was no easy short-cut to the production of good synthetic military tires, no

[89] Lemon, Story of Rubber, pp. 113–50, OHF. A chart on p. 114 of this reference summarizes the progress in converting tank tracks and bogies up to the fall of 1944.

CHART 18—MONTHLY AVERAGE USE OF SYNTHETIC RUBBER BY THE ORDNANCE DEPARTMENT: 4TH QUARTER, 1942; 3D QUARTER, 1943

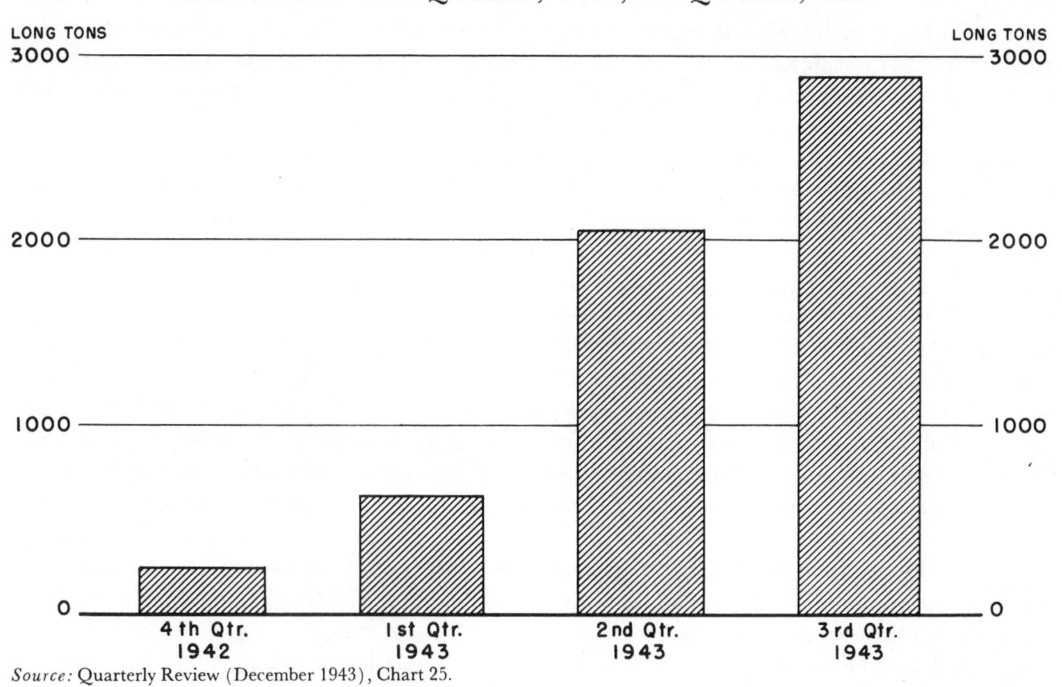

Source: Quarterly Review (December 1943), Chart 25.

way to solve the problem except through the painstaking trial-and-error process of building and testing tires by the thousands. The highways and country roads adjacent to Aberdeen Proving Ground provided a permanent testing ground on which the rubber components of tanks, trucks, and amphibian vehicles were tried out. At Camp Shilo, Manitoba, in the winter of 1942–43, and on the Alaska Highway during the winter of 1943–44, Aberdeen detachments conducted tests of synthetic rubber products in snow and ice and subzero temperatures. The Army Desert Test Command at Camp Seeley, California, established in March 1942, conducted endurance tests in extremely high temperatures over miles of hot, dry terrain. The most extensive tire-testing operation of this kind was carried on under Ordnance auspices at Normoyle Field in Texas where from 200 to 300 vehicles ran for 24 hours a day, 7 days a week, over a 165-mile test course, completing 22,000,000 vehicle test miles by June 1945.

In the Army's small-tire group the most important tire was the 6.00-16 for ¼-ton jeeps and passenger cars. The first tests of this tire with synthetic tread on a natural rubber carcass in 1942 were so promising that new tests were conducted with tires made entirely of synthetic rubber. These tires performed so well, most of them running twice the required mileage, that the Ordnance Technical Committee approved their procurement in December 1942. Before conversion to synthetic rubber, each 6.00-16 tire required 10 pounds of natural rubber and nearly 6 pounds of reclaimed rubber; after conversion, only 4 ounces of natural rubber and 2 pounds of reclaimed rubber went into each tire. By June 1943 the use of synthetic rubber was extended to all tires in the small-tire group.[90]

Of the three size groups of Army tires, by far the most important, in terms of rubber conservation, was the medium-size group, including tires from seven to ten inches wide. Nearly three fourths of all the rubber used for Ordnance tires went into these sizes, which were used on trucks of all weights up to six tons. In contrast to the quick and relatively easy conversion of the smaller tires, the use of synthetic rubber in medium-size tires presented many difficult problems. Because these tires had thick sidewalls and carried heavy loads, they ran at high temperatures, which weakened both the rubber and the tire cord. A partial solution to this problem was found in the use of rayon cord, which stood up much better under high temperatures than did cotton cord. Tires made with rayon cord required fewer plies and therefore less rubber than did cotton-cord tires, and tests demonstrated that, in the medium-size tire group, synthetic tires made with rayon gave nearly as good service as did natural rubber tires.[91] The only difficulty lay in the shortage of the particular kind of rayon needed. In spite of rapid expansion of rayon cord production facilities, through the efforts of the War Production Board, there was enough rayon cord only for the 9.00-20 and larger tires in which cotton was totally unsatisfactory. For the other sizes, reinforcing cotton plies known as "cap plies" had to be placed over the regular plies to give added strength. As a result of these and other efforts, the production of all medium-size tires with 35 percent synthetic content—synthetic tread on natural rubber carcass—was approved by the Ordnance Technical Committee in June 1943, and a month later the percentage of synthetic was doubled. For medium-size tires with highway tread this percentage remained at 70 for the rest of the war, but in October 1943 the percentage of synthetic rubber authorized for medium-size tires with mud and snow tread was raised to 90, and later to 92.[92]

Conversion of large-size tires to synthetic rubber was delayed for three main reasons: it was difficult to make them of synthetic rubber; the military requirement for large tires was comparatively small until the end of 1943; and the smaller tires used practically all the available synthetic rubber. During the winter of 1943–44 extensive tests were made of large tires in sizes from 11.00-20 to 13.00-24 made of 70 percent synthetic rubber with rayon instead of cotton cord. The results led the Ordnance Technical Committee to give its approval to these tires in April 1944. The 14.00-inch truck and trailer tires were not made with synthetic rubber except for the 14.00-20 tire with mud and snow tread, for which 35 percent synthetic rubber was approved in the spring of 1945.

Conversion to synthetic rubber was by no means complete at the end of the war. In many items natural rubber still had to be used if performance was not to be seri-

[90] OCM 19323, 10 Dec 42 and 20730, 10 Jun 43.

[91] Memo, CG T-AC for CG SOS, 27 Feb 43, sub: Rayon Versus Cotton Cord in Military Tires, Exhibit 18, Lemon, Story of Rubber, OHF. See also OCM 19389, 24 Dec 42, and 24823, 24 Aug 44. Experiments were also conducted with wire for tire cord but the results were not altogether satisfactory.

[92] For dates of conversion to synthetic rubber for each tire size, and OCM citations, see R&D Div, Rubber for Mechanized Warfare, Chronology of Important Steps in Production of Synthetic Tires, Tubes and Flaps, OHF.

TABLE 14—SUMMARY OF CONVERSIONS TO SYNTHETIC RUBBER BY V-J DAY

Product	Percent Synthetic	Markings on Sidewalls
Tires:		
5.50 through 7.00, 8-ply	100	S-3
7.50-20 and 9.00-16	93	S-8
9.00 and 10.00 (10-ply and up)	90	S-4
11.00 through 13.00	70	S-6
14.00-20, 12-ply	70	S-6
14.00-20, 20-ply	35	S-7
14.00-24	5–10	S-11
Combat tires:		
6.00-16	100	S-3
8.00-16	90	S-4
8.25 and 9.00	70	S-6
14.00-20	5–10	S-11
Tubes	100	Blue stripe
Flaps	100	Red stripe
Tank track blocks	100	Red rectangle
Tank track bushings	crude rubber	
Bogie tires, 20x9x16	crude rubber	
Bogie tires, other size	100	Red rectangle
Band tracks	70	Red medallion

Source: Ordnance Digest, 27, 9 (September, 1945), 10, OHF.

ously impaired. In addition to use in large-size tires, small quantities of natural rubber were used in all tires as an adhesive between tread and carcass, and in scores of very small items, such as the cores of tire valves and tire gauges, natural rubber was essential. By the summer of 1945, 86 percent of all Ordnance tire production had been converted to synthetic rubber, and conversion of mechanical rubber items to synthetic construction was over 95 percent complete. The more difficult conversion of tank tracks and bogies stood at 65 percent. Efforts continued during the summer of 1945 to curtail the use of natural rubber in Ordnance items, but everyone recognized that the worst of the rubber crisis was over. "Primarily owing to the Ordnance Department's program," the Ordnance Research and Development Service reported, "the total of crude rubber required by the industry for mixing with . . . synthetic was only 10,000 tons per month in 1945, a rate that equalled imports. The Ordnance Department required about 2500 tons per month, a figure far below its proportionate share of the consumption before conversion and one indicating the success of the Ordnance program." [93]

Preservative Materials

Closely allied to the Ordnance conservation program was the effort to preserve finished items of equipment by the use of rust-preventive and corrosion-preventive coatings and the employment of advanced packaging methods to save shipping space

[93] R&D Div, Rubber for Mechanized Warfare, p. 7, OHF.

and prevent damage from rough handling. The waste of material resulting from breakage or from corrosion was just as real as the waste resulting from improper use of critical materials in the original design. It was, in some respects, even worse. "If, for any reason," an Ordnance report stated, "matériel arrived in an overseas theater in unusable condition due to improper packaging, . . . it represented a loss of the raw materials from which it was manufactured, a loss of man-hours which were required to process and move it, a loss of packaging materials, a loss of space in trucks, depots, railroad cars and ships—in short, so much loss that it would have been far better if the item had never been made."[94] And, of course, the morale of combat troops suffered when unserviceable ammunition or equipment was received.

At the outset of World War II the methods and materials used for preserving and packaging Ordnance matériel were little more advanced than they were at the close of World War I. No special consideration had been given to the problem of developing preservative materials during the 1920's and 1930's because War Department plans in those years did not envisage the shipment of vast quantities of military equipment to widely scattered overseas battlefronts. Contracts with manufacturers ordinarily called for no higher standards of packaging for military supplies than those prescribed by common carriers for shipment of commercial goods at the lowest applicable freight rates.[95] These packaging methods had proved reasonably satisfactory for normal shipments of commercial material in time of peace, but they proved wholly inadequate for the shipment of military equipment in time of war. Packaging materials and preservatives in World War II not only had to protect matériel against a wide variety of climatic conditions, from subzero temperatures in Alaska to steaming jungles in the South Pacific, but they also had to guarantee that equipment would arrive in serviceable condition after it had made a long sea voyage, been exposed to rain, corrosive salt spray, and abrupt changes in temperature, and been landed with primitive equipment at a bombed-out port or newly won beachhead.

Although responsibility for the development of packaging methods for Ordnance matériel rested with Field Service during the early months of the war and was then transferred to Industrial Service, the Research and Development Service played an important role in developing the preservatives needed to prevent rust, corrosion, and fungus growth.[96] An industrial packaging expert, Mr. Neil A. Fowler, was engaged early in 1942 to serve as a consultant to General Barnes on packaging and preserving Ordnance matériel, and later Dr. G. A. Greathouse of the Department of Agriculture was employed to study means of protecting matériel from damage by mold. The Materials Branch gave its attention primarily to protection against fungi and to the development of preservative greases, oils, and paints, while Field

[94] Development of Packaging in Ord Dept, 1941–45, PSP 58 (hereafter cited as PSP 58), p. 5, OHF.

[95] Memo, Col Raaen, Exec Off OCO, to Mr. Julius H. Amberg, 14 Jul 44, sub: Packaging of Automotive Spare Parts, Exhibit 2 in PSP 58, II, OHF.

"Items of artillery were presumably to be shipped on a magic carpet," wrote the author of an Ordnance report on prewar packaging, "through an atmosphere everlastingly free of rain, snow, fungus, or any other hazardous influence." Hist of Packaging and Marking International Aid Materiel, Exhibit 7 in PSP 58, II, OHF.

[96] PSP 58, p. 52, OHF. For a discussion of packaging methods, see Thomson and Mayo, Procurement and Supply of Munitions, MS, OHF.

Service and Industrial Service, working in close co-operation with industry and the Forest Products Laboratory of the Department of Agriculture, developed protective wrapping materials and devised improved methods of using the materials in packing and crating Ordnance supplies. These measures furthered the Ordnance conservation program by preventing waste all along the supply lines which stretched for thousands of miles from factories to fighting fronts.

The essence of the problem facing the Materials Branch was that most Ordnance matériel, being made of metal, was subject to rust or corrosion when it became wet or dirty. Even minute quantities of water, dirt, or salt spray could work havoc. The moisture in the air within a package, if it condensed on metal parts when the temperature dropped suddenly, could cause rust; the moisture in a man's fingerprint was capable of causing rust on an exposed metal part. The solution to the problem, although difficult to achieve, was clear enough: matériel had to be kept clean and bone dry either by enclosing it in moisture-proof packages or by covering it with a protective coating such as paint, oil, grease, or a plating material. The search for, and standardization of, such protective coatings and wrapping materials for Ordnance matériel became vitally important during World War II.

Painting and Plating

Two of the most widely used methods of protecting Ordnance matériel against rust and corrosion before the war were painting and plating. Wherever practicable, exposed parts were given a coat of paint that served the dual purpose of protecting the finish and providing camouflage coloring. Parts for which paint was not suitable, and for which permanent protection was needed, were plated with such metals as zinc, cadmium, nickel, or chromium. When the outbreak of war brought an acute shortage of plating materials, Ordnance was forced to adopt a thinner plating on many items and to eliminate plating altogether on others. At the same time, while paint itself was rapidly becoming a scarce material, experience in overseas operations revealed that many of the paints used in 1941 did not provide adequate protection for military equipment. Ordnance, as the custodian of Army paint specifications, therefore undertook a program to conserve paint, standardize military paints, and develop paints with better protective qualities.[97]

Late in 1942, as reports came in of excessive corrosion of the metal boxes in which small arms ammunition was packed, the Materials Branch started work on developing a rust-inhibiting paint for these containers to replace the lusterless olive-drab paint originally adopted primarily for camouflage purposes. Modifications made in a one-coat paint used by the Engineer Board on aircraft landing mats produced a remarkably effective semigloss paint for ammunition containers. Its use was soon extended to a wide variety of other containers. Later, when hermetically sealed boxes were adopted for small arms ammunition, the method of packing and painting these boxes required a quick-drying paint. Industrial chemists promptly developed a paint that permitted painting, stencilling, and packaging the container within twenty minutes. At the same time, intensive efforts were made to provide a

[97] Hist of Materials Branch, Pt. III, OHF.

suitable protective finish for steel cartridge cases under development during 1942 and 1943.

Oils, Greases, Plastics

Not all classes of Ordnance items could be protected by paint. Many had to be coated with oil or grease and enclosed in a protective wrapper while in storage and transit. Aircraft machine guns fell into this category, and the effort to develop suitable preservative materials for them may be cited as a typical example of the work of the Materials Branch. At the start of World War II the Ordnance Department was still using a heavy grease, popularly known as cosmoline, to rustproof such weapons. It gave excellent results, but it was hard to remove. When weapons coated with this compound arrived overseas they had to be given a thorough cleaning or "degreasing" before they were fit to use, and if even a small portion of the grease were left on the weapon, it might fail to function in extremely low temperatures. In 1942 Ordnance engineers, working in close co-operation with a machine gun manufacturer, discarded the heavy grease in favor of a light preservative oil that would lubricate working parts satisfactorily and provide a certain amount of protection against rust. To supplement the action of this protective oil, a wrapping material was needed that would be not only waterproof but also moisture-vaporproof. Experience had shown that in damp weather the moisture in the air was able to pass through most waterproof materials and then condense on the metal parts within the package. After extensive experiments a material was found that was moisture-vaporproof, flexible, tough, and transparent. But, when tests were made on weapons coated with oil and enclosed in the moisture-vaporproof material, the weapons still rusted. The explanation lay in the condensation of moisture from the air trapped within the package and within the gun itself. The problem was solved by placing a dehydrating agent within the package to absorb the moisture before it did any harm. "In the past two years," the Small Arms Division reported in June 1945, "not a single case of a rusted machine gun packaged in this manner has been reported." [98]

In the fall of 1943 a new type of material was adopted for protecting Ordnance parts and assemblies of moderate size and weight. This was a thermoplastic material composed of oils, waxes, and ethyl-cellulose which, after application to the item by a hot-dip bath, formed a tough elastic coating that not only gave good protection against corrosion but could be quickly removed by slitting and peeling.[99] For many types of parts, use of this strippable coating was more economical than the light oil in a moisture-vaporproof wrap. In 1945 it was estimated that Ordnance installations and contractor plants were using the new compound at the rate of 150,000 pounds a month.[100] Another strippable compound, attracting wide attention in the spring of 1945 but not adopted before the end of the war, was a cellulose-acetate-butyrate-base material that had the advantages over the ethyl-cellulose compound of being fairly transparent, applicable at lower temperatures, and more easily stripped from recesses. Further studies, in which Ordnance co-operated with other branches of the service, were begun in the fall of 1944 on

[98] Hist of Packaging of Cal. .50 Aircraft Machine Gun, Exhibit 33, PSP 58, OHF.

[99] PSP 58, pp. 59–60, OHF.

[100] *Ibid.*, pp. 59–60.

a spray-type strippable compound developed by the Navy for long-time storage of all types of war matériel and production equipment.

Automotive Matériel

The preservation of automotive matériel, including tanks, trucks, and spare parts, was one of the most important phases of the Ordnance program and was one of infinite complexity. Late in 1942 when the problem was referred to the SAE War Engineering Board for study, the board appointed numerous subcommittees to deal with the preservation of such items as engines, cooling systems, batteries, and service parts, and to recommend cleaning methods, corrosion-prevention compounds, and packaging materials. As the subcommittee recommendations were received, tested, and approved they were incorporated into the appropriate Ordnance specifications or packaging regulations.[101] One of the most successful developments in this field was the application of alkyd resin varnishes to the electrical systems of vehicles to prevent them from "drowning out" after exposure to heavy rains or submersion in water. Tank hulls were prepared for shipment in the same way as aircraft machine guns—a moisture-proof and vaporproof wrap enclosing a dehydrating substance. Less successful was the effort to develop an exterior paint for automotive vehicles. Before the war, lusterless enamel was specified for this purpose largely because of its camouflage value, but it was too porous to give adequate protection in areas of extreme humidity and heavy rainfall. Because the paint shortage precluded using two coats—the semigloss covered with the lusterless—the Ordnance Department recommended that, in spite of the sacrifice of camouflage protection, semigloss enamel be adopted for all vehicles. This recommendation was not finally approved by higher authority until very near the end of the war.[102]

Perhaps the most unusual problem of matériel preservation that Ordnance faced during World War II was the rapid deterioration of equipment caused by mold or mildew in extremely hot and humid areas. It was not a new problem by any means, but it had never before assumed such large proportions as in 1944 when fighting started on a large scale in the South Pacific. Supplies deteriorated at an alarming rate. Textiles rotted and fell apart; cork and paper gaskets disintegrated; leather holsters and instrument cases became covered with fungi that caused the threads to break; electrical instruments failed because fungus growth on the fabric-sheathed wires caused short circuits. The Materials Branch began studying methods of protecting equipment against mold early in 1944 and in April of that year published a pamphlet on the subject.[103] In September 1944 an Artillery Tropicalization Mission was sent to the Panama Canal Department to investigate measures used in that area to prevent deterioration of Ordnance matériel by mold. With the aid of industry and other branches of the Army, Ordnance soon developed means of controlling mold on a wide variety of items and issued several of the early Army specifications in this field. A varnish containing a fungicide

[101] C. E. Heussner and C. O. Durbin, "Materials for Preparation and Preservation of Vehicles and Component Parts for Storage and Shipment," *SAE Journal,* Vol. 52, 12 (December, 1944), 564–72. See also Hist of Materials Branch, Pt. III, OHF.

[102] Hist of Materials Branch, Pt. III, OHF.

[103] The Prevention of Deterioration of Material by Mold, copy in Hist of Materials Branch, OHF.

proved effective in controlling mold on electrical equipment and gaskets. For leather items, neat's-foot oil mixed with a fungicide gave excellent protection. Gun covers, tarpaulins, vehicle tops, and cotton cordage were protected by the use of copper naphthenate as a fungicide. Difficulties were experienced with some items. For example, the fungicide used on wooden ammunition boxes caused dermatitis, but the fungus problem was generally well under control by the spring of 1945.[104]

The successful efforts of the Materials Branch to develop effective preservatives provided a fitting supplement to its efforts to promote the conservation of strategic materials in the design and manufacture of Ordnance items. It constituted the "follow through" that was essential to the safe arrival of supplies in the theaters of operations. It sharply reduced some of the appalling losses of equipment that occurred early in the war, and entirely eliminated others. When combined with the extensive efforts of the Field Service and the Industrial Service in developing and applying advanced packing methods it contributed in very large measure to the success of the Ordnance program to conserve strategic materials.

[104] Interv with Mr. Clayton R. Cornthwaite, Ord Materials Br, 5 Sep 51. For details as to specification numbers and chemical compositions of fungicides, see Hist of Materials Branch, Pt III, OHF.

CHAPTER XIX

Unresolved Problems of Research and Development

The end of fighting in World War II found the Ordnance Research and Development Service with several hundred projects under way and scores of problems still unsolved. The long list of specific questions that had arisen but remained unanswered showed no lack of energy or of imagination on the part of Ordnance engineers, but rather the complex interrelatedness of factors to be considered in any major development and the vastness of the realm of applicable science still scarcely explored. That neither Ordnance specialists nor scientists of the National Defense Research Committee had, for example, learned what made predictable the behavior of a shaped charge must be recognized as the consequence of the limited knowledge of aerodynamics, explosives, chemistry, and physics generally. In time, such phenomena could either be analyzed and sorted out into categories in which comprehended natural laws applied or be relegated to the area of natural forces usable but not understood. In view of the tremendous facilities for scientific investigation in the United States, Americans could safely cherish the belief that problems solvable by scientific research would be dealt with as quickly, perhaps more rapidly, in the United States than in any other country in the world. That such a program might take years could cause no profound dismay since, in the competition with other nations that underlies war, the scientific progress in other countries might outstrip the United States in some particular applications but could surely not keep pace in others. So German science had preceded Allied in developing guided missiles but, providentially for the armies fighting the Axis, had lagged far behind in making possible the employment of proximity fuzes.

Comforting though these reflections might be in the long view, for the Ordnance Department the series of problems that were unresolved on V-J Day constituted an abiding challenge. They were of two kinds, those requiring patient investigation of means of improving any given weapon, and those involving matters of tactical usage, logistics, and the basic theories of how a citizens' army should be equipped. To cite a single example of the first kind, research into ways of producing a longer-ranged, accurate, and more powerful rocket to be fired from a shoulder launcher was a project calling for extensive postwar work. Far more fundamental were the controversial questions arising from conflicting views of what types of weapons modern warfare demanded. The Ordnance Department, as has been repeatedly stated, had no final voice in those decisions.

291064 O—55——34

Yet its opinion carried weight, at the end of the war perhaps more than in 1941 when experience had not yet lent force to the Ordnance line of reasoning.[1]

Global war had, to be sure, manifested the undesirability of having a single type of weapon for universal use. Thus, the Ordnance Department learned that to limit design of tanks, whether light or medium, to one standard pattern was to court disaster. Wide tracks to give flotation in mud and swamps were needed in some actions; narrower tracks and less powerful engines were adequate in others. Rubber tracks gave better service over paved roads and smooth surfaces; steel were all but essential for rocky terrain and coral reefs. But acceptance of the thesis of variations of design did not settle the argument of whether many relatively thinly armored, rather lightly gunned combat vehicles were more valuable than fewer very heavy tanks that were harder to ship and much more expensive to build and operate. Six years after V-J Day the proponents of the lumbering, powerful, heavy tank were to encounter occasionally the criticism that the U.S. Army had let itself be overmechanized; repeating the argument heard about the Italian campaigns of 1943–45, the contention was that a few units of horse cavalry in Korea could have cleaned out pockets of resistance where a vehicle was unable to go.

Still, granting the wisdom of adaptations of some features of a weapon to give the versatility required for effective use under various conditions of combat, climate, and terrain, the question remained as to whether multiplicity of design created more problems than it solved. Quite apart from any difficulties in production, supplying special spare parts for, and training troops in the use of, a variety of weapons might make the drawbacks more considerable than the advantages. The Ordnance Department's largely successful effort to make all ammunition of a given caliber usable in any model of any type of gun of that size paid off again and again. The much less successful endeavor to have parts for vehicles interchangeable between one make and another convinced Ordnance automotive engineers that uniformity of mechanisms was vitally important. Yet within the Ordnance Department, as in the Army at large, differences of opinion endured over whether to place emphasis upon multipurpose weapons or on special equipment for special purposes. The visible effectiveness of the German 88-mm. gun at once as a field artillery piece, an antitank weapon, and an antiaircraft gun inspired design features of the American 90-mm. that warranted General Barnes' calling the 90-mm. a "triple-threat" gun. But the result was a series of compromises that made the gun less well suited to any one of the three uses than would otherwise have been possible.

Even what constituted the most essential features of infantry weapons was a matter of some argument throughout the war. The fast cyclic rate and thirty-round magazine of the 8.5-pound M3 submachine gun provided the infantryman and paratrooper with a spray of fire, but precluded aiming shots carefully. Conversely, the Browning automatic rifle, though capable of short bursts at an even higher cyclic rate, had only a 20-round magazine and, with its bipod, weighed over 19 pounds. But it could achieve an accuracy unobtainable

[1] In the brief summarizing paragraphs that follow, unless otherwise noted, the substantiating documentary evidence covering the particular examples alluded to here is in the chapters where the development of each item in turn is discussed.

with the more portable submachine gun and had double the range. So the question arose whether, when choice was necessary, the scatter fire of the lighter, short-range weapon was more useful than the accurately aimed longer-range fire of the heavier. Attempts to copy a very lightweight German machine gun and a machine pistol seemed waste effort to men who believed the .30-caliber Browning machine gun and the BAR the best weapons foot soldiers on the move could have. Troops advancing through the villages and wooded stretches of Lorraine and the Ardennes found reassurance in the sound of their submachine guns rattling away at scattered enemy, but the fact that "nearly every unit carried more BAR's than called for in the Tables of Equipment" testifies to the faith American soldiers placed in the heavier weapon.[2] True, an infantry company might be given a diversity of small arms so that the BAR's of some squads would supplement the submachine guns and rifles of others. But the new emphasis put upon the individual soldier's combat capacity and his indoctrination in fighting not only as a member of a team but, when necessary, as a one-man army carried implicitly the assumption that every individual must be armed as adequately as possible. One man could not pack both a "Tommy" gun and a BAR.

How much the factor of weight should be considered in infantry equipment was a question as controversial as that of aimed versus area fire. The M1 rifle gave the infantryman a weapon of greater power than the short-ranged carbine but saddled him with over four pounds more weight. Which was more important for the individual soldier, the utmost mobility and least possible fatigue or more, longer-range killing power, and hence greater self-confidence? Ordnance Research and Development Service, neither able nor invited to give a categorical answer, could only strive to develop infantry weapons combining light weight and fire power more satisfactorily than those of the enemy.

The importance of achieving light weight and sturdiness in equipment was heightened, moreover, by the growing role of air warfare and the introduction of the parachute technique to drop men and supplies behind enemy lines. Obviously matériel that would survive parachuting or delivery by glider must still possess lethal characteristics if it were to be of any use. A serviceable airborne tank had not been developed by V-J Day, and even the 105-mm. airborne howitzer, because of its reduced range, proved less valuable than its designers had hoped.

Whether extensive recourse to night fighting demanded special equipment not only for bombers but for ground troops was another moot question. Whether infra-red rays, for example, could be effectively used to facilitate driving vehicles at night was a matter for further study. Though the Corps of Engineers had primary responsibility for infra-red applications, Ordnance assistance was enlisted on the problem. On V-J Day its future was uncertain. Battlefield flood lighting had scarcely been tried at all. In late 1942 interest in a secret British development had run high. Five hundred Canal Defense Light vehicles were built in the United States under high priority, in anticipation of need of powerful searchlight illumination for night tank battles. Mounted on General Grant medium tanks, some sixty of these were employed in the Rhine river crossings in February 1945, but no other use occurred. The "illumi-

[2] Cole, *The Lorraine Campaign*, p. 603.

nated front" that was to be widely advocated in Korea was after all not part of the tactics of the 1944–45 campaigns in either Europe or the Pacific.

The logistical and tactical considerations to be borne in mind in determining what length of life American weapons should have were never fully evaluated during World War II. Shortages of tungsten, chromium, molybdenum, rubber, and a dozen other materials obliged the Ordnance Department to find substitutes even at the expense of producing less long-wearing items, but it was usually necessity rather than reasoned choice that changed the specifications. Nevertheless, as the war progressed, the observant could see the logic of frequently using stamped metal parts in place of forgings or a wide variety of cheap, readily worked materials in lieu of more durable but more expensive kinds. German and Russian infantry weapons proved that inexpensive short-lived articles, produceable at fractional cost and therefore cheaply replaceable, in many cases served every purpose adequately. The American submachine gun M3, with most of its parts stamped out of sheet metal, was one application of the new realization that great durability was not necessarily a vital requirement for any small weapon.

But while tacitly admitting the validity of the thesis in the case of small arms, the General Staff and the Ordnance Department were far less persuaded of the soundness of the principle applied to more complex items. Where replacements must be shipped halfway around the world, the cost of having equipment wear out needlessly fast was naturally too high to contemplate. On the other hand, enemy fire could demolish in a moment matériel with years of life left in it when struck. Unlike machines designed to run until deliberately scrapped, weapons of war were constantly subject to destruction long before they wore out. The Germans put the Panther tank into action with an engine requiring replacement after, at most, 625 miles of travel, whereas Sherman engines were known sometimes to have a life of over 3,000 miles. Advantageous though the greater endurance must be if achieved without sacrifice of essential features and without large additional expense or slowing of quantity production, the reasonable chance that enemy fire would destroy the tank before the engine had lived out its life made its durability a doubtful asset. The Soviet Army, like the German, accepted matériel with a service life span far below what the U.S. Army demanded. In the Russian view, usable, albeit makeshift, equipment was good enough to be blown up. But in the United States the century-old concept of building military equipment with a solidity to last at least through an entire war was too deeply ingrained to be cast off readily. The question of what items were best made as cheaply as possible with scant regard to service life was one that the Ordnance Department was only beginning to study at the end of the war.

Equally fundamental was the question of overelaboration versus oversimplification of military equipment. Improvisations in the field often did a job as well as a device carefully worked out on drawing board and production line. When the research and development staff in Washington learned that American soldiers in the jungles of the Pacific had been sticking razor blades into tree trunks to prevent Japanese snipers who had infiltrated through the lines at night from taking position in the trees, draftsmen immediately began making drawings of a device by which a bristle of knife blades could be clamped to a tree trunk. A commercial company under contract produced several experimental versions of this gadget before the scheme was vetoed as quite needless.[3] More bizarre and amusing than significant, this episode nevertheless exemplified a growing tendency to gild the lily of simplicity on the one hand and to develop and nurture the extremely elaborate on the other.

When armies had been supplied only with rifles, bayonets, revolvers, and sabres, with cannon and howitzers, mortars, and hand grenades, or even with machine guns, designing, manufacturing, and keeping satisfactory weapons in usable condition was relatively easy. Training soldiers to use them properly was correspondingly routine. When World War I inaugurated both air and tank warfare, the task became far more complex, and by the end of World War II the advances of science made the possible applications to military usage so infinitely various as to tempt the general staffs of all countries to junk most earlier types of killing devices. Just as the single-shot rifle was largely superseded by the semiautomatic, and the revolver by the semiautomatic carbine or the submachine gun, so artillery fire control instruments directed by eye, hand, and prefigured firing tables were replaced by highly intricate electrical computers, frequently fed data by radar. To train soldiers in the use of such equipment and to teach crews to maintain it meant lengthy courses of instruction meticulously planned and executed.

Any Russian peasant trooper could see in a moment how to use the "Molotov Cocktail," a bottle filled with gasoline and stoppered with a rag set alight and hurled into a tank to set it on fire. Had he needed to be taught how to use a proximity fuze on a rocket, preliminary schooling would have been necessary. Nor was the better-educated soldier of the U.S. Army always ready to make use of new equipment, advance instruction in its employment notwithstanding. Thus the patience, ingenuity, and money spent in the United States on developing gyrostabilizers for tank guns proved largely wasted until the very end of the war, inasmuch as hastily trained tank crews, finding them too difficult to manage, usually disconnected them. When they were used, specially schooled maintenance teams stationed far to the rear had to adjust and repair them at frequent intervals, with the consequence that gunners of most armored units through much of the war preferred tanks minus this refinement. If the U.S. Army must count on having little more than a year in which to prepare draftees for military service, dare it rely on equipping its forces with weapons so complicated that the high school graduates composing the citizens' army could comprehend the principles of employment and care of only a very few items? Might the dangers inherent in this kind of specialization not exceed any benefits? Though these were not questions for the Ordnance Department to answer alone, they were problems the nation's Military Establishment had to face before it could arrive at an intelligently planned development program.

Hand-in-hand with these questions ran the matter of over-all costs in both money and materials for complex new weapons. Bred in the belief that its natural resources, if not inexhaustible, were at least ample for immediate national needs, the American people at the opening of World War II had been unprepared to accept the idea that some matériel might be too expensive to use, and that less than perfection must do. The Russians put into action tanks the ex-

[3] SA & SA Ammo, Book 1, Pt. 3, p. 134.

terior finish of which was so rough that American engineers deemed them unsuitable because somewhat less likely to cause a projectile to glance off than would the rounded contours of the American. Again the provision for crew comfort within American combat vehicles had no counterpart in Russian-built tanks. Here, to be sure, the argument lay in the relative value of unfatigued crews versus cheaper tanks. Yet World War II experience forced recognition of the possibility that American design and fabrication was refined to the point of extravagance. A German general, comparing Russian and American tanks, remarked: "In my opinion, your Western tank is much too complicated, much too expensive." [4]

After the war, so one story runs, military tacticians were startled by the dollars and cents aspect of wider use of proximity fuzes in place of impact or time fuzes; when inquiry revealed that the cost differential was close to ten to one, the plea for issue of a larger proportion of influence fuzes was withdrawn. In the heat of combat, soldiers naturally forgot that they were taxpayers as well as fighting men, but the Ordnance research and development staff was coming to realize that it must keep costs constantly in mind. National policy had of course to determine the balance to be maintained between the armament program and the national economy as a whole. For the Ordnance Research and Development Division the problem remained of how to carry out any policy when settled.

The swiftness with which combat conditions and doctrine of tactical employment of weapons shifted in World War II naturally made carefully thought-out tables of equipment extremely difficult to compile and revise. Piecemeal standardization of items from 1940 onward multiplied models from which to choose matériel for any particular type of engagement, but the War Department had made no thorough overall study of what a modern army would need since the Westervelt Board report, completed in 1919. By early 1943 the Ordnance Department believed a careful reappraisal overdue. In March Brig. Gen. Roland P. Shugg, then attached to the Office, Chief of Ordnance, pointed out to General Somervell and Lt. Gen. Joseph T. McNarney the desirability of "a comprehensive survey of the necessary modern gun power and armor to win the European campaign. We need immediately another Westervelt Report." [5] Though in late 1943 and during 1944 several special missions, such as the Eddy mission to Europe and the Borden "Jungle Warfare" mission to the Pacific, brought back a series of recommendations, the "comprehensive survey" wanted by the Ordnance Department had to wait till a year after the war.

The upshot was inevitably not only considerable waste effort spent during the war on specific developments requested by the using arms and then canceled before results could be tried but, after the war, a tangle of conflicting views about what projects should be pursued and fitted into an all-embracing armament plan. The new weapons employed in the last year of fighting, the Axis' dreaded V-2 rocket, the proximity fuzes, and above all, the atom bomb, unavoidably introduced elements of confusion. Why expend time and money on improving conventional weapons likely to be outmoded at the drop of a hat or an

[4] Transcript of discussion following lecture by Lt. Gen. Anton von Bechtolsheim on German Strategy versus the USSR in World War II, given at National War College, Jan 52.

[5] Memo, Gen Shugg for Gen Somervell and Gen McNarney, 5 Mar 43, OO 350.05/2578 SW, DRB AGO.

A-bomb? Hints thrown out in the press that warfare would soon be revolutionized by the use of very-long-range artillery firing an atomic warhead tended to raise questions of the utility of such a weapon as the 914-mm. mortar. Admittedly only guesses, these rumors affected public opinion and made Ordnance research and development planning more difficult. Until the first report of the Army Equipment Review Board appeared in the summer of 1946, uncertainty left the Ordnance Department with no logically constructed long-range program of development to follow.

Achievements during the war had exceeded the most optimistic hopes of men familiar with the obstacles to overcome in designing military equipment. Science, allied as never before with military research and development, had sent weapons into action that rivaled Buck Rogers' extravagancies. But if much of the development program had been haphazard, Ordnance Committee attempts at co-ordination notwithstanding, the fundamental difficulty was more subtle. Clearer differentiation of the respective roles of the pure scientist, the design engineer, and the technician engaged in testing and modifying the products of the first two was needed. "The world," said Brig. Gen. Leslie E. Simon, in speaking of the applications of science, "muddled through by random processes rather than through the application of purposive procedure."[6] Perhaps John Dewey's pronouncement on adjusting to life could be applied to devising ways to kill: "If ever we are to be governed by intelligence, not by things and by words, science must have something to say about what we do, and not merely about how we may do it most easily and economically."[7]

[6] Brig. Gen. Leslie E. Simon, ACofOrd, "On Bridging the Gap Between Research and Development," speech given at Fifth Annual Conference on Administration of Research, Ann Arbor, Mich., 24 Sep 51, copy in OHF.

[7] Quoted, *ibid.*

Bibliographical Note

In the preparation of this volume the authors have relied primarily upon four collections—the studies, copies of supporting documents and personal records of individual Ordnance officers, which together comprise the Ordnance Historical Files; the papers assembled in the Departmental Records Branch of the Adjutant General's Office in Alexandria, Virginia; the materials housed in the War Department section of the National Archives; and reports and correspondence still in possession of the subdivisions of the Office, Chief of Ordnance, in the Pentagon. In addition, several manuscripts prepared by the Office of the Chief of Military History have proved useful, as have several published works, notably the volumes of the series *Science in World War II,* Scientific Research and Development. *Army Ordnance,* the bimonthly publication of the American Ordnance Association, has been of far more use than any other periodical.

The Ordnance Historical Files were collected during the war by the staff of the Ordnance Historical Branch. The backbone of this material is the series of typescript historical reports submitted by the divisions and staff branches of the Office, Chief of Ordnance, and by all the major field installations, including the arsenals, districts, depots, proving grounds, training centers, OCO–Detroit, the Field Director of Ammunition Plants, and others. In this collection is a group of project papers, that is, studies of particular Ordnance problems, and of project supporting papers, prepared during or immediately after the war either by members of the Historical Branch or by specialists in other branches of the Department. The quality and coverage of the project papers varies greatly, but many of them contain photographs, charts, and statistical tables of interest, and the copies of pertinent documents assembled in the project supporting papers are both intrinsically valuable to the historian and indirectly useful because of the leads they give to the whereabouts of further data. Of the collections of individuals' papers in the Ordnance Historical Files, the Barnes file, a partial transcript of General Barnes' conferences and some of his semiofficial correspondence, and General Barnes' diary are particularly helpful on questions involving research and development. For over-all problems and organizational matters, a useful source is the record of General Wesson's regular 11 o'clock conferences at which he discussed with his staff most of the problems facing the Department during the defense period.

For the history of the Department in the years before 1940, the records in the National Archives are essential, though material such as the bound volumes of Ordnance Department Orders are still available in the Executive Office of the Office, Chief of Ordnance. For the war period, a major source is the collection of Ordnance papers, both classified and unclassified, in the custody of the Departmental Records Branch of the Adjutant General's Office in Alexandria. Information on certain controversial subjects, moreover, was found in the central files of the Adjutant General's Office, and in the files of the Army Service Forces, Army Ground Forces, the Under Secretary of War, and the G–4 Division of the General Staff. For data on German equipment, the authors made extensive use of the files in the Foreign Studies Branch of the Office, Chief of Military History, and in the German Documents Section of the Departmental Records Branch, AGO.

The most important single source for the history of research and development from 1919 through World War II is the series of Ordnance Committee Minutes. These are still housed in the Pentagon in the keeping of the Ordnance Technical Committee Secretariat. The Minutes list the action taken and frequently some of the discussion about each Ordnance item on which the Department undertook research and development from the end of World War I to the present. Other materials in files of the subdivisions of the Research and Development Division of the Office, Chief of Ordnance, in the Pentagon are only less useful. Among these the Summary Technical Reports prepared on particular problems by units of the National Defense Research Committee should be singled out for mention. Unclassified information in the Executive Office is contained in such volumes as the *Ordnance Reports* published in 1889 and in the typescript volumes "Ordnance Developmental and Experimental Projects 1920–1925." Officially published statistics of the Army, the Official Munitions Production of the United States, by month, July 1, 1940–August 31, 1945, popularly known as OMPUS, is cited for World War II; Leonard P. Ayres and Benedict Crowell for World War I.

Supplementary to these written records is the information the authors have obtained in a host of interviews and from correspondence with men intimately concerned with the work discussed in this book.

List of Abbreviations

AA	Antiaircraft
AAF	Army Air Forces
ACofAS	Assistant Chief of Air Staff
ACofOrd	Assistant Chief of Ordnance
ACofS	Assistant Chief of Staff
Actg	Acting
Admin	Administrative
AEF	American Expeditionary Forces (1917–18)
AF	Air Force
AFV	Armored Fighting Vehicles
AG	Adjutant General
AGCT	Army General Classification Test
AGD	Adjutant General's Department
AGF	Army Ground Forces
AGO	Adjutant General's Office
AGWAR	Adjutant General, War Department
Ammo	Ammunition
A&N	Army and Navy
ANMB	Army and Navy Munitions Board
Ann	Annual
APC	Armor-piercing-capped
APG	Aberdeen Proving Ground
AR	Army Regulations
Arty	Artillery
ASF	Army Service Forces
ASW	Assistant Secretary of War
AT	Antitank
Atchd	Attached
ATSC	Air Technical Service Command
Auto	Automotive
BAR	Browning automatic rifle
Bd	Board
Br	Branch
BRL	Ballistic Research Laboratory
BT	Base detonating
Bull	Bulletin
CA	Coast Artillery
CBI	China-Burma-India
CC	Clearance Committee
CDL	Canal defense light
CG	Commanding general
CIOS	Combined Intelligence Objectives Subcommittee
Cir	Circular
Civ	Civilian
CO	Commanding officer
CofAC	Chief of Air Corps
CofAS	Chief of Air Staff
CofCA	Chief of Coast Artillery
CofCav	Chief of Cavalry
CofEngrs	Chief of Engineers
CofFA	Chief of Field Artillery
CofInf	Chief of Infantry
CofOrd	Chief of Ordnance
CofS	Chief of Staff
Conf	Conference
CPD	Civilian Personnel Division
DA	Defense aid
DCofS	Deputy Chief of Staff
Dev	Development
Dir	Director
Dist	District
Div	Division
Doc	Document
DRB AGO	Departmental Records Branch, Adjutant General's Office
EDNA	Ethylenedinitramine
Eng	England
Engr	Engineer (s) (ing)

ETO	European Theater of Operations
ETOUSA	European Theater of Operations, U.S. Army
EUCOM	European Command
Exec	Executive
FA	Field Artillery
FDAP	Field Director of Ammunition Plants
Fisc	Fiscal
FM	Field manual
FNH	Flashless nonhygroscopic powder
FS	Field Service
FY	Fiscal year
G–2	Intelligence Division of the War Department General Staff
G–3	Operations and Training Division of the War Department General Staff
G–4	Supply Division of the War Department General Staff
GHQ	General Headquarters
GMDS	German Military Documents Section
GO	General Order
GOCO	Government-owned, contractor-operated
Gp	Group
GP	General purpose
GPF	*Grande Puissance Filloux*
GS	General Staff
HE	High explosive
HEAT	High-explosive, antitank (ammunition)
Hist	History
HP	Horsepower
Hq	Headquarters
HR	House of Representatives
HVAP	High-velocity, armor-piercing
HVAR	High-velocity aircraft rocket
ICAF	Industrial College of the Armed Forces
IG	Inspector General
Incl	Inclosure
Ind	Industrial, indorsement
Inf	Infantry
Intel	Intelligence
Interv	Interview
IPF	Initial Protective Force
JAC	Joint Aircraft Committee
JIT	Job Instructor Training
JMT	Job Methods Training
JRT	Job Relations Training
LL	Lend-lease
Ltr	Letter
Maint	Maintenance
MAT	Mechanical Aptitude Test
MG	Machine gun
MID	Military Intelligence Division
Mil	Military
Min	Minutes
MNAM	Military North African Mission
MPTS	Military Plans and Training Service
Mtg	Meeting
MTP	Military Training Program
MTS	Motor Transport Service
NA	National Archives
NADA	National Automobile Dealers Association
NATOUSA	North African Theater of Operations, U.S. Army
NCO	Noncommissioned officer
NDRC	National Defense Research Committee
NE	National Emergency
OASW	Office of the Assistant Secretary of War
OC	Ordnance Committee
OCD	Office of Civilian Defense
OCM	Ordnance Committee Minutes
OCMH	Office of the Chief of Military History
OCO	Office, Chief of Ordnance

OCO-D	Office, Chief of Ordnance–Detroit
OCT	Office, Chief of Transportation
OD	Ordnance Department
ODEP	Ordnance Developmental and Experimental Projects
ODFS	Ordnance Department Field Service
ODO	Ordnance Department Order
Off	Officer
OHF	Ordnance Historical File
OKH	*Oberkommando des Heeres* (High Command of the Army)
OMPUS	Official Munitions Production of the United States
OO	Ordnance Office
OPD	Operations Division
Opns	Operations
Ord	Ordnance
Orgn	Organization
ORTC	Ordnance Replacement Training Center
OSW	Office of the Secretary of War
OTC	Ordnance Training Center
OUSW	Office of the Under Secretary of War
Pers	Personnel, personal
PETN	Pentaerythritol tetranite
PL	Public Law
PMP	Protective Mobilization Plan
POA	Pacific Ocean Area
POW	Prisoner of war
PSP	Project Supporting Paper
PT	Point detonating
Pub	Public
PWA	Public Works Administration
QMC	Quartermaster Corps
RAF	Royal Air Force
R&D	Research and Development
RDX	Research development explosive cyclonite
Regt	Regiment
Res	Resolution
Ret	Retired
Rpt	Report
Rqmts	Requirements
RTC	Replacement Training Center
S	Senate
SA	Small arms
SAE	Society of Automotive Engineers
SAIC	Special Allied Interrogation Commission
SAP	Semi-armor-piercing
SC	Service command
Sec	Section
Secy	Secretary
Serv	Service
SHAEF	Supreme Headquarters, Allied Expeditionary Force
SNL	Standard Nomenclature List
SO	Special Order
SOS	Services of Supply
Stat	Statistics, statistical
STM	Strength of the Army Reports
Supp	Supplement
Supt	Superintendent
SW	Secretary of War
T-AC	Tank-Automotive Center
TAG	The Adjutant General
Tech	Technical
TIG	The Inspector General
TM	Training manual
Tng	Training
TNT	Trinitrotoluene
TQMG	The Quartermaster General
TWI	Training Within Industry
U.K.	United Kingdom
USAF	United States Air Force
USAFCBI	United States Army Forces in China-Burma-India
USAFIME	United States Army Forces in the Middle East
USSAFE	U.S. Strategic Air Forces, Europe

USSR	Union of Socialist Soviet Republics
USW	Under Secretary of War
UTC	Unit Training Center
UXB	Unexploded bomb
V-E	Victory in Europe
VHB	Very heavy bomber
V-J	Victory in Japan
WD	War Department
WDAB	War Department appropriations bill
WDGS	War Department General Staff
WPA	Works Progress Administration
WP	White phosphorus
WPB	War Production Board
WPD	War Plans Division

UNITED STATES ARMY IN WORLD WAR II

The multivolume series, UNITED STATES ARMY IN WORLD WAR II, consists of a number of subseries which are tentatively planned as follows: The War Department, The Army Air Forces, The Army Ground Forces, The Army Service Forces, The Defense of the Western Hemisphere, The War in the Pacific, The European Theater of Operations, the War in the Mediterranean, The Middle East Theater, The China-Burma-India Theater, Civil Affairs, The Technical Services, Special Studies, and Pictorial Record.

The following volumes have been published or are in press:*

The War Department
Chief of Staff: Prewar Plans and Preparations
Washington Command Post: The Operations Division
Strategic Planning for Coalition Warfare: 1941–1942
Global Logistics and Strategy: 1940–1943

The Army Ground Forces
The Organization of Ground Combat Troops
The Procurement and Training of Ground Combat Troops

The Army Service Forces
The Organization and Role of the Army Service Forces

The War in the Pacific
Okinawa: The Last Battle
Guadalcanal: The First Offensive
The Approach to the Philippines
The Fall of the Philippines
Leyte: The Return to the Philippines
Seizure of the Gilberts and Marshalls
Victory in Papua

The European Theater of Operations
The Lorraine Campaign
Cross-Channel Attack
Logistical Support of the Armies, Volume I
The Supreme Command

---

*Volumes on the Army Air Forces, published by the University of Chicago Press, are not included.

The Middle East Theater

The Persian Corridor and Aid to Russia

The China-Burma-India Theater

Stilwell's Mission to China
Stilwell's Command Problems

The Technical Services

The Transportation Corps: Responsibilities, Organization, and Operations
The Transportation Corps: Movements, Training, and Supply
The Quartermaster Corps: Organization, Supply and Services, Volume I
The Quartermaster Corps: Organization, Supply, and Services, Volume II
The Ordnance Department: Planning Munitions for War
The Signal Corps: The Emergency
The Medical Department: Hospitalization and Evacuation, Zone of Interior

Special Studies

Three Battles: Arnaville, Altuzzo, and Schmidt
The Women's Army Corps

Pictorial Record

The War Against Germany and Italy: Mediterranean and Adjacent Areas
The War Against Germany: Europe and Adjacent Areas
The War Against Japan

Index

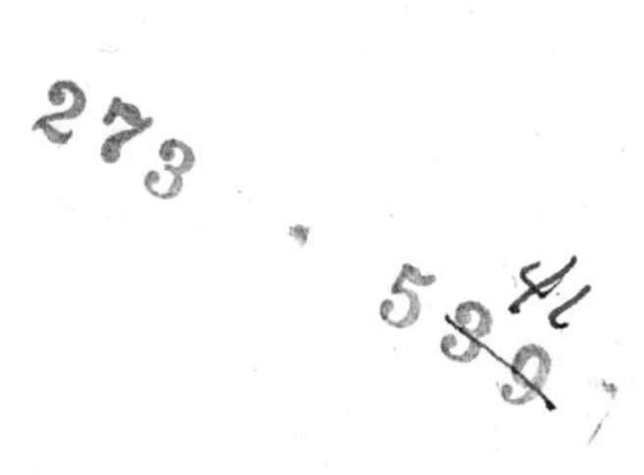

U. S. GOVERNMENT PRINTING OFFICE: 1955 O-F—291064